MW01000927

Introduction to Modern Finsler Geometry

Introduction to Modern Finsler Geometry

Yi-Bing Shen

Zhejiang University, China

Zhongmin Shen

Indiana University–Purdue University Indianapolis, USA

Higher Education Press

World Scientific

Published by

Higher Education Press Limited Company
4 Dewai Dajie, Beijing 100120, P. R. China
and
World Scientific Publishing Co. Pte. Ltd.
5 Toh Tuck Link, Singapore 596224

Library of Congress Cataloging-in-Publication Data
Names: Shen, Yibing. | Shen, Zhongmin, 1963–
Title: Introduction to modern Finsler geometry / by Yi-Bing Shen (Zhejiang University, China),
   Zhongmin Shen (Indiana University-Purdue University, Indianapolis, USA).
Description: New Jersey : Higher Education Press Limited Company :
   World Scientific Publishing Co., 2016.
Identifiers: LCCN 2015047992| ISBN 9789814704908 (hardcover : alk. paper) |
   ISBN 9789814713160 (pbk. : alk. paper)
Subjects: LCSH: Finsler spaces. | Geometry, Differential. | Differentiable manifolds.
Classification: LCC QA689 .S538 2016 | DDC 516.3/75--dc23
LC record available at http://lccn.loc.gov/2015047992

British Library Cataloguing-in-Publication Data
A catalogue record for this book is available from the British Library.

Copyright © 2016 by Higher Education Press Limited Company and
World Scientific Publishing Co. Pte. Ltd.

All rights reserved. This book, or parts thereof, may not be reproduced in any form or by any means, electronic or mechanical, including photocopying, recording or any information storage and retrieval system now known or to be invented, without written permission from the publishers.

For photocopying of material in this volume, please pay a copying fee through the Copyright Clearance Center, Inc., 222 Rosewood Drive, Danvers, MA 01923, USA. In this case permission to photocopy is not required from the publishers.

Printed in P. R. China

Preface

"Finsler geometry is just Riemannian geometry without quadratic restriction", commented by the past famous geometer, S. S. Chern. In fact, early in 1854, B. Riemann had introduced the concept of Finsler geometry in his ground-breaking Habilitationsvortrag. He had seen the difference between metrics of quadratic type (i.e. Riemannian metrics) and those in the general case. No essential development was made until 1918 when P. Finsler studied the geometry of curves and surfaces in the general case. Therefore, more precisely, we should call this subject Riemann-Finsler geometry.

Since more than twenty years ago, substantial progress has been made in Finsler geometry, especially in global Finsler geometry, so that we have seen a completely new outlook. Informally speaking, Riemannian geometry studies spaces with only black and white colors, while Finsler geometry studies a colorful world. The methods and ideas used in Finsler geometry not only are closely related to other mathematical branches such as differential equations, Lie groups, algebra, topology, nonlinear analysis, etc., but also have more and more applications to mathematical physics, theoretical physics, mathematical biology, control theory, informatics, etc. Therefore, not just in theory but also in application, Finsler geometry has shown its strong vitality and great value.

In order to meet the need of education for senior undergraduate and graduate students, under the influence of books [10, 103], we wrote this textbook, based on many years of teaching experience. The whole book is divided into 11 chapters: in the first five chapters, we discuss differential manifolds, Finsler metrics, the Chern connection, Riemannian and non-Riemannian quantities. The rest is written for further studies. This second part covers projective transformations, comparison theorems, fundamental group, minimal immersions, harmonic maps, Einstein metrics, conformal transformations and conformal vector fields, the Finsler Laplacian and its first eigenvalue, etc. At the end of every chapter there are some exercises, which are important complements for the contents. The final Appendix is to provide Maple programs on the computations of geometric quantities in Finsler geometry.

With the main tool of tensor analysis, we systematically introduce the basic concepts and methods in Finsler geometry, and we do our best to include the classical theory as well as the newest developments, so that readers can do research independently after studying this book. This book may be used as a selective textbook for senior undergraduate students and a regular textbook for graduate students. It can also be used as a reference book for mathematical physics, theoretical physics, control theory, etc. We believe that this book is of positive significance as an addition and improvement to current textbooks in colleges.

We would like to take this opportunity to thank the National Natural Science Foundation of China (No. 11171297), the Center of Mathematical Sciences and the Department of Mathematics at Zhejiang University, and our many students who contributed to this book.

In conclusion we acknowledge the Higher Education Press in China and World Scientific Publishing Company in Singapore for their great support.

Yi-Bing Shen
Zhongmin Shen
March 2015

Contents

PART I
Foundations

Chapter 1

Differentiable Manifolds

1.1 Differentiable manifolds

1.1.1 Differentiable manifolds

Definition 1.1. An n-dimensional *differentiable manifold* is a Hausdorff topological space M and a family of diffeomorphisms $\phi_\alpha : U_\alpha \subset M \to \phi_\alpha(U_\alpha) \subset \mathbb{R}^n$ such that the following conditions are satisfied:

(i) $\{U_\alpha\}$ is an open covering of M, i.e., U_α is open and $\bigcup_\alpha U_\alpha = M$;

(ii) If $U_\alpha \cap U_\beta = V \neq \emptyset$, then $\phi_\alpha(V)$ and $\phi_\beta(V)$ are open sets in $\mathbb{R}^n$, and $\phi_\alpha \circ \phi_\beta^{-1}|_{\phi_\beta(V)}$ is a diffeomorphism;

(iii) The family $\{(U_\alpha, \phi_\alpha)\}$ is maximal relative to (i) and (ii).

For a point $p \in U_\alpha$, (U_α, ϕ_α) is called a *coordinate neighborhood* of p, and the coordinate of $\phi_\alpha(q) \in \phi_\alpha(U_\alpha)$, $\forall q \in U_\alpha$, in $\mathbb{R}^n$ can be viewed as the coordinate of $q \in U_\alpha \subset M$. A family $\{(U_\alpha, \phi_\alpha)\}$ satisfying (i) and (ii) is called a *differentiable structure* on M. The condition (iii) is included for purely technical reasons.

1.1.2 Examples of differentiable manifolds

Example 1.1. The Euclidean space $\mathbb{R}^n$.

Example 1.2. The unit sphere in $\mathbb{R}^{n+1}$

$$\mathbb{S}^n = \left\{ (y^1, \cdots, y^{n+1}) \in \mathbb{R}^{n+1} \,\middle|\, \sum_{\alpha=1}^{n+1} (y^\alpha)^2 = 1 \right\} \subset \mathbb{R}^{n+1}.$$

Take the topology of $\mathbb{S}^n$ as the sub-topology in $\mathbb{R}^{n+1}$, i.e., $U \subset \mathbb{S}^n$ is open if and only if there is an open $\widetilde{U} \subset \mathbb{R}^{n+1}$ such that $U = \widetilde{U} \cap \mathbb{S}^n$. Thus, $\mathbb{S}^n$ is a Hausdorff topological space. We are going to introduce a differentiable structure on $\mathbb{S}^n$.

For all $1 \leq \alpha \leq n+1$, let

$$\widetilde{U}_\alpha^+ = \{(y^1, \cdots, y^{n+1}) | y^\alpha > 0\}, \quad \widetilde{U}_\alpha^- = \{(y^1, \cdots, y^{n+1}) | y^\alpha < 0\}.$$

$\widetilde{U}_\alpha^\pm$ are two open sets in $\mathbb{R}^{n+1}$ separated by the hyperplane $y^\alpha = 0$. Then the family $\{U_\alpha^\pm = \widetilde{U}_\alpha^\pm \cap \mathbb{S}^n\}$ covers $\mathbb{S}^n$. Take the orthogonal projection $\phi_\alpha^\pm : U_\alpha^\pm \to \mathbb{R}^n$

$$\phi_\alpha^\pm(y^1, \cdots, y^{n+1}) = (y^1, \cdots, \widehat{y^\alpha}, \cdots, y^{n+1}),$$

where $\widehat{y^\alpha}$ means the corresponding term is omitted. It is easy to see that $\phi_\alpha^\pm$ are diffeomorphisms from $U_\alpha^\pm$ to the open set $W_\alpha = \{(y^1, \cdots, \widehat{y^\alpha}, \cdots, y^{n+1}) \in \mathbb{R}^n | \sum_{\beta \neq \alpha} (y^\beta)^2 < 1\}$. Moreover, coordinate transformations are smooth. In fact, for example, the transformation $\phi_2^- \circ (\phi_1^+)^{-1}$ on $U_2^- \cap U_1^+$ is

$$(y^2, \cdots, y^{n+1}) \xrightarrow{(\phi_1^+)^{-1}} \left(\sqrt{1 - \sum_{\alpha=2}^{n+1} (y^\alpha)^2}, y^2, \cdots, y^{n+1} \right)$$

$$\xrightarrow{\phi_2^-} \left(\sqrt{1 - \sum_{\alpha=2}^{n+1} (y^\alpha)^2}, y^3, \cdots, y^{n+1} \right).$$

Instead of $(y^2, \cdots, y^{n+1})$ and $(y^1, y^3, \cdots, y^{n+1})$ on U_1^+ and U_2^-, we use $(x^1, x^2, \cdots, x^n)$ and $(\overline{x}^1, \overline{x}^2, \cdots, \overline{x}^n)$, respectively. Then we have

$$\overline{x}^1 = \sqrt{1 - \sum_{i=1}^n (x^i)^2}, \quad \overline{x}^j = x^j, \quad j = 2, \cdots, n.$$

Hence, $\mathbb{S}^n$ is an n-dimensional smooth manifold.

Example 1.3. The *real projective space* $\mathbb{R}P^n$.

This is the set of lines of $\mathbb{R}^{n+1}$ that pass through the origin $O = (0, \cdots, 0)$. Thus, $\mathbb{R}P^n$ can be viewed as the quotient space of the unit sphere $\mathbb{S}^n = \{p \in \mathbb{R}^{n+1} | \, |p| = 1\}$ by the equivalence relation A that identifies $p \in \mathbb{S}^n$ with its antipodal point $A(p) = -p$. Indeed, each line that passes through the origin determines two antipodal points and $\mathbb{R}P^n = \mathbb{S}^n/A$.

Let $\pi : \mathbb{S}^n \to \mathbb{R}P^n$ be the canonical projection, i.e., $\pi(p) = \{p, -p\}$. By using the differentiable structure of $\mathbb{S}^n$ as in Example 1.2, one can see that $\pi(U_\alpha^+) = \pi(U_\alpha^-)$ and $\{\pi(U_\alpha^\pm)\}$ covers $\mathbb{R}P^n$. Thus, $\phi_\alpha = \phi_\alpha^\pm \circ \pi^{-1}$ is a diffeomorphism from $\pi(U_\alpha^\pm)$ to $W_\alpha \subset \mathbb{R}^n$. This gives a differentiable structure on $\mathbb{R}P^n$. Hence, $\mathbb{R}P^n$ is a smooth manifold, and $\mathbb{S}^n$ can be viewed as the two-fold covering of $\mathbb{R}P^n$.

Let $(x^1, \cdots, x^{n+1})$ be the coordinates of $\mathbb{R}^{n+1}$. Define an equivalent relation $\sim$ in $\mathbb{R}^{n+1} \setminus \{0\}$ as follows: For any two points $\bar{x} = (\bar{x}^1, \cdots, \bar{x}^{n+1})$ and $x = (x^1, \cdots, x^{n+1})$, if there is a real number $\lambda \neq 0$ such that $\bar{x} = \lambda x$, then $\bar{x} \sim x$. Thus, the real projective space $\mathbb{R}P^n$ is the quotient space $(\mathbb{R}^{n+1} \setminus \{0\}) / \sim$, and $(x^1, \cdots, x^{n+1}) \neq (0, \cdots, 0)$ is called the *homogeneous coordinate* of $\mathbb{R}P^n$.

Example 1.4. The *Grassmann manifold*

$G_{k,n} = \{k\text{-dimensional linear subspaces in } \mathbb{R}^n \text{passing through the origin}\}.$

Fix an orthonormal base $\{e_1, \cdots, e_n\}$ in $\mathbb{R}^n$. The orthogonal group $O(n)$ acts on $\mathbb{R}^n$ via the matrix multiplication. On the other hand, any non-singular linear transformation $\sigma \in O(n)$ maps a k-dimensional linear subspace P to a k-dimensional linear subspace $Q = \mathcal{A}(\sigma, P)$, where

$$\mathcal{A} : O(n) \times G_{k,n} \to G_{k,n}.$$

Let P_0 denote the k-dimensional linear subspace spanned by $e_1, \cdots, e_k$. Let $H \subset O(n)$ be the subgroup preserving P_0 invariant. We have

$$H = \left\{ \begin{pmatrix} \alpha & 0 \\ 0 & \beta \end{pmatrix} \in O(n) | \alpha \in O(k), \beta \in O(n-k) \right\}.$$

Thus, H is the closed subgroup of $O(n)$ which is isomorphic to $O(k) \times O(n-k)$. The map $\sigma(O(k) \times O(n-k)) \mapsto \mathcal{A}(\sigma, P_0)$ from the quotient space $O(n)/O(k) \times O(n-k)$ to $G_{k,n}$ is bijective. We make the above map diffeomorphic, so that $G_{k,n}$ is a $k(n-k)$-dimensional differentiable manifold. It is easy to see that the manifold structure of $G_{k,n}$ is independent of a particular choice of the base in R^n. In particular, $G_{1,n+1} = \mathbb{R}P^n$.

Example 1.5. The *product manifold* $M \times N$.

Let $\{(U_\alpha, \phi_\alpha)\}$ and $\{(V_\beta, \psi_\beta)\}$ be differentiable structures of M and N, respectively. Clearly, we have $\bigcup_{\alpha,\beta} U_\alpha \times V_\beta = M \times N$. Define the diffeomorphism $\phi_\alpha \times \psi_\beta : U_\alpha \times V_\beta \to \phi_\alpha(U_\alpha) \times \psi_\beta(V_\beta) \subset \mathbb{R}^m \times \mathbb{R}^n = \mathbb{R}^{m+n}$ as follows:

$$(\phi_\alpha \times \psi_\beta)(p, q) = (\phi_\alpha(p), \psi_\beta(q)), \quad \forall (p, q) \in U_\alpha \times V_\beta.$$

Then $\{(U_\alpha \times V_\beta, \phi_\alpha \times \psi_\beta)\}$ is a differentiable structure of $M \times N$.

An important example of product manifolds is the n-torus $T^n = \mathbb{S}^1 \times \cdots \times \mathbb{S}^1$, which is the n-multiple Descartes product of circles.

Let $f : M \to N$ be a map from a differentiable manifold M to another N. For $p \in M$, if there are a coordinate neighborhood (U, ϕ) of p and a coordinate neighborhood (V, ψ) of $f(p)$ such that $f(U) \subset V$ and the map $\widehat{f} = \psi \circ f \circ \phi^{-1} : \phi(U) \subset \mathbb{R}^n \to \psi(V) \subset \mathbb{R}^m$ is differentiable at $\phi(p)$, then f is called to be differentiable at p. If $f : M \to N$ is differentiable at each point of M, then f is said to be differentiable on M. Particularly, a differentiable map $f : M \to \mathbb{R}$ is called a differentiable *function* on M. A differentiable *curve* in M is a differentiable map $\gamma : (a, b) \subset \mathbb{R} \to M$.

1.2   Vector fields and tensor fields

1.2.1   Vector bundles

Let M be a differentiable manifold and $p \in M$ a point. Consider a curve $\gamma : (-\varepsilon, \varepsilon) \to M$ with $\gamma(0) = p$. Let $\mathcal{C}(M)$ be the set of differentiable functions at the point p on M. The *tangent vector* of a curve γ at $t = 0$ is the map $\gamma'(0) : \mathcal{C}(M) \to \mathbb{R}$ defined by

$$\gamma'(0)f = \frac{d(f \circ \gamma)}{dt}\bigg|_{t=0}, \quad \forall f \in \mathcal{C}(M).$$

A *tangent vector* at p on M is the tangent vector of a curve $\gamma : (-\varepsilon, \varepsilon) \to M$ $(\gamma(0) = p)$ at $t = 0$. The set of tangent vectors at $p \in M$ is called the *tangent space* of M at p, denoted by $T_p M$.

Given a coordinate neighborhood (U, ϕ) of p with the local coordinates $\{x^i\}$, a function f and a curve γ can be expressed as

$$f(q) = f(x^1, \cdots, x^n), \quad (x^1, \cdots, x^n) = \phi(q) \in \phi(U),$$

$$\phi \circ \gamma(t) = (x^1(t), \cdots, x^n(t)).$$

By restricting f to γ, we have

$$\gamma'(0)f = \frac{d}{dt}(f \circ \gamma)\bigg|_{t=0} = \frac{d}{dt}f(x^1(t), \cdots, x^n(t))\bigg|_{t=0}$$
$$= \sum_i x'^i(0)\frac{\partial f}{\partial x^i}\bigg|_p = \left(\sum_i x'^i(0)\frac{\partial}{\partial x^i}\bigg|_p\right)f,$$

which implies that $\gamma'(0)$ can be denoted by

$$\gamma'(0) = \sum_i x'^i(0)\frac{\partial}{\partial x^i}\bigg|_p. \tag{1.2.1}$$

Clearly, $\frac{\partial}{\partial x^i}\big|_p$ is just the tangent vector of the coordinate curve $x^i \mapsto \phi^{-1}(0, \cdots, 0, x^i, 0, \cdots, 0)$ at p. It follows that $(1.2.1)$ that any vector of $T_p M$ can be expressed linearly in terms of $\{\frac{\partial}{\partial x^i}|_p\}$, which is a natural base for T_pM. Given a coordinate transformation $\overline{x}^i = \overline{x}^i(x^1, \cdots, x^n)$, we have

$$\frac{\partial}{\partial \overline{x}^i} = \frac{\partial x^j}{\partial \overline{x}^i} \frac{\partial}{\partial x^j}. \tag{1.2.2}$$

Here and from now on, the Einstein sum convention is used.

As a linear space, the dual space of T_pM consists of all linear functionals on T_pM, called the *cotangent space* at p and denoted by T_p^*M. Clearly, $\{dx^i|_p\}$ is a base for T_p^*M, called the *natural dual base* of $\{\frac{\partial}{\partial x^i}|_p\}$. Similarly, we have

$$d\overline{x}^i = \frac{\partial \overline{x}^i}{\partial x^j} dx^j. \tag{1.2.3}$$

The set $TM := \bigcup_{p \in M} T_pM = \{(p,v)|p \in M, v \in T_pM\}$ can be endowed a differentiable structure such that TM becomes a $2n$-dimensional differentiable manifold, called the *tangent bundle* of M. Let $\{x^i\}$ be the local coordinates on a neighborhood $U \subset M$. Any tangent vector $y \in T_pM$ ($p \in U$) can be expressed as $y = y^i \frac{\partial}{\partial x^i}$. So, the coordinates of (p,y) in $TU \subset TM$ can be written as $\{x^1, \cdots, x^n, y^1, \cdots, y^n\}$, from which a differentiable structure on TM follows. The mapping $(p,y) \mapsto p$ defines a natural projection $\pi : TM \to M$. Similarly, $T^*M := \bigcup_{p \in M} T_p^*M$ is also a $2n$-dimensional differentiable manifold, called the *cotangent bundle* of M.

By means of the tensor product, we can define the following vector space

$$T_s^r M_p := \underbrace{T_pM \otimes \cdots \otimes T_pM}_{r} \otimes \underbrace{T_p^*M \otimes \cdots \otimes T_p^*M}_{s},$$

called the (r,s)-*tensor space* induced by T_pM, which is a multilinear functional: $T_p^*M \times \cdots \times T_p^*M \times T_pM \times \cdots \times T_pM \to \mathbb{R}$. The natural base of the tensor space $T_s^r M_p$ is

$$\left\{ \left(\frac{\partial}{\partial x^{i_1}} \otimes \cdots \otimes \frac{\partial}{\partial x^{i_r}} \otimes dx^{j_1} \otimes \cdots \otimes dx^{j_s} \right)_p \right\}.$$

The set $T_s^r M := \bigcup_{p \in M} T_s^r M_p$ is called the (r,s)-*tensor bundle* on M.

1.2.2 Tensor fields

A *vector field* X on M is a function which assigns to each point $p \in M$ a tangent vector $X_p \in T_pM$. In other words, a vector field on M is a section $X : M \to TM$ in TM such that $\pi \circ X = \text{id}$. A vector field X is said to be differentiable if the map $X : M \to TM$ is differentiable. In a local coordinate system $\{x^i\}$ X can be expressed by

$$X = X^i(x)\frac{\partial}{\partial x^i}, \quad X^i = Xx^i,$$

where the components $X^i(x)$ are functions of (x^j), which transform under a coordinate transformation $\overline{x}^i = \overline{x}^i(x^1, \cdots, x^n)$ as follows

$$\overline{X}^i = X^j\frac{\partial \overline{x}^i}{\partial x^j} \quad \text{with} \quad X = \overline{X}^i\frac{\partial}{\partial \overline{x}^i}. \tag{1.2.4}$$

A *1-form* θ on M is also a function assigning to each point $p \in M$ a cotangent vector $\theta_p \in T^*M_p$. Similarly, a 1-form θ may be viewed as a section $\theta : M \to T^*M$ in T^*M. In a local coordinate system $\{x^i\}$, θ can be expressed by

$$\theta = \theta_i(x)dx^i, \quad \theta_i = \theta\left(\frac{\partial}{\partial x^i}\right),$$

where θ_i satisfy

$$\overline{\theta}_i = \theta_j\frac{\partial x^j}{\partial \overline{x}^i} \quad \text{with} \quad \theta = \overline{\theta}_i d\overline{x}^i. \tag{1.2.5}$$

In a similar way, we can define the (r,s)-*tensor field*. For example, let

$$\Phi = \Phi^{i_1 i_2}_{j_1 j_2}(x)\frac{\partial}{\partial x^{i_1}} \otimes \frac{\partial}{\partial x^{i_2}} \otimes dx^{j_1} \otimes dx^{j_2}$$

be a $(2,2)$-tensor field. We then have

$$\overline{\Phi}^{i_1 i_2}_{j_1 j_2} = \Phi^{k_1 k_2}_{l_1 l_2}\frac{\partial \overline{x}^{i_1}}{\partial x^{k_1}}\frac{\partial \overline{x}^{i_2}}{\partial x^{k_2}}\frac{\partial x^{l_1}}{\partial \overline{x}^{j_1}}\frac{\partial x^{l_2}}{\partial \overline{x}^{j_2}}.$$

Let $\varphi : M \to N$ be a differentiable map. The *pull back* φ^* of φ maps functions on N into functions $\varphi^*f := f \circ \varphi$ on M, i.e., $\varphi^*f(p) = f(\varphi(p))$ for any point $p \in M$. The *differential* $d\varphi \equiv \varphi_*$ of φ maps a tangent vector $X \in TM_p$ on M to a tangent vector $\varphi_*X \in TN_{\varphi(p)}$ on N defined by

$$\varphi_*X(f) = X(\varphi^*f), \tag{1.2.6}$$

where $f : N \to \mathbb{R}$ is a differentiable function on N. Furthermore, a 1-form ω on N can be pulled back to M, denoted by $\varphi^*\omega$, which is defined by

$$\varphi^*\omega(X) = \omega(\varphi_*X), \tag{1.2.7}$$

where X is a vector field on M.

1.3 Exterior forms and exterior differentials

1.3.1 Exterior differential operators

Let M be an n-manifold. An *exterior differential form θ of degree r* on M is just an alternating $(0, r)$-tensor field, simply called an *r-form*. By the exterior multiplication, θ may be expressed as

$$\theta = \theta_{i_1 \cdots i_r}(x) dx^{i_1} \wedge \cdots \wedge dx^{i_r} \tag{1.3.1}$$

in a local coordinate system $\{x^i\}$. Denote by $\Lambda^r(M)$ the set of all r-forms on M. Clearly, $0 \leq r \leq n$, and $\Lambda^0(M) = \mathcal{C}(M)$ is the set of smooth functions on M.

Definition 1.2. The *exterior differential operator* is a mapping $d : \Lambda^r(M) \to \Lambda^{r+1}(M)$ satisfying

(i) d is $\mathbb{R}$-linear;

(ii) For $f \in \Lambda^0(M)$, df is the usual differential of f, and $d(df) = 0$;

(iii) $d(\theta \wedge \sigma) = d\theta \wedge \sigma + (-1)^r \theta \wedge d\sigma$, where $\theta \in \Lambda^r(M)$, and σ is arbitrary.

The existence and uniqueness of the operator d are shown as follows. In fact, since d is a local operator, we need only define it in any coordinate neighborhood $U \subset M$ with coordinates $\{x^i\}$.

For $\theta \in \Lambda^r(M)$ denoted by (1.3.1), define

$$\begin{aligned} d\theta &= d\theta_{i_1 \cdots i_r} \wedge dx^{i_1} \wedge \cdots \wedge dx^{i_r} \\ &= (\partial_j \theta_{i_1 \cdots i_r}) dx^j \wedge dx^{i_1} \wedge \cdots \wedge dx^{i_r} \in \Lambda^{r+1}(M). \end{aligned} \tag{1.3.2}$$

It is easy to see that (i)-(iii) are satisfied.

Lemma 1.1 (Poincaré lemma).

$$d^2 = 0,$$

i.e., $d(d\theta) = 0$ *for any* $\theta \in \Lambda^r(M)$.

By a simply computation we can obtain the following

Lemma 1.2. *Let* $\omega \in \Lambda^1(M)$ *and* $X, Y \in \mathcal{C}(TM)$. *We have*

$$d\omega(X, Y) = X(\omega(Y)) - Y(\omega(X)) - \omega([X, Y]).$$

Let M and N be differentiable manifolds, and $\varphi : M \to N$ a smooth map. Denote by d_M and d_N the exterior differential operators on M and N, respectively. It may be proved that

$$\varphi^*(d_N \psi) = d_M(\varphi^* \psi)$$

for any $\psi \in \Lambda^r(N)$ ([169]). It can be expressed simply as

$$\varphi^* \circ d = d \circ \varphi^*. \tag{1.3.3}$$

1.3.2   de Rham theorem

We now assume M is an oriented compact manifold without boundary, and $\theta \in \Lambda^r(M)$. θ is called a *closed form* if $d\theta = 0$; and it is called an *exact form* if there is an $(r-1)$-form $\sigma \in \Lambda^{r-1}(M)$ such that $d\sigma = \theta$. By Lemma 1.1, an exact form must be closed. Let $Z^r(M, \mathbb{R})$ be the set of all closed r-forms. Clearly, $Z^r(M)$ is a linear subspace of $\Lambda^r(M)$ since it is the kernel of the homomorphism $d : \Lambda^r(M) \to \Lambda^{r+1}(M)$. Similarly, the set $B^r(M, \mathbb{R})$ of all exact r-forms is also a linear subspace of $\Lambda^r(M)$ since it is the image of $d : \Lambda^{r-1}(M) \to \Lambda^r(M)$. It follows from Lemma 1.1 (Poincaré lemma) that $B^r(M, \mathbb{R}) \subset Z^r(M, \mathbb{R})$. We obtain a quotient space $H^r(M, \mathbb{R}) := Z^r(M, \mathbb{R})/B^r(M, \mathbb{R})$, which is called the r-th *de Rham cohomology group*. Set

$$H^*(M, \mathbb{R}) = H^0(M, \mathbb{R}) \oplus H^1(M, \mathbb{R}) \oplus \cdots \oplus H^n(M, \mathbb{R}),$$

which becomes an algebra associated with the exterior multiplication. The importance of the algebra $H^*(M, \mathbb{R})$ is due to the following de Rham theorem.

Theorem 1.1 (de Rham). *There is a natural isomorphism of $H^*(M, \mathbb{R})$ and the cohomology ring of M under which $H^r(M, \mathbb{R})$ corresponds to the r-th cohomology group of M.*

An r-form ω can be integrated over an oriented r-dimensional region. The well-known Stokes' formula may be stated as follows.

Theorem 1.2 (Stokes). *Let M be an n-dimensional oriented differentiable manifold with smooth boundary ∂M. For an $(n-1)$-form ω on M we have*

$$\int_M d\omega = \int_{\partial M} \omega,$$

where ∂M has the orientation induced from one of M.

See [169] for details on the proof of these theorems.

1.4   Vector bundles and connections

1.4.1   Connection of the vector bundle

Let M be an n-dimensional differentiable manifold. A *vector bundle of rank k* with the *base space* M is an $(n+k)$-dimensional differentiable manifold $\mathcal{A}$ and a differentiable map $\pi : \mathcal{A} \to M$ such that for any coordinate neighborhood $U \subset M$, $\pi^{-1}(U)$ is diffeomorphic to $U \times \mathbb{R}^k$, i.e., $\pi^{-1}(x)$ is diffeomorphic to $\{x\} \times \mathbb{R}^k$ for each point $x \in U$. The set $\mathcal{A}_x = \pi^{-1}(x)$ is called the *fiber* at $x \in M$ which is a k-dimensional vector space. $\mathcal{A}$ is called the *total space* and π is called the *projection*. For example, the tangent bundle TM of M is a vector bundle of rank n. Let $\mathcal{A}_x^*$ be the dual space to $\mathcal{A}_x$ at $x \in M$. Then

$$\mathcal{A}^* := \bigcup_{x \in M} \mathcal{A}_x^*$$

is a vector bundle of rank k, called the *dual bundle* to $\mathcal{A}$.

Let $\pi : \mathcal{A} \to M$ be a vector bundle, and $\phi : N \to M$ a smooth map from another manifold N to M. We can construct the *induced vector bundle* $\widetilde{\pi} : \widetilde{\mathcal{A}} \to N$ on N as follows.

(i) Consider $\widetilde{x} \in N$ and $\xi \in \mathcal{A}$. The total space is the set

$$\widetilde{\mathcal{A}} = \{(\widetilde{x}, \xi) \in N \times \mathcal{A} \,|\, \phi(\widetilde{x}) = \pi(\xi)\}.$$

(ii) The projection $\widetilde{\pi} : \widetilde{\mathcal{A}} \to N$ is defined by $\widetilde{\pi}(\widetilde{x}, \xi) = \widetilde{x}$. By putting $\widetilde{\phi}(\widetilde{x}, \xi) = \xi$, we have the following commutative diagram

$$
\begin{array}{ccc}
\widetilde{\mathcal{A}} \cong \phi^{-1}\mathcal{A} & \xrightarrow{\ \widetilde{\phi}\ } & \mathcal{A} \\
\widetilde{\pi} \downarrow & & \downarrow \pi \\
N & \xrightarrow[\ \phi\ ]{} & M
\end{array}
$$

It is easy to check that $\widetilde{\pi} : \widetilde{\mathcal{A}} \to N$ is a vector bundle of rank k, denoted simply by $\phi^{-1}\mathcal{A}$. In particular, one can obtain the induced vector bundle $\phi^{-1}TM$ from the map $\phi : N \to M$.

A section of the vector bundle $\pi : \mathcal{A} \to M$ is a map $s : M \to \mathcal{A}$ satisfying $\pi \circ s = \mathrm{id}$. Denote by $\mathcal{C}(\mathcal{A})$ the set of all smooth sections. In particular, $\mathcal{C}(TM)$ is just the set of all smooth vector fields on M.

Definition 1.3. A *linear connection* on the vector bundle $\pi : \mathcal{A} \to M$ is a map $\nabla : \mathcal{C}(TM) \times \mathcal{C}(\mathcal{A}) \to \mathcal{C}(\mathcal{A})$, written as

$$\nabla : (X, \xi) \in \mathcal{C}(TM) \times \mathcal{C}(\mathcal{A}) \mapsto \nabla_X \xi \in \mathcal{C}(\mathcal{A}),$$

which satisfies the following properties:

(i) $\nabla_{(fX)}\xi = f\nabla_X \xi$;

(ii) $\nabla_X(f\xi + h\eta) = df(X)\xi + f\nabla_X \xi + dh(X)\eta + h\nabla_X \eta$,

where $f, h \in C^\infty(M)$, $X, Y \in \mathcal{C}(TM)$, $\xi, \eta \in \mathcal{C}(\mathcal{A})$. $\nabla_X \xi$ is called the *covariant derivative* of ξ in the direction of X.

It should be remarked that the value $(\nabla_X\xi)_x$ of $\nabla_X\xi$ at $x \in M$ depends only on the vector value X_x and the restriction ξ to a curve C in the direction of X_x.

In order to describe the connection ∇ concretely, we take a local frame field $\{e_\alpha\}_{\alpha=1}^k$ in the vector bundle $\mathcal{A}$, i.e., $\{e_\alpha\}|_x$ is the base of the fiber space $\mathcal{A}_x$ for any point $x \in U \subset M$. Putting $\xi = \xi^\alpha e_\alpha$, we have

$$\nabla_X\xi = \left\{d\xi^\alpha(X) + \xi^\beta\omega_\beta^\alpha(X)\right\}e_\alpha \quad (1 \le \alpha, \beta, \cdots \le k) \tag{1.4.1}$$

where 1-forms ω_β^α are determined by

$$\nabla_X e_\beta = \omega_\beta^\alpha(X)e_\alpha. \tag{1.4.2}$$

$\{\omega_\beta^\alpha\}$ are called the *connection forms* of ∇ with respect to $\{e_\alpha\}$. Since X is arbitrary, (1.4.1) is equivalent to

$$\nabla\xi = \left\{d\xi^\alpha + \xi^\beta\omega_\beta^\alpha\right\}e_\alpha \in T^*M \otimes \mathcal{A},$$

which is a 1-form on M with values in the vector bundle $\mathcal{A}$.

1.4.2 Curvature of a connection

By using exterior differential, we obtain the following curvature 2-forms

$$\Omega_\beta^\alpha := d\omega_\beta^\alpha - \omega_\beta^\gamma \wedge \omega_\gamma^\alpha. \tag{1.4.3}$$

In particular, if $\mathcal{A} = TM$ and $\{e_i\}$ is a local frame field in TM, whose dual field is $\{\omega^i\}$, we have

$$\nabla_X e_j = \omega_j^i(X)e_i, \quad \omega_j^i := \Gamma_{jk}^i\omega^k. \tag{1.4.4}$$

It follows that

$$\nabla_X Y = \left(dY^i(X) + Y^j\Gamma_{jk}^i\omega^k(X)\right)e_i \tag{1.4.5}$$

for $X = X^i e_i$ and $Y = Y^i e_i$. These $\{\Gamma_{jk}^i\}$ in (1.4.4) are called the *connection coefficients* of ∇, by which the connection ∇ is determined completely. It can be easily proved that there exists the affine connection in a differentiable manifold with countable topological base.

By using exterior differential, we can define the *torsion* of ∇ as

$$T = T^i e_i, \quad T^i := d\omega^i - \omega^j \wedge \omega_j^i, \tag{1.4.6}$$

which, by Lemma 1.2, is equivalent to

$$T(X,Y) = \nabla_X Y - \nabla_Y X - [X,Y]. \tag{1.4.6'}$$

If $T = 0$, then the connection ∇ is said to be *torsion free*, or *symmetric*.

For TM (1.4.3) becomes

$$\Omega_j^i = d\omega_j^i - \omega_j^k \wedge \omega_k^i, \tag{1.4.7}$$

which is equivalent to

$$\Omega_j^i(X,Y)e_i = \left(\nabla_X \nabla_Y - \nabla_Y \nabla_X - \nabla_{[X,Y]}\right)e_j := \Omega(X,Y)e_j. \tag{1.4.7'}$$

The equations (1.4.6) and (1.4.7) are called the *structure equations* of ∇ related to $\{e_i\}$.

The covariant derivative $\nabla_X Y$ can be generalized to tensor fields. Let Φ be a $(0,r)$-tensor field on (M,g). The *covariant derivative* $\nabla_X \Phi$ of Φ in the direction of X is a $(0,r)$-tensor field defined by

$$(\nabla_X \Phi)(Y_1, \cdots, Y_r) = X(\Phi(Y_1, \cdots, Y_r)) - \sum_{a=1}^{r} \Phi(Y_1, \cdots, \nabla_X Y_a, \cdots, Y_r),$$
$$\tag{1.4.8}$$

where $X, Y_1, \cdots, Y_r \in \mathcal{C}(TM)$. Clearly,

$$\nabla_X f = Xf = df(X) \tag{1.4.9}$$

for any function f on M. Thus, the *covariant differential* $\nabla \Phi$ of Φ is a $(0, r+1)$-tensor field defined by

$$\nabla \Phi(Y_1, \cdots, Y_r, X) = (\nabla_X \Phi)(Y_1, \cdots, Y_r). \tag{1.4.10}$$

Φ is said to be *parallel* with respect to ∇ if $\nabla \Phi = 0$.

In a local base $\{e_i\}$ dual to $\{\omega^i\}$, let $\Phi = \Phi_{i_1 \cdots i_r} \omega^{i_1} \otimes \cdots \otimes \omega^{i_r}$. Then $\nabla \Phi$ can be expressed as

$$\nabla \Phi = \Phi_{i_1 \cdots i_r | j} \omega^j \otimes \omega^{i_1} \otimes \cdots \otimes \omega^{i_r}, \tag{1.4.11}$$

where

$$\Phi_{i_1 \cdots i_r | j} \omega^j := d\Phi_{i_1 \cdots i_r} - \sum_{k=1}^{r} \Phi_{i_1 \cdots i_{k-1} j i_{k+1} \cdots i_r} \omega_{i_k}^j. \tag{1.4.12}$$

Here $\Phi_{i_1 \cdots i_r | j}$ is called the *covariant derivative* of $\Phi_{i_1 \cdots i_r}$ with respect to ∇.

Exercises

1.1   Let M and N be differentiable manifolds, and $f : M \to N$ a smooth map. If the rank of f equals the dimension of M, then f is called an *immersion*, and M is called an *immersed submanifold* of N. Furthermore, if $f : M \to f(M) \subset N$ is a diffeomorphism, then M is called a *regular submanifold* of N. Prove that if M is compact, then there is a positive integer m and a smooth map $f : M \to \mathbb{R}^m$, such that M is a regular submanifold of a Euclidean space $\mathbb{R}^m$.

1.2 Let X be a smooth vector field on an n-manifold M, and $p \in M$ a regular point of X, i.e., $X(p) \neq 0$. Prove that there exists a local coordinate neighborhood (U, ϕ) including p with the local coordinates $(x^1, \cdots, x^n)$, such that

$$X\Big|_U = \frac{\partial}{\partial x^1}.$$

1.3 Prove Lemma 1.2 and the formula (1.3.3).

1.4 Let M be an n-dimensional differentiable manifold. If there is an n-form ω on M which is non-zero everywhere, then M is said to be *orientable*. Prove that the real projective space RP^n is orientable if n is odd, and not orientable if n is even.

1.5 Prove that (1.4.6) and (1.4.7) are equivalent to (1.4.6′) and (1.4.7′), respectively.

1.6 Prove (1.4.11) in detail by virtue of (1.4.8) and (1.4.10).

1.7 Let (M, g) and (N, h) be smooth Riemannian manifolds, $f : M \to N$ a smooth map. For each point $p \in M$, pulling the tangent space $T_{f(p)}N$ at $f(p) \in N$ back at p, we obtain a vector bundle,

$$f^{-1}TN := \bigcup_{x \in M} T_{f(p)}N,$$

called the *pull-back bundle* of f. Deduce the covariant differential operation acting on sections of the pull-back bundle by means of Riemannian connections on (M, g) and (N, h).

1.8 In the case of Ex. 1.7, let $\{x^i\}$ and $\{\tilde{x}^\alpha\}$ be local coordinates on (M, g) and (N, h), respectively. The differential of the map $f : M \to N$ is $df = f_i^\alpha dx^i \otimes \frac{\partial}{\partial \tilde{x}^\alpha}$, where $f_i^\alpha := \frac{\partial f^\alpha}{\partial x^i}$. By using the Riemannian connection ∇ on the pull-back bundle $f^{-1}TN$, write out the expression of the covariant differential ∇df for df in the local coordinates.

Chapter 2

Finsler Metrics

2.1 Finsler metrics

2.1.1 Finsler metrics

As a general rule, a metric in a space is used to measure the "distance" between two points of the space. Thus a distance function from one point to another point is called a *metric*. Throughout this book, we always assume that a space means a finite dimensional, connected, smoothly differentiable manifold, and a metric given in the space is a distance function which can be used to compute the length of a curve in the space. Precisely, a metric is a function of both the point and the tangent vector on the manifold. We consider sometimes the non-positively definite "metric" in order to generalize it to the space-time in the Einstein relative theory.

Let M be an n-dimensional smooth manifold. A parameterized curve segment $c = c(t)$ on M is a continuous map $c : [a, b] \to M$, $t \in [a, b]$, for real numbers a and b. In a local coordinate system $\{x^i\}$ in M, it can be expressed by $x^i = x^i(t)$, $t \in [a, b]$. The tangent vector field $\dot{c}$ of c can be written as $\dot{x}^i = \frac{dx^i}{dt}$. To measure the length of c, we need a metric (resp. an arc element) ds on M. For example, if we are given a Riemannian metric

$$ds = \sqrt{g_{ij}(x)dx^i dx^j}$$

on M, then the length $L_g(c)$ of c is

$$L_g(c) = \int_a^b \sqrt{g_{ij}(x(t))\dot{x}^i \dot{x}^j}\, dt.$$

Here the square of the integrand function is a positively definite quadric form with respect to $\dot{x}^i$. In general, it is not necessary to restrict the integrand function in such a way. We may admit that the integrand function is a non-negative function $F(c(t), \dot{c}(t))$ with $2n$ variables defined on the tangent bundle TM such that the length $L_F(c)$ of c becomes

$$L_F(c) = \int_a^b F(c(t), \dot{c}(t))dt.$$

It is required that $L_F(c)$ be independent of positive parametrization. So, $F(x, y)$ should be positively homogenous with degree one, i.e.,

$$F(x, \lambda y) = \lambda F(x, y), \quad \lambda > 0.$$

From now on we always adopt the notations that $x = (x^1, \cdots, x^n)$, $y = (y^1, \cdots, y^n)$ with the tangent vector $y = y^i \frac{\partial}{\partial x^i}$. The length structure induces a distance function $d_F : M \times M \to [0, +\infty)$ by

$$d_F(p, q) = \inf_c L_F(c), \quad p, q \in M,$$

where the infimum is taken over all curves c from $p = x(a)$ to $q = x(b)$. In general, d_F is irreversible, i.e., $d_F(p, q) \neq d_F(q, p)$. Furthermore, we impose a convexity condition on F, i.e.,

$$F(x, y_1 + y_2) \leq F(x, y_1) + F(x, y_2), \quad y_1, y_2 \in T_x M,$$

where the equality holds if and only if $y_1 = ay_2$ for some $a > 0$.

Definition 2.1. Let M be an n-dimensional smooth manifold, $F : TM \to [0, +\infty)$ be a non-negative function on the tangent bundle. F is called a *Finsler metric* in M if it satisfies the following conditions:

(1) *Positive homogeneity*: $F(x, \lambda y) = \lambda F(x, y), \forall \lambda > 0$;

(2) *Smoothness*: $F(x, y)$ is a C^∞ function on the slit tangent bundle $M_0 := TM \backslash \{0\}$;

(3) *Strong convexity*: For any non-zero vector $y \neq 0$, the Hessian matrix formed by following

$$g_{ij}(x, y) = \frac{1}{2} \frac{\partial^2 F^2}{\partial y^i \partial y^j}(x, y) = \frac{1}{2}[F^2]_{y^i y^j}$$

is positively definite.

The bilinear symmetric form

$$g = g_{ij}(x, y)dx^i \otimes dx^j$$

on M_0 is called the *fundamental form* or *fundamental tensor*.

A differentiable manifold M equipped with a Finsler metric F is called a *Finsler manifold* or *Finsler space* denoted by (M, F).

It follows from the definition that $F(x, y) \geq 0$ where the equality holds if and only if $y = 0$. By the Euler theorem on the homogeneous function we have

$$y^i F_{y^i} = F, \quad y^j F_{y^i y^j} = 0, \quad F^2 = g_{ij} y^i y^j. \tag{2.1.1}$$

More general, let $L : TM \to \mathbb{R}$ be a function with the following properties:

(1) *Homogeneity*: $L(x, \lambda y) = \lambda^2 L(x, y), \forall \lambda > 0$;

(2) *Smoothness*: $L(x, y)$ is a C^∞ function on the slip tangent bundle M_0;

(3) *Regularity*: For any non-zero vector $y \neq 0$, $g_{ij}(x, y) = \frac{1}{2} \frac{\partial^2 L}{\partial y^i \partial y^j}(x, y)$ form a non-singular matrix.

Then L is called a *generic Finsler metric* in M. If (g_{ij}) is a positively definite matrix, then $L = F^2$ is just the Finsler metric. L is called a *pseudo-Finsler metric* if (g_{ij}) has the negative eigenvalue. In this case, strictly speaking, L is not a metric. If the dimension of M is 4 and (g_{ij}) has one negative eigenvalue, then L is called a *space-time Finsler metric*.

2.1.2 Examples of Finsler metrics

We now look at some important examples of Finsler metrics. For simplicity, we assume that Finsler metrics are defined on an open subset of $\mathbb{R}^n$.

Example 2.1. Let $(g_{ij}(x))$ be a smooth, symmetric, positively definite matrix defined on an open subset $U \subset \mathbb{R}^n$. Set

$$F^2(x, y) = g(x, y) = g_{ij}(x) y^i y^j,$$

where $y = (y^i) \in T_x U \approx \mathbb{R}^n$ is the tangent vector at the point $x = (x^i) \in U$. This is the usual *Riemannian metric*.

Writing $\langle x, y \rangle = \sum_{i=1}^n x^i y^i$, $|x| = \sqrt{\sum_{i=1}^n (x^i)^2}$, $|y| = \sqrt{\sum_{i=1}^n (y^i)^2}$, we set

$$g_\mu = \frac{|y|^2 + \mu(|x|^2 |y|^2 - \langle x, y \rangle^2)}{(1 + \mu|x|^2)^2} = g_{ij}(x) y^i y^j,$$

$$g_{ij}(x) = \frac{\delta_{ij} + \mu(|x|^2 \delta_{ij} - x^i x^j)}{(1 + \mu|x|^2)^2},$$

where μ is a constant, (g_{ij}) is a symmetric positively definite matrix on the ball $B^n(r)$, where $r = +\infty$ if $\mu \geq 0$ and $r = \pi/\sqrt{-\mu}$ if $\mu < 0$. Clearly, this is a Riemannian metric with constant sectional curvature μ. $g_0 = |y|^2$ is just the standard Euclidean metric when $\mu = 0$.

It is easy to prove that a Finsler metric in Definition 2.1 satisfies the convexity condition as in §2.1.1. Hence, for any fixed point $x \in U$, $F_x = F(x, \cdot)$ is a "norm" on $T_x M$ and $(T_x U, F_x)$ is a space endowed with a norm. Thus, for any $y \in T_x U$, $F_x(y) = F(x, y)$ is called the *F-length* of y.

If a Finsler metric $F(x, y) = F(y)$ on $U \subset \mathbb{R}^n$ is independent of x, then it is called a *Minkowski metric*, which is a generalization of the Euclidean metric. Obviously, at each point x, $F_x(y)$ is a Minkowski metric on $T_x M \equiv \mathbb{R}^n$. A vector space equipped with a Minkowski metric is called a *Minkowski space*. The tangent space at each point in a Finsler manifold is a Minkowski space. Intuitively, the Minkowski unit ball $\mathcal{B}_x := \{x \in T_x M | F_x(y) < 1\}$ at a point $x \in M$ is an infinitesimal color pattern and it varies over the whole manifold. Thus, a Finsler manifold is a "colorful" curved space.

Example 2.2. Let $\alpha = \sqrt{a_{ij}(x)y^i y^j}$ be a Riemannian metric defined on an open subset $U \subset \mathbb{R}^n$, $\beta = b_i(x)y^i$ one form.
(1) Define

$$F := \alpha + \beta. \qquad (2.1.2)$$

On putting $||\beta_x||_\alpha := \sup_{y \in T_x U} \frac{\beta(x,y)}{\alpha(x,y)}$, we have $||\beta_x||_\alpha = \sqrt{a^{ij}(x)b_i(x)b_j(x)}$, where $(a^{ij}(x)) = (a_{ij}(x))^{-1}$. If F is positively definite, then $F(x, y) \geq 0$ for any non-zero tangent vector y. Thus, we obtain the following necessary condition

$$||\beta_x||_\alpha < 1.$$

It is easy to see that this is also a sufficient condition for F (2.1.2) to be a Finsler metric (see Lemma 2.1 below for detail). Finsler metrics defined by (2.1.2) are called *Randers metrics*, which were first introduced by a physicist G. Randers in 1941 ([31]).

A famous example of Randers metrics is the following

$$\alpha = \frac{\sqrt{|y|^2 + \mu(|x|^2|y|^2 - \langle x, y \rangle^2)}}{1 + \mu|x|^2}, \quad \beta = \frac{\sqrt{-\mu}\langle x, y \rangle}{1 + \mu|x|^2}, \quad \mu < 0, \qquad (2.1.3)$$

where $x \in B^n(r_\mu) \subset \mathbb{R}^n$, $r_\mu = 1/\sqrt{-\mu}$, $y \in T_x B^n(r_\mu)$. When $\mu = -1$, we have

$$F = \frac{\sqrt{|y|^2 - (|x|^2|y|^2 - \langle x, y \rangle^2)} + \langle x, y \rangle}{1 - |x|^2} := \Theta(x, y). \qquad (2.1.4)$$

This is the *Funk metric* defined on the unit ball $B^n(1) \subset \mathbb{R}^n$.
(2) Put

$$F := (\alpha + \beta)^2/\alpha. \qquad (2.1.5)$$

It follows from Lemma 2.1 below that F defined by (2.1.5) is Finslerian if and only if $||\beta_x||_\alpha < 1$. A special case is as follows.

Let

$$\alpha = \frac{\sqrt{|y|^2 + \mu(|x|^2|y|^2 - \langle x, y \rangle^2)}}{(1 + \mu|x|^2)}, \quad \beta = \frac{\sqrt{-\mu}\langle x, y \rangle}{1 + \mu|x|^2},$$

where $y \in T_x B^n(r_\mu) \approx \mathbb{R}^n$, $x \in B^n(r_\mu) \subset \mathbb{R}^n$, $\mu < 0$ is a constant. Then

$$F = \frac{(\alpha + \beta)^2}{\alpha} = \frac{(\sqrt{|y|^2 + \mu(|x|^2|y|^2 - \langle x, y \rangle^2)} + \sqrt{-\mu}\langle x, y \rangle)^2}{(1 + \mu|x|^2)^2 \sqrt{|y|^2 + \mu(|x|^2|y|^2 - \langle x, y \rangle^2)}}. \quad (2.1.6)$$

In particular, for $\mu = -1$, we have

$$F = \frac{(\sqrt{|y|^2 - (|x|^2|y|^2 - \langle x, y \rangle^2)} + \langle x, y \rangle)^2}{(1 - |x|^2)^2 \sqrt{|y|^2 - (|x|^2|y|^2 - \langle x, y \rangle^2)}}. \quad (2.1.6')$$

Finsler metrics defined by (2.1.5) are called *quadratic metrics*, which will appear in many geometric problems discussed below.

(3) By using a Riemannian metric α and a 1-form β, we may construct many interesting Finsler metrics.

Let $\phi : (-b_0, b_0) \to (0, \infty)$ be a smooth positive function. Suppose that $\alpha(x, y) = \sqrt{a_{ij}(x)y^i y^j}$ is a Riemannian metric on an open subset $U \subset \mathbb{R}^n$ and $\beta(x, y) = b_i(x)y^i$ is a 1-form satisfying $b := ||\beta||_\alpha < b_0$. Define

$$F(x, y) = \alpha(x, y)\phi(s), \quad s = \frac{\beta(x, y)}{\alpha(x, y)}. \quad (2.1.7)$$

Applying some Maple programs (Appendix A), we may obtain ([36])

$$g_{ij} = \rho a_{ij} + \rho_0 b_i b_j + \rho_1 (b_i \alpha_j + b_j \alpha_i) - s\rho_1 \alpha_i \alpha_j,$$

where $\alpha_i = \alpha_{y^i}$,

$$\rho = \phi^2 - s\phi\phi', \quad \rho_0 = \phi\phi'' + (\phi')^2, \quad \rho_1 = -s(\phi\phi'' + (\phi')^2) + \phi\phi'.$$

According to Lemma 4.1 in Chapter 4, we have

$$\det(g_{ij}) = \phi^{n+1}(\phi - s\phi')^{n-2}\{(\phi - s\phi') + (b^2 - s^2)\phi''\} \det(a_{ij}). \quad (2.1.7')$$

Lemma 2.1. $F = \alpha\phi(\frac{\beta}{\alpha})$ *defined by (2.1.7) is a Finsler metric for any α and β with $||\beta||_\alpha < b_0$ if and only if the function $\phi(s)$ satisfies*

$$\phi(s) > 0, \quad (\phi(s) - s\phi'(s)) + (b^2 - s^2)\phi''(s) > 0, \quad (*)$$

where s and b are arbitrary real numbers with $|s| \le b < b_0$.

Such a metric $F = \alpha\phi(\beta/\alpha)$ is called an (α, β)-*metric*.

Proof. Assume $(*)$ is satisfied. By taking $b = s$ in $(*)$, we see that

$$\phi(s) - s\phi'(s) > 0 \qquad (**)$$

for any s with $|s| < b_0$. Consider the following families of functions and metrics

$$\phi_t(s) := 1 - t + t\phi(s), \quad F_t := \alpha\phi_t\left(\frac{\beta}{\alpha}\right), \quad g_{ij}^t := \frac{1}{2}[F_t^2]_{y^iy^j}.$$

It follows from $(*)$ and $(**)$ that the following inequalities hold for any s, b with $|s| < b_0$ and $0 \le t \le 1$

$$\phi_t - s\phi_t' = 1 - t + t(\phi - s\phi') > 0,$$

$$(\phi_t - s\phi_t') + (b^2 - s^2)\phi_t'' = 1 - t + t\{(\phi - s\phi') + (b^2 - s^2)\phi''\} > 0.$$

Thus $\det(g_{ij}^t) > 0$ for all $0 \le t \le 1$. Since (g_{ij}^0) is positively definite, then (g_{ij}^t) is positively definite for any $0 \le t \le 1$. Hence, F_t is a Finsler metric for any $t \in [0.1]$. In particular, $F = F_1$ is Finslerian.

Conversely, assume that F defined by (2.1.7) is Finslerian. Then $\phi(s) > 0$ for any s with $|s| < b_0$. Note the formula (2.1.7'). If n is even, then $\det(g_{ij}) > 0$ implies that $(*)$ holds for any s with $|s| < b$. If $n > 1$ is odd, then $\det(g_{ij}) > 0$ implies that the following inequality holds for s with $|s| < b$

$$\phi(s) - s\phi'(s) \neq 0.$$

Since $\phi(s) > 0$, the above inequality implies $(**)$ holds for any s with $|s| < b$. Since b with $0 \le b \le b_0$ is arbitrary, we conclude that $(**)$ holds for any s with $|s| < b_0$. Finally, it is easy to see that $\det(g_{ij}) > 0$ implies that $(*)$ holds for any s with $|s| \le b < b_0$. $\qquad\square$

Clearly, the Randers metric is an (α, β)-metric with $\phi(s) = 1 + s$.

The quadratic metric (2.1.5) is an (α, β)-metric with $\phi(s) = (1 + s)^2$.

The *Matsumoto metric* $F = \frac{\alpha^2}{\alpha-\beta}$ is an (α, β)-metric with $\phi(s) = (1 - s)^{-1}$ $(|s| < 1)$.

The *Kropina metric* $F = \frac{\alpha^2}{\beta}$ is an (α, β)-metric with $\phi(s) = 1/s$ $(s > 0)$, which is not regular.

Let us look at the following example. Define

$$F := \alpha + \epsilon\beta + 2\frac{k\beta^2}{\alpha} - \frac{k^2\beta^4}{3\alpha^3},$$

where ϵ and $k \neq 0$ are constant. By Lemma 2.1, the above F is Finslerian if and only if $b := \|\beta_x\|_\alpha < 1/\sqrt{|k|}$. This is an (α, β)-metric with $\phi(s) = 1 + \epsilon s + 2ks^2 - \frac{1}{3}k^2s^4$ ([133]).

Example 2.3. Let m be a positive even integer. Define

$$F = \{a_{i_1 \cdots i_m}(x)y^{i_1} \cdots y^{i_m}\}^{\frac{1}{m}} = (F^m)^{\frac{1}{m}}, \qquad (2.1.8)$$

where $F^m = a_{i_1 \cdots i_m}(x)y^{i_1} \cdots y^{i_m}$ is a positive homogeneous polynomial of degree m. F is called an *m-th root metric*. Clearly, such metrics include Riemannian metrics.

We are interested in the 4-th root metrics, i.e.,

$$F = \sqrt[4]{a_{ijkl}(x)y^i y^j y^k y^l},$$

and its generalization,

$$F = \sqrt{\sqrt{A} + B} + C, \quad A = a_{ijkl}(x)y^i y^j y^k y^l, \quad B = b_{ij}(x)y^i y^j, \quad C = c_i(x)y^i.$$
$$(2.1.9)$$

Such metrics would have special geometric properties which will be discussed further. When $C = 0$, $F = \sqrt{\sqrt{A} + B}$ is a *reversible metric*, i.e., $F(x, y) = F(x, -y)$.

Example 2.4. Let $f : [0, \infty) \times [0, \infty) \to \mathbb{R}$ be a smooth positive function satisfying $f(\lambda s, \lambda t) = \lambda f(s, t)$, $\lambda > 0$. Suppose that α_1 and α_2 are Riemannian metrics on $U_1 \subset \mathbb{R}^{n_1}$ and $U_2 \subset \mathbb{R}^{n_2}$, respectively. Define

$$F(x, y) = \sqrt{f([\alpha_1(x_1, y_1)]^2, [\alpha_2(x_2, y_2)]^2)}, \qquad (2.1.10)$$

where $x = (x_1, x_2)$, $y = (y_1, y_2)$. If $F(s, t)$ satisfies the following conditions:

$$f_s > 0, \quad f_t > 0, \quad f_s + 2s f_{ss} > 0, \quad f_t + 2t f_{tt} > 0, \quad f_s f_t - 2f f_{st} > 0,$$

then (2.1.10) defines a positively definite Finsler metric, which is a *Berwald metric* (see Chapter 3, §3.1.2). A straightforward computation gives (cf. Lemma 4.1 in Chapter 4, below)

$$(g_{ij}) = \begin{pmatrix} 2f_{ss}y_{i_1}y_{j_1} + f_s g_{i_1 j_1} & 2f_{st}y_{i_1}y_{j_2} \\ 2f_{st}y_{i_2}y_{j_1} & 2f_{tt}y_{i_2}y_{j_2} + f_t g_{i_2 j_2} \end{pmatrix}, \qquad (2.1.10')$$

$$\det(g_{ij}) = h([\alpha_1]^2, [\alpha_2]^2) \det(g_{i_1 j_1}) \det(g_{i_2 j_2}),$$

$$h(s, t) := (f_s)^{n_1 - 1}(f_t)^{n_2 - 1}\{f_s f_t - 2f f_{st}\}.$$

A concrete example of f is

$$f(s, t) = s + t + \varepsilon(s^k + t^k)^{1/k},$$

where ε is a non-negative number and k is a positive integer.

In the following we consider some pseudo-Finsler metrics.

Example 2.5. Let $\alpha = \sqrt{a_{ij}(x)y^i y^j}$ be a Riemannian metric on an open subset $U \subset \mathbb{R}^3$. Define a product metric on $U \times \mathbb{R}$ as follows. Let $\overline{x} = (x, s)$ be the point in $U \times \mathbb{R}$, $\overline{y} = (y, u)$ the tangent vector at $\overline{x}$. Define

$$g(\overline{x}, \overline{y}) = a_{ij}(x)y^i y^j - u^2 + \varepsilon \sqrt{[a_{ij}(x)y^i y^j]^2 + u^4},$$

where ε is a constant. Then g is the fundamental form of a non-positively definite pseudo-Finsler metric when ε is small enough.

A time-space Finsler metric should satisfy the requirements of homogeneity, isotropy and closure. An example of such metrics is the following $F = \alpha + \beta$ where

$$\alpha^2 = R^2(t)\left(\frac{dx^2}{1 - kx^2} + x^2 dy^2 + x^2 \sin^2 y dz^2\right) - (dt)^2.$$

$$\beta = b_1 dx + b_2 dy + b_3 dz - b_4 dt.$$

It can be seen from Definition 2.1 that for any fixed $y \in T_x M$ the fundamental tensor g can be represented by the following non-coordinate form:

$$g_y(u, v) := \frac{1}{2}\frac{\partial^2}{\partial t_1 \partial t_2}F^2(y + t_1 u + t_2 v)\Big|_{t_1 = t_2 = 0}$$

for $u, v \in TM_0$. The fundamental form $g(x, y)$ determines an *inner product* $\langle \cdot, \cdot \rangle$ on $T_x M$. Thus, the following notations can be used:

$$\langle v, w \rangle_y := g_y(v, w) := g_{ij}(x, y)v^i w^j, \tag{2.1.11}$$

where $v = v^i \frac{\partial}{\partial x^i}$, $w = w^i \frac{\partial}{\partial x^i} \in T_x M$. Particularly, the third formula of (2.1.1) can be written as

$$\langle y, y \rangle_y = g_y(y, y) = F^2(x, y). \tag{2.1.12}$$

Such notations are called sometimes the global representation, of which the advantage is to avoid the choice of local coordinate frames.

2.2 Cartan torsion

2.2.1 Cartan torsion

Let M be an n-dimensional manifold. For a point $p \in M$, we have a local coordinate map $\varphi : U_p \to \mathbb{R}^n$. By φ we obtain a local coordinate system $\widehat{\varphi} : TU_p \to \mathbb{R}^n \times \mathbb{R}^n$ in TM, which is defined by $\widehat{\varphi} : y = y^i \frac{\partial}{\partial x^i}|_p \to (x^i, y^i)$, where x^i are the coordinates of p and $(\frac{\partial}{\partial x^i}, \frac{\partial}{\partial y^i})$ are the local natural frames in $T(TM)$.

Let $\pi : TM \to M$ be the natural projection from the tangent bundle TM. Define an equivalent relation $\sim$ in the slip tangent bundle $TM_0 := TM \setminus \{0\}$: $X \sim Y$ if two non-zero tangent vectors X and Y satisfy $Y = \lambda X$ ($\forall \lambda \in \mathbb{R}^+$). The quotient space $TM_0 / \sim$ is called the *projective tangent bundle* over M, denoted by PTM, which is isomorphic to the *unit sphere bundle* $SM := \{y \in TM_0 | F(\cdot, y) = 1\}$ over (M, F). Thus, $\dim PTM = \dim SM = 2n - 1$. The local coordinates on PTM can be denoted by (x^i, y^i), where $\{y^i\}$ are the homogeneous coordinates.

For a point $x \in M$, the fiber of SM at x is

$$S_x M \equiv \mathcal{I}_x := \{y \in T_x M | F_x(y) = F(x, y) = 1\}.$$

It is called the *indicatrix* of (M, F) at x. If F is Riemannian, the indicatrix at any point is a Euclidean unit sphere. However, if F is non-Riemannian, the indicatrix of (M, F) at a point $x \in M$ is a hypersurface $\{y \in T_x M | F_x(y) = F(x, y) = 1\}$ in the Minkowski space $(T_x M, F_x)$, which varies over M.

Denote by $\rho : PTM \to M$ the natural projection from the projective tangent bundle. Let $\pi^* TM$ be the pull-back tangent bundle over PTM induced by π, which is also the pull-back tangent bundle over TM_0. Thus, we have the following commutative diagram:

$$
\begin{array}{ccc}
\pi^* TM & \xrightarrow{\ \pi\ } & PTM \cong SM \\
{\scriptstyle \rho} \downarrow & & \downarrow {\scriptstyle \rho} \\
TM & \xrightarrow[\ \pi\ ]{} & M
\end{array}
$$

Since $F(x, y)$ is a homogeneous function of degree 1 with respect to y, $F(x, y)$ is actually defined on PTM and the fundamental tensor g is defined on $\pi^* TM$.

To characterize Riemannian metrics among Finsler metric, we present the following geometric quantity introduced by E. Cartan in 1934.

Definition 2.2. Let (M, F) be an n-dimensional Finsler manifold. The *Cartan torsion* $\mathbf{C}$ is a symmetric $(0, 3)$-tensor field defined on $\pi^* TM$:

$$\mathbf{C} = C_{ijk}(x, y) dx^i \otimes dx^j \otimes dx^k, \quad C_{ijk} := \frac{1}{4}[F^2]_{y^i y^j y^k} = \frac{1}{2}\frac{\partial g_{ij}}{\partial y^k}. \quad (2.2.1)$$

The mean value $\mathbf{I}$ of $\mathbf{C}$ is called the *mean Cartan torsion* defined by

$$\mathbf{I} = \mathbf{I}_k dx^k, \quad \mathbf{I}_k = g^{ij} C_{ijk}, \quad (g^{ij}) = (g_{ij})^{-1}. \quad (2.2.2)$$

$\mathbf{C}$ and $\mathbf{I}$ are also called the *Cartan tensor* and *Cartan form*, respectively.

C and **I** can be also rewritten as

$$\mathbf{C}_y(u,v,w) := \frac{1}{4}\frac{\partial^3}{\partial t_1 \partial t_2 \partial t_3}F^2(y + t_1 u + t_2 v + t_3 w)\Big|_{t_1 = t_2 = t_3 = 0}, \qquad (2.2.1')$$

$$\mathbf{I}(v) = \mathrm{tr}_g \mathbf{C}(\cdot, \cdot, v), \qquad (2.2.2')$$

where $u, v, w \in TM_0$. In virtue of (2.1.1) and (2.2.1), we have

$$C_{ijk}y^i = C_{ijk}y^j = C_{ijk}y^k = 0, \quad \text{or} \quad \mathbf{C}_y(u,v,w) = 0. \qquad (2.2.3)$$

By means of (2.1.1) and (2.2.2), we have

$$\mathbf{I}_k = \frac{\partial}{\partial y^k}\left[\ln\sqrt{\det(g_{ij})}\right]. \qquad (2.2.4)$$

It follows from (2.2.1) that a Finsler metric is Riemannian if and only if its Cartan torsion vanishes identically. Moreover, we have the following Deicke theorem.

2.2.2   Deicke theorem

Theorem 2.1 (A. Deicke). *A Finsler metric is Riemannian if and only if its mean Cartan torsion vanishes identically.*

Proof. The necessity is obvious. We now prove the sufficiency. Assume that the mean Cartan torsion vanishes identically. Fixed a point $x \in M$, $F_x^2(y) = F^2(x,y) = g_{ij}(x,y)y^i y^j$ becomes a Riemannian metric on $T_x M$. On putting $(g^{ij}) = (g_{ij})^{-1}$, we consider the following elliptic operator $\Delta_x := g^{ij}\frac{\partial^2}{\partial y^i \partial y^j}$ on $(T_x M, F_x^2(y))$. For each g_{kl}, by using (2.2.1) and (2.2.2), we have

$$\begin{aligned}
\Delta_x g_{kl} &= g^{ij}[g_{kl}]_{y^i y^j} = \frac{1}{2}g^{ij}[F^2]_{y^i y^j y^k y^l} = 2g^{ij}[C_{ijk}]_{y^l}\\
&= 2[g^{ij}C_{ijk}]_{y^l} - 2[g^{ij}]_{y^l}C_{ijk} = 2[\mathbf{I}_k]_{y^l} + 2g^{ip}g^{jq}[g_{pq}]_{y^l}C_{ijk}\\
&= 4g^{ip}g^{jq}C_{ijk}C_{pql}.
\end{aligned}$$

Thus, the matrix $(\Delta_x g_{kl})$ is semi-positively definite. In particular, $\Delta_x g_{kk} \geq 0$ for each k.

Let $B(r) := \{y \in T_x M | F_x(y) < r\}$, where $r > 1$ is a real number. Since g_{kk} is homogeneous with respect to y, g_{kk} must achieve its maximum in the interior of the domain $B(r) \setminus B(1/r)$. By the maximum principle, g_{kk} must be constant in $B(r) \setminus B(1/r)$, i.e., g_{kk} is independent of y. Letting $r \to +\infty$, we see that g_{kk} is constant on $T_x M \setminus \{0\}$ for each k, from which it follows that $\Delta_x g_{kk} = 0$ for each k. Hence, the trace of the matrix $(\Delta_x g_{kl})$

is zero on $T_xM \setminus \{0\}$. Since the matrix is semi-positively definite, we see $(\Delta_x g_{kl})$ is a zero matrix, i.e., $\Delta_x g_{kl} = 0$ for every pair $\{kl\}$.

Applying the maximum principle to each g_{kl}, we conclude that g_{kl} are independent of y on $T_xM \setminus \{0\}$. Since the point $x \in M$ is arbitrary, g_{kl} are independent of y on TM_0 everywhere, i.e., F is Riemannian. □

To characterize Randers metrics, M. Matsumoto introduced the following symmetric $(0,3)$-tensor field ([74, 75])

$$M_{ijk} := C_{ijk} - \frac{1}{n+1}\left(\mathbf{I}_i h_{jk} + \mathbf{I}_j h_{ki} + \mathbf{I}_k h_{ij}\right), \tag{2.2.5}$$

where

$$h_{ij} := F[F]_{y^i y^j} = g_{ij} - g_{ip}g_{jq}\frac{y^p}{F}\frac{y^q}{F}.$$

Theorem 2.2 (M. Matsumoto). *For $n \geq 3$, a Finsler metric F is a Randers metric if and only if the tensor field defined by (2.2.5) vanishes identically.*

Proof. The necessity follows from a direct calculation (see Ex. 2.5 and 2.6, Chapter 2). The proof for the sufficiency is given in the following two steps.

Step I: Algebraic transformations. Suppose that the tensor field M_{ijk} of F vanishes identically, i.e.,

$$C_{ijk} = \frac{1}{n+1}\left(\mathbf{I}_i h_{jk} + \mathbf{I}_j h_{ki} + \mathbf{I}_k h_{ij}\right). \tag{2.2.6}$$

Fix arbitrary point $x \in M$. We have a Riemannian metric on $T_xM \setminus \{0\}$ induced by F

$$g_x := g_{ij}(x,y)dy^i \otimes dy^j.$$

The Levi-Civita connection $\widetilde{\nabla}$ in the Riemannian manifold $(T_xM \setminus \{0\}, g_x)$ is determined by the Christoffel symbol

$$\widetilde{\Gamma}^i_{jk} = C^i_{jk} = g^{il}C_{jkl}.$$

Denoting by "," the covariant differential with respect to $\widetilde{\nabla}$, we have

$$g_{ij,k} = 0, \quad \ell_{i,j} = \frac{h_{ij}}{F}, \quad \ell_i := F_{y^i}, \quad h_{ij} = g_{ij} - \ell_i \ell_j, \tag{2.2.7}$$

$$h_{ij,k} = -\frac{1}{F}(h_{ik}\ell_j + h_{jk}\ell_i), \tag{2.2.8}$$

$$C_{ijk,l} = C_{ijl,k}, \quad \mathbf{I}_{i,j,k} - \mathbf{I}_{i,k,j} = \mathbf{I}_i(C^s_{ij}C^l_{sk} - C^s_{ik}C^l_{sj}). \tag{2.2.9}$$

It follows from (2.2.6)-(2.2.9) that

$$\mathbf{I}_{i,j} = \frac{1}{(n-1)F}[F\mathcal{I}h_{ij} - (n-1)(\mathbf{I}_i \ell_j + \mathbf{I}_j \ell_i)], \quad \mathcal{I} := g^{ij}\mathbf{I}_{i,j}. \tag{2.2.10}$$

Put

$$D_i := \frac{1}{(n-1)} \left[\left(\frac{2(n-1)\|\mathbf{I}\|^2}{(n+1)^2} - \frac{n-1}{F^2} \right) \mathbf{I}_i - \frac{2\mathcal{I}}{F} \ell_i - \mathcal{I}_{,i} \right], \quad \|\mathbf{I}\|^2 := g^{ij}\mathbf{I}_i\mathbf{I}_j.$$

$$(2.2.11)$$

It is easy from (2.2.6), (2.2.9) and (2.2.10) to get

$$h_{ij}D_k = h_{ik}D_j. \tag{2.2.12}$$

Noting that $D_i y^i = 0$ and contracting (2.2.12) with g^{ij}, we get $(n-2)D_k = 0$. Since $n \geq 3$, $D_k = 0$, i.e.,

$$\mathcal{I}_{,i} = (n-1) \left[\frac{2\|\mathbf{I}\|^2}{(n+1)^2} - \frac{1}{F^2} \right] \mathbf{I}_i - \frac{2\mathcal{I}}{F} \ell_i. \tag{2.2.13}$$

On the other hand, it follows from (2.2.10) that

$$\frac{1}{2}(\|\mathbf{I}\|^2)_{,i} = \frac{\mathcal{I}}{n-1} \mathbf{I}_i - \frac{\|\mathbf{I}\|^2}{F} \ell_i. \tag{2.2.14}$$

On putting

$$\mathcal{A} := \frac{\mathcal{I}}{n-1} + \frac{\|\mathbf{I}\|^2}{n+1}, \tag{2.2.15}$$

we have from (2.2.13) and (2.2.14)

$$\mathcal{A}_{,i} = 2\mathcal{A} \left[\left(\frac{1}{n+1} - \frac{1}{2\mathcal{A}F^2} \right) \mathbf{I}_i - \frac{\ell_i}{F} \right]. \tag{2.2.16}$$

Step II: Solving equations. By using the well-known formula of the covariant differential and substituting (2.2.6) into the left hand side of (2.2.8), we can obtain

$$\frac{\partial h_{ij}}{\partial y^k} = \frac{2}{n+1}(\mathbf{I}_i h_{jk} + \mathbf{I}_j h_{ki} + \mathbf{I}_k h_{ij}) - \frac{1}{F}(h_{ik}\ell_j + h_{jk}\ell_i). \tag{2.2.17}$$

By the same method, we can get from (2.2.6), (2.2.15) and (2.2.10)

$$\frac{\partial \mathbf{I}_i}{\partial y^j} = \mathcal{A}h_{ij} + \frac{2\mathbf{I}_i\mathbf{I}_j}{n+1} - \frac{1}{F}(\mathbf{I}_i\ell_j + \mathbf{I}_j\ell_i). \tag{2.2.18}$$

On the other hand, (2.2.4) may be rewritten as

$$\mathbf{I}_i = -\frac{n+1}{2}\frac{\partial \log G}{\partial y^i}, \quad G := [\det(g_{ij})]^{-\frac{1}{n+1}}. \tag{2.2.19}$$

By means of (2.2.17)-(2.2.19), the equation (2.2.16) can be reduced to

$$\frac{\partial(GF^2\mathcal{A})}{\partial y^i} + G\mathbf{I}_i = 0.$$

Inserting (2.2.19) into the above equation and integrating with respect to y, we obtain

$$(2F^2\mathcal{A} - (n+1))G = 2a, \qquad (2.2.20)$$

where $a = a(x)$ depends only on x. In virtue of (2.2.19), the equation (2.2.18) may be reduced to

$$\frac{\partial \mathbf{I}_i}{\partial y^j} + \frac{\partial \log(GF)}{\partial y^j}\mathbf{I}_i = \mathcal{A}h_{ij} - \frac{\mathbf{I}_j\ell_i}{F},$$

i.e.,

$$\frac{\partial(GF\mathbf{I}_i)}{\partial y^j} = G(F\mathcal{A}h_{ij} - \mathbf{I}_j\ell_i).$$

By using (2.2.19) and (2.2.20), we can rewrite the above equation as

$$\frac{\partial}{\partial y^j}(GF\mathbf{I}_i) = \frac{\partial}{\partial y^j}\left[\left(a + \frac{n+1}{2}G\right)\ell_i\right].$$

Integrating in the left and right hand sides of the above formula, we get

$$GF\mathbf{I}_i = \left(a + \frac{n+1}{2}G\right)\ell_i + a_i, \qquad (2.2.21)$$

where $a_i = a_i(x)$ $(1 \le i \le n)$ depend only on x.

It follows from (2.2.17) and (2.2.21) that

$$\frac{\partial h_{ij}}{\partial y^k} - \frac{2}{n+1}h_{ij}\mathbf{I}_k = \frac{2}{(n+1)GF}\left[(a\ell_i + a_i)h_{jk} + (a\ell_j + a_j)h_{ik}\right],$$

which is just

$$\frac{\partial(Gh_{ij})}{\partial y^k} = \frac{2}{n+1}\frac{\partial}{\partial y^k}(a\ell_i\ell_j + a_i\ell_j + a_j\ell_i).$$

Integrating the above equation yields

$$Gh_{ij} = \frac{2}{n+1}(a\ell_i\ell_j + a_i\ell_j + a_j\ell_i + a_{ij}),$$

where $a_{ij} = a_{ij}(x) = a_{ji}(x)$ depend only on x. Contracting the above formula with $y^i y^j$, we obtain

$$aF^2 + 2(a_i y^i)F + a_{ij}y^i y^j = 0. \qquad (2.2.22)$$

By solving the quadratic equation (2.2.22), we see that F is a Randers metric. $\qquad \square$

2.3   Hilbert form and sprays

2.3.1   Hilbert form

Let (M, F) be an n-dimensional Finsler manifold, and (x, y) the local coordinates on PTM. Define

$$\omega := F_{y^i} dx^i = F^{-1} y^j g_{ji} dx^i. \tag{2.3.1}$$

ω is called *Hilbert form*, of which the dual vector field is

$$\ell = \ell^i \frac{\partial}{\partial x^i} := F^{-1} y^i \frac{\partial}{\partial x^i}. \tag{2.3.2}$$

If $(\widetilde{x}, \widetilde{y})$ are the another coordinates on PTM, then we have

$$\widetilde{y}^i = \frac{\partial \widetilde{x}^i}{\partial x^j} y^j, \quad F_{y^i} = \frac{\partial \widetilde{x}^j}{\partial x^i} F_{\widetilde{y}^j}.$$

Thus,

$$\omega = F_{y^i} dx^i = F_{\widetilde{y}^i} d\widetilde{x}^i,$$

i.e., ω is independent of the choice of local coordinates on PTM, so that ω is well defined on PTM globally. With the Hilbert form and (2.1.1), the arc integral in the beginning of §2.1 may be written as

$$L_F(C) = \int_C \omega.$$

The 1-form ω was proposed by D. Hilbert at the 1900 International Congress in Paris when he devoted the problem of the geometry of simple integral, namely Problem 23, to the subject. The Hilbert form plays an important role in the study of Finsler geometry.

By using the exterior differential on PTM, one can prove (cf. [10]) that

$$\omega \wedge (d\omega)^{n-1} \neq 0.$$

Thus, the Hilbert form ω deduces a *contact structure* on the $(2n - 1)$-dimensional manifold PTM. Viewing PTM as a base space, we may make up a $2n$-dimensional line bundle $\iota : \mathcal{S} \to PTM$, whose fiber is $\lambda \omega$ ($\lambda \neq 0$). Then there is a *symplectic structure* $\Omega := d\omega$ on the $2n$-dimensional manifold $\mathcal{S}$ because $(\Omega)^n = (d\omega)^n \neq 0$.

We should observe that the tangent bundle TM (resp. PTM) has a local coordinate basis $\{\frac{\partial}{\partial x^i}, \frac{\partial}{\partial y^i}\}$. Under the coordinate transformation on TM induced by a coordinate change on M, the vectors $\{\frac{\partial}{\partial x^i}\}$ transform in a somewhat complicated manner, as follows

$$\frac{\partial}{\partial \widetilde{x}^i} = \frac{\partial x^k}{\partial \widetilde{x}^i} \frac{\partial}{\partial x^k} + \frac{\partial^2 x^k}{\partial \widetilde{x}^i \partial \widetilde{x}^j} \widetilde{y}^j \frac{\partial}{\partial y^k},$$

and the set of vector fields $\{\frac{\partial}{\partial y^i}\}$ do not have this property. So, in order to remedy this we replace $\{\frac{\partial}{\partial x^i}\}$ by the following vector fields:

$$\frac{\delta}{\delta x^i} := \frac{\partial}{\partial x^i} - N_i^j \frac{\partial}{\partial y^i}, \qquad (2.3.3)$$

where

$$N_i^j := \gamma_{ik}^j y^k - g^{jl} C_{ikl} \gamma_{pq}^k y^p y^q, \quad \gamma_{jk}^i := \frac{1}{2} g^{il} \left(\frac{\partial g_{jl}}{\partial x^k} + \frac{\partial g_{kl}}{\partial x^j} - \frac{\partial g_{jk}}{\partial x^l} \right). \qquad (2.3.4)$$

It is easy to check that

$$\frac{\delta}{\delta \widetilde{x}^i} = \frac{\partial x^k}{\partial \widetilde{x}^i} \frac{\delta}{\delta x^k}.$$

Thus, the tangent bundle $T(TM_0)$ of TM_0 can be decomposed the sum of the *horizontal part* $\mathcal{H}TM$ spanned by $\{\frac{\delta}{\delta x^i}\}$ and the *vertical part* $\mathcal{V}TM$ spanned by $\{\frac{\partial}{\partial y^i}\}$. The dual basis of $\{\frac{\partial}{\partial x^i}, \frac{\partial}{\partial y^i}\}$ is $\{dx^i, \delta y^i\}$, where

$$\delta y^i := dy^i + N_j^i dx^j. \qquad (2.3.5)$$

In other words, we have

$$T(TM_0) = \mathcal{H}TM \bigoplus \mathcal{V}TM = \text{span} \left\{ \frac{\delta}{\delta x^i} \right\} \bigoplus \text{span} \left\{ \frac{\partial}{\partial y^i} \right\},$$

$$T^*(TM_0) = \mathcal{H}^*TM \bigoplus \mathcal{V}^*TM = \text{span} \left\{ dx^i \right\} \bigoplus \text{span} \left\{ \delta y^i \right\}.$$

Denote by $\pi : TM_0 \to M$ the natural projection, which induces $d\pi : T(TM_0) \to TM$. Note that the vertical part $\mathcal{V}TM = \text{span}\{\frac{\partial}{\partial y^i}\}$ is just the $\ker(d\pi)$. Such a decomposition is very important because we are proceeding on TM_0, but not M, in Finsler geometry, which is different from the case of Riemannian geometry.

Proposition 2.1. *Any Finsler metric function F is horizontally constant, i.e.,*

$$X(F) = dF(X) = 0$$

for any horizontal vector $X = X^i \frac{\delta}{\delta x^i} \in \mathcal{H}TM$.

Proof. By means of (2.2.3), (2.3.4) and (2.3.5), a direct calculation gives

$$d(F^2) = (dg_{ij})y^i y^j + 2g_{ij}y^i dy^j = \frac{\partial g_{ij}}{\partial x^k} y^i y^j dx^k + 2g_{ij}y^i dy^j$$

$$= 2g_{ij}y^i \delta y^j \in \mathcal{V}^*TM,$$

which means that $dF^2 = 2FdF$ satisfies $dF^2(X) = 0$ for any horizontal vector $X = X^i \frac{\delta}{\delta x^i} \in \mathcal{H}TM$. Hence, $dF(X) = 0$ for any horizontal vector X. $\qquad \square$

Remark. It follows from the above argument that the main difference between Finsler geometry and Riemannian geometry lies in the fundamental manifold, which is PTM, but not M, in Finsler geometry. Various tensor bundles over M may be pulled back at PTM. It is certain that the readers will understand more well after learning the first five chapters of this book.

2.3.2 Sprays

Definition 2.3. A *spray* $\mathbf{G}$ on a smooth manifold M is a special vector field on the split tangent bundle TM_0 with the following properties:

(1) In a standard coordinate system (x, y) on TM, $\mathbf{G}$ can be expressed as

$$
\begin{aligned}
\mathbf{G} &= y^i \frac{\partial}{\partial x^i} - 2G^i(x, y) \frac{\partial}{\partial y^i} \\
&= y^i \frac{\delta}{\delta x^i} - \left[2G^i(x, y) - y^k N_k^i \right] \frac{\partial}{\partial y^i},
\end{aligned}
\tag{2.3.6}
$$

where $G^i(x, \lambda y) = \lambda^2 G^i(x, y), \forall \lambda > 0$. G^i are called the *spray coefficients*;

(2) G^i are smooth at $(x, y \neq 0) \in TM_0$.

A spray is a map $\mathbf{G} : TM_0 \to T(TM_0)$, such that $d\pi \circ \mathbf{G} = \mathrm{id}.$, i.e., we have the following commutative diagram:

$$
\begin{array}{ccc}
TM_0 & \xrightarrow{\ \mathbf{G}(y)\ } & T(TM_0) \\
{\scriptstyle \pi}\downarrow & & \downarrow{\scriptstyle d\pi} \\
M & \xrightarrow[\ y\ ]{} & TM_0
\end{array}
$$

where y is an arbitrary non-zero vector field on M. In the following, we shall look at some interesting examples on an open subset U in the Euclidean space $\mathbb{R}^n$.

Example 2.6. Let $P : U \times \mathbb{R}^n \to \mathbb{R}$ be a function with the following properties:

(1) $P(x, \lambda y) = \lambda P(x, y), \forall \lambda > 0$;

(2) $P(x, y)$ is C^∞ at points $(x, y \neq 0)$.

On putting $G^i(x, y) = P(x, y) y^i$, we see that

$$
\mathbf{G} = y^i \frac{\partial}{\partial x^i} - 2G^i \frac{\partial}{\partial y^i} = y^i \frac{\partial}{\partial x^i} - 2P y^i \frac{\partial}{\partial y^i}
\tag{2.3.7}
$$

is a spray on U, which is called a *projectively flat spray*.

Example 2.7. Let $\Gamma^i_{jk}(x)$ be C^∞ on U, and $\Gamma^i_{jk}(x) = \Gamma^i_{kj}(x)$. Set $G^i = \frac{1}{2}\Gamma^i_{jk}(x)y^j y^k$, which are homogeneous functions of degree two with respect to y. Then

$$\mathbf{G} = y^i \frac{\partial}{\partial x^i} - 2G^i \frac{\partial}{\partial y^i} = y^i \frac{\partial}{\partial x^i} - \Gamma^i_{jk}(x)y^j y^k \frac{\partial}{\partial y^i} \qquad (2.3.8)$$

is a spray on U, which is called a *quadratic spray*, or a *Berwald spray*.

Example 2.8. Let $P(x, y)$ and $\Gamma^i_{jk}(x)$ be the same as Example 2.6 and 2.7. Set $G^i = \frac{1}{2}\Gamma^i_{jk}(x)y^j y^k + P(x, y)y^i$. Then the spray

$$\mathbf{G} = y^i \frac{\partial}{\partial x^i} - 2G^i \frac{\partial}{\partial y^i}$$

is called a *quadratic projective spray*, or a *Douglas spray*, on U.

Example 2.9. Let $G^i = (A^i_j y^j)|y|$, where (A^i_j) is a skew-symmetric matrix, $|y| = \sqrt{\sum_{i=1}^n (y^i)^2}$. Then

$$\mathbf{G} = y^i \frac{\partial}{\partial x^i} - 2G^i \frac{\partial}{\partial y^i}$$

is a spray on U.

2.4 Geodesics

2.4.1 Geodesics

Let $\mathbf{G}$ be a spray on a manifold M, $\gamma = \gamma(t)$ a curve on TM_0. If

$$\dot{\gamma} = \mathbf{G}|_\gamma, \qquad (2.4.1)$$

where "$\cdot$" denotes the derivative with respect to t, then γ is called an *integral curve* of $\mathbf{G}$. Under the local coordinate system (x, y), (2.4.1) can be expressed by

$$\dot{x}^i(t) = y^i(t), \quad \dot{y}^i(t) + 2G^i(x(t), y(t)) = 0. \qquad (2.4.1')$$

Denote by $\pi : TM_0 \to M$ the natural projection. Let $\sigma(t) = \pi(\gamma(t))$ be the projection of $\gamma(t)$ by π. Then the local coordinates $\sigma^i(t)$ of $\sigma(t)$ satisfy

$$\ddot{\sigma}^i(t) + 2G^i(\sigma(t), \dot{\sigma}(t)) = 0, \qquad (2.4.2)$$

where $\dot{\sigma}(t) = \dot{\sigma}^i(t)\frac{\partial}{\partial x^i}$.

Conversely, given a curve $\sigma = \sigma(t)$ in M, its *canonical lift* on TM_0 is the integral curve generated by the tangent vector field $\dot{\sigma}(t) = \dot{\sigma}^i(t)\frac{\partial}{\partial x^i}|_{\sigma(t)}$, so that the coordinates of the lift are $(\sigma^i(t), \dot{\sigma}^i(t))$. Clearly, if $\sigma(t)$ satisfies (2.4.2), then $(x, y) = (\sigma(t), \dot{\sigma}(t))$ satisfies (2.4.1), i.e., the canonical lift of $\sigma(t)$ is the integral curve of $\mathbf{G}$.

Definition 2.4. Let **G** be a spray on a manifold M, $\sigma(t)$ a curve in M. If the canonical lift of $\sigma(t)$ is the integral curve of **G**, i.e., the equation (2.4.2) is satisfied, then σ is called a *geodesic* of **G** in M, and G^i are called the *geodesic coefficients*.

By the theory of ODE, for any $y \in TM_0$, there is a unique integral curve $\gamma_y(t) \subset TM_0$ of **G**, such that $\gamma_y(0) = y$. By writing $\varphi_t(y) := \gamma_y(t)$, we obtain a family of diffeomorphisms $\varphi_t : TM_0 \to TM_0$, which satisfy the following homogeneous condition

$$\varphi_t(\lambda y) = \lambda \varphi_t(y), \quad \lambda \in \mathbb{R}^+.$$

By the definition of geodesics, the curve $\pi(\gamma_y(t)) = \pi \circ \varphi_t(y)$ is the geodesic satisfying $\pi(\gamma_y(0)) := \pi \circ \varphi_0(y) = y$. φ_t is called the *geodesic flow* of the spray **G**. By Proposition 2.1, we have

$$\frac{d}{dt}\left[F(\varphi_t(y))\right] = dF\left[\mathbf{G}|_{\varphi_t(y)}\right] = 0,$$

which implies that the geodesic flow preserves the Finsler metric F, i.e., $F(\varphi_t(y)) = F(y)$.

2.4.2 Geodesic coefficients

A Finsler metric F on a manifold M induces a spray **G**, of which the coefficients G^i are given by

$$G^i = \frac{1}{4}g^{ij}\left\{[F^2]_{y^j x^k}y^k - [F^2]_{x^j}\right\}. \tag{2.4.3}$$

(2.4.2) is the geodesic equation in (M, F). Hence, the spray coefficients G^i defined by (2.4.3) are called the *geodesic coefficients* of (M, F).

Proposition 2.2. *If $\sigma(t)$ is a geodesic on a Finsler manifold (M, F), then the length of its tangent vector is constant, i.e., $F(\sigma(t), \dot{\sigma}(t))$ is constant.*

Proof. By means of (2.4.2) and (2.4.3), we have

$$\frac{d}{dt}\left[F^2(\sigma(t), \dot{\sigma}(t))\right] = \frac{\partial g_{ij}}{\partial x^k}\dot{\sigma}^k\dot{\sigma}^i\dot{\sigma}^j + 2\frac{\partial g_{ij}}{\partial y^k}\ddot{\sigma}^k\dot{\sigma}^i\dot{\sigma}^j + 2g_{ij}\ddot{\sigma}^i\dot{\sigma}^j$$

$$= (g_{mj}N_i^m + g_{im}N_j^m)\dot{\sigma}^i\dot{\sigma}^j - 4g_{ij}G^i\dot{\sigma}^j = 0.$$

Hence, $F(\sigma(t), \dot{\sigma}(t))$ is constant. $\qquad\square$

Let $p, q \in M$ be two points in a manifold, C a piecewise smooth curve from p to q. If

$$d_F(p, q) = L_F(C),$$

then C is called the *shortest path* from p to q. By the variation of the arc length, we can prove the following

Theorem 2.3. *Let C be a smooth curve from p to q on a Finsler manifold (M, F), whose tangent vector has constant length. If C is the shortest path, then C is a smooth geodesic on (M, F). Conversely, the length of a smooth geodesic on (M, F) is locally minimizing.*

Proof. Let $\sigma = \sigma(t)$, $a \le t \le b$, be a smooth curve from $p = \sigma(a)$ to $q = \sigma(b)$ on (M, F). Consider a smooth variation $\psi : (-\varepsilon, \varepsilon) \times [a, b] \to M$ of σ, such that

$$\psi(0, t) = \sigma(t), \ a \le t \le b, \quad \psi(s, a) = \sigma(a) = p, \quad \psi(s, b) = \sigma(b) = q, \ |s| < \varepsilon.$$

This is a variation fixing the ends of the curve. The length of $\sigma_s(t) := \psi(s, t)$ is

$$L(s) = \int_a^b F(\sigma_s(t), \dot{\sigma}_s(t)) dt.$$

Put

$$v(t) := \frac{\partial \psi}{\partial s}(0, t) := v^i(t) \frac{\partial}{\partial x^i}, \quad a \le t \le b,$$

which is called the *variation vector field*. Clearly, $v(a) = v(b) = 0$. By using (2.4.3) and computing directly, we have

$$L'(0) = \int_a^b \frac{1}{2F} \left(\frac{dF^2}{ds} \right)\Big|_{s=0} dt = \int_a^b \frac{1}{2F} \left[[F^2]_{x^k} v^k + [F^2]_{y^k} \frac{dv^k}{dt} \right] dt$$

$$= \int_a^b \frac{1}{2F} \left[[F^2]_{x^k} - [F^2]_{x^i y^k} \dot{\sigma}^i - [F^2]_{y^k y^i} \ddot{\sigma}^i \right] v^k dt + \frac{1}{2F} [F^2]_{y^k} v^k \Big|_a^b$$

$$= -\int_a^b \frac{1}{F} \{ \ddot{\sigma}^i + 2G^i(\sigma, \dot{\sigma}) \} v^k dt. \tag{2.4.4}$$

Since the variation is arbitrary, (2.4.4) equals zero if and only if (2.4.2) holds, i.e., $\sigma(t)$ is a geodesic. $\square$

Remark. (2.4.4) is just the first variation formula of the arc length, which holds also for piecewise smooth curves (cf. [103]).

2.4.3 Geodesic completeness

Let (M, F) be an n-dimensional Finsler manifold, G^i the geodesic coefficients given by (2.4.3). The geodesic equations on (M, F) are (2.4.2) (cf. Chapter 3, §3.1). Now fixing a point $x \in M$, for any vector $y \in T_x M$, there exists a unique geodesic $\sigma_y(t) : (-\varepsilon, \varepsilon) \to M$, such that $\sigma_y(0) = x$ and $\dot{\sigma}_y(0) = y$ according to the theory of the ordinary differential equation.

Since G^i are homogeneous with respect to y, for any constant $a > 0$, the curve $\sigma_y(at) : (-\varepsilon/a, \varepsilon/a) \to M$ is the same geodesic satisfying the initial conditions $\sigma_y(0) = x$ and $\dot{\sigma}_y(0) = ay$, i.e.,

$$\sigma_y(at) = \sigma_{ay}(t).$$

Thus, similar to Riemannian geometry, one can define *exponential mapping* $\exp_x : T_xM \to M$

$$\exp_x(y) = \sigma_y(1), \quad \forall y \in T_xM, \quad ||y|| < a \quad (\text{resp. } +\infty).$$

Since $G^i(x, y)$ is C^∞ except for $y = 0$ where it is C^1, then $\exp_x$ is C^∞ on $T_xM \setminus \{0\}$, while it is C^1 at $y = 0$ and $d(\exp_x)|_0 = id$. Thus, the exponential mapping is a local diffeomorphism.

Fixing a point $x \in M$, we define

$$S_x(r) := \{y \in T_xM | F(x, y) = r\}, \quad B_x(r) := \{y \in T_xM | F(x, y) < r\}$$

called respectively the *tangent sphere* $S_x(r)$ and the *open tangent ball* $B_x(r)$ of radius r. Clearly, the exponential mapping $\exp_x$ is well defined on $S_x(r)$ and $B_x(r)$ when r is small enough. Thus, $\exp_x[S_x(r)]$ is called the *geodesic sphere* on M of radius r at the center x, and $\exp_x[B_x(r)]$ is called the *geodesic ball* (resp. *geodesic disk*).

In $T_xM \setminus \{0\}$ a Riemannian metric induced by F is

$$g_x(y) := g_{ij}(x, y)dy^i \otimes dy^j.$$

Since F is constant on $S_x(r)$, we have

$$0 = v^i F_{y^i} = v^i g_{ij} \frac{y^j}{r}$$

for any tangent vector $v = v^i \frac{\partial}{\partial y^i}$ to the tangent sphere $S_x(r)$. It implies that the radius vector ty for any $t > 0$ is g_x-orthogonal to the tangent sphere $S_x(r)$.

Gauss Lemma. *For a point $x \in M$, let $y \in S_x(r)$. Assume that $T(t)$ is the tangent vector of the radius geodesic $\exp_x(ty)$ $(0 \leq t \leq 1)$ and $V(t)$ is tangent to the tangent sphere $S_x(tr)$. Then, for any $t \in [0, 1]$, we have*

$$g_T(d\exp_x V, T) = 0.$$

Proof. For any fixed number $a \in [0, 1]$, we have $ay \in S_x(ar)$. Let $\gamma(s)$, $s \in (-\epsilon, \epsilon)$, be the curve issued at the point $ay(s = 0)$ on $S_x(ar)$. Denote by V the tangent vector to the curve. Construct the variation of the geodesic $\sigma(t) = \exp_x(t(ay))$:

$$\psi(t, s) = \sigma(t, s) := \exp_x[t\gamma(s)], \quad 0 \leq t \leq 1, \quad -\epsilon \leq s \leq \epsilon.$$

Clearly, $\sigma_s(t) = \psi(t, s)$ are all geodesics, which have the same arc length. Moreover, the lengths of their tangent vectors are equal to the same constant ar, and $L'(0) = 0$.

The variation vector field v satisfies $v(0) = 0$, $v(1) = d\exp_x V$. The vector $v(1)$ is tangent to the geodesic sphere $\exp_x[S_x(ar)]$. Since the tangent vector of the geodesic $\exp_x(ty)$ is T, the tangent vector of the geodesic $\sigma(t) = \exp_x(tay)$ is aT.

Recall the first variation formula (2.4.4) of the arc length. Since $v(1)$ does not vanish and $\sigma(t)$ satisfies (2.4.2), we have

$$0 = L'(0) = \frac{1}{2F}[F^2]_{y^k} v^k \Big|_{t=1}.$$

Since the tangent vector T of the radius geodesic is parallel to $y = y^i \frac{\partial}{\partial x^i}$ and $y^i = g^{ij} F F_{y^j}$, the above formula is equivalent to

$$0 = g_{jk} y^j v^k = g_T(d\exp_x V, T) = \langle d\exp_x V, T\rangle_T. \qquad \square$$

By the Gauss lemma, we can introduce the geodesically polar coordinate system in the geodesic ball $\exp_x[B_x(r)] \subset M$. Let $t = F(y)$ $(0 < t < r)$ be the radius coordinate, and $\{\theta^\alpha\}$ $(\alpha = 2, \cdots, n)$ the coordinates on the geodesic sphere $\exp_x[S_x(ar)]$. Then the Riemannian metric $g_x(y)$ has the following form

$$g_x = dt \otimes dt + t^2 \dot{g}, \quad \dot{g} := \dot{g}_{\alpha\beta}(t, \theta)d\theta^\alpha \otimes \theta^\beta.$$

(t, θ^α) are called the *geodesically polar coordinates* of the point $x \in M$, or simply, the *polar coordinates*.

A Finsler manifold (M, F) is said to be *positively* (resp. *negatively*) *geodesically complete* if every geodesic $\sigma(t)$ defined in an interval $[a, b]$ on (M, F) can be extended to $[a, +\infty)$ (resp. $(-\infty, b]$). In such a case, (M, F) is said also to be *forward* (resp. *backward*) *geodesically complete*.

Let d_F be the distant function induced from F such that (M, d_F) becomes a *(general)* metric space (cf. §8.3.1 below). A sequence of points $\{x_i\}$ in (M, d_F) is called a *forward* (resp. *backward*) *Cauchy sequence* if for any $\varepsilon > 0$, there is a natural number N such that $d_F(x_i, x_j) < \varepsilon$ (resp. $d_F(x_j, x_i) < \varepsilon$) when $j > i \geq N$.

A sequence of points $\{x_i\} \subset M$ is said to be *forward* (resp. *backward*) *convergent* if there exists a point $x \in M$ such that

$$\lim_{i \to \infty} d_F(x_i, x) = 0 \quad (\text{resp. } \lim_{i \to \infty} d_F(x, x_i) = 0).$$

(M, d_F) is said to be *positively* (resp. *negatively*) *complete* if any forward (resp. backward) Cauchy sequence in (M, d_F) is forward (resp. backward) convergent.

As in the Riemannian case, we have the following Hopf-Rinow theorem, of which the proof is omitted, for details see [10] and [103].

Theorem 2.4 (Hopf-Rinow). *Let (M, F) be a connected Finsler manifold. The following statements are equivalent:*

(1) (M, F) is positively geodesically complete.

(2) (M, d_F) is positively complete.

(3) In (M, F) there is a point $x \in M$ such that $\exp_x$ is defined on all of $T_x M$.

(4) At every point $x \in M$, $\exp_x$ is defined on all of $T_x M$.

(5) Every closed and forward bounded subset of (M, d_F) is compact.

Moreover, if any one of the above is true, then every pair of points in (M, F) can be joined by a minimizing geodesic.

It should be pointed out that, in general, we have $F(x, y) \neq F(x, -y)$ for a Finsler metric F. Thus, being different from the Riemannian case, it is not necessary that a positively complete Finsler manifold (M, F) is also negatively complete. For example, a Randers metric (2.1.2) satisfies $F(x, y) = F(x, -y)$ if and only if $\beta = 0$, i.e., it is Riemannian. Hence, a positively complete Randers metric (2.1.2), which is not Riemannian, could not be negatively complete. A Finsler metric F is called a *complete metric* if F is both positively and negatively complete. For example, the $2k$-th root metrics in Example 2.3 of §2.1 are complete.

Definition 2.5. For a Finsler manifold (M, F), the number

$$\lambda_F := \sup_{(x,y) \in TM_0} \left\{ \frac{F(x, -y)}{F(x, y)} \right\} \tag{2.4.5}$$

is called the *reversibility* of (M, F).

Obviously, $\lambda_F \geq 1$, where the equality holds if and only if F is *reversible*, i.e., $F(x, -y) = F(x, y)$. Moreover, when $\lambda_F < \infty$, we have clearly

$$(1/\lambda_F)F(x, y) \leq F(x, -y) \leq \lambda_F F(x, y). \tag{2.4.6}$$

Thus, it is easy to prove that (129) the positive completeness is equivalent to the negative completeness when $\lambda_F < \infty$. In particular, every closed compact Finsler manifold is complete. The reversibility λ_F plays an important role in global Finsler geometry.

Exercises

    2.1   Prove that the Riemannian metric g_μ given in Example 2.1 has constant sectional curvature μ.

2.2 By using (2.1.1), prove that $F_{y^i} = F^{-1}y^j g_{ij}$.

2.3 Write down the expressions of g_{ij} for metrics (2.1.4) and (2.1.6).

2.4 Prove that a positively definite Finsler metric $F(x, y)$ satisfies the following the triangle inequality

$$F(x, u + v) \le F(x, u) + F(x, v),$$

where the equality holds if and only if u and v lie in a same line.

2.5 Let $F = \alpha + \beta$ be a Randers metric, where

$$\alpha = \sqrt{a_{ij}(x)y^i y^j}, \quad \beta = b_i(x)y^i.$$

Set

$$y_i = y^j a_{ji}, \quad b^i = a^{ij}b_j.$$

Prove that

$$g_{ij} = \frac{F}{\alpha}\left\{a_{ij} - \frac{y_i}{\alpha}\frac{y_j}{\alpha} + \frac{\alpha}{F}\left(b_i + \frac{y_i}{\alpha}\right)\left(b_i + \frac{y_i}{\alpha}\right)\right\},$$

$$g^{ij} = \frac{\alpha}{F}a^{ij} - \frac{\alpha}{F^2}(b^i y^j + b j y^i) + \frac{\alpha\|\beta\|_\alpha^2 + \beta}{\alpha^3}y^i y^j.$$

2.6 For the above Randers metric, by using (2.2.4), prove that

$$\mathbf{I}_i = \frac{n+1}{2(\alpha + \beta)}\left(b_i - \frac{\beta}{\alpha^2}y_i\right),$$

$$h_{ij} = \frac{\alpha + \beta}{\alpha}\left(a_{ij} - \frac{y_i}{\alpha}\frac{y_j}{\alpha}\right),$$

from which it follows that

$$C_{ijk} = \frac{1}{n+1}\left(\mathbf{I}_i h_{jk} + \mathbf{I}_j h_{ki} + \mathbf{I}_k h_{ij}\right).$$

2.7 By means of the fundamental quadric form of a Finsler metric F, we can define the *norms* of the Cartan tensor and the mean Cartan tensor:

$$\|\mathbf{I}\|^2 := \sup_{x \in M}\sup_{F(y)=1}\{g^{ij}\mathbf{I}_i\mathbf{I}_j\}, \quad \|\mathbf{C}\|^2 := \sup_{x \in M}\sup_{F(y)=1}\{g^{ip}g^{jq}g^{kr}C_{ijk}C_{pqr}\}.$$

Prove that (cf. [59])

$$\|\mathbf{I}\|^2 = \frac{(n+1)^2}{2}\left[1 - \sqrt{1 - \|\beta\|_\alpha^2}\right] < \frac{(n+1)^2}{2}$$

for a Randers metric $F = \alpha + \beta$, so that

$$\|\mathbf{C}\|^2 \le \frac{9}{2}\left[1 - \sqrt{1 - \|\beta\|_\alpha^2}\right] < \frac{9}{2}.$$

2.8   Prove that the Finsler metric F determined by the quadric equation (2.2.22) is a Randers metric.

2.9   Verify that $d(F^2) = 2g_{ij}y^i\delta y^j$.

2.10   Prove that $\omega \wedge (d\omega)^{n-1} \neq 0$, where ω is the Hilbert form of an n-dimensional Finsler metric F.

2.11   Prove that the positive completeness is equivalent to the negative completeness when the reversibility λ_F is finite.

Chapter 3

Connections and Curvatures

3.1 Connections

A connection on a Finsler manifold (M, F) is a linear connection on the vector bundle $\rho : \pi^*TM \to TM_0$ (see Chapter 1, §1.4), which can be defined in various ways. Several famous great geometers, E. Cartan, S. S. Chern, etc. have made their contributions to this subject. Here we would introduce mainly a connection for Finsler metrics discovered firstly by S. S. Chern in 1943, which is called now the *Chern connection*. Later on, H. Rund independently introduced this connection in a different setting. So, the Chern connection is also called the Rund connection in some literatures ([101], [11], p.171).

3.1.1 Chern connection

Let (M, F) be an n-dimensional Finsler manifold, and $TM_0 = TM \setminus \{0\}$ its slit tangent bundle. The natural projection $\pi : TM_0 \to M$ induces a vector bundle π^*TM on TM_0 (see Chapter 2, §2.2), whose fiber at a point $(x, y) \in TM_0$ is

$$\pi^*TM|_{(x,y)} := \{(x, y, v)|v \in T_xM\} \cong T_xM.$$

In other words, π^*TM is a vector bundle of rank n with the base space TM_0. Its dual bundle is π^*T^*M, whose fiber is the dual space T_x^*M of the fiber T_xM.

Theorem 3.1 (S. S. Chern). *Let (M, F) be an n-dimensional Finsler manifold. On the pull-back tangent bundle π^*TM, there exists a unique linear connection ∇ without torsion and with almost metric-compatibility. In detail, for any local frame field $\{e_i\}$ on π^*TM and its dual field $\{\omega^i\}$ on*

π^*T^*M, *there is a unique set of local 1-forms* $\{\omega_j^i\}$ *on* TM_0 *such that*

$$d\omega^i - \omega^j \wedge \omega_j^i = 0, \tag{3.1.1}$$

$$dg_{ij} - g_{kj}\omega_i^k - g_{ik}\omega_j^k = 2C_{ijk}\omega^{n+k}, \quad \omega^{n+k} := dy^k + y^j\omega_j^k, \tag{3.1.2}$$

where $g_{ij}\omega^i \otimes \omega^j$ *is the fundamental form,* $C_{ijk}\omega^i \otimes \omega^j \otimes \omega^k$ *is the Cartan tensor and* $y = y^i e_i \in TM_0$ *is a tangent vector.*

(3.1.1) and (3.1.2) can be also written as (see Chapter 1, §1.4 and Chapter 2, §2.2)

$$\nabla_u v - \nabla_v u = [u, v], \quad \forall u, v, w \in TM_0, \tag{3.1.1'}$$

$$w(\langle u, v \rangle_y) - \langle \nabla_w u, v \rangle_y - \langle u, \nabla_w v \rangle_y = 2\mathbf{C}_y(\nabla_w y, u, v). \tag{3.1.2'}$$

Remark. Since the Chern connection is defined on the pull-back tangent bundle π^*TM, it should be remarked that $\nabla_u v$ and $[u, v]$ in the above formulas have to be understood as $\nabla_n(\rho^{-1}v)$ and $[\rho^{-1}u, \rho^{-1}v] = \rho^{-1}[u, v]$, according to the commutative diagram in §2.2.1. The rest can be deduced similarly, and will not be remarked.

Proof of Theorem 3.1. Without loss of generality, we may prove the theorem in a standard local coordinate system (x^i, y^i) in TM_0. Thus, the local frame field in the pull-back tangent bundle π^*TM is $\{\partial_i = \frac{\partial}{\partial x^i}\}$, whose dual frame field is $\{dx^i\}$ in the dual bundle π^*T^*M.

The required local 1-forms ω_j^i can be expressed as

$$\omega_j^i = \Gamma_{jk}^i dx^k + \Pi_{jk}^i dy^k.$$

(3.1.1) is equivalent to

$$dx^j \wedge \left(\Gamma_{jk}^i dx^k + \Pi_{jk}^i dy^k\right) = d(dx^i) = 0,$$

from which it follows that

$$\Pi_{jk}^i = 0, \quad \Gamma_{jk}^i = \Gamma_{kj}^i, \quad \omega_j^i = \Gamma_{jk}^i dx^k. \tag{3.1.3}$$

Substituting (3.1.3) into (3.1.2) reduces

$$dg_{ij} = g_{mj}\Gamma_{ik}^m dx^k + g_{im}\Gamma_{jk}^m dx^k + 2C_{ijl}\left(dy^l + \Gamma_{km}^l y^m dx^k\right). \tag{3.1.4}$$

By means of (2.2.1) and $dg_{ij} = \frac{\partial g_{ij}}{\partial x^k}dx^k + \frac{\partial g_{ij}}{\partial y^k}dy^k$, one gets from (3.1.4)

$$\frac{\partial g_{ij}}{\partial x^k} = g_{mj}\Gamma_{ik}^m + g_{im}\Gamma_{jk}^m + 2C_{ijl}\Gamma_{km}^l y^m. \tag{3.1.5}$$

Permutating the indices i, j, k, one also gets

$$\frac{\partial g_{jk}}{\partial x^i} = g_{mk}\Gamma_{ji}^m + g_{jm}\Gamma_{ki}^m + 2C_{jkl}\Gamma_{im}^l y^m, \tag{3.1.6}$$

$$\frac{\partial g_{ki}}{\partial x^j} = g_{mj}\Gamma^m_{kj} + g_{km}\Gamma^m_{ij} + 2C_{kil}\Gamma^l_{jm}y^m. \tag{3.1.7}$$

Adding (3.1.6) and (3.1.7), then subtracting (3.1.5), one obtains

$$\Gamma^l_{ij} = \gamma^l_{ij} - g^{lk}\left(C_{jkp}\Gamma^p_{im} + C_{kip}\Gamma^p_{jm} - C_{ijp}\Gamma^p_{km}\right)y^m, \tag{3.1.8}$$

where γ^l_{ij} are defined by (2.3.4).

Contracting (3.1.8) with y^i and using (2.2.3), one obtains

$$\Gamma^l_{ij}y^i = \gamma^l_{ij}y^i - g^{lk}C_{jkp}\Gamma^p_{im}y^iy^m. \tag{3.1.9}$$

Contracting (3.1.9) with y^j yields

$$\Gamma^l_{ij}y^iy^j = \gamma^l_{ij}y^iy^j. \tag{3.1.10}$$

Plugging (3.1.10) into the right hand side of (3.1.9) and using (2.3.4), we have

$$\Gamma^l_{ij}y^i = \gamma^l_{ij}y^i - g^{lk}C_{jkp}\gamma^p_{im}y^iy^m = N^l_j. \tag{3.1.11}$$

Plugging (3.1.11) into the right hand side of (3.1.8) yields

$$\Gamma^l_{ij} = \gamma^l_{ij} - g^{lk}\left(C_{jkp}N^p_i + C_{kip}N^p_j - C_{ijp}N^p_k\right). \tag{3.1.12}$$

This means that Γ^l_{ij} are determined by the metric $F(x,y)$ completely, and so are ω^i_j. This proves the theorem. $\square$

γ^l_{ij} defined by the second formula of (2.3.4) are called the *formal Christoffel symbols* of the second kind. By using (2.2.3) and the operator (2.3.3), it follows from (3.1.12)

$$\Gamma^l_{ij} = \frac{1}{2}g^{lk}\left(\frac{\delta g_{ik}}{\delta x^j} + \frac{\delta g_{jk}}{\delta x^i} - \frac{\delta g_{ij}}{\delta x^k}\right). \tag{3.1.12'}$$

Thus, Γ^l_{ij} are called the *Christoffel symbols* (or the *connection coefficients*) of the Chern connection.

In virtue of (3.1.11), (3.1.3) and (2.3.5), we can rewrite the second formula of (3.1.2) as follows

$$\omega^{n+k} = dy^k + y^l\Gamma^k_{lj}dx^j = dy^k + N^k_j dx^j = \delta y^k. \tag{3.1.13}$$

Thus, in the local natural basis, (3.1.2) becomes

$$dg_{ij} - g_{kj}\omega^k_i - g_{ik}\omega^k_j = 2C_{ijk}\delta y^k.$$

Using

$$[F^2]_{x^k} = \frac{\partial g_{ij}}{\partial x^k}y^iy^j, \quad [F^2]_{x^ky^l}y^k = 2\frac{\partial g_{ij}}{\partial x^k}y^iy^k, \tag{3.1.14}$$

we have

$$G^i = \frac{1}{2}\gamma^i_{jk}y^jy^k = \frac{1}{2}\Gamma^i_{jk}y^jy^k, \tag{3.1.15}$$

where G^i are the spray coefficients defined by (2.4.3). Thus, the geodesic equation (2.4.2) in (M, F) can be written as

$$\ddot{\sigma}^i(t) + \Gamma^i_{jk}(\sigma(t), \dot{\sigma}(t))\dot{\sigma}^j(t)\dot{\sigma}^k(t) = 0, \tag{3.1.16}$$

which is similar to the Riemannian case.

By differentiating (3.1.15) with respect to y^j and using (3.1.11), we have

$$N^i_j = \frac{\partial G^i}{\partial y^j}. \tag{3.1.17}$$

So, the local functions N^i_j are also called the *connection coefficients*, which depend only on G^i.

3.1.2 Berwald metrics and Landsberg metrics

Definition 3.1. Let F be a Finsler metric in a manifold M. F is called a *Berwald metric* if, in any local coordinate system (x^i, y^i) on TM_0, the Christoffel symbols $\Gamma^l_{ij} = \Gamma^l_{ij}(x)$ of the Chern connection are only functions of the point x in M.

It follows from (3.1.15) that a characteristic of a Berwald metric is $G^i = \frac{1}{2}\Gamma^i_{jk}(x)y^jy^k$, i.e., G^i is a quadric form with respect to y. Clearly, a Riemannian metric is a Berwald metric. There are many non-Riemannian Berwald metrics. For example, for a Randers metric $F = \alpha + \beta$ (see Chapter 2, Example 2.2), if the 1-form β is parallel with respect to the Riemannian metric α, then it is a Berwald metric. Moreover, Example 2.4 in Chapter 2 is a non-Riemannian Berwald metric (see §3.3.1 below).

The *Landsberg tensor* in a Finsler manifold (M, F) is defined by

$$\mathbf{L} := L^i_{jk}\partial_i \otimes dx^j \otimes dx^k, \quad L^i_{jk} := [G^i]_{y^jy^k} - \Gamma^i_{jk}, \tag{3.1.18}$$

which is symmetric with respect to indices j and k. The *mean Landsberg tensor* is defined by

$$\mathbf{J} := J^i\partial_i, \quad J^i := L^i_{jk}g^{jk}. \tag{3.1.19}$$

By (3.1.18), one can easily verifies that

$$L^i_{jk} = y^l[\Gamma^i_{kl}]_{y^j} = y^l[\Gamma^i_{jl}]_{y^k}. \tag{3.1.20}$$

Definition 3.2. A Finsler metric F with vanishing the (resp. mean) Landsberg tensor is called a (resp. *weak*) *Landsberg metric*.

It follows from (3.1.20) that every Berwald metric is a Landsberg metric. But, vice versa, is every Landsberg metric a Berwald metric? This is an open question up to now.

For a Randers metric, a straightforward calculation (or use (4.3.5) in Chapter 4 below) yields the following result, which can be found in [36].

Theorem 3.2. *Let $F = \alpha + \beta$ be an n-dimensional Randers metric. The following are equivalent:*

(i) F is a Landsberg metric;

(ii) F is a Berwald metric;

(iii) β is parallel with respect to α, i.e., $\nabla^\alpha \beta = 0$, where ∇^α denotes the Riemannian connection of α.

In a Finsler manifold (M, F), except for the Chern (resp. Rund) connection, there are other connections, among which the following three connections are well-known:

(i) **Cartan connection**. Its connection forms are given by

$$^c\omega^i_j := \omega^i_j + C^i{}_{jk}\delta y^k,$$

where ω^i_j are Chern's connection forms, $C^i{}_{jk} = g^{il}C_{ljk}$, δy^k are defined by (3.1.13). It is metric-compatible, but has torsion (cf. [3]).

(ii) **Berwald connection**. Its connection forms are given by

$$^b\omega^i_j = \omega^i_j + \dot{A}^i{}_{jk}dx^k,$$

where ω^i_j are Chern's connection forms,

$$A^i{}_{jk} = FC^i{}_{jk}, \quad \dot{A}^i{}_{jk} = A^i{}_{jk|m}\ell^m,$$

$$A^i{}_{jk|m} = \frac{\delta A^i{}_{jk}}{\delta x^m} + A^p{}_{jk}\Gamma^i_{pm} - A^i{}_{pk}\Gamma^p_{jm} - A^i{}_{jp}\Gamma^p_{km}.$$

It is a connection without torsion, of which the connection coefficients are

$$B^i_{jk} =^b \Gamma^i_{jk} = \Gamma^i_{jk} + \dot{A}^i{}_{jk}, \qquad (3.1.21)$$

where Γ^i_{jk} are Chern's connection coefficients. By using (2.2.1) and (3.1.15), one can obtain

$$\frac{1}{2}[G^i]_{y^j y^k} = \Gamma^i_{jk} + \dot{A}^i{}_{jk} = B^i_{jk}. \qquad (3.1.22)$$

(iii) **Hashiguchi connection**. Its connection forms are

$$^h\omega^i_j := \omega^i_j + C^i{}_{jk}\delta y^k + \dot{A}^i{}_{jk}dx^k,$$

where ω^i_j are Chern's connection forms.

These connections all become the Riemannian (or Levi-Civita) connection when F is Riemannian.

3.2 Curvatures

3.2.1 Curvature form of the Chern connection

Let (M, F) be an n-dimensional Finsler manifold. For any local frame field $\{e_i\}$ on the pull-back tangent bundle π^*TM and its dual field $\{\omega^i\}$ in the dual bundle π^*T^*M, we have Chern's connection forms $\{\omega_j^i\}$ defined by (3.1.1) and (3.1.2). Its curvature 2-forms (see Chapter 1, §1.4) are defined by

$$\Omega_j^i = d\omega_j^i - \omega_j^k \wedge \omega_k^i. \tag{3.2.1}$$

Equivalently,

$$\left(\nabla_X \nabla_Y - \nabla_Y \nabla_X - \nabla_{[X,Y]} \right) Z := \Omega(X, Y)Z \tag{3.2.1'}$$

for $X, Y, Z \in \mathcal{C}(\pi^*TM)$.

Exterior differentiating (3.1.1) and using (3.1.1) and (3.2.1), one can obtain

$$\begin{aligned}
0 = d^2\omega^i &= d\omega^j \wedge \omega_j^i - \omega^j \wedge d\omega_j^i \\
&= -\omega^j \wedge \Omega_j^i
\end{aligned} \tag{3.2.2}$$

which is called the *first Bianchi identity*.

In π^*T^*M the 2-form Ω_j^i is a linear combination of $\omega^i \wedge \omega^j$, $\omega^i \wedge \omega^{n+j}$ and $\omega^{n+i} \wedge \omega^{n+j}$. Because of (3.2.2), Ω_j^i can be expressed as

$$\Omega_j^i := \frac{1}{2} R_j{}^i{}_{kl} \omega^k \wedge \omega^l + P_j{}^i{}_{kl} \omega^k \wedge \omega^{n+l}, \tag{3.2.3}$$

where $R_j{}^i{}_{kl}$ is called the *first Chern curvature tensor* (or *hh-curvature tensor*), $P_j{}^i{}_{kl}$ is called the *second Chern curvature tensor* (or *hv-curvature tensor*).

Equivalently, (3.2.3) can be denoted by

$$\Omega(X, Y)Z = R(X, Y)Z + P(X, \nabla_Y(y), Z). \tag{3.2.3'}$$

By (3.2.2) and (3.2.3) we have

$$R_j{}^i{}_{kl} + R_j{}^i{}_{lk} = 0, \quad R_j{}^i{}_{kl} + R_k{}^i{}_{lj} + R_l{}^i{}_{jk} = 0. \tag{3.2.4}$$

$$P_j{}^i{}_{kl} = P_k{}^i{}_{jl}. \tag{3.2.5}$$

In a local coordinate system (x^i, y^i) of TM_0, we obtain from (3.1.3) and (3.1.13)

$$\omega^i = dx^i, \quad \omega^{n+i} = dy^i + N_j^i dx^j = \delta y^i, \quad \omega_j^i = \Gamma_{jk}^i dx^k. \tag{3.2.6}$$

Thus, (3.2.3) becomes

$$\Omega_j^i := \frac{1}{2} R_j{}^i{}_{kl} dx^k \wedge dx^l + P_j{}^i{}_{kl} dx^k \wedge \delta y^l. \qquad (3.2.3^*)$$

On the other hand, substituting the third formula of (3.2.6) into (3.2.1) and comparing with (3.2.3*), we easily obtain

$$R_j{}^i{}_{kl} = \frac{\delta \Gamma_{jl}^i}{\delta x^k} - \frac{\delta \Gamma_{jk}^i}{\delta x^l} + \Gamma_{km}^i \Gamma_{jl}^m - \Gamma_{lm}^i \Gamma_{jk}^m, \qquad (3.2.7)$$

$$P_j{}^i{}_{kl} = -\frac{\partial \Gamma_{jk}^i}{\partial y^l}, \qquad (3.2.8)$$

where the operator (2.3.3) is used. By means of (3.1.11) and (3.1.17), we obtain from (3.2.8) that

$$-y^j P_j{}^i{}_{kl} = y^j \frac{\partial \Gamma_{jk}^i}{\partial y^l} = \frac{\partial (y^j \Gamma_{jk}^i)}{\partial y^l} - \Gamma_{kl}^i = [G^i]_{y^k y^l} - \Gamma_{kl}^i.$$

By (3.1.18) we obtain

$$L^i{}_{kl} = -y^j P_j{}^i{}_{kl}. \qquad (3.2.9)$$

By Definition 3.1 and (3.2.8), we directly obtain the following

Corollary 3.1. *The second Chern curvature tensor $P_j{}^i{}_{kl}$ vanishes identically if and only if F is a Berwald metric.*

3.2.2 Flag curvature and Ricci curvature

By using the first Chern curvature tensor $R_j{}^i{}_{kl}$, we can introduce the notion of the *flag curvature* on a Finsler manifold, which is a natural generalization of the sectional curvature on a Riemannian manifold. Firstly, we write

$$R_{ijkl} := g_{js} R_i{}^s{}_{kl}. \qquad (3.2.10)$$

For a fixed point $(x, y) \in TM_0$, let $\Pi_y(v) = \text{span}\{y, v\} \subset T_x M$ be a two-dimensional plane in $T_x M$ containing y, $y = y^i \partial_i$, $v = v^i \partial_i$. Here the fixed y may be viewed as the *"flagpole"* of the *"flag"* $\Pi_y(v)$, and $v \in T_x M$ is the another edge of $\Pi_y(v)$. Then, the *flag curvature* of $\Pi_y(v)$ with the flagpole y at $x \in M$ is defined by

$$K(\Pi_y)(v) := \frac{-R_{ijkl} y^i v^j y^k v^l}{(g_{ik} g_{jl} - g_{il} g_{jk}) y^i v^j y^k v^l}, \qquad (3.2.11)$$

where g_{ij} and R_{ijkl} are calculated at the based point $(x, y) \in TM_0$. Obviously, the flag curvature of $\Pi_y(v)$ is independent of the choice of v in $\Pi_y(v)$.

If F is a Riemannian metric, g_{ij} and R_{ijkl} are independent of y and the flag curvature is just the sectional curvature of $\Pi_y(v)$ at $x \in M$.

Using the notations as in (2.1.11) and (3.2.3′), we can write the flag curvature formula (3.2.11) as follows

$$K(\Pi_y)(v) = \frac{-\langle R(y,v)y, v\rangle_y}{\langle y,y\rangle_y \langle v,v\rangle_y - \langle y,v\rangle_y^2}. \qquad (3.2.11^*)$$

Put

$$R^i{}_k := y^j R_j{}^i{}_{kl} y^l, \quad R_{jk} := g_{ij} R^i{}_k = y^i R_{ijkl} y^l = -R_{ijlk} y^i y^l. \qquad (3.2.12)$$

Taking v which is unit and orthogonal to y at $(x,y) \in TM_0$, i.e., $g_{ij} v^i v^j = 1$ and $g_{ij} v^i y^j = 0$, and noting $g_{ij} y^i y^j = F^2$, we can simplify (3.2.11) as

$$K(\Pi_y)(v) := F^{-2} R_{jk} v^j v^k. \qquad (3.2.11')$$

$R^i{}_k$ (resp. R_{jk}) defined by (3.2.12) is called the *flag curvature tensor*. It is also called the *Riemann curvature tensor*, or the *Riemann curvature* in some literatures. One can check R_{jk} defined in (3.2.12) is symmetric with respect to j and k (see Proposition 3.2 in next section). The flag curvature tensor $\mathbf{R}_y := R^i{}_j dx^j \otimes \frac{\partial}{\partial x^i}$ induces a linear map $T_x M \to T_x M$ defined by

$$\mathbf{R}_y(v) := R^i{}_j v^j \frac{\partial}{\partial x^i}.$$

Clearly, we have

$$\mathbf{R}_y(y) = 0, \quad \mathbf{R}_{\lambda y} = \lambda^2 \mathbf{R}_y, \quad \lambda > 0, \qquad (3.2.12')$$

and

$$K(\Pi_y)(v) = \frac{\langle \mathbf{R}_y(v), v\rangle_y}{\langle y,y\rangle_y \langle v,v\rangle_y - \langle y,v\rangle_y^2}.$$

In $T_x M$ we choose an orthonormal base $\{e_1, \cdots, e_{n-1}, e_n = y/F\}$ with respect to g_y. Then, the *Ricci curvature* of F at the point $(x,y) \in TM_0$ is defined by

$$Ric := \sum_{a=1}^{n-1} K(\Pi_y)(e_a) = g^{jk} R_{jk} = R^k{}_k. \qquad (3.2.13)$$

This is a well-defined scalar function on TM_0. *Ric* is also called the *Ricci scalar*, which is an average of flag curvatures with the flagpole y.

For a local orthonormal frame field $\{e_i\}$ ($e_n = y/F$) with respect to g_y on $\pi^* TM$ and its dual frame field $\{\omega^i\}$ on $\pi^* T^*M$, (3.1.1) and (3.1.2) reduce

$$d\omega^i - \omega^j \wedge \omega^i_j = 0,$$

$$\omega_j^i + \omega_i^j = -2C_{ijk}\omega^{n+k}, \quad \omega^{n+k} := \delta_n^k dF + F\omega_n^k, \tag{3.2.14}$$

since $y = Fe_n = F\delta_n^i e_i$ and

$$g_{ij} = g(e_i, e_j) = \delta_j^i, \quad g^{ij} = \delta_j^i.$$

In this case we have

$$e_n = \frac{y}{F} = \ell, \quad \omega^n = F_{y^i} dx^i = \omega,$$

where ω and ℓ are the Hilbert 1-form and its dual vector field (cf. Chapter 2, §2.3). Exterior differentiating ω^n and choosing $\omega_n^n = 0$ (cf. 21), we have

$$d\omega^n = \omega^a \wedge \omega_a^n, \quad \omega_a^n + \omega_n^a = 0, \quad 1 \le a, b, \cdots, \le n-1 \tag{3.2.15}$$

because of $C_{njk} = 0$ (see (2.2.3)).

The curvature 2-forms are as same as in (3.2.1) and (3.2.3) formally. However, it should be remarked that we denote often some geometric quantities by the same notations in the different local frame fields. For example, in the above orthonormal frame field (3.2.12) and (3.2.13) become

$$R^i{}_k = R_{ik} = F^2 R_{nikn}, \quad Ric = \sum_i R_{ii}.$$

If F is Riemannian, i.e., $F^2 = g_{ij}(x)y^i y^j$, one can see from (3.1.12$'$) and (3.2.7) that $R_j{}^i{}_{kl}$ are functions of positions $x \in M$ only. Thus,

$$R^i{}_k = R_j{}^i{}_{kl}(x)y^j y^l, \quad Ric = R^k{}_k = S_{ij}(x)y^i y^j, \quad S_{ij} := R_i{}^k{}_{kj} = \frac{1}{2}[Ric]_{y^i y^j}, \tag{3.2.16}$$

where S_{ij} is just the Ricci tensor in Riemannian geometry ([169]).

In Finsler geometry the flag curvature and the Ricci curvature are the most important Riemannian type quantities, which play a major role in studying Finsler geometric problems. On the other hand, there are many other non-Riemannian type quantities, for example, the Cartan tensor, the Landsberg tensor and the so-called **S**-curvature (see the next Chapter for details).

3.3 Bianchi identities

3.3.1 Covariant differentiation

Let (M, F) be an n-dimensional Finsler manifold, $\{e_i\}$ a local frame field on $\pi^* TM$, $\{\omega^i, \omega^{n+i}\}$ the corresponding co-frame field on $T^*(TM_0)$, and $\{\omega_j^i\}$ the corresponding Chern connection 1-forms (cf. §3.1). We are going to define the covariant differentiation for tensor fields on TM_0 with respect to the Chern connection. Since the pull-back bundle $T^*(TM_0)$ may be decomposed as the horizontal part and the vertical part, so is the covariant differentiation. For example, consider a $(1,1)$-type tensor field $T = T^i{}_j e_i \otimes \omega^j$. The covariant differentiation $\nabla T^i{}_j$ of $T^i{}_j$ is defined by

$$\nabla T^i{}_j := dT^i{}_j + T^k{}_j \omega^i_k - T^i{}_k \omega^k_j = T^i{}_{j|k} \omega^k + T^i{}_{j;k} \omega^{n+k}, \qquad (3.3.1)$$

where the second equality defines $T^i{}_{j|k}$ and $T^i{}_{j;k}$, called the *horizontal co-variant derivative* and the *vertical covariant derivative*, respectively. In particular, we have

$$\nabla f = df = f_{|k} \omega^k + f_{;k} \omega^{n+k} \qquad (3.3.2)$$

for a scalar function $f(x,y)$ on TM_0. In a local coordinate system (x^i, y^i), $\omega^i = dx^i$, $e_i = \frac{\partial}{\partial x^i}$, $\omega^i_j = \Gamma^i_{jk} dx^k$, $\omega^{n+k} = \delta y^k$, we then have

$$T^i{}_{j|k} = \frac{\partial T^i{}_j}{\partial x^k} + T^s{}_j \Gamma^i_{sk} - T^i{}_s \Gamma^s_{jk} - T^i{}_{j;s} N^s_k = \frac{\delta T^i{}_j}{\delta x^k} + T^s{}_j \Gamma^i_{sk} - T^i{}_s \Gamma^s_{jk},$$

$$T^i{}_{j;k} = \frac{\partial T^i{}_j}{\partial y^k}.$$

$$(3.3.3)$$

For the fundamental tensor field $g = g_{ij} \omega^i \otimes \omega^j$, using (3.1.2), we have

$$g_{ij|k} = 0, \quad g_{ij;k} = 2C_{ijk}. \qquad (3.3.4)$$

Moreover, we have from the second formula of (3.1.2)

$$y^i_{|k} = 0, \quad y^i_{;k} = \delta^i_k \qquad (3.3.5)$$

for the standard section $y = y^i e_i$. Thus,

$$[F^2]_{|k} = (g_{ij} y^i y^j)_{|k} = g_{ij|k} y^i y^j = 0.$$

This proves Proposition 2.1 in Chapter 2 again.

Let $c = c(t)$ be a smooth curve in M, $V = V^i(t) \frac{\partial}{\partial x^i}|_{c(t)}$ a smooth vector field along $c(t)$. The *linear covariant derivative* of $V(t)$ along $c(t)$ is defined by

$$\nabla_{\dot{c}} V(t) := \left\{ \frac{dV^i}{dt} + V^j(t) N^i_j(c(t), \dot{c}(t)) \right\} \frac{\partial}{\partial x^i}\Big|_{c(t)},$$

where $N^i_j(x,y)$ is the connection coefficients denoted by (3.1.11) or (3.1.17). Clearly, $\nabla_{\dot{c}} V(t)$ is well-defined, i.e., it is independent of the choice of local coordinate systems.

Definition 3.3. If $\nabla_{\dot{c}} V(t) = 0$ along $c(t)$ identically, then $V(t)$ is called a *linearly parallel vector field* along $c(t)$, or the *linearly parallel translation* of $V_0 = V(0)$ along $c(t)$.

According to the theory of ODE, given an initial vector, there is a unique linearly parallel vector field along $c(t)$. It follows from (3.1.16) that a geodesic on (M, F) is a curve along which its tangent vector field is linearly parallel, called the *self-parallel curve*. Similar to the Riemannian case, we have the following

Lemma 3.1. *If $c(t)$ be a geodesic on (M, F), then the linearly parallel translation along $c(t)$ preserves both the norm of any linearly parallel vector field along $c(t)$ and the angle between two linearly parallel vector fields along $c(t)$.*

Proof. Let $U(t)$ and $V(t)$ be parallel vector fields along the geodesic $c(t)$. We have from the definition

$$\frac{d}{dt} g_{\dot{c}}(U, V) = \frac{d}{dt} \left[g_{ij} U^i V^j \right] = \left\{ \frac{\partial g_{ij}}{\partial x^k} \dot{c}^k - g_{kj} N_i^k - g_{ik} N_j^k - 4 C_{ijk} G^k \right\} U^i V^j.$$

On the other hand, contracting (3.1.5) with y^k and using (3.1.16), we have

$$\frac{\partial g_{ij}}{\partial x^k} y^k = g_{kj} N_i^k + g_{ik} N_j^k + 4 C_{ijk} G^k.$$

It follows from the above two formulas that

$$\frac{d}{dt} g_{\dot{c}}(U, V) = 0.$$

The proof is completed. $\square$

We now define another covariant derivative $\widetilde{\nabla}_{\dot{c}}$ along a curve $c(t)$. Set

$$\widetilde{\nabla}_{\dot{c}} V(t) := \left\{ \frac{dV^i}{dt} + \dot{c}^j(t) N_j^i(c(t), V(t)) \right\} \frac{\partial}{\partial x^i} \bigg|_{c(t)}.$$

In general, the connection $\widetilde{\nabla}$ is not linear.

Definition 3.4. If $\widetilde{\nabla}_{\dot{c}} V(t) = 0$ holds along $c(t)$ identically, then $V(t)$ is called the *parallel vector field* along $c(t)$.

Lemma 3.2. *Let $c(t)$ be a smooth curve, $V(t)$ a parallel vector field along $c(t)$. We have*

$$F(c(t), V(t)) = \text{const.}$$

along $c(t)$.

Proof. Since

$$F^2(c(t), V(t)) = g_{ij}(c(t), V(t))V^i(t)V^j(t),$$

noting that $C_{ijk}(c(t), V(t))V^i(t) = 0$, we obtain from (3.1.16), (3.1.11) and Definition 3.4 that

$$\frac{d}{dt}\left[F^2(c(t), V(t))\right] = \frac{\partial g_{ij}}{\partial x^k}\dot{c}^k V^i V^j + 2g_{ij}V^i\frac{dV^j}{dt}$$
$$= 2g_{ik}\Gamma^k_{jl}\dot{c}^l V^i V^j - 2g_{ik}N^k_l\dot{c}^l V^i = 0.$$

The proof is completed. □

Let $p, q \in M$ be two arbitrary points in (M, F), $c(t)$ ($a \leq t \leq b$) a smooth curve from p ($t = a$) to q ($t = b$) on M. Define a map $P_c : T_pM \to T_qM$ by

$$P_c(v) := V(b), \quad v \in T_pM,$$

where $V(t)$ is a parallel vector field along $c(t)$ with initial value $V(a) = v$. Thus, P_c is called the *parallel translation* along $c(t)$. By Lemma 3.2, the parallel translation P_c is a C^∞ diffeomorphism from $T_pM\setminus\{0\}$ to $T_qM\setminus\{0\}$, which is positively homogeneous of degree one,

$$P_c(\lambda v) = \lambda P_c(v), \quad \lambda > 0, \ v \in T_pM.$$

However, P_c is not linear, in general.

Let (M, F) be a Berwald manifold (cf. Definition 3.1). In a standard coordinate system (x, y),

$$v^j N^i_j(x, y) = v^j\Gamma^i_{jk}(x)y^k = y^j\Gamma^i_{jk}(x)v^k = y^j N^i_j(x, v)$$

for any vector $v \in T_xM\setminus\{0\}$. Thus for any curve $c(t)$ and any vector field $V(t)$ along $c(t)$,

$$\nabla_{\dot{c}}V(t) = \widetilde{\nabla}_{\dot{c}}V(t).$$

Hence, any parallel vector field along a curve linearly depends on its initial value. By Lemma 3.2, we immediately have the following

Proposition 3.1. *Let (M, F) be a Berwald manifold, $p, q \in M$ two arbitrary points. For any smooth curve $c(t)$ from p to q on M, the parallel translation P_c is a linear isometry between (T_pM, F_p) and (T_qM, F_q).*

Example 3.1. Consider Example 2.4 in §2.1.2. The Finsler metric in (2.1.10) is given by Riemannian metrics α_1 and α_2. Let

$$\overline{F}(x, y) := \sqrt{[\alpha_1(x_1, y_1)]^2 + [\alpha_2(x_2, y_2)]^2},$$

which is a product Riemannian metric. A straightforward computation yields that the spray coefficients of $\overline{F}$ can be decomposed as a direct sum of spray coefficients of α_1 and α_2:

$$\overline{G}^{i_1}(x_1, y_1) = G_{\alpha_1}^{i_1}(x_1, y_1), \quad \overline{G}^{i_2}(x_2, y_2) = G_{\alpha_2}^{i_2}(x_2, y_2).$$

It is easy to prove that (cf. [36], §4.3) the Finsler metric in (2.1.10) and the Riemannian metric $\overline{F}$ have the same spray coefficients. Hence,

$$G^i = \overline{G}^i = \frac{1}{2}\overline{\Gamma}^i_{jk}(x)y^j y^k,$$

i.e., F is a Berwald metric.

3.3.2 Bianchi identities

Exterior differentiating the first formula in (3.1.2) yields

$$g_{ik}\Omega^k_j + g_{kj}\Omega^k_i = -2(C_{ijk|l}\omega^l + C_{ijk;l}\omega^{n+l}) \wedge \omega^{n+k} - 2C_{ijk}\Omega^k_l y^l.$$

Inserting (3.2.3) into the above identity and using (3.2.9) and (3.2.10), we obtain

$$R_{jikl} + R_{ijkl} = -2C_{ijs}R^s{}_{kl}, \quad R^i{}_{kl} = y^s R_s{}^i{}_{kl}, \tag{3.3.6}$$

$$P_{jikl} + P_{ijkl} = 2C_{ijs}L^s{}_{kl} - 2C_{ijl|k}, \quad P_{ijkl} = g_{js}P_i{}^s{}_{kl}. \tag{3.3.7}$$

It follows from (3.2.4) that

$$2(R_{klji} - R_{jikl}) = (R_{klji} + R_{lkji}) - (R_{jikl} + R_{ijkl})$$
$$+ (R_{kilj} + R_{iklj}) + (R_{ljki} + R_{jlki}) + (R_{iljk} + R_{lijk}) + (R_{jkil} + R_{kjil}).$$

By means of (3.3.6), the above formula is reduced as

$$R_{klji} - R_{jikl} = -C_{kls}R^s{}_{ji} + C_{jis}R^s{}_{kl} - C_{kis}R^s{}_{lj}$$
$$- C_{ljs}R^s{}_{ki} - C_{ils}R^s{}_{jk} - C_{jks}R^s{}_{il}. \tag{3.3.8}$$

(3.3.8) together with (3.2.4) is called the *first Bianchi identity*. Contracting (3.3.8) with y^j and y^k and using (3.2.12), one gets

$$R_{ij} = R_{ji}. \tag{3.3.9}$$

Therefore, we obtain the following

Proposition 3.2. R_{ij} *defined in (3.2.12) is symmetric.*

Put

$$\mathbf{R} := R^k_{\ j} dx^j \otimes \frac{\partial}{\partial x^k}, \quad \left\langle \mathbf{R}\left(\frac{\partial}{\partial x^j}\right), \frac{\partial}{\partial x^i} \right\rangle_y = R_{ij}, \qquad (3.3.9')$$

which is also called the *Riemann curvature tensor* (compare with (3.2.12)).
Exterior differentiating the second equation in (3.1.2) yields

$$
\begin{aligned}
d\omega^{n+k} &= dy^j \wedge \omega^k_j + y^j d\omega^k_j \\
&= (\omega^{n+j} - y^s \omega^j_s) \wedge \omega^k_j + y^j (\Omega^k_j + \omega^s_j \wedge \omega^k_s) \qquad (3.3.10)\\
&= y^j \Omega^k_j + \omega^{n+j} \wedge \omega^k_j.
\end{aligned}
$$

Exterior differentiating (3.2.1), we obtain the following *second Bianchi identity*:

$$d\Omega^i_j = -\Omega^k_j \wedge \omega^i_k + \omega^k_j \wedge \Omega^i_k.$$

Inserting (3.2.3) into the above equation and using (3.1.1), (3.2.1) and (3.3.10), we obtain

$$
\begin{aligned}
0 = {}&\frac{1}{2}(R_j^{\ i}{}_{kl|m} - P_j^{\ i}{}_{ks}R^s_{\ lm})\omega^k \wedge \omega^l \wedge \omega^m \\
&+ \frac{1}{2}(R_j^{\ i}{}_{kl;m} - 2P_j^{\ i}{}_{km|l} + 2P_j^{\ i}{}_{ks}L^s_{\ lm})\omega^k \wedge \omega^l \wedge \omega^{n+m} \\
&+ P_j^{\ i}{}_{kl;m}\omega^k \wedge \omega^{n+l} \wedge \omega^{n+m},
\end{aligned}
$$

where $R_j^{\ i}{}_{kl|m}$ is defined by an analogy of (3.3.3), $R^s_{\ lm}$ is defined by the second formula of (3.3.6), $L^s_{\ lm}$ is expressed by (3.2.9). Then we obtain the second Bianchi identity in the tensor form:

$$
\begin{aligned}
&R_j^{\ i}{}_{kl|m} + R_j^{\ i}{}_{lm|k} + R_j^{\ i}{}_{mk|l} = P_j^{\ i}{}_{ms}R^s_{\ kl} + P_j^{\ i}{}_{ks}R^s_{\ lm} + P_j^{\ i}{}_{ls}R^s_{\ mk}, \\
&R_j^{\ i}{}_{kl;m} = P_j^{\ i}{}_{km|l} - P_j^{\ i}{}_{lm|k} - P_j^{\ i}{}_{ks}L^s_{\ lm} + P_j^{\ i}{}_{ls}L^s_{\ km}, \\
&P_j^{\ i}{}_{kl;m} - P_j^{\ i}{}_{km;l} = 0.
\end{aligned}
$$

$$(3.3.11)$$

Contracting the first formula of (3.3.11) with y^j and y^l and using (3.2.12) and (3.3.5), we get

$$R^i_{\ k|m} - R^i_{\ m|k} + R^i_{\ mk|l}y^l = L^i_{\ ks}R^s_{\ m} - L^i_{\ ms}R^s_{\ k}. \qquad (3.3.12)$$

Observe that

$$R^i_{\ kl;j} = (y^s R_s^{\ i}{}_{kl});j = R_j^{\ i}{}_{kl} + y^t R_t^{\ i}{}_{kl;j}.$$

Using the second formula of (3.3.11), we have

$$
\begin{aligned}
R_j^{\ i}{}_{kl} &= R^i_{\ kl;j} - y^s R_s^{\ i}{}_{kl;j} \\
&= R^i_{\ kl;j} - y^t (P_t^{\ i}{}_{kj|l} - P_t^{\ i}{}_{lj|k} - P_t^{\ i}{}_{ks}L^s_{\ lj} + P_t^{\ i}{}_{ls}L^s_{\ kj}).
\end{aligned}
$$

By virtue of (3.2.9) and (3.3.5), we finally obtain

$$R_j^{\ i}{}_{kl} = R^i_{\ kl;j} + L^i_{\ kj|l} - L^i_{\ lj|k} - L^i_{\ ks}L^s_{\ lj} + L^i_{\ ls}L^s_{\ kj}. \qquad (3.3.13)$$

3.3.3   Other formulas

It follows from (3.2.7), (3.1.11) and the third formula of (3.3.6) that

$$R^i{}_{jk} = \frac{\partial N^i_k}{\partial x^j} - \frac{\partial N^i_j}{\partial x^k} + N^s_k \frac{\partial N^i_j}{\partial y^s} - N^s_j \frac{\partial N^i_k}{\partial y^s}. \tag{3.3.14}$$

Contracting (3.3.14) with y^k and using (3.1.17), we obtain

$$R^i{}_j = 2\frac{\partial G^i}{\partial x^j} - y^k \frac{\partial^2 G^i}{\partial x^k \partial y^j} + 2G^k \frac{\partial^2 G^i}{\partial y^k \partial y^j} - \frac{\partial G^i}{\partial y^k} \frac{\partial G^k}{\partial y^j}. \tag{3.3.15}$$

From (3.3.14) and (3.3.15) we immediately obtain

$$R^i{}_{jk} = \frac{1}{3}(R^i{}_{j;k} - R^i{}_{k;j}). \tag{3.3.16}$$

Lemma 3.3.

$$C_{ijk|p|q}y^p y^q + C_{ijs}R^s{}_k = -\frac{1}{3}\{g_{is}R^s{}_{k;j} + g_{sj}R^s{}_{k;i}\} - \frac{1}{6}\{g_{is}R^s{}_{j;k} + g_{sj}R^s{}_{i;k}\},$$

$$\mathbf{I}_{k|p|q}y^p y^q + \mathbf{I}_s R^s{}_k = -\frac{2}{3}R^s{}_{k;s} - \frac{1}{3}R^s{}_{s;k}.$$

Proof. Set $L_{ijk} = g_{is}L^s{}_{jk} = -y^s P_{sijk}$. By virtue of (3.2.9) and (3.3.7), noting (2.2.3), we have

$$L_{ijk} = -\frac{1}{2}y^s P_{sijk} - \frac{1}{2}y^s P_{jisk} = \frac{1}{2}y^s P_{isjk} + \frac{1}{2}y^s P_{sijk} + y^s C_{ijk|s} = y^s C_{ijk|s}, \tag{3.3.17}$$

which implies that L_{ijk} are symmetric and

$$L_{ijk}y^k = L_{ijk}y^j = L_{ijk}y^i = 0. \tag{3.3.17'}$$

Put

$$J_i = g_{ik}J^k = g^{jk}L_{ijk}.$$

Contracting (3.3.17) with g^{jk} and noting (2.2.2), one may get

$$J_i = \mathbf{I}_{i|s}y^s. \tag{3.3.18}$$

It follows from (3.3.13) that

$$R_j{}^i{}_{ks}y^s = R^i{}_{ks;j}y^s + L^i{}_{jk|s}y^s = R^i{}_{k;j} + R^i{}_{jk} + L^i{}_{jk|s}y^s.$$

Thus,

$$R_{jiks}y^s = g_{is}\{R^s{}_{k;j} + R^s{}_{jk}\} + L_{ijk|s}y^s. \tag{3.3.19}$$

By means of (3.3.19) and (3.3.6) we have

$$L_{ijk|s}y^s + C_{ijs}R^s{}_k = -\frac{1}{2}g_{is}\{R^s{}_{k;j} + R^s{}_{jk}\} - \frac{1}{2}g_{js}\{R^s{}_{k;i} + R^s{}_{ik}\}. \tag{3.3.20}$$

Contracting (3.3.20) with g^{ij} and using (3.3.16) and (3.3.18) yields the second formula in Lemma 3.3. Inserting (3.3.16) into (3.3.20) and using (3.3.17), one obtains the first formula in Lemma 3.3. The lemma is proved.

$\square$

These related formulas play an important role in the local calculations of Finsler geometry. We see that relations among geometric quantities in Finsler geometry are more complicated than the Riemannian case. Therefore, Finsler geometry is enable better to portray the colorful geometric world.

3.4 Legendre transformation

3.4.1 The dual norm in the dual space

As it is well-known, in Riemannian geometry a covariant (resp. contravariant) index of a tensor can be transformed to a contravariant (resp. covariant) index by means of the Riemannian metric tensor g_{ij} and its inversion g^{ij}. In other words, g_{ij} (resp. g^{ij}) gives a linear isomorphism between the tangent space and the cotangent space. However, this is more complicated in Finsler geometry. So, we have to introduce the following Legendre transformation, which comes from the Hamilton system in classical mechanics.

Let (M, F) be an n-dimensional Finsler manifold with positive definite Finsler metric. Fixing a point $x \in M$, $F(x, y) = F(y)$ is a Minkowski norm on $T_x M$ (see Chapter 2, §2.1). On putting $T_x M_0 = T_x M \setminus \{0\}$, we define the *dual norm* F^* in the dual space $T_x^* M$ by

$$F^*(\theta) = \sup_{F(y)=1} \theta(y), \quad \theta \in T_x^* M. \tag{3.4.1}$$

Clearly, we have $F^*(\lambda\theta) = \lambda F^*(\theta)$ for $\lambda \in \mathbb{R}^+$.

Proposition 3.3. *For a fixed point $x \in M$, the co-vector $\theta := g(y, \cdot) \in T_x^* M$ for any vector $y \in T_x M_0$ satisfies*

$$F(y) = F^*(\theta) = \frac{\theta(y)}{F(y)}. \tag{3.4.2}$$

Conversely, for any co-vector $\theta \in T_x^* M \setminus \{0\} = T_x^* M_0$, there exists an unique vector $y \in T_x M_0$ such that $\theta = g(y, \cdot)$.

Proof. By the definition of the fundamental tensor g and (3.4.1) we have

$$F(y) = \frac{g(y, y)}{F(y)} = \frac{\theta(y)}{F(y)} \le F^*(\theta)$$

at the point (x, y). On the other hand, it follows from the Cauchy inequality $\theta(v) = g(y, v) \le F(y)F(v)$ that

$$F^*(\theta) = \sup_{v \in T_x M \setminus \{0\}} \frac{\theta(v)}{F(v)} \le F(y).$$

By virtue of these formulas above, we obtain (3.4.2) directly.

Conversely, for any co-vector $\theta \in T_x^* M_0$, the level sets

$$\mathcal{K}^c := \{v \in T_x M \mid \theta(v) = c = \text{const.}\}$$

are parallel hyperplanes in $T_x M$. Since the indicatrix $S_x M = F^{-1}(1)$ (see Chapter 2, §2.2) is strictly convex, there are uniquely a positive number $c_0 > 0$ and a vector $y \in S_x M$, such that $\mathcal{K}^{c_0}$ is tangent to $S_x M$ at y. Thus,

$$\theta(v) = c_0, \quad v \in T_y(S_x M) = \mathcal{K}^{c_0}.$$

On the other hand, the equation of the tangent hyperplane of $S_x M$ at y can be written as $g(y, v) - 1 = 0$, i.e.,

$$T_y(S_x M) = \{v \in T_x M \mid g(y, v) = 1\}.$$

Hence,

$$\theta(v) = c_0 g(y, v), \quad v \in T_x M.$$

On putting $\widetilde{y} = c_0 y$, we obtain the required vector $\widetilde{y}$ satisfying $\theta = g(\widetilde{y}, \cdot)$. The proof is completed. $\qquad\qquad\square$

3.4.2 Legendre transformation

Definition 3.5. For any point $x \in M$, the Legendre transformation $\mathcal{L} : T_x M \to T_x^* M$ is defined by

$$\mathcal{L}(y) = g(y, \cdot) = \theta, \quad \forall \ y \in T_x M_0, \quad \mathcal{L}(0) = 0.$$

Proposition 3.3 implies that the Legendre transformation is smooth on $T_x M_0$. Obviously,

$$\mathcal{L}(\lambda y) = \lambda \mathcal{L}(y), \quad \lambda > 0.$$

It follows from (3.4.2) that

$$F(y) = F^*(\mathcal{L}(y)) = F^*(\theta).$$

In a local coordinate system (x^i, y^i) we have

$$\mathcal{L}(y) = \theta = \theta_i dx^i = g_{ij}(y) y^j dx^i, \quad \theta_i = g_{ij}(y) y^j, \qquad (3.4.3)$$

where $g_{ij}(y) = \frac{1}{2}[F^2]_{y^i y^j}(y)$. Thus, the Jacobian of the Legendre transformation $\mathcal{L}$ is

$$\det\left(\frac{\partial \theta_i}{\partial y^j}(y)\right) = \det\left(g_{ij}(y)\right) > 0. \qquad (3.4.4)$$

Therefore, we have the following

Proposition 3.4. *The Legendre transformation* $\mathcal{L}$ *is a diffeomorphism from* $T_x M_0$ *to* $T_x^* M_0$.

It should be remarked that the Legendre transformation is not a linear isomorphism, in general. We now consider the inverse $\mathcal{L}^{-1}$ of the Legendre transformation $\mathcal{L}$. For $\theta \in T_x^* M_0$, let

$$g^{*ij} := \frac{1}{2}[F^{*2}]_{\theta_i \theta_j}(\theta), \quad \mathcal{L}^{-1}(\theta) = y.$$

By differentiating the equality $F^2(y) = F^{*2}(\theta)$ with respect to y^i and using (3.4.2) and (3.4.4), we get

$$\frac{1}{2}[F^2]_{y^i}(y) = \frac{1}{2}\sum_k [F^{*2}]_{\theta_k}(\theta)g_{ki}(y). \tag{3.4.5}$$

Thus, we have from (3.4.5) and $y^i g_{ij} = \frac{1}{2}[F^2]_{y^j}$

$$g^{*jk}(\theta)\theta_k = \frac{1}{2}[F^{*2}]_{\theta_j}(\theta) = \frac{1}{2}g^{jk}(y)[F^2]_{y^k}(y) = y^j,$$

from which it follows that

$$g^{*kl}\theta_l \frac{\partial g_{ki}}{\partial y^j} = y^k \frac{\partial g_{ki}}{\partial y^j} = 2y^k C_{kij} = 0.$$

Differentiating (3.4.5) with respect to y^j yields

$$g_{ij} = g^{*kl}(\theta)g_{ik}(y)g_{jl}(y) + g^{*kl}(\theta)\theta_l \frac{\partial g_{ik}}{\partial y^j}(y) = g^{*kl}(\theta)g_{ik}(y)g_{jl}(y),$$

i.e.,

$$g^{*kl}(\theta) = g^{kl}(y). \tag{3.4.6}$$

This proves the following

Proposition 3.5. *The dual norm* F^* *defined by (3.4.1) is a Minkowski norm in* $T_x^* M$.

Since the point $x \in M$ is arbitrary, $F^*(x, \theta)$ defines a *dual Finsler metric*. The relation between $F^*(x, \theta)$ and $F(x, y)$ is given in (3.4.6).

3.4.3 Example

Let $F = \alpha + \beta$ be a Randers metric (see Chapter 2, §2.1, Example 1.2).

$$\alpha = \sqrt{a_{ij} y^i y^j}, \quad \beta = b_i y^i, \quad y = y^i \frac{\partial}{\partial x^i}.$$

We have

$$\|\beta\| = \sqrt{a^{ij} b_i b_j}, \quad (a^{ij}) = (a_{ij})^{-1}.$$

Its dual Finsler metric is also a Randers metric:

$$F^* = \alpha^* + \beta^*, \quad \alpha^*(\theta) = \sqrt{a^{*ij}\theta_i\theta_j}, \quad \beta^*(\theta) = b^{*i}\theta_i, \quad \theta = \theta_i dx^i,$$

where

$$a^{*ij} = \frac{(1 - ||\beta||^2)a^{ij} + b^i b^j}{(1 - ||\beta||^2)^2}, \quad b^i = a^{ij}b_j, \quad b^{*i} = -\frac{b^i}{1 - ||\beta||^2}.$$

Putting $(a^*_{ij}) = (a^{*ij})^{-1}$, we have

$$a^*_{ij} = (1 - ||\beta||^2)(a_{ij} - b_i b_j).$$

Thus, the norm $||\beta^*|| := \sup_{\alpha^*(\theta)=1} \beta^*(\theta)$ is given by

$$||\beta^*||^2 = a^*_{ij} b^{*i} b^{*j} = \frac{1}{1 - ||\beta||^2} (a_{ij} - b_i b_j) b^i b^j = ||\beta||^2.$$

This means that the norm of β^* with respect to α^* equals the norm of β with respect to α.

By Definition 3.4, the Legendre transformation is

$$\theta = \mathcal{L}(y) = g_{ij}(y)y^j dx^i = F(y)\left\{\frac{a_{ij}y^j}{\alpha(y)} + b_i\right\} dx^i, \tag{3.4.7}$$

of which the inverse is

$$y = \mathcal{L}^{-1}(\theta) = g^{*ij}(\theta)\theta_j \frac{\partial}{\partial x^i} = F^*(\theta)\left\{\frac{a^{*ij}\theta_j}{\alpha^*(\theta)} + b^{*i}\right\} \frac{\partial}{\partial x^i}. \tag{3.4.8}$$

Exercises

3.1 By using the operator (2.3.3) prove the formula (3.1.12′).

3.2 Check the formula (3.1.15).

3.3 Check the formula (3.1.22) and prove that $\dot{A}_{ijk} = -\frac{1}{4}y_l[G^l]_{y^i y^j y^k}$.

3.4 Prove formulas (3.2.7) and (3.2.9) in detail.

3.5 Prove that the hh-curvature tensor of the Berwald connection is

$$^b R_j{}^i{}_{kl} = R_j{}^i{}_{kl} + \dot{A}^i_{jl|k} - \dot{A}^i_{jk|l} + \dot{A}^i_{sk}\dot{A}^s_{jl} - \dot{A}^i_{sl}\dot{A}^s_{jk},$$

where $R_j{}^i{}_{kl}$ is the first Chern curvature tensor.

3.6 Let (M, F) be a Finsler manifold, $x \in M$ a fixed point. In the tangent space $T_x M$ there is an induced Riemannian metric

$$\widehat{g}_x := g_{ij}(y)dy^i \otimes dy^j.$$

Prove that the Christoffel symbols and the curvature tensor of $\widehat{g}_x$ are respectively

$$\widehat{\Gamma}^i_{jk} = C^i_{jk} := g^{is}C_{jks}, \quad \widehat{R}_j{}^i{}_{kl} = C^i_{sl}C^s_{jk} - C^i_{sk}C^s_{jl}.$$

3.7 Denote by $\Delta_{\widehat{g}}$ the Laplacian with respect to $\widehat{g}_x$ as above. Prove that

$$\Delta_{\widehat{g}} = g^{ij} \left(\frac{\partial^2}{\partial y^i \partial y^j} - C_{ij}^k \frac{\partial}{\partial y^k} \right).$$

3.8 Let (M, F) be a Landsberg manifold, $p, q \in M$. Denote by P_c the parallel translation from p to q along a smooth curve $c : [a, b] \to M$. Prove that P_c induces an isometric transformation from the Riemannian space $(T_p(M), \widehat{g}_p)$ to $(T_q(M), \widehat{g}_q)$ (cf. [36]).

3.9 Prove that the product Riemannian metric $\overline{F}$ in Example 3.1 has the same spray coefficients as that of the Finsler metric (2.1.10).

3.10 Let (M, F) be a Finsler manifold, $f : M \to \mathbb{R}$ a smooth function on M. By means of the Legendre transformation, write down the vector field dual to the differential $df = \frac{\partial f}{\partial x^i} dx^i$ of f and the Hessian ∇df with respect to the Chern connection in a local coordinate system (x^i, y^i).

Chapter 4

S-Curvature

4.1 Volume measures

In Riemannian geometry, the Riemannian metric $g = g_{ij}(x)dx^i \otimes dx^j$ determines uniquely the Riemannian volume element

$$dV_g = \sqrt{\det(g_{ij}(x))}dx^1 \wedge \cdots \wedge dx^n.$$

However, there are various volume elements in Finsler geometry, among which two volume elements are used usually. They are reduced to the Riemannian volume element when the Finsler metric is Riemannian.

4.1.1 Busemann-Hausdorff volume element

Let (M, F) be an n-dimensional oriented Finsler manifold. For any fixed point $x \in M$, let $\{e_i\}$ be an oriented base in T_xM, whose dual base is $\{\omega^i\}$. As a measurable metric space, the volume element of (M, F) may be denoted by

$$dV_F := \sigma(x)\omega^1 \wedge \cdots \wedge \omega^n,$$

where $\sigma(x)$ is a measure function which satisfies some conditions such that dV_F is an invariant n-form. Various volume elements may be obtained whenever a measure functions is chosen.

The *Busemann-Hausdorff volume element* at a point x is defined by

$$dV_F := \sigma_B(x)\omega^1 \wedge \cdots \wedge \omega^n, \tag{4.1.1}$$

where

$$\sigma_B(x) := \frac{\text{Vol}(B^n(1))}{\text{Vol}\left(y = y^i e_i \in T_xM | F(x, y) < 1\right)}.$$

Here Vol denotes the Euclidean volume and $B^n(1)$ is a unit ball in $\mathbb{R}^n$. Particularly, in a local coordinate system we have

$$dV_F := \sigma_B(x)dx^1 \wedge \cdots \wedge dx^n, \qquad (4.1.1')$$

where

$$\sigma_B(x) := \frac{\text{Vol}(B^n(1))}{\text{Vol}\left(y^i \frac{\partial}{\partial x^i} \in T_xM \,|\, F(x,y) < 1\right)}.$$

By such a volume element, the second author of this book established the co-area formula and volume comparison theorems in Finsler geometry and introduced the mean curvature of Finsler submanifolds ([103]).

For general Finsler metrics, the Busemann-Hausdorff volume element may be expressed hardly by element functions. However, it can be done for the Randers metric. Firstly, we need the following result in linear algebra.

Lemma 4.1. *Let $G = (g_{ij})$ and $A = (a_{ij})$ be two $n \times n$ symmetric matrices, $B = (b_i)$ an n-dimensional vector. Suppose that $A = (a_{ij})$ is reversible and write $A^{-1} = (A^{ij})$. If*

$$g_{ij} = a_{ij} + cb_ib_j,$$

then

$$\det G = (1 + cb^2)\det A,$$

where $b^2 = a^{ij}b_ib_j$. Moreover, if $1 + cb^2 \neq 0$, then G is reversible and $G^{-1} = (g^{ij})$ can be expressed by

$$g^{ij} = a^{ij} - \frac{cb^ib^j}{1 + cb^2}, \quad b^i = a^{ij}b_j.$$

We now consider a Randers metric $F = \alpha + \beta$, where $\alpha = \sqrt{a_{ij}(x)y^iy^j}$ and $\beta = b_i(x)y^i$. Put

$$b = ||\beta||_\alpha = \sqrt{a^{ij}(x)b_i(x)b_j(x)} < 1.$$

For any point x, let $\{e_i\}$ be a local orthonormal base at x with respect to the Riemannian metric α, such that $a_{ij} = \delta_{ij}$ and $\det(a_{ij}) = 1$. Without loss of generality, suppose that $\beta = by^1$. Thus, the following domain

$$\Omega := \{y^ie_i \in \mathbb{R}^n \cong T_xM \,|\, F(y^ie_i) < 1\}$$

can be denoted by

$$(1 - b^2)^2 \left(y^1 + \frac{b}{1 - b^2}\right)^2 + (1 - b^2)\sum_{k=2}^{n}(y^k)^2 < 1,$$

which is a convex one in $\mathbb{R}^n$. We make a transformation $\phi : (y^i) \to (v^i)$ as follows:

$$v^1 = (1 - b^2)\left(y^1 + \frac{b}{1 - b^2}\right), \quad v^k = \sqrt{1 - b^2} y^k, \quad 2 \le k \le n. \quad (4.1.2)$$

ϕ maps Ω into $B^n(1) \subset \mathbb{R}^n$, whose Jacobi is

$$\det\left(\frac{\partial v^i}{\partial y^j}\right) = (1 - b^2)^{\frac{n+1}{2}}.$$

Then,

$$\text{Vol}(B^n(1)) = \int_{B^n(1)} dv^1 \cdots dv^n = \int_\Omega (1 - b^2)^{\frac{n+1}{2}} dy^1 \cdots dy^n$$
$$= (1 - b^2)^{\frac{n+1}{2}} \text{Vol}(\Omega).$$

Clearly, in the general base we have

$$\text{Vol}(B^n(1)) = (1 - b^2)^{\frac{n+1}{2}} \sqrt{\det(a_{ij}(x))} \text{Vol}(\Omega).$$

Hence, it follows from (4.1.1) that

$$\sigma_B(x) = (1 - b^2(x))^{\frac{n+1}{2}} \sqrt{\det(a_{ij}(x))}. \quad (4.1.3)$$

This is the Busemann-Hausdorff volume measure function of $F = \alpha + \beta$. In a local coordinate system, the volume element is

$$dV_F = (1 - b^2(x))^{\frac{n+1}{2}} \sqrt{\det(a_{ij}(x))} dx^1 \wedge \cdots \wedge dx^n.$$

Example 4.1. Let $F = \alpha + \beta$ be a Randers metric defined on the unit ball $B^n(1) \subset \mathbb{R}^n$ be determined by

$$\alpha = \frac{\sqrt{|y|^2 - (|x|^2|y|^2 - \langle x, y \rangle^2)}}{1 - |x|^2},$$

$$\beta = \frac{\langle x, y \rangle}{1 - |x|^2} + \frac{\langle u, y \rangle}{1 + \langle u, x \rangle},$$

where $y \in T_x\mathbb{R}^n$, the vector $u \in B^n(1)$, and $|\cdot|$ and $\langle \, , \, \rangle$ denote the standard Euclidean norm and inner product, respectively. When $u = 0$, F is just the Funk metric defined by (2.1.4) in Chapter 2, §2.1. Hence, it is a Finsler metric whenever $|u|$ small enough. In fact, for any u, $|u| < 1$, F is a Finsler metric on $\mathbf{B}^n(1)$.

Applying Lemma 4.1 to the following matrix (a_{ij})

$$a_{ij} = \frac{1}{1 - |x|^2}\left(\delta_{ij} + \frac{x^i x^j}{1 - |x|^2}\right),$$

one can obtain

$$\det(a_{ij}) = \frac{1}{(1 - |x|^2)^{n+1}}.$$

Thus, the volume element of the Riemannian metric α is given by

$$dV_\alpha = \left(1 - |x|^2\right)^{-\frac{n+1}{2}} dx^1 \wedge \cdots \wedge dx^n.$$

By Lemma 4.1, we see

$$a^{ij} = (1 - |x|^2)(\delta^{ij} - x^i x^j).$$

The norm of β with respect to α is

$$\|\beta\|_\alpha = \sqrt{a^{ij}(x)b_i(x)b_j(x)} = \sqrt{1 - \frac{(1 - |x|^2)(1 - |u|^2)}{(1 + \langle u, x \rangle)^2}}.$$

Inserting these into (4.1.3) yields the Busemann-Hausdorff volume element for the Randers metric in Example 4.1.

$$dV_F = \sigma_B(x)dx^1 \wedge \cdots \wedge dx^n = \left\{ \frac{1 - |u|^2}{(1 + \langle u, x \rangle)^2} \right\}^{\frac{n+1}{2}} dx^1 \wedge \cdots \wedge dx^n.$$

4.1.2 The volume element induced from SM

As known (cf. Chapter 2, §2.2), the projective sphere bundle SM of an n-dimensional oriented Finsler manifold (M, F) is

$$SM = \bigcup_{x \in M} S_x M, \quad S_x M = \{y \in T_x M | F(x, y) = 1\}.$$

Clearly, SM is compact when M is compact. At every fiber of $\pi^* T^* M$ there is a positively oriented orthonormal coframe $\{\omega^i\}$ such that $\omega^n = \omega$ (the Hilbert form, Chapter 2, §2.3). Let $\{e_i\}$ be the dual frame. We can denote $\omega^i = v^i_j dx^j$ and $e_i = u^i_j \partial_j$, where the matrix (u^i_j) is the inversion of the matrix (v^i_j). Thus, $\delta_{ij} = g(e_i, e_j) = u^k_i u^l_j g(\partial_k, \partial_l) = u^k_i u^l_j g_{kl}$ and $\sum_i v^i_k v^i_l = g_{kl}$. It follows from the orientation that $\det(v^i_j) = \sqrt{\det(g_{ij})}$.

We now can take a local orthonormal base and its dual base on $T(TM_0)$ and $T^*(TM_0)$:

$$\widetilde{e}_i = u^j_i \frac{\delta}{\delta x^j}, \quad \widetilde{e}_{n+i} = u^j_i F \frac{\partial}{\partial y^j},$$

$$\omega^i = v^i_j dx^j, \quad \omega^{n+i} = v^i_j \frac{\delta y^j}{F},$$

where $\frac{\delta}{\delta x^j}$ and δy^j are defined by (2.3.3) and (2.3.5), respectively. So, in TM_0 we have the following Sasaki metric

$$\mathcal{G}_S = \sum_i \left(\omega^i \otimes \omega^i + \omega^{n+i} \otimes \omega^{n+i}\right) = g_{ij} dx^i \otimes dx^j + g_{ij} \frac{\delta y^i}{F} \otimes \frac{\delta y^j}{F}.$$

Note that $\omega^{2n} = F_{y^i} \frac{\delta y^i}{F} = d(\log F)$, which is dual to the "radius" vector $y^i \frac{\partial}{\partial y^i}$, so that ω^{2n} vanishes on SM.

Clearly, $\mathcal{G}_S$ is invariant under the transformation $y \to \lambda y$ ($\lambda > 0$). Hence, they are well defined on SM. The restriction of the Sasaki metric $\mathcal{G}_S$ to SM is a Riemannian metric

$$\widehat{g} = g_{ij} dx^i \otimes dx^j + \sum_{a=1}^{n-1} \omega^{n+a} \otimes \omega^{n+a}$$

$$= g_{ij} dx^i \otimes dx^j + F F_{y^i y^j} \frac{\delta y^i}{F} \otimes \frac{\delta y^j}{F}$$

$$= g_{ij} dx^i \otimes dx^j + F_{y^i y^j} \delta y^i \otimes \delta y^j.$$

Here we have used $F(y) = 1$.

The Riemannian volume element of the $(2n-1)$-dimensional Riemannian manifold $(SM, \widehat{g})$ is

$$dV_{SM} = \omega^1 \wedge \cdots \wedge \omega^{2n-1} = \sqrt{\det(g_{ij})} dx \wedge d\xi,$$

where

$$dx := dx^1 \wedge \cdots \wedge dx^n, \quad d\xi = \omega^{n+1} \wedge \cdots \wedge \omega^{2n-1}.$$

According to $\omega^{n+i}\|_{SM} = v^i_j \delta y^j$, noting that $F(y) = 1$, a simple algebraic computation yields that

$$d\xi = \frac{\sqrt{\det(g_{ij})}}{F^n} \sum_i (-1)^{i-1} y^i \delta y^1 \wedge \cdots \wedge \widehat{\delta y^i} \wedge \cdots \wedge \delta y^n$$

$$= \sqrt{\det(g_{ij})} \sum_i (-1)^{i-1} y^i \delta y^1 \wedge \cdots \wedge \widehat{\delta y^i} \wedge \cdots \wedge \delta y^n.$$

Thus, we can write

$$dV_{SM} = \det(g_{ij}) d\eta \wedge dx = \sqrt{\det(g_{ij})} d\nu \wedge dx, \qquad (4.1.4)$$

where

$$d\eta := \sum_i (-1)^{i-1} y^i dy^1 \wedge \cdots \wedge \widehat{dy^i} \wedge \cdots \wedge dy^n,$$

$$d\nu := \sqrt{\det(g_{ij})} d\eta. \qquad (4.1.5)$$

Here $\{y^i\}$ can be considered as the homogeneous coordinates on the fiber $S_x M = \{y \in T_x M | F(y) = 1\}$. Therefore, at a point $x \in M$ the volume element of (M, F) induced from the projective sphere bundle is defined by
$$dV_F := \sigma_H(x)dx,$$

$$\sigma_H(x) := \frac{1}{c_{n-1}} \int_{S_x M} \det(g_{ij})d\eta = \frac{1}{c_{n-1}} \int_{S_x M} \sqrt{\det(g_{ij})}d\nu, \qquad (4.1.6)$$

where c_{n-1} is the Euclidean volume of the $(n-1)$-dimensional sphere $\mathbb{S}^{n-1}$. This volume element is also called the *Holmes-Thompson volume element* ([103]).

By using this volume element, the famous Gauss-Bonnet theorem can be generalized to Finsler manifolds under some conditions ([9]), the energy variation of the smooth map between Finsler manifolds can be computed ([128]), and the volume variation of Finsler submanifolds can be calculated ([56]), etc.

For Randers metrics we have the following

Proposition 4.1 ([57]). *The Holmes-Thompson volume element $dV_F = \sigma_H(x)dx$ of a Randers metric $F = \alpha + \beta$ is equal to the Riemannian volume element dV_α of the corresponding Riemannian metric α.*

Proof. Let $\alpha = \sqrt{a_{ij}(x)y^i y^j}$, $\beta = b_i(x)y^i$. For any fixed point $x \in M$, $T_x M \cong \mathbb{R}^n$, let $\{\lambda_i\}$ be the eigenvalues of the symmetric matrix (a_{ij}) with respect to the Euclidean inner product of $\mathbb{R}^n$, of which the corresponding eigenvectors are $\{v_k = v_k^i e_i\}$. Put
$$y^i = \sum_k v_k^i \frac{z^k}{\sqrt{\lambda_k}} \quad \text{with} \quad ||z||^2 = 1.$$
Thus, it follows from (4.1.5) that
$$dV_{S_x M} = \sqrt{\det(a_{ij})} \sum_i (-1)^{i-1} y^i dy^1 \wedge \cdots \wedge \widehat{dy^i} \wedge \cdots \wedge dy^n$$

$$= \sum_i (-1)^{i-1} z^i dz^1 \wedge \cdots \wedge \widehat{dz^i} \wedge \cdots \wedge dz^n = dV_{\mathbb{S}^{n-1}}.$$

Since each z^k is a symmetric odd function on $\mathbb{S}^{n-1}$, then
$$\int_{S_x M} y^i dV_{S_x M} = \sum_k v_k^i \frac{1}{\sqrt{\lambda_k}} \int_{\mathbb{S}^{n-1}} z^k dV_{\mathbb{S}^{n-1}} = 0.$$

Hence,
$$dV_F = \frac{\sqrt{\det(a_{ij})}}{c_{n-1}} dx \int_{S_x M} (1 + b_i y^i)dV_{S_x M} = \sqrt{\det(a_{ij})}dx = dV_\alpha.$$
The proposition is proved. $\qquad\qquad\qquad\qquad\qquad\qquad\qquad\qquad\qquad\qquad\qquad \square$

Remark. For general (α, β)-metrics, see §9.2.2 below.

4.2 S-curvature

4.2.1 Distortion

Let (M, F) be an n-dimensional oriented Finsler manifold, $\{\omega^i\}$ a co-frame field in T^*M, whose dual field is $\{e_i\}$. Thus, the components of the fundamental tensor are $g_{ij}(x, y) = g(e_i, e_j) = \frac{1}{2}[F^2]_{y^i y^j}$, $y = y^i e_i$. Denote the volume element of (M, F) by

$$dV_F := \sigma_F(x)\omega^1 \wedge \cdots \wedge \omega^n,$$

where $\sigma_F(x)$ is the volume measure function. Clearly, σ_F depends on the choice of the frame field. When the frame field is changed, the change of $\sigma_F(x)$ is the same as that of $\sqrt{\det(g_{ij})}$. Thus, we give the following

Definition 4.1. The *distortion* of a Finsler metric F is defined by

$$\tau := \ln \frac{\sqrt{\det(g_{ij})}}{\sigma_F}. \tag{4.2.1}$$

Clearly, F is Riemannian if and only if $\tau \equiv 0$. On the other hand, a direct computation gives

$$\tau_{y^i} = \frac{\partial}{\partial y^i}\left(\ln \sqrt{\det(g_{ij})}\right) = \mathbf{I}_i, \tag{4.2.1'}$$

where $\mathbf{I}_i$ is the mean Cartan tensor (Chapter 2, §2.3, (2.2.4)). By Deicke theorem (Chapter 2, Theorem 2.1), one can obtain

Proposition 4.2. *Let F be a Finsler metric. The following three statements are equivalent: (1) F is Riemannian; (2) $\tau \equiv 0$; (3) τ is independent of y.*

4.2.2 S-curvature and E-curvature

As it is well known, volume comparison theorems in Riemannian geometry are the foundation of the modern geometric analysis and the powerful tool in developing the global differential geometry. In studying the volume comparison for Finsler manifolds ([105]), the second author of this book considered the rate of changes of the distortion along geodesics, which leads to the so-called **S**-curvature.

Definition 4.2. For a point $x \in M$ and a vector $y \in T_x M_0$, let $\gamma = \gamma(t)$ be the geodesic with $\gamma(0) = x$ and $\dot{\gamma}(0) = y$. Set

$$\mathbf{S}(x, y) := \frac{d}{dt}\left[\tau\left(\gamma(t), \dot{\gamma}(t)\right)\right]\Big|_{t=0}. \tag{4.2.2}$$

The quantity $\mathbf{S} = \mathbf{S}(x, y)$ is called the **S**-*curvature* of the Finsler metric F.

Clearly, $\mathbf{S}(x, y)$ is positively y-homogeneous of degree one, i.e.,

$$\mathbf{S}(x, \lambda y) = \lambda \mathbf{S}(x, y), \quad \lambda > 0. \tag{4.2.3}$$

Let (x, y) be the local coordinate system in (M, F), $G^i(x, y)$ the spray coefficients (Chapter 2, §2.3). From (3.1.17), (3.1.15) and (3.1.11) it follows that

$$\sum_k \frac{\partial G^k}{\partial y^k} = \frac{1}{2} g^{kl} \frac{\partial g_{kl}}{\partial x^i} y^i - 2\mathbf{I}_i G^i. \tag{4.2.4}$$

Thus,

$$
\begin{aligned}
\mathbf{S}(x, y) &= y^i \frac{\partial \tau}{\partial x^i} - 2 \frac{\partial \tau}{\partial y^i} G^i \\
&= \frac{1}{2} g^{kl} \frac{\partial g_{kl}}{\partial x^i} y^i - 2\mathbf{I}_i G^i - y^k \frac{\partial}{\partial x^k} (\ln \sigma_F(x)) \\
&= \sum_k \frac{\partial G^k}{\partial y^k} - y^k \frac{\partial}{\partial x^k} (\ln \sigma_F(x)),
\end{aligned}
\tag{4.2.5}
$$

where $\sigma_F(x)$ is the volume measure function, i.e., $dV_F = \sigma_F dx^1 \wedge \cdots \wedge dx^n$.

By Proposition 4.2, the $\mathbf{S}$-curvature of a Riemannian metric vanishes identically.

Proposition 4.3. *For any Berwald metric with Busemann-Hausdorff volume measure function $\sigma_F = \sigma_B$, the $\mathbf{S}$-curvature vanishes, i.e., $\mathbf{S} = 0$.*

Proof. Fix any point $(x, y) \in TM_0$ and let $\gamma = \gamma(t)$ be a geodesic with $\gamma(0) = x$ and $\dot{\gamma}(0) = y$. Let $\{e_i(t)\}$ be a linearly parallel frame along $\gamma(t)$, i.e., $e_i(t)$ is linearly parallel along $\gamma(t)$. (Chapter 3, §3.3.1)

Let $g_{ij}(t) = g_{\dot{\gamma}}(e_i(t), e_j(t))$. By Lemma 3.1, $g_{ij}(t) = $ const. Thus, $\det(g_{ij}(t)) = $ const. On the other hand, for any $(y^i) \in \mathbb{R}^n$, the vector field $V := y^i e_i$ is linearly parallel along γ. By Lemma 3.2,

$$F(\gamma(t), y^i e_i(t)) = \text{const.}$$

Thus, the following convex subset $\mathcal{U}_t \subset \mathbb{R}^n$ is independent of t,

$$\mathcal{U}_t := \left\{ (y^i) \in \mathbb{R}^n \mid F(\gamma(t), y^i e_i(t)) < 1 \right\}.$$

This implies that the volume measure function σ_B is constant,

$$\sigma_B(\gamma(t)) = \frac{\text{Vol}(B^n(1))}{\text{Vol}(\mathcal{U}_t)} = \text{const.}$$

Therefore, by (4.2.1) and (4.2.2), $\mathbf{S} = 0$ at $(x, y) \in TM_0$. Since $(x, y) \in TM_0$ is arbitrary, we see that $\mathbf{S} = 0$ everywhere. $\square$

Below is a geometric quantity related to the **S**-curvature. Let

$$E_{ij} := \frac{1}{2}\mathbf{S}_{y^i y^j} = \frac{1}{2}\left[\frac{\partial G^s}{\partial y^s}\right]_{y^i y^j}, \tag{4.2.6}$$

where the last equality is due to (4.2.5).

Definition 4.3. The two-order symmetric tensor $E := E_{ij}(x,y)dx^i \otimes dx^j$ is called the *E-tensor*. $\mathbf{E} := \{\mathbf{E}_y | y \in TM_0\}$ is called the **E**-*curvature*, or the *mean Berwald curvature*, where $\mathbf{E}_y(u,v) := E_{ij}(x,y)u^i v^j$, $u = u^i \partial_i$, $v = v^i \partial_i$.

From the definition one see easily that

$$\mathbf{E}_y(y,v) = \mathbf{E}_y(v,y) = 0,$$

since **S** is positively y-homogeneous of degree one. Clearly, $\mathbf{E} = 0$ if $\mathbf{S} = 0$. However, the converse might not be true. But so far, no counter-example has been found yet.

By Lemma 3.3, we have the following formula between the **S**-curvature and the Riemann curvature $R^i{}_j$.

Proposition 4.4.

$$\mathbf{S}_{;k|s}y^s - \mathbf{S}_{|k} = \mathbf{I}_{k|p|q}y^p y^q + \mathbf{I}_s R^s{}_k = -\frac{2}{3}R^s{}_{k;s} - \frac{1}{3}R^s{}_{s;k}.$$

Proof. In a general local frame field $\{\omega^i, \omega^{n+i}\}$, let

$$d\tau = \tau_{|i}\omega^i + \tau_{;i}\omega^{n+i}. \tag{4.2.7}$$

Note that

$$d\tau_{|i} - \tau_{|j}\omega_i^j = \tau_{|i|j}\omega^j + \tau_{|i;j}\omega^{n+j}, \quad d\mathbf{I}_i - \mathbf{I}_j\omega_i^j = \mathbf{I}_{i|j}\omega^j + \mathbf{I}_{i;j}\omega^{n+j}.$$

Exterior differentiating (4.2.7) and using (3.2.3), (3.3.10) and (4.2.1′), we have

$$0 = (\tau_{|i|j}\omega^j + \tau_{|i;j}\omega^{n+j}) \wedge \omega^i + (\mathbf{I}_{i|j}\omega^j + \mathbf{I}_{i;j}\omega^{n+j}) \wedge \omega^{n+i}$$
$$+ \mathbf{I}_i y^j (\frac{1}{2}R_j{}^i{}_{kl}\omega^k \wedge \omega^l + P_j{}^i{}_{kl}\omega^k \wedge \omega^{n+l}).$$

Thus, we obtain the following Ricci type identities

$$\tau_{|k|l} - \tau_{|l|k} = \mathbf{I}_s R^s{}_{kl}, \tag{4.2.8}$$

$$\tau_{|k;l} - \mathbf{I}_{l|k} = -\mathbf{I}_s L^s{}_{kl}. \tag{4.2.9}$$

By the definition of **S**-curvature, we have

$$\mathbf{S} = \tau_{|s}y^s. \tag{4.2.10}$$

Contracting (4.2.9) with y^k and using (4.2.10), one can get

$$\begin{aligned}
\mathbf{S}_{;k} &= \tau_{|s;k}y^s + \tau_{|k} = \mathbf{I}_{k|s}y^s - \mathbf{I}_i L^i{}_{sk}y^s + \tau_{|k} \\
&= \mathbf{I}_{k|s}y^s + \tau_{|k} = J_k + \tau_{|k},
\end{aligned}$$
(4.2.11)

from which it follows that

$$\mathbf{S}_{;k|l} = J_{k|l} + \tau_{|k|l}.$$
(4.2.12)

From (4.2.8) and (4.2.12) we have

$$\begin{aligned}
\mathbf{S}_{;k|s}y^s - \mathbf{S}_{|k} &= (\mathbf{S}_{;k|s} - \mathbf{S}_{;s|k})y^s \\
&= (J_{k|s} - J_{s|k})y^s + (\tau_{|k|s} - \tau_{|s|k})y^s = J_{k|s}y^s + \mathbf{I}_s R^s{}_k.
\end{aligned}$$

Since $J_{k|s}y^s = \mathbf{I}_{k|p|q}y^p y^q$, we obtain the first equality in Proposition 4.4. The second equality is due to the second formula in Lemma 3.3. □

4.3   Isotropic S-curvature

4.3.1   Isotropic S-curvature and isotropic E-curvature

Definition 4.4. Let (M, F) be an n-dimensional Finsler manifold, $\mathbf{S}(x, y)$ its **S**-curvature. Suppose that $c = c(x)$ is a scalar function in M and $\eta = \eta_i(x)y^i$ is a one form in M.

(i) If

$$\mathbf{S} = (n+1)cF + \eta,$$
(4.3.1)

then F is said to have *weakly isotropic* **S***-curvature*;

(ii) F is said to have *almost isotropic* **S***-curvature* if the 1-form η in (4.3.1) is closed, i.e., $d\eta = 0$;

(iii) F is said to have *isotropic* **S***-curvature* if $\eta = 0$;

(iv) F is said to have *constant* **S***-curvature* if $\eta = 0$ and $c = \text{const}$.

For **E**-curvature, we have the similar definitions.

Definition 4.5. Let (M, F) be an n-dimensional Finsler manifold. The *angle metric* of F (cf. (2.2.5)) is defined by

$$\mathbf{h} = h_{ij}(x, y)dx^i \otimes dx^j, \quad h_{ij} = g_{ij} - \ell_i\ell_j = FF_{y^iy^j}, \quad \ell_i = g_{ij}\ell^j. \quad (4.3.2)$$

If

$$\mathbf{E} = \frac{1}{2}(n+1)cF^{-1}\mathbf{h},$$
(4.3.3)

then F is said to have *isotropic* **E***-curvature*.

Example 4.2. Consider the Randers metric $F = \alpha + \beta = \Theta(x,y) + \frac{\langle u,y \rangle}{1+\langle u,x \rangle}$ in Example 4.1, where $\Theta(x,y)$ denotes the Funk metric. A direct computation shows that the above metric satisfies

$$F_{x^k y^j} y^k = F_{x^j}, \quad G^i = P y^i, \quad P = \frac{F_{x^k} y^k}{2F} = \frac{1}{2}\left\{\Theta(x,y) - \frac{\langle u,y \rangle}{1+\langle u,x \rangle}\right\}.$$

By using the homogeneity of P, we have

$$\sum_k \frac{\partial G^k}{\partial y^k} = (n+1)P.$$

Thus, using the expression of σ_B in Example 4.1, a direct computation gives

$$\mathbf{S} = (n+1)P - y^s \frac{\partial}{\partial x^s}(\ln \sigma_B) = \frac{n+1}{2}F.$$

This implies that F has constant **S**-curvature.

By Definition 4.3 and the above formula of **S**-curvature, it is easy to see that

$$\mathbf{E} = \frac{1}{4}(n+1)F^{-1}\mathbf{h}.$$

Thus, F has constant **E**-curvature.

4.3.2 Randers metrics of isotropic S-curvature

Let $F = \alpha + \beta$ be a Randers metric, where $\alpha = \sqrt{a_{ij}(x)y^i y^j}$, $\beta = b_i(x)y^i$. Denote by "," the covariant differentiation with respect to the Riemannian connection of α. We shall use the following notations:

$$r_{ij} := \frac{1}{2}(b_{i,j} + b_{j,i}), \quad s_{ij} := \frac{1}{2}(b_{i,j} - b_{j,i}) = \frac{1}{2}(\partial_j b_i - \partial_i b_j),$$
$$s^i{}_j := a^{ik}s_{kj}, \quad s^i{}_0 = s^i{}_j y^j, \quad s_j := b_k s^k{}_j, \quad s_0 = s_j y^j,$$
$$r_{00} := r_{ij}y^i y^j, \quad e_{ij} = r_{ij} + b_i s_j + b_j s_i, \quad e_{00} = e_{ij}y^i y^j,$$
$$b^i = a^{ij}b_j, \quad b^2 := a^{ij}b_i b_j, \quad (a^{ij}) = (a_{ij})^{-1}.$$
(4.3.4)

Denote by G^i and G^i_α spray (or geodesic) coefficients of F and α, respectively. By (2.4.3), a direct computation gives

$$G^i = G^i_\alpha + P y^i + Q^i, \quad P = \frac{e_{00}}{2F} - s_0, \quad Q^i = \alpha s^i{}_0.$$
(4.3.5)

(4.3.5) can be applied to prove Theorem 3.2 in Chapter 3.
    Put

$$\rho(x) := \ln \sqrt{1 - ||\beta||^2_\alpha}.$$
(4.3.6)

By means of (4.1.3), the volume elements dV_F and dV_α are related by the following

$$dV_F = e^{(n+1)\rho(x)}dV_\alpha.$$

By using the homogeneity of P and the skew-symmetry of s_{ij}, we have

$$\frac{\partial(Py^s)}{\partial y^s} = \frac{\partial P}{\partial y^s}y^s + nP = (n+1)P,$$

$$\frac{\partial Q^s}{\partial y^s} = \alpha^{-1}s_{00} + \alpha s^s{}_s = 0.$$

For the Riemannian metric α, we have from (2.4.3)

$$\frac{\partial G_\alpha^s}{\partial y^s} = \frac{1}{2}a^{kl}\frac{\partial a_{kl}}{\partial x^s}y^s = \frac{y^s}{\sqrt{\det(a_{ij})}}\frac{\partial}{\partial x^s}\left(\sqrt{\det(a_{ij})}\right) = y^s\frac{\partial}{\partial x^s}\left(\ln\sigma_\alpha\right).$$

By virtue of these formulas, we obtain from (4.2.5) and (4.3.5)

$$\begin{aligned}
\mathbf{S} &= \frac{\partial G_\alpha^s}{\partial y^s} + \frac{\partial(Py^s)}{\partial y^s} + \frac{\partial Q^s}{\partial y^s} - (n+1)y^s\frac{\partial\rho}{\partial x^s} - y^s\frac{\partial}{\partial x^s}\left(\ln\sigma_\alpha\right) \\
&= (n+1)(P - \rho_0) = (n+1)\left[\frac{e_{00}}{2F} - (s_0 + \rho_0)\right],
\end{aligned} \tag{4.3.7}$$

where $\rho_0 = \frac{\partial\rho}{\partial x^i}y^i$.

Theorem 4.1 ([36]). *For a Randers metric $F = \alpha + \beta$ on M, the following are equivalent*
(i) $\mathbf{S} = (n+1)cF$,
(ii) $\mathbf{E} = \dfrac{1}{2}(n+1)cF^{-1}\mathbf{h}$,
(iii) $e_{00} = 2c(\alpha^2 - \beta^2)$,
where $c = c(x)$ is a scalar function on M.

Proof. From Definitions 4.4 and 4.5, it is obvious that $(i) \Rightarrow (ii)$.
 $(ii) \Rightarrow (iii)$. The condition (ii) implies that

$$E_{ij} = \frac{1}{2}(n+1)cF_{y^iy^j} = \frac{1}{2}(n+1)c\alpha_{y^iy^j}. \tag{4.3.8}$$

On the other hand, from (4.2.6) and (4.3.7) we have

$$E_{ij} = \frac{1}{4}(n+1)\left[\frac{e_{00}}{F}\right]_{y^iy^j}. \tag{4.3.9}$$

It follows from (4.3.8) and (4.3.9) that

$$\left[\frac{e_{00}}{F}\right]_{y^iy^j} = 2cF_{y^iy^j}.$$

Thus, at any point $x \in M$ we have

$$\frac{e_{00}}{F} = 2cF + \theta + a,$$

where $\theta \in T_x^* M$ is a 1-form, a is a constant. By the homogeneity, one can see that $a = 0$, i.e.,

$$\frac{e_{00}}{F} = 2cF + \theta.$$

This equation equals the following

$$e_{00} = 2c(\alpha^2 + \beta^2) + \theta\beta,$$
$$0 = 4c\beta + \theta.$$
(4.3.10)

Substituting the second formula into the first formula in (4.3.10) yields (iii).

$(iii) \Rightarrow (i)$. The condition (iii) together with (4.3.7), yields

$$\mathbf{S} = (n+1)\{c(\alpha - \beta) - (s_0 + \rho_0)\}.$$
(4.3.11)

On the other hand, contracting (iii) with b^j gives

$$s_i + \rho_i + 2cb_i = 0.$$

Thus, $s_0 + \rho_0 = -2c\beta$, substituting which into (4.3.11) yields (i). $\square$

Example 4.3. Consider a Randers metric $F = \alpha + \beta$ defined on $\mathbb{R}^n$, where

$$\alpha = \frac{\sqrt{(1 - \varepsilon^2)\langle x, y\rangle^2 + \varepsilon|y|^2(1 + \varepsilon|x|^2)}}{1 + \varepsilon|x|^2}, \qquad \beta = \frac{\sqrt{1 - \varepsilon^2}\langle x, y\rangle}{1 + \varepsilon|x|^2}.$$

Here ε is a constant satisfying $|\varepsilon| < 1$, and β is closed. Clearly, $s_{ij} = 0$ and $s_i = 0$. By computing $b_{i,j}$, one obtains

$$e_{ij} = \frac{\varepsilon\sqrt{1 - \varepsilon^2}}{(1 + \varepsilon|x|^2)(\varepsilon + |x|^2)}\delta_{ij}.$$

Moreover,

$$a_{ij} - b_i b_j = \frac{\varepsilon}{1 + \varepsilon|x|^2}\delta_{ij}.$$

Hence,

$$e_{ij} = 2c(a_{ij} - b_i b_j), \quad \text{where} \quad c := \frac{\sqrt{1 - \varepsilon^2}}{2(\varepsilon + |x|^2)}.$$

By Theorem 4.1, we see that F has isotropic **S**-curvature and isotropic **E**-curvature, i.e.,

$$\mathbf{S} = (n+1)cF, \quad \mathbf{E} = \frac{1}{2}cF^{-1}\mathbf{h}.$$

Note that α is not Riemannian if $\varepsilon \neq 0$. Thus, it is different from Example 4.2.

A global result is the following

Proposition 4.5. *Let (M, F) be an n-dimensional closed compact Finsler manifold. If **S**-curvature of (M, F) is a constant c, then $c = 0$.*

Proof. Suppose that F has constant **S**-curvature. By Definition 4.4, $\mathbf{S} = (n + 1)cF$, where c is constant. According to Definition 4.2, along any unit velocity geodesic $\gamma(t)$, we have (noting $F(\dot{\gamma}(t)) = 1$)

$$\frac{d}{dt}\left[\tau\left(\gamma(t), \dot{\gamma}(t)\right)\right]|_{t=0} = (n+1)c.$$

Since t is arbitrary, then

$$\tau(t) = (n+1)ct + c_0$$

along the geodesic $\gamma(t)$. Since (M, F) is compact, it is complete, and $\tau(t)$ is bounded. Hence, $c = 0$. Because $\gamma(t)$ is arbitrary, so $c = 0$ on M everywhere. □

Remark. For an n-dimensional Randers metric $F = \alpha + \beta$, if there is a volume element $dV_F = \sigma(x)dx^1 \wedge \cdots \wedge dx^n$ such that its **S**-curvature vanishes identically, then β is a Killing form of constant length with respect to α. Moreover, the volume element dV_F coincides with the Busemann-Hausdorff volume element up to a constant multiplication ([89]). In fact, in such a case, the volume element dV_F coincides with the Riemannian volume element of α up to a constant multiplication. The similar results hold for general (α, β)-metrics $F = \alpha\phi(s)$, $s = \alpha/\beta$ ([125]).

4.3.3 Geodesic flow

Let (M, F) be an n-dimensional Finsler manifold, of which the Finsler spray on TM_0 is (2.3.6), where coefficients $G^i(x, y)$ are given by (2.4.3). Since G^i is y-homogeneous of degree two, we see from (3.1.17) that

$$\mathbf{G} = y^i\left(\frac{\partial}{\partial x^i} - N_i^k\frac{\partial}{\partial y^k}\right) = y^i\frac{\delta}{\delta x^i}. \qquad (4.3.12)$$

Assume that the geodesic flow of $\mathbf{G}$ is $\varphi_t : TM_0 \to TM_0$, which preserves F invariant (see §2.4.1, behind Definition 2.4). Recall that the Hilbert form ω on TM_0 (§2.3) is defined by (2.3.1). Set

$$\hat{\omega} := F\omega = \frac{1}{2}[F^2]_{y^i}dx^i = g_{ij}y^j dx^i. \qquad (4.3.13)$$

$\hat{\omega}$ has the following property.

Lemma 4.2. *For any t,*

$$\frac{d}{dt}\left((\varphi_t)^*\widehat{\omega}\right) = \frac{1}{2}d\left((\varphi_t)^*(F^2)\right). \tag{4.3.14}$$

Hence,

$$(\varphi_t)^*d\widehat{\omega} = d\widehat{\omega}.$$

Proof. Let $(\varphi^i(t), \psi^i(t))$ be the local coordinates of $y(t) := \varphi_t(y)$ on TM, $y(t)$ be an integral curve of the geodesic flow $\mathbf{G}$. In other words,

$$\begin{cases} \dfrac{d\varphi^i(t)}{dt} = \psi^i(t), \\ \dfrac{d\psi^i(t)}{dt} = -2G^i(y(t)). \end{cases}$$

It follows that

$$(\varphi_t)^*\widehat{\omega} = \frac{1}{2}[F^2]_{y^i}(y(t))\left(\frac{\partial \varphi_t^i}{\partial x^j}dx^j + \frac{\partial \varphi_t^i}{\partial y^j}dy^j\right).$$

Note that

$$\left(\frac{\partial \varphi_t^i}{\partial x^j}dx^j + \frac{\partial \varphi_t^i}{\partial y^j}dy^j\right)\Bigg|_{t=0} = dx^i, \quad \frac{d}{dt}\left(\frac{\partial \varphi_t^i}{\partial x^j}dx^j + \frac{\partial \varphi_t^i}{\partial y^j}dy^j\right)\Bigg|_{t=0} = dy^i.$$

We then obtain immediately

$$\frac{d}{dt}\left[(\varphi_t)^*\widehat{\omega}\right]\Bigg|_{t=0} = \frac{1}{2}\left([F^2]_{x^k y^i}y^k - 2[F^2]_{y^k y^i}G^k(y)\right)dx^i + \frac{1}{2}[F^2]_{y^i}dy^i. \tag{4.3.15}$$

It follows from (2.4.3) that

$$2[F^2]_{y^k y^i}G^k = [F^2]_{x^k y^i}y^k - [F^2]_{x^i},$$

inserting which into (4.3.15) yields

$$\frac{d}{dt}\left[(\varphi_t)^*\widehat{\omega}\right]\Bigg|_{t=0} = \frac{1}{2}\left\{[F^2]_{x^i}dx^i + [F^2]_{y^i}dy^i\right\} = \frac{1}{2}d[F^2](y).$$

Since $\varphi_{t+s} = \varphi_t \circ \varphi_s$, we obtain (4.3.14). By using (4.3.14), we have

$$\frac{d}{dt}\left[(\varphi_t)^*d\widehat{\omega}\right] = d\frac{d}{dt}\left[(\varphi_t)^*\widehat{\omega}\right] = \frac{1}{2}d^2\left[(\varphi_t)^*[F^2]\right] = 0.$$

Hence,

$$(\varphi_t)^*d\widehat{\omega} = (\phi_0)^*d\widehat{\omega} = d\widehat{\omega}. \qquad \square$$

Recall that there is a Sasaki metric $\mathcal{G}_S$ on TM_0 (see §4.1.2), which induces a Riemannian volume form

$$dV_{\mathcal{G}} := \det(g_{ij})dx^1 \wedge \cdots \wedge dx^n \wedge \frac{\delta y^1}{F} \wedge \cdots \wedge \frac{\delta y^n}{F}$$

$$= \frac{1}{F^n}\det(g_{ij})dx^1 \wedge \cdots \wedge dx^n \wedge dy^1 \wedge \cdots \wedge dy^n.$$

Put

$$\widehat{dV_{\mathcal{G}}} := F^n dV_{\mathcal{G}} = \det(g_{ij})dx^1 \wedge \cdots \wedge dx^n \wedge dy^1 \wedge \cdots \wedge dy^n.$$

From (4.3.13) we have

$$d\widehat{\omega} = \frac{\partial g_{ik}}{\partial x^j}y^k dx^j \wedge dx^i - g_{ij}dx^i \wedge \delta y^j.$$

Thus,

$$\widehat{dV_{\mathcal{G}}} = (-1)^{\frac{n(n+1)}{2}}\frac{1}{n!}d\widehat{\omega} \wedge \cdots \wedge d\widehat{\omega}. \tag{4.3.16}$$

Proposition 4.6 ([43]). *The geodesic flow φ_t preserves the Riemannian volume form $dV_{\mathcal{G}}$ of the Sasaki metric $\mathcal{G}_S$.*

Proof. By Proposition 2.1 (§2.3.1) and the definition of geodesic flow (§2.4.1), the geodesic flow preserves F invariant. It follows from Lemma 4.2 that the geodesic flow preserves $d\widehat{\omega}$ invariant. Therefore, the proposition follows from (4.3.16). □

Let $i : SM \to TM_0$ be the natural imbedding of the projective sphere bundle SM (§4.1.2) to TM_0. Since the geodesic flow φ_t preserves F, then $\varphi_t : SM \to SM$. Let $i^*\widehat{\omega} := \mathring{\omega}$. From Lemma 4.2 one can see that

$$\frac{d}{dt}[(\varphi_t)^*\mathring{\omega}] = 0,$$

i.e., the geodesic flow φ_t preserves $\mathring{\omega}$.

By using $\mathring{\omega}$, the volume form dV_{SM} (4.1.4) induced by the Riemannian metric $\widehat{g}$ on SM may be expressed as (cf. [103])

$$dV_{SM} = (-1)^{\frac{(n-1)(n+2)}{2}}\frac{1}{(n-1)!}\mathring{\omega} \wedge d\mathring{\omega} \cdots \wedge d\mathring{\omega}.$$

Hence, we have immediately the following

Proposition 4.7 ([43]). *The geodesic flow φ_t preserves the Riemannian volume form dV_{SM} on SM, i.e.,*

$$\varphi_t^*(dV_{SM}) = dV_{SM}.$$

Exercises

4.1 Prove Lemma 4.1 in detail.

4.2 Check the formula (4.3.16).

4.3 Prove Theorem 3.2 in Chapter 3 by using (4.3.5).

4.4 Let $F = \alpha\phi(s)$, $s := \beta/\alpha$, be (α, β)-metric (§2.1.2, (2.1.5)). Let G_α^i be geodesic coefficients of α. Prove that geodesic coefficients G^i of F can be expressed as ([112])

$$G^i = G_\alpha^i + \alpha Q s^i{}_0 + \alpha^{-1}\Theta(-2\alpha Q s_0 + r_{00})y^i + \Psi(-2\alpha Q s_0 + r_{00})b^i,$$

$$Q = \frac{\phi'}{\phi - s\phi'}, \quad \Theta = \frac{Q - sQ'}{2\Delta}, \quad \Psi = \frac{Q'}{2\Delta}, \quad \Delta = 1 + sQ + (b^2 - s^2)Q'.$$

$$(1)$$

4.5 For the above (α, β)-metric, prove ([17]) that

$$\frac{\partial G^m}{\partial y^m} = y^m \frac{\partial}{\partial x^m}(\ln \sigma_\alpha) + 2\Psi(r_0 + s_0) - \alpha^{-1}\frac{\Phi}{2\Delta^2}(r_{00} - 2\alpha Q s_0), \quad (2)$$

where

$$\Phi := -(Q - sQ')(n\Delta + 1 + sQ) - (b^2 - s^2)(1 + sQ)Q'',$$

$$\sigma_\alpha(x) = \sqrt{\det(a_{ij})}.$$

4.6 For a fixed local coordinate system $\{x^i\}_{i=1}^n$, let $\mu(dx) = \sigma(x)dx^1 \wedge dx^2 \wedge \cdots \wedge dx^n$ be a volume measure on M. By using (2), prove that the **S**-curvature of this volume measure for the (α, β)-metric may be expressed as

$$S = \frac{\partial G^m}{\partial y^m} - y^m\frac{\partial}{\partial x^m}(\ln \sigma) = 2\Psi(r_0 + s_0) - \alpha^{-1}\frac{\Phi}{2\Delta^2}(r_{00} - 2\alpha Q s_0) + y^m t_m,$$

$$(3)$$

where

$$t_m = \frac{\partial}{\partial x^m}\left(\ln \frac{\sigma_\alpha}{\sigma}\right).$$

4.7 Let $F = \alpha\phi(\beta/\alpha)$ be an (α, β)-metric as above. Prove that the mean Cartan tensor of F can be expressed as ([39])

$$I_i = -\frac{\Phi}{2F\Delta}(\phi - s\phi')h_i, \quad h_i = b_i - \alpha^{-1}sy_i. \quad (4)$$

4.8 Let (M^n, F, μ), $n \geq 3$, be a measurable non-Riemannian (α, β)-space, where $F = \alpha\phi(s)$, $s = \beta/\alpha$, $b := \|\beta\|_\alpha$, and μ is a volume measure on M^n. Prove that ([125]) F has vanishing **S**-curvature everywhere if and only if there is a constant $c \in \mathbb{R}$ such that β is a Killing form with respect to the Riemannian metric $\bar{\alpha} = \sqrt{(a_{ij} + cb_ib_j)y^iy^j}$ and $b = \text{const}$.

Moreover, μ coincides with the Riemannian volume measure of α up to a constant multiplication.

4.9 Let $(M, F = \alpha\phi(s))$ be an n-dimensional (α, β)-space, $b := \|\beta\|_\alpha$. Let $dV_F = dV_{BH} = \sigma_B dx$ or $dV_{HT} = \sigma_H dx$. Prove that ([28]) $dV_F = f(b)dv_\alpha = f(b)\sqrt{\det(a_{ij})}\, dx$, where

$$
f(b) := \begin{cases} \dfrac{\int_0^\pi \sin^{n-2} t\, dt}{\int_0^\pi \frac{\sin^{n-2} t}{\phi(b\cos t)^n}\, dt}, & dV_F = dV_{BH}, \\[4mm] \dfrac{\int_0^\pi (\sin^{n-2} t)T(b\cos t)dt}{\int_0^\pi \sin^{n-2} dt}, & dV_F = dV_{HT}, \end{cases} \tag{5}
$$

where

$$
T(s) := \phi(\phi - s\phi')^{n-2}[(\phi - s\phi') + (b^2 - s^2)\phi''].
$$

Chapter 5

Riemann Curvature

5.1 The second variation of arc length

Finsler geometry originated in the variation calculus of arc length in a sense. At the 1900 International Congress in Paris, D. Hilbert gave the integral of the Hilbert form described in §2.3. The notation of Riemann type has arisen in the second variation formula of a geodesic.

5.1.1 The second variation of length

The first variation of arc length gives that any shortest path is a geodesic (cf. Theorem 2.3). We now consider the second variation of a geodesic. Let (M, F) be an n-dimensional connected Finsler manifold, $\sigma = \sigma(t)$, $a \leq t \leq b$, be a geodesic from the point $p = \sigma(a)$ to the point $q = \sigma(b)$ in M. Consider a smooth variation $\psi : (-\varepsilon, \varepsilon) \times [a, b] \to M$ of σ such that

$$\psi(0, t) = \sigma(t), \ a \leq t \leq b, \quad \psi(s, a) = \sigma(a) = p, \quad \psi(s, b) = \sigma(b) = q, \ |s| < \varepsilon.$$

This is a variation preserving ends of the geodesic. Thus, the length of the curve $\sigma_s(t) := \psi(s, t)$ is

$$L(s) = \int_a^b F(\sigma_s(t), \dot\sigma_s(t))dt. \tag{5.1.1}$$

Since $\sigma(t)$ is a geodesic, we have according to Proposition 2.2 in Chapter 2

$$||\dot\sigma_0(t)|| = ||\dot\sigma(t)|| = F(\sigma, \dot\sigma) = \text{const.} := F_0. \tag{5.1.2}$$

Set

$$v(t) := \frac{\partial\psi}{\partial s}(0, t) := v^i(t)\frac{\partial}{\partial x^i}, \quad a \leq t \leq b, \tag{5.1.3}$$

which is called a *variation vector field*. Clearly, $v(a) = v(b) = 0$.

We now lift canonically $\psi(s,t) = \sigma_s(t)$ on TM_0 (cf. Chapter 2, §2.4). Let

$$\overline{T} := d\psi\left(\frac{\partial}{\partial t}\right) = \frac{\partial \psi}{\partial t} = \dot{\sigma}_s, \quad \overline{V} := d\psi\left(\frac{\partial}{\partial s}\right) = \frac{\partial \psi}{\partial s}. \qquad (5.1.4)$$

We use the same notations to denote their canonical lift along $\sigma_s(t)$, i.e., they are pulled back at the point $(\sigma_s, \dot{\sigma}_s) \in TM_0$, which may be viewed as differentiable sections (vector fields) of the vector bundle $\pi^* TM$. They then are projected to M after some necessary computations. So, these statements will be omitted from now on, and then should be understood in the contents.

Since the Chern connection is torsion free, we have (Chapter 3, §3.1)

$$\nabla_{\overline{T}} \overline{V} - \nabla_{\overline{V}} \overline{T} = [\overline{T}, \overline{V}] = d\psi\left[\frac{\partial}{\partial t}, \frac{\partial}{\partial s}\right] = 0. \qquad (5.1.5)$$

With the property of the variation ψ, we get

$$\overline{V}(s,a) = \overline{V}(s,b) = 0, \quad \overline{V}(0,t) = v(t), \quad \overline{T}(0,t) = \dot{\sigma}(t). \qquad (5.1.6)$$

Differentiating (5.1.1) and using (2.1.11), (2.2.3) and (3.1.2′), we obtain

$$\begin{aligned}
L'(s) &= \int_a^b \frac{1}{2F} \frac{\partial}{\partial s} F^2(\sigma_s(t), \dot{\sigma}_s(t)) dt = \int_a^b \frac{1}{2F} \overline{V}(\langle \overline{T}, \overline{T} \rangle_{\overline{T}}) dt \\
&= \int_a^b \frac{1}{F} \langle \nabla_{\overline{V}} \overline{T}, \overline{T} \rangle_{\overline{T}} dt.
\end{aligned} \qquad (5.1.7)$$

Considering the curvature of the Chern connection ∇ (cf. Chapter 3, §3.2) and noting (5.1.5), we have

$$\nabla_{\overline{V}} \nabla_{\overline{T}} \overline{V} - \nabla_{\overline{T}} \nabla_{\overline{V}} \overline{V} = \Omega(\overline{V}, \overline{T}) \overline{V} = R(\overline{V}, \overline{T}) \overline{V} + P(\overline{V}, \nabla_{\overline{T}} y) \overline{V}. \qquad (5.1.8)$$

Differentiating (5.1.7) and using (5.1.5) and (5.1.8), we obtain

$$\begin{aligned}
L''(s) &= \int_a^b \frac{1}{F} \left\{ \langle \nabla_{\overline{V}} \nabla_{\overline{T}} \overline{V}, \overline{T} \rangle_{\overline{T}} + ||\nabla_{\overline{T}} \overline{V}||^2 \right\} dt - \int_a^b \frac{1}{F^3} \langle \nabla_{\overline{T}} \overline{V}, \overline{T} \rangle_{\overline{T}}^2 dt \\
&= \int_a^b \frac{1}{F} \langle \nabla_{\overline{T}} \nabla_{\overline{V}} \overline{V}, \overline{T} \rangle_{\overline{T}} dt + \int_a^b \frac{1}{F} \langle \Omega(\overline{V}, \overline{T}) \overline{V}, \overline{T} \rangle_{\overline{T}} dt \\
&\quad + \int_a^b \frac{1}{F} \left\{ ||\nabla_{\overline{T}} \overline{V}||^2 \right\} dt - \int_a^b \frac{1}{F^3} \langle \nabla_{\overline{T}} \overline{V}, \overline{T} \rangle_{\overline{T}}^2 dt.
\end{aligned} \qquad (5.1.9)$$

Now we deal with (5.1.9) along $\sigma(t)$ term by term. From (3.1.2′) and (2.2.3) it follows that

$$\langle \nabla_{\overline{T}} \nabla_{\overline{V}} \overline{V}, \overline{T} \rangle_{\overline{T}} = \overline{T} \langle \nabla_{\overline{V}} \overline{V}, \overline{T} \rangle_{\overline{T}} - \langle \nabla_{\overline{V}} \overline{V}, \nabla_{\overline{T}} \overline{T} \rangle_{\overline{T}} - 2C_{\overline{T}}(\nabla_{\overline{T}} \overline{T}, \nabla_{\overline{V}} \overline{V}, \overline{T}).$$

Noting $\nabla_{\dot{\sigma}}\dot{\sigma} = 0$ and using (5.1.3) and (5.1.6), we have

$$\int_a^b \frac{1}{F}\langle \nabla_{\overline{T}}\nabla_{\overline{V}}\overline{V}, \overline{T}\rangle_{\overline{T}}|_{s=0}dt = \frac{1}{F_0}\langle \nabla_v v, \dot{\sigma}\rangle_{\dot{\sigma}}|_a^b - \frac{1}{F_0}\int_a^b \langle \nabla_v v, \nabla_{\dot{\sigma}}\dot{\sigma}\rangle_{\dot{\sigma}}dt = 0.$$
(5.1.10)

In the same way we have

$$\|\nabla_{\overline{T}}\overline{V}\|^2 = \langle \nabla_{\overline{T}}\overline{V}, \nabla_{\overline{T}}\overline{V}\rangle_{\overline{T}}$$
$$= \overline{T}\langle \nabla_{\overline{T}}\overline{V}, \overline{V}\rangle_{\overline{T}} - \langle \nabla_{\overline{T}}\nabla_{\overline{T}}\overline{V}, \overline{V}\rangle_{\overline{T}} - 2C_{\overline{T}}(\nabla_{\overline{T}}\overline{T}, \nabla_{\overline{T}}\overline{V}, \overline{V}).$$

Thus

$$\int_a^b \frac{1}{F}\left\{\|\nabla_{\overline{T}}\overline{V}\|^2\right\}|_{s=0}dt = \frac{1}{F_0}\langle \nabla_{\dot{\sigma}}v, v\rangle_{\dot{\sigma}}|_a^b - \frac{1}{F_0}\int_a^b \langle \nabla_{\dot{\sigma}}\nabla_{\dot{\sigma}}v, v\rangle_{\dot{\sigma}}dt$$

$$= -\frac{1}{F_0}\int_a^b \langle \nabla_{\dot{\sigma}}\nabla_{\dot{\sigma}}v, v\rangle_{\dot{\sigma}}dt.$$
(5.1.11)

Since

$$\langle \nabla_{\overline{T}}\overline{V}, \overline{T}\rangle_{\overline{T}} = \overline{T}\langle \overline{V}, \overline{T}\rangle_{\overline{T}} - \langle \overline{V}, \nabla_{\overline{T}}\overline{T}\rangle_{\overline{T}},$$

then

$$\int_a^b \frac{1}{F^3}\langle \nabla_{\overline{T}}\overline{V}, \overline{T}\rangle_{\overline{T}}^2 dt|_{s=0} = \frac{1}{F_0^3}\int_a^b (\dot{\sigma}\langle v, \dot{\sigma}\rangle_{\dot{\sigma}})^2 dt.$$
(5.1.12)

Along the geodesic $\sigma(t)$ let $\dot{\sigma} = y$. By (3.2.3') and $\nabla_y y = \nabla_{\dot{\sigma}}\dot{\sigma} = 0$ we have

$$\langle \Omega(v,y)v, y\rangle_y = \langle R(v,y)v, y\rangle_y + \langle P(v, \nabla_y y, v), y\rangle_y = \langle R(v,y)v, y\rangle_y$$
$$= v^k y^l v^j y^i g_{is} R_j{}^s{}_{kl} = v^k y^l v^j y^i R_{ijlk} = -v^k v^j R_{jk}.$$

Here we have used (3.3.6) and (3.2.12). By means of (3.3.9'), the above can be rewritten as

$$\langle \Omega(v,y)v, y\rangle_y = -\langle \mathbf{R}(v), v\rangle.$$

Hence, we have

$$\int_a^b \frac{1}{F}\langle \Omega(\overline{V}, \overline{T})\overline{V}, \overline{T}\rangle_{\overline{T}}dt|_{s=0} = -\frac{1}{F_0}\int_a^b \langle \mathbf{R}(v), v\rangle dt.$$
(5.1.13)

Inserting (5.1.10)-(5.1.13) into (5.1.9) yields the second variation formula of a geodesic

$$L''(0) = -\frac{1}{F_0}\int_a^b \langle \nabla_{\dot{\sigma}}\nabla_{\dot{\sigma}}v + \mathbf{R}(v),\ v\rangle_{\dot{\sigma}}dt - \frac{1}{F_0^3}\int_a^b (\dot{\sigma}\langle v, \dot{\sigma}\rangle_{\dot{\sigma}})^2 dt.$$ (5.1.14)

In particular, if the variation vector field v is orthogonal to $\dot{\sigma}$ everywhere, then (5.1.14) becomes

$$L''(0) = -\frac{1}{F_0}\int_a^b \langle \nabla_{\dot{\sigma}}\nabla_{\dot{\sigma}}v + \mathbf{R}(v),\ v\rangle_{\dot{\sigma}}dt.$$
(5.1.14')

5.1.2   Elements of curvature and topology

From the above section we see that the Riemann curvature $\mathbf{R}$ appears in the second variation formula of a geodesic. This leads to the following

Definition 5.1. If a vector field $J(t)$ along a geodesic $\sigma(t)$ satisfies the following equation

$$\nabla_{\dot{\sigma}}\nabla_{\dot{\sigma}}J + \mathbf{R}(J) = 0, \tag{5.1.15}$$

then $J(t)$ is called a *Jacobi field* along $\sigma(t)$.

Let the tangent vector of the geodesic $\sigma(t)$ be unit, i.e., $F(\sigma(t), \dot{\sigma}(t)) = 1$, so that $F_0 = 1$ (see §2.4.2). Such a geodesic is called a *normal geodesic*. According to (5.1.14), we define the *index form* along a normal geodesic $\sigma(t)$ by

$$I(v, w) := \int_a^b \langle \nabla_{\dot{\sigma}}v, \nabla_{\dot{\sigma}}w \rangle_{\dot{\sigma}}dt - \int_a^b \langle \nabla_{\dot{\sigma}}\nabla_{\dot{\sigma}}v + \mathbf{R}(v), \ w \rangle_{\dot{\sigma}}dt, \tag{5.1.16}$$

where v, w are vector fields along $\sigma(t)$ which are orthogonal to $\dot{\sigma}$.

As the same as the case of Riemannian geometry, Jacobi fields play an important role in Finsler geometry. For example, by the theory on the second variation and Jacobi fields along a geodesic, one can obtain many global geometric results for Finsler manifolds.

In the following, we enumerate some results without proofs. See [10] and [36] for detail.

Index Lemma. *Let $\sigma(t)$, $a \leq t \leq b$, be a normal minimal geodesic from $p \in M$ to $q \in M$ in a forward complete Finsler manifold (M, F), and J be a Jacobi field along $\sigma(t)$ such that $J(a) = 0$. If v is a vector field along $\sigma(t)$ orthogonal to $\dot{\sigma}$ such that $v(a) = J(a) = 0$, $v(q) = J(q)$, then*

$$I(v, v) \geq I(J, J),$$

where the equality holds if and only if $v = J$.

Theorem 5.1 (Synge)**.** *Let (M, F) be an even-dimensional compact Finsler manifold without boundary. If (M, F) has positive flag curvature, then it is simply connected.*

Theorem 5.2 (Cartan-Hadamard)**.** *Let (M, F) be a forward complete Finsler manifold. If it has non-positive flag curvature, then the exponential map $\exp$ of M is regular everywhere.*

Theorem 5.3 (Bonnet-Myers). *Let (M, F) be an n-dimensional forward complete Finsler manifold. If its Ricci curvature satisfies $Ric \geq (n-1)k > 0$, then the diameter of M is not larger than $\pi/\sqrt{k}$, so that M is compact and its fundamental group is finite.*

In Riemannian geometry, the famous sphere theorem says that a simply-connected and closed Riemannian manifold with sectional curvature K satisfying $\frac{1}{4} < K \leq 1$ is homeomorphic to the a standard sphere ([62]). P. Dazord extended this theorem to reversible Finsler manifold ([43]). For general Finsler manifolds (not necessary reversible), H. B. Rademacher gave the following sphere theorem.

Theorem ([95]). *Let (M, F) be a simply-connected, closed, n-dimensional ($n \geq 3$) Finsler manifold with finite reversibility λ_F. If its flag curvature K satisfies*

$$\left(1 - \frac{1}{1 + \lambda_F}\right)^2 < K \leq 1,$$

then M is homotopy equivalent to an n-sphere.

The proof of the theorem can be found in [95] for details.

Before concluding this section, we would introduce some differential operators in Finsler manifolds.

Let $f = f(x)$ be a differentiable function in a Finsler manifold (M, F), and its differential be $df = f_{x^i} dx^i$. By using the Legendre transformation $\mathcal{L}$ (Chapter 3, §3.4), we define the *gradient* (vector field) of f by

$$\nabla f := \mathcal{L}^{-1}(df) := \ell_f,$$

which can be written locally as

$$\nabla f = \ell_f = \ell_f{}^i \frac{\partial}{\partial x^i}, \quad \ell_f{}^i := g^{ij}(\ell_f)\frac{\partial f}{\partial x^j}. \tag{5.1.17}$$

Set $\mathcal{U}_f := \{p \in M | df(p) \neq 0\}$. On $\mathcal{U}_f$ the *Hessian* $H(f)$ of f may be defined by

$$H(f)(u, v) := uv(f) - \nabla_u^{\ell_f} v(f), \quad \forall\, u, v \in T\mathcal{U}_f \subset TM,$$

where ∇^{ℓ_f} denotes the Chern connection ∇ valued in the direction $\ell_f := \nabla f$. By the property of ∇ (cf. §3.1.1), it is easy to see that

$$H(f)(u, v) = \langle \nabla_u^{\ell_f} \nabla f, v \rangle_{g_{\ell_f}} = \langle \nabla_v^{\ell_f} \nabla f, u \rangle_{g_{\ell_f}} = H(f)(v, u),$$

where g_{ℓ_f} denotes the fundamental tensor g valued in $\ell_f = \nabla f$. In a local coordinate system we have

$$H(f)_{ij} = \frac{\partial^2 f}{\partial x^i \partial x^j} - \Gamma_{ij}^k(\ell_f)\frac{\partial f}{\partial x^k}. \tag{5.1.18}$$

Let $d\mu = \sigma(x)dx^1 \wedge \cdots \wedge dx^n$ be a volume form of (M, F), $v = v^i(x)\frac{\partial}{\partial x^i}$ be a differentiable vector field in (M, F) without singular points. Thus, the *divergence* div v of v with respect to $d\mu$ is defined by (cf. [103], §2.4)

$$(\text{div } v)d\mu = d(v \rfloor d\mu),$$

where $v\rfloor$ denotes the inner differential related to v. A direct computation gives

$$\begin{aligned}
\text{div } v &= \frac{1}{\sigma}\frac{\partial}{\partial x^i}(\sigma v^i) \\
&= \frac{1}{\sigma}\left(\frac{\partial}{\partial x^i}(\sigma v^i) + \sigma v^i \Gamma_{ij}^j(v) - \sigma v^i \Gamma_{ij}^j(v)\right) \\
&= \frac{1}{\sigma}\nabla_i^v(\sigma v^i) - v^i \Gamma_{ij}^j(v) \\
&= \nabla_i^v v^i + v^i \nabla_i(\log \sigma) - v^i \Gamma_{ij}^j(v).
\end{aligned}$$

Noting that $\Gamma_{ij}^j(v) = (\nabla_i \log \sqrt{\det(g_{jk})}\,)|_v$ and recalling the definition of **S**-curvature related to $d\mu$ (§4.2), we have

$$\mathbf{S}(v) = v^i(\nabla_i \tau)|_v = v^i \nabla_i \log\left(\frac{\sqrt{\det(g_{jk})}}{\sigma}\right).$$

Hence,

$$\text{div } v = \nabla_i^v v^i - \mathbf{S}(v). \qquad (5.1.19)$$

On $\mathcal{U}_f$, the *Laplacian* Δf of a differentiable function $f : M \to \mathbb{R}$ is defined by

$$\Delta f := \text{div}(\nabla f).$$

Lemma 5.1. *Let $(M, F, d\mu)$ be an n-dimensional Finsler manifold with volume form $d\mu$, $f = f(x)$ be a differentiable function in M, $\mathcal{U}_f := \{p \in M | df(p) \neq 0\}$. We then have*

$$tr_{g_{\ell_f}} H(f) = \Delta f + \mathbf{S}(\nabla f)$$

on $\mathcal{U}_f$, where $\mathbf{S}$ is the $\mathbf{S}$-curvature related to $d\mu$.

Proof. By using (5.1.19) and putting $v = \nabla f := \ell_f$, we have

$$\Delta f = \text{div}(\nabla f) = (\nabla_i^{\ell_f} \ell_f{}^i) - \mathbf{S}(\ell_f) = tr_{g_{\ell_f}} H(f) - \mathbf{S}(\ell_f). \qquad (5.1.20)$$

$\square$

5.2   Scalar flag curvature

The flag curvature of a Finsler manifold (Chapter 3, §3.2) is similar to the sectional curvature of a Riemannian manifold. In the two-dimensional case, it reduces the well-known Gauss curvature.

5.2.1   Schur theorem

Let (M, F) be an n-dimensional Finsler manifold, of which the flag curvature $K(\Pi_x, y)$, in general, depends on not only the point $(x, y) \in TM_0$, but also the section Π_x (see (3.2.11)).

Definition 5.2. A Finsler manifold (M, F) is said to have *scalar flag curvature* if $K(\Pi_x, y) = K(x, y)$ is only a function of $(x, y) \in TM_0$. (M, F) is said to have *isotropic flag curvature* if $K(\Pi_x, y) = K(x)$ is only a function of $x \in M$. (M, F) is said to have *constant flag curvature* if $K(\Pi_x, y) = $ constant everywhere.

From (3.2.11) and (3.3.9$'$) it follows that a Finsler manifold (M, F) has scalar flag curvature if and only if

$$\mathbf{R}(v) = K(x, y)\{g(y, y)v - g(y, v)y\} = K\{F^2 v - g(y, v)y\}, \qquad (5.2.1)$$

which can be expressed as (cf. (3.2.12) and (2.2.5))

$$R^i{}_j = KF^2 h^i{}_j, \quad h^i{}_j = g^{ik}h_{kj} = \delta^i_j - F^{-2}g_{jk}y^k y^i. \qquad (5.2.1')$$

From (5.2.1$'$) and (3.3.16) one can get

$$R^i{}_{kl} = \frac{1}{3}F^2\left\{K_{;l}h^i{}_k - K_{;k}h^i{}_l\right\} + K\left\{g_{lp}\delta^i_k - g_{kp}\delta^i_l\right\}y^p. \qquad (5.2.2)$$

On the other hand, by (5.2.1$'$), the formula (3.3.12) can be reduced to

$$R^i{}_{k|j} - R^i{}_{j|k} + R^i{}_{jk|s}y^s = 0. \qquad (5.2.3)$$

Substituting (5.2.1$'$) and (5.2.2) into (5.2.3) yields

$$K_{|j}h^i{}_k - K_{|k}h^i{}_j - \frac{1}{3}\left\{K_{;j|s}h^i{}_k - K_{;k|s}h^i{}_j\right\}y^s$$
$$- F^{-2}K_{|s}y^s(g_{jp}\delta^i_k - g_{kp}\delta^i_j)y^p = 0.$$

Contracting the above with respect to i and k, we obtain

$$(n-2)\left\{K_{|j} - F^{-2}K_{|s}y^s g_{jp}y^p - \frac{1}{3}K_{;j|s}y^s\right\} = 0. \qquad (5.2.4)$$

Moreover, from $d^2 K = 0$ one can obtain the following Ricci type identity

$$K_{;j|l} = K_{|l;j} + K_{;k}L^k{}_{lj}.$$

Contracting the above with y^l yields

$$K_{;j|l}y^l = K_{|l;j}y^l = (K_{|l}y^l)_{;j} - K_{|j}.$$

Inserting this formula into (5.2.4), we may get

$$(n-2)\left\{4F^3 K_{|j} - (F^3 K_{|l}y^l)_{;j}\right\} = 0. \tag{5.2.5}$$

Theorem 5.4 (Schur). *Let (M, F) be an n-dimensional $(n \geq 3)$ Finsler manifold. If (M, F) has isotropic flag curvature, i.e., $K = K(x)$, then K must be constant.*

Proof. Since $K = K(x)$ is a scalar function, then $K_{|j} = [K]_{x^j}$. Thus, $K_{|j;l} = 0$. When $n \geq 3$, by using $FF_{y^j} = F_{y^j}F_{y^p}y^p = g_{jp}y^p$, we obtain from (5.2.5)

$$F^2 K_{|j} = (K_{|l}y^l)g_{js}y^s. \tag{5.2.6}$$

Differentiating the above with respect to y^k yields

$$K_{|l}y^l g_{jk} = 2K_{|j}g_{ks}y^s - K_{|k}g_{js}y^s. \tag{5.2.7}$$

Contracting (5.2.7) with g^{jk}, one can get $K_{|l}y^l = 0$. Substituting this into (5.2.6) yields $K_{|j} = 0$, i.e., $K = $ constant. $\square$

Remark. Theorem 5.4 is a direct generalization of the Schur theorem in Riemannian geometry ([169], [26]), namely, Riemannian manifolds with isotropic sectional curvature must be of constant curvature.

Proposition 5.1. *Let (M, F) be an n-dimensional Finsler manifold with scalar flag curvature $K = K(x, y)$. If the $\mathbf{S}$-curvature of F is isotropic, i.e., (4.3.1)-(ii) holds, then there is a scalar function $\sigma = \sigma(x)$ on M such that*

$$K = 3\frac{c_{x^k}y^k}{F} + \sigma(x).$$

Proof. Since (M, F) has scalar flag curvature $K(x, y)$, then (5.2.1') holds. Differentiating (5.2.1') with respect to y^k yields

$$R^i_{\ j;k} = K_{;k}F^2 h^i_{\ j} + K\{2g_{pk}y^p\delta^i_j - g_{jp}y^p\delta^i_k - g_{jk}y^i\}. \tag{5.2.7'}$$

Substituting (5.2.7') into the formula in Proposition 4.4, one can get

$$\mathbf{S}_{;k|s}y^s - \mathbf{S}_{|k} = -\frac{n+1}{3}K_{;k}F^2.$$

By using (4.3.1) and noting that η is closed, we have

$$\mathbf{S}_{;k|s}y^s - \mathbf{S}_{|k} = (n+1)\{c_{|s}y^s F_{;k} - c_{|k}F + (\eta_{k|s} - \eta_{s|k})y^s\}$$
$$= (n+1)\{c_{|s}y^s F_{;k} - c_{|k}F\}.$$

Thus,

$$c_{|s}y^s F_{;k} - c_{|k}F = -\frac{1}{3}K_{;k}F^2.$$

It is obvious that $c_{|k} = c_{x^k} = \partial c/\partial x^k$. We then rewrite the above as

$$\left[\frac{1}{3}K - \frac{c_{x^s}y^s}{F}\right]_{y^k} = 0,$$

which implies that $\sigma := K - \frac{3c_{x^s}y^s}{F}$ is a scalar function on M. The proof is completed. $\qquad\square$

Corollary 5.1. *Let (M, F) be an n-dimensional Finsler manifold with scalar flag curvature $K = K(x, y)$. If F has constant **S**-curvature (4.3.1)-(iv), then F has isotropic flag curvature $K = K(x)$. Hence, K is constant for $n \geq 3$.*

5.2.2 Constant flag curvature

Assume that the flag curvature of a Finsler metric F is a constant a, i.e., $K = a$. Then (5.2.2) deduces

$$R^i_{\ kl} = a\left\{g_{lp}\delta^i_k - g_{kp}\delta^i_l\right\}y^p. \tag{5.2.8}$$

Substituting (5.2.8) into (3.3.13) yields

$$R_j{}^i{}_{kl} = a(g_{jl}\delta^i_k - g_{jk}\delta^i_l) + L^i_{\ jk|l} - L^i_{\ jl|k} - L^i_{\ ks}L^s_{\ jl} + L^i_{\ ls}L^s_{\ jk}. \tag{5.2.9}$$

By using (5.2.9), the second formula of the second Bianchi identity (3.3.11) can be reduced as

$$\begin{aligned}
2a(C_{jlm}\delta^i_k &- C_{jkm}\delta^i_l) \\
&= P_j{}^i{}_{km|l} - P_j{}^i{}_{lm|k} + P_j{}^i{}_{ks}L^s_{\ lm} - P_j{}^i{}_{ls}L^s_{\ km} \\
&\quad - L^i_{\ ls;m}L^s_{\ jk} + L^i_{\ ks;m}L^s_{\ jl} - L^i_{\ ls}L^s_{\ jk;m} + L^i_{\ ks}L^s_{\ jl;m} \\
&\quad + L^i_{\ jl|k;m} - L^i_{\ jk|l;m}.
\end{aligned} \tag{5.2.10}$$

Theorem 5.5 ([103]). *Let (M, F) be a Finsler manifold with constant flag curvature $a \neq 0$. If its mean Landsberg tensor $\mathbf{J} = 0$, then F is Riemannian.*

Proof. Contracting (5.2.10) with $g_{is}y^s$ yields

$$a(C_{jlm}g_{ks} - C_{jkm}g_{ls})y^s = L_{jkm|l} - L_{jlm|k}.$$

By contracting the above with y^l, we obtain

$$L_{jkm|l}y^l + aF^2C_{jkm} = 0. \tag{5.2.11}$$

Contracting (5.2.11) with g^{jm} yields

$$J_{k|l}y^l + aF^2I_k = 0. \tag{5.2.12}$$

Hence, if $J_k = 0$, then $I_k = 0$. According to Theorem 2.1 (Deicke theorem), we see that F is Riemannian. $\qquad\square$

Remark. Theorem 5.5 improves a result of [87] in the case when the flag curvature is constant, where the assumption that $\mathbf{L} = 0$ instead.

Since Berwald metrics are Landsberg metrics (Chapter 3, §3.1), Theorem 5.5 implies that a Berwald metric with non-zero constant flag curvature is Riemannian. In order to consider the case of zero flag curvature, we introduce the following

Definition 5.3. A Finsler metric F is said to be *flat* if its spray $\mathbf{G}$ is flat, namely, at every point, there is a local coordinate system, in which the spray coefficients $G^i = 0$ identically.

Let (M, F) be a Finsler manifold. F is said to be *locally Minkowskian* if at any point $x \in M$, there is a standard local coordinate system (x^i, y^i) in which $F = F(y)$ is a function of y^i only. Clearly, any locally Minkowskian metric is locally flat. The converse is true too. Assume that F is flat, i.e., $G^i = 0$ in a local coordinate system (x^i, y^i). From (3.1.17) we have $N^j_k = 0$, from which and (3.1.5), (3.1.11) it follows that

$$[F^2]_{x^k} = \frac{\partial g_{ij}}{\partial x^k} y^i y^j = 2 y^i g_{ij} N^j_k = 0.$$

Thus F is locally Minkowskian. For a flat Finsler metric F, from (3.3.15) we see that $\mathbf{R} = 0$.

Theorem 5.6 (Berwald). *A Berwald metric F is flat if and only if $\mathbf{R} = 0$. Thus the flag curvature vanishes identically.*

Proof. We need only to prove the sufficiency. By Definition 3.1, the characterization of a Berwald metric is that G^i is a quadratic form with respect to y (see (3.1.15)). Moreover, by Proposition 3.1, $P_j{}^i{}_{kl} = 0$. According to (3.2.7), in such a case, $R_j{}^i{}_{kl}$ are functions of x only. By virtue of (3.2.12), $R^i{}_k$ is a quadratic form related to y. If $\mathbf{R} = 0$, then there is a local coordinate system (x^i, y^i), in which we have $R^i{}_k = 0$. By using (3.3.16), we get $R^i{}_{jk} = 0$. By means of (3.3.6), we have

$$R_j{}^i{}_{kl} = \frac{\partial (y^s R_s{}^i{}_{kl})}{\partial y^j} = \frac{\partial R^i{}_{kl}}{\partial y^j} = 0.$$

Thus, from (3.2.3) it follows that the curvature of the Chern connection vanishes identically, i.e., the connection is flat. Hence, there is a local coordinate system (x^i) in which $\Gamma^i_{jk} = 0$ (cf. [49]). By (3.1.15) we see that $G^i = 0$, i.e., the Berwald metric is flat. $\qquad\square$

In the two-dimensional case we have the following result, of which the proof can be found in [137] or [10].

Proposition 5.2 ([137]). *Let (M, F) be a 2-dimensional connected Berwald surface, whose flag curvature is K. (1) If K vanishes identically, then F is locally Minkowskian; (2) If K is not identically zero, then F is Riemannian.*

The following example is a non-Berwaldian Finsler metric with $\mathbf{R} = 0$.

Example 5.1. Let $B^n(1) \subset \mathbb{R}^n$ be a standard unit Euclidean ball and define

$$F(x, y) = \frac{\left(\sqrt{|y|^2 - (|x|^2|y|^2 - \langle x, y\rangle^2)} + \langle x, y\rangle\right)^2}{(1 - |x|^2)^2 \sqrt{|y|^2 - (|x|^2|y|^2 - \langle x, y\rangle^2)}}, \tag{5.2.13}$$

where $y \in T_x B^n(1) \equiv \mathbb{R}^n$. It is easy to verify that the metric (5.2.13) satisfies $R^i{}_k = 0$. However, it is not flat. Thus, it is non-Berwaldian. (cf. [36], Example 2.3.3).

The following example provides a Finsler metric of constant flag curvature $K = 1$ with vanishing **S**-curvature.

Example 5.2 ([15]). We view $\mathbb{S}^3 = Sp(1)$ as a compact Lie group. Let ζ^i $(i = 1, 2, 3)$ be the standard right invariant 1-forms on $\mathbb{S}^3$ satisfying

$$d\zeta^1 = 2\zeta^2 \wedge \zeta^3, \quad d\zeta^2 = 2\zeta^3 \wedge \zeta^1, \quad d\zeta^3 = 2\zeta^1 \wedge \zeta^2.$$

The metric

$$\alpha_1(y) := \sqrt{(\zeta^1(y))^2 + (\zeta^2(y))^2 + (\zeta^3(y))^2}$$

is the standard Riemannian metric of constant curvature 1. For $k \geq 1$, define

$$\alpha_k(y) := \sqrt{(k\zeta^1(y))^2 + k(\zeta^2(y))^2 + k(\zeta^3(y))^2}, \quad \beta_k(y) := \sqrt{k(k-1)}\zeta^1(y).$$

Thus,

$$F_k := \alpha_k + \beta_k \tag{5.2.14}$$

is a Randers metric on $\mathbb{S}^3$. In the following, we show that for any $k \geq 1$, **S**-curvature (related to the Busemann-Hausdorff volume element, §4.1.1) of F_k vanishes identically.

Take an orthonormal coframe for $T^*\mathbb{S}^3$

$$\theta^1 := k\zeta^1, \quad \theta^2 := \sqrt{k}\zeta^2, \quad \theta^3 := \sqrt{k}\zeta^3,$$

so that

$$\alpha_k(y) = \sqrt{\sum_{i=1}^{3}(\theta^i(y))^2}, \quad \beta_k(y) = \sum_{i=1}^{3} b_i(\theta^i(y))^2,$$

$$b_1 = \sqrt{k(k-1)}/k, \quad b_2 = b_3 = 0.$$

Clearly, β_k has constant length with respect to α_k, i.e.,

$$||\beta_k||_{\alpha_k} = \sqrt{k(k-1)}/k.$$

The Levi-Civita connection forms related to α_k are

$$\theta_2^1 = \theta^3, \quad \theta_3^1 = -\theta^2, \quad \theta_3^2 = \left(\frac{2}{k}-1\right)\theta^1, \quad \theta_j^i + \theta_i^j = 0. \qquad (5.2.15)$$

By the definition of covariant differentiation, $b_{i,j}\theta^j := db_i - b_j\theta_i^j$, we get

$$b_{1,i} = b_{2,1} = b_{2,2} = b_{3,1} = b_{3,3} = 0,$$

$$b_{2,3} = -\sqrt{k(k-1)}/k, \quad b_{3,2} = \sqrt{k(k-1)}/k.$$

Thus, $b_{i,j} + b_{j,i} = 0$, i.e., β_k is a Killing field with respect to α_k. It follows from (4.3.4) that $r_{ij} = 0$. By the above computation and (4.3.4), we have

$$s_{12} = s_{13} = 0, \quad s_{23} = -\sqrt{k(k-1)}/k, \quad s_{ij} + s_{ji} = 0, \quad s^i{}_j = s_{ij}.$$

Thus, $s_j := b_i s^i{}_j = b_1 s_{1j} = 0$. From (4.3.4) we see that $e_{00} = 0$. By virtue of Theorem 4.1 (§4.3.2), we obtain $c = 0$, $\mathbf{S} = \mathbf{E} = 0$.

We now consider the flag curvature of F_k. Firstly, by the above computation, β_k satisfies the following (see Formula (9.29) in [103])

$$\sum_{i=1}^{3} b_{i,j}b_{i,l} = ||\beta_k||_{\alpha_k}^2 \delta_{jl} - b_j b_l. \qquad (5.2.16)$$

Next, by definition, the curvature tensor $\overline{R}_j{}^i{}_{kl}$ of α_k are defined by

$$\frac{1}{2}\overline{R}_j{}^i{}_{kl}\theta^k \wedge \theta^l = d\theta_j^i - \theta_j^k \wedge \theta_k^i.$$

By (5.2.15), a direct computation gives

$$\overline{R}_2{}^1{}_{12} = \overline{R}_3{}^1{}_{13} = 1, \quad \overline{R}_2{}^1{}_{13} = \overline{R}_3{}^1{}_{12} = \overline{R}_3{}^1{}_{23} = 0,$$

$$\overline{R}_3{}^2{}_{23} = \frac{4}{k} - 3, \quad \overline{R}_3{}^2{}_{13} = \overline{R}_3{}^2{}_{12} = \overline{R}_1{}^2{}_{31} = 0.$$

Other components of $\overline{R}_j{}^i{}_{kl}$ can be obtained by (3.2.4). Let $\{e_i\}$ be the dual frame to $\{\theta^i\}$. Write $y = y^i e_i$, $\overline{R}^i{}_j := \overline{R}_k{}^i{}_{jl}y^k y^l$. It is easy to verify (see Formula (9.31) of [103]) that

$$\overline{R}^i{}_j = \left[(1 - ||\beta_k||_{\alpha_k}^2)\alpha_k^2 + \beta_k^2\right]\delta_{ij} + \alpha_k^2 b_i b_j - (1 - ||\beta_k||_{\alpha_k}^2)y^i y^j$$
$$\qquad - \beta_k(b_j y i + b_i y^j) - 3(b_{i,p}y^p)(b_{j,q}y^q). \qquad (5.2.17)$$

Thus, by Proposition 9.3.1 in [103], we conclude that F_k defined by (5.2.14) has constant flag curvature $K = 1$.

Remark. Other examples of Finsler metrics with constant flag curvature can see Exercises 5.5 and 5.7 ([103]).

5.3 Global rigidity results

5.3.1 Flag curvature with special conditions

Let $\gamma(t)$ be a geodesic with unit velocity in a Finsler manifold (M, F), $v = v(t)$ be a parallel vector field along $\gamma(t)$. Along $\gamma(t)$ let (see (2.2.1′) and (3.1.18))

$$\mathbf{C}(t) := \mathbf{C}_{\dot\gamma(t)}(v(t), v(t), v(t)), \quad \mathbf{L}(t) := \mathbf{L}_{\dot\gamma}(v(t), v(t), v(t)),$$
$$\mathbf{I}(t) := \mathbf{I}_{\dot\gamma(t)}(v(t)), \quad \mathbf{J}(t) := \mathbf{J}_{\dot\gamma(t)}(v(t)).$$

It follows from (3.3.17) and (3.3.18) that

$$\mathbf{L}(t) = \dot{\mathbf{C}}(t), \quad \mathbf{J}(t) = \dot{\mathbf{I}}(t), \tag{5.3.1}$$

where "·" denotes differentiation with respect to t along $\gamma(t)$.

Assume that (M, F) has constant flag curvature. Noting that $F(\dot\gamma(t)) = 1$ along $\gamma(t)$ and using (5.2.11) and (5.2.12), we get

$$\dot{\mathbf{L}}(t) + a\mathbf{C}(t) = 0, \quad \dot{\mathbf{J}}(t) + a\mathbf{I}(t) = 0.$$

Inserting (5.2.14) into the above equations, one can see that $\mathbf{C}(t)$ and $\mathbf{I}(t)$ satisfy the following equations:

$$\ddot{\mathbf{C}}(t) + a\mathbf{C}(t) = 0, \quad \ddot{\mathbf{I}}(t) + a\mathbf{I}(t) = 0. \tag{5.3.2}$$

The general solution of equations (5.3.2) is

$$\mathbf{C}(t) = \mathfrak{s}_a(t)\mathbf{L}(0) + \mathfrak{s}_a'(t)\mathbf{C}(0),$$
$$\mathbf{I}(t) = \mathfrak{s}_a(t)\mathbf{J}(0) + \mathfrak{s}_a'(t)\mathbf{I}(0), \tag{5.3.3}$$

where $\mathfrak{s}_a(t)$ is the unique solution of the following equation

$$\ddot{f}(t) + af(t) = 0, \quad f(0) = 0, \quad \dot{f}(0) = 1. \tag{5.3.4}$$

By means of (5.3.2)-(5.3.4), we may show the following

Theorem 5.7 ([5]). *Let (M, F) be a complete Finsler manifold with constant flag curvature $K = a$. Assume that the Cartan (resp. mean Cartan) tensor of (M, F) is bounded.*
(i) If $a < 0$, then F is Riemannian;
(ii) If $a = 0$, then F is Landsbergian (resp. weakly Landsbergian).

Proof. Since (M, F) is complete (Chapter 2, §2.4), any geodesic $\gamma(t)$ may be defined on $(-\infty, +\infty)$. We now consider two cases separately.

Case (i): $a = -1$. (5.3.3) gives

$$\mathbf{C}(t) = \text{sh}(t)\mathbf{L}(0) + \text{ch}(t)\mathbf{C}(0).$$

If $\mathbf{C}$ is bounded, then $\mathbf{L}(0) = 0 = \mathbf{C}(0)$. Since $\gamma(t)$ is arbitrary, we conclude $\mathbf{C} = 0$, i.e., F is Riemannian.

If $\mathbf{I}$ is bounded, in the same way, we can conclude $\mathbf{I} = 0$. By the Deicke theorem, F is Riemannian.

Case (ii): $a = 0$. (5.3.2) gives

$$\mathbf{C}(t) = t\mathbf{L}(0) + \mathbf{C}(0).$$

If $\mathbf{C}$ is bounded, then $\mathbf{L}(0) = 0$. Since $\gamma(t)$ is arbitrary, then $\mathbf{L} = 0$, i.e., F is Landsbergian.

If $\mathbf{I}$ is bounded, in the same way, we can conclude $\mathbf{J} = 0$. Thus, F is weakly Landsbergian. $\square$

Remark. According to Schur theorem (Theorem 5.4), for $n \geq 3$, in the above theorem the assumption that (M, F) has constant flag curvature can be replaced by the assumption that (M, F) has isotropic flag curvature. For the general case when (M, F) has isotropic flag curvature, see §7.2 in [36]. When M is compact, the assumption that the Cartan (resp. mean Cartan) tensor is bounded can be omitted. Furthermore, it can be proved that a compact Finsler manifold with zero flag curvature must be locally Minkowskian ([36], §7.2).

Theorem 5.8. *Let (M, F) be a compact closed Finsler manifold with negative flag curvature. If one of the following conditions is satisfied:*
(i) F has constant flag curvature;
(ii) F has constant $\mathbf{S}$-curvature;
(iii) F is weakly Landsbergian,
then F is Riemannian.

To prove Theorem 5.8 we need the following lemma, whose proof is omitted here, see [142] for detail.

Lemma 5.2 ([142]). *Let (M, F) be a compact closed Finsler manifold with negative flag curvature, f be a function defined on TM_0, which is positively y-homogeneous of degree zero. For any $(x, y) \in TM_0$, let*

$$\dot{f}(x, y) := \frac{d}{dt} f(\gamma(t), \dot{\gamma}(t))|_{t=0},$$

where $\gamma(t)$ is a geodesic satisfying $\gamma(0) = x$ and $\dot{\gamma}(0) = y$. If $\dot{f}$ does not change its $\pm$-symbol on TM_0, then f must be constant.

Proof of Theorem 5.8. (i) may follow from Theorem 5.7.

(ii) If F has constant **S**-curvature, by Definition 4.4 (§4.2), $\mathbf{S} = (n + 1)cF$, where c is constant. By virtue of Definition 4.2, we have

$$\dot{\tau} = \frac{d}{dt}\left[\tau\left(\gamma(t), \dot{\gamma}(t)\right)\right]|_{t=0} = (n + 1)c$$

along any geodesic $\gamma(t)$ of unit velocity, where τ is the distortion of F. By Lemma 5.2, $\tau(t) = $ const. It follows from $(4.2.1')$ that

$$\mathbf{I}_i = [\tau]_{y^i} = 0, \quad \mathbf{I} = 0.$$

Applying Deicke theorem yields that F is Riemannian.

(iii) If F is weakly Landsbergian, then $\mathbf{J} = J_i dx^i = 0$. Set $f := F^2|\mathbf{I}|^2 = F^2 g^{ij}\mathbf{I}_i\mathbf{I}_j$. One can see easily that f is a positively y-homogeneous function of degree zero on TM_0. Since $\mathbf{J} = 0$, $\dot{f} = 0$. By Lemma 5.2, f is constant. At the maximum point of τ we have $\mathbf{I}_i = \tau_{;i} = 0$. Thus, $f = F^2|\mathbf{I}|^2 = 0$ at that point. Since f is constant, f vanishes everywhere, i.e., $\mathbf{I} = 0$. Hence, by Deicke theorem, F is Riemannian. $\qquad\square$

5.3.2 Manifolds with non-positive flag curvature

Theorem 5.9 ([111]). *Let (M, F) be a complete Finsler manifold with non-positive flag curvature. If F has the constant **S**-curvature and the finite bounded Cartan tensor, then F is a weak Landsberg metric $(\mathbf{J} = 0)$ satisfying $\mathbf{R}_y(\mathbf{I}_y) = 0$. Particularly, F is Riemannian at the point where F has negative flag curvature.*

Proof. Take any local coordinate system (x^i, y^i) in (M, F). Let

$$\mathbf{I} = \mathbf{I}_i dx^i, \quad \mathbf{I}^i = g^{ij}\mathbf{I}_j, \quad \mathbf{J} = J_i dx^i, \quad J^i = g^{ij}J_j.$$

Then

$$\mathbf{R}_y(\mathbf{I}_y) = R^i{}_j \mathbf{I}^j \frac{\partial}{\partial x^i}.$$

If (M, F) has constant **S**-curvature, then $\mathbf{S} = (n + 1)cF$, where c is a constant. We then have

$$\mathbf{S}_{;k|s}y^s - \mathbf{S}_{|k} = (n + 1)c\{F_{;k|s}y^s - F_{|k}\} = 0.$$

It follows from Proposition 4.4 and the above that

$$J^i_{|s}y^s + R^i{}_s\mathbf{I}^s = 0. \tag{5.3.5}$$

Let $\gamma(t)$ be a geodesic with the unit velocity in (M, F). Since (M, F) is complete (Chapter 2, §2.4), any geodesic $\gamma(t)$ can extend to $(-\infty, +\infty)$. Along $\gamma(t)$ let

$$\mathbf{I}(t) := \mathbf{I}^i(\gamma(t), \dot{\gamma}(t))\frac{\partial}{\partial x^i}|_{\gamma(t)}, \quad \mathbf{J}(t) := J^i(\gamma(t), \dot{\gamma}(t))\frac{\partial}{\partial x^i}|_{\gamma(t)}.$$

By (3.3.18), we have $J^i = \mathbf{I}^i_{|s} y^s$, so that

$$\nabla_{\dot\gamma} \mathbf{I}(t) = \dot\gamma^k(t) \mathbf{I}^i_{|k}(\gamma(t), \dot\gamma(t)) \frac{\partial}{\partial x^i}|_{\gamma(t)} = \mathbf{J}(t), \qquad (5.3.6)$$

$$\nabla_{\dot\gamma} \mathbf{J}(t) = \dot\gamma^k(t) J^i_{|k}(\gamma(t), \dot\gamma(t)) \frac{\partial}{\partial x^i}|_{\gamma(t)} = \nabla_{\dot\gamma} \nabla_{\dot\gamma} \mathbf{I}(t). \qquad (5.3.7)$$

Restricting (5.3.5) to $\gamma(t)$ yields

$$\nabla_{\dot\gamma} \nabla_{\dot\gamma} \mathbf{I}(t) + \mathbf{R}_{\dot\gamma}(\mathbf{I}(t)) = 0, \qquad (5.3.8)$$

which implies that the mean Cartan tensor $\mathbf{I}$ is a Jacobi field along the geodesic $\gamma(t)$.

Set

$$f(t) := \langle \mathbf{I}(t), \mathbf{I}(t) \rangle_{g_{\dot\gamma}} = g_{ij}(\gamma, \dot\gamma) \mathbf{I}^i(t) \mathbf{I}^j(t).$$

It then follows from (5.3.6)-(5.3.8) that

$$\begin{aligned}\ddot f(t) &= 2\langle \nabla_{\dot\gamma} \nabla_{\dot\gamma} \mathbf{I}(t), \mathbf{I}(t) \rangle_{g_{\dot\gamma}} + 2\langle \nabla_{\dot\gamma} \mathbf{I}(t), \nabla_{\dot\gamma} \mathbf{I}(t) \rangle_{g_{\dot\gamma}} \\ &= -2\langle \mathbf{R}_{\dot\gamma}(\mathbf{I}(t)), \mathbf{I}(t) \rangle_{g_{\dot\gamma}} + 2\langle \mathbf{J}(t), \mathbf{J}(t) \rangle_{g_{\dot\gamma}}.\end{aligned} \qquad (5.3.9)$$

By the hypothesis of the theorem, we have $\langle \mathbf{R}_{\dot\gamma}(\mathbf{I}(t)), \mathbf{I}(t) \rangle_{g_{\dot\gamma}} \leq 0$ and $f(t)$ is bounded. From (5.3.9) we have

$$\ddot f(t) \geq 0.$$

Thus, $f(t)$ is convex and non-positive. We now show $\dot f(t) = 0$. We will use reductio ad absurdum. Suppose that there exists a t_0 such that $\dot f(t_0) \neq 0$. If $\dot f(t_0) < 0$, then

$$f(t) \geq f(t_0) - \dot f(t_0)(t_0 - t), \quad \forall t < t_0.$$

If $\dot f(t_0) > 0$, then

$$f(t) \geq f(t_0) - \dot f(t_0)(t - t_0), \quad \forall t > t_0.$$

In any case, we would have either $\lim_{t \to +\infty} f(t) = \infty$ or $\lim_{t \to -\infty} f(t) = \infty$. This contradicts to the boundness of $f(t)$. Therefore, $\dot f(t) = 0$ and $\ddot f(t) = 0$. Thus, from (5.3.9) we obtain

$$\mathbf{R}_{\dot\gamma}(\mathbf{I}(t)) = 0, \quad \mathbf{J}(t) = 0.$$

Since $\gamma(t)$ is arbitrary,

$$\mathbf{R}_y(\mathbf{I}_y) = 0, \quad \mathbf{J}_y = 0.$$

This implies that F is weakly Landsbergian.

We now assume that F has negative flag curvature at a point $x \in M$. Since $\mathbf{I}_y$ is orthogonal to y with respect to g_y and $\mathbf{R}_y(\mathbf{I}_y) = 0$, we conclude that $\mathbf{I}_y = 0$ for all $y \in T_x M_0$. By Deicke Theorem, F is Riemannian. $\square$

Remark. As a corollary of Theorem 5.9, we just obtain (ii) of Theorem 5.8. An example satisfying Theorem 5.9 is as follows.

Example 5.3. Let $f : [0, +\infty) \times [0, +\infty)$ be a smooth function defined as in Example 1.5, which satisfies $f(\lambda s, \lambda t) = \lambda f(s, t)$. Let (M_k, α_k) $(k = 1, 2)$ be two arbitrary Riemannian manifolds. Put $M = M_1 \times M_2$ and

$$F(x, y) := \sqrt{f\left([\alpha_1(x_1, y_1)]^2, [\alpha_2(x_2, y_2)]^2\right)}, \quad x = (x_1, x_2), \quad y = y_1 \oplus y_2,$$

where $x_k \in M_k$ and $y_k \in T_{x_k}M_k$ $(k = 1, 2)$. (M, F) is a Berwald manifold since its spray is $G = G_1 \oplus G_2$ where $G_k = G_{\alpha_k}$ is the spray of α_k $(k = 1, 2)$ (cf. [36], §4.3). By Proposition 4.3, we see the **S**-curvature of (M, F) vanishes identically.

A direct computation gives the Riemann curvature tensor of F

$$\left(R^i_{\ j}\right) = \begin{pmatrix} {}^{(1)}R^{i_1}_{\ j_1} & 0 \\ 0 & {}^{(2)}R^{i_2}_{\ j_2} \end{pmatrix},$$

where ${}^{(1)}R^{i_1}_{\ j_1}$ and ${}^{(2)}R^{i_2}_{\ j_2}$ denote Riemannian curvature tensors of α_1 and α_2, respectively. By using the computation of Example 1.5, we have

$$(R_{ij}) = \begin{pmatrix} f_s \ {}^{(1)}R_{i_1 j_1} & 0 \\ 0 & f_t \ {}^{(2)}R_{i_2 j_2} \end{pmatrix}.$$

For any vector $v = v^i \frac{\partial}{\partial x^i} \in T_x M$, we have

$$\langle \mathbf{R}_y(v), v \rangle_{g_y} = f_s \ {}^{(1)}R_{i_1 j_1} v^{i_1} v^{j_1} + f_t \ {}^{(2)}R_{i_2 j_2} v^{i_2} v^{j_2}.$$

Thus, if α_k $(k = 1, 2)$ have non-positive sectional curvature, then F has non-positive flag curvature. By means of $(4.2.1')$ and the computation of Example 1.5, we have

$$\mathbf{I}_i = \frac{\partial}{\partial y^i}\left[\ln \sqrt{\det(g_{ij})}\right] = \frac{\partial}{\partial y^i}\left[\ln \sqrt{h([\alpha_1]^2, [\alpha_2]^2)}\right].$$

One then gets

$$\mathbf{I}_{i_1} = h^{-1}h_s y_{i_1}, \quad \mathbf{I}_{i_2} = h^{-1}h_t y_{i_2},$$

where $y_{i_k} = y^{j_k}g_{j_k i_k}$ $(k = 1, 2)$. Clearly, the mean Cartan tensor is bounded.

Since $y_{i_k} \ {}^{(k)}R^{i_k}_{\ j_k} = 0$, we have

$$\langle \mathbf{R}_y(\mathbf{I}_y), \mathbf{I}_y \rangle_{g_y} = \mathbf{I}_i R^I_{\ j} I^j = h^{-1}h_s y_{i_1} \ {}^{(1)}R^{i_1}_{\ j_1} \mathbf{I}^{j_1} + h^{-1}h_t y_{i_2} \ {}^{(2)}R^{i_2}_{\ j_2} \mathbf{I}^{j_2} = 0.$$

Since F is Berwaldian, it is Landsbergian, i.e., $\mathbf{J} = 0$. Hence, this is an example satisfying Theorem 5.9.

Example 5.4 ([110]). Let $n \geq 2$ and $U := \{x = (s, t, \overline{x}) \in \mathbb{R}^2 \times \mathbb{R}^{n-2} | s^2 + t^2 < 1\}$. Define

$$F(x, y) := (1 - s^2 - t^2)^{-1} \left\{ \sqrt{(-tu + sv)^2 + |y|^2(1 - s^2 - t^2)} - (-tu + sv) \right\},$$

where $y = (u, v, \overline{y}) \in T_x U \cong \mathbb{R}^n$. It is easy to check that F is a Finsler metric with zero flag curvature and zero **S**-curvature on U. However, it can be shown that $\mathbf{J} \neq 0$. Therefore, Theorem 5.9 does not hold when (M, F) is not complete.

5.4   Navigation

5.4.1   Navigation problem

Consider an object moving in a metric space, such as Euclidean space, pushed by an internal force and an external force field. The shortest time problem is to determine a curve from one point to another in the space, along which it takes the least time for the object to travel. This is so-called *Zermelo navigation problem*, which was studied by E. Zermelo in some special cases.

Now suppose that an object in a Finsler manifold (M, F) is pushed by an internal U with constant length, $F(x, U_x) = c$, and while it is pushed by an external force field V with $F(x, -V_x) < c$. The combined force at x is

$$W_x = U_x + V_x.$$

The condition, $F(x, -V_x) < c$, guarantees that the object can move forward in any direction (see Figure 5.1).

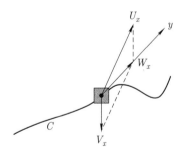

Figure 5.1

For the sake of simplicity, we can assume that $c = 1$ and the velocity vector at any point $x \in M$ is W_x. Set

$$y_0 := \frac{W_x}{F(x, W_x)}. \tag{5.4.0}$$

Since $F(x, y_0) = 1$ and

$$W_x = F(x, W_x)y_0,$$

we then have

$$F(x, F(x, W_x)y_0 - V_x) = F(x, W_x - V_x) = F(x, U_x) = 1. \tag{5.4.1}$$

The indicatrix $S_x M = F^{-1}(1)$ is a smooth convex hypersurface in $T_x M$. By the triangle inequality

$$F(x, y) \leq F(x, y - V) + F(x, V),$$

we get

$$F(x, y - V) \geq F(x, y) - F(x, V) = 1 - F(x, V) > 0.$$

Write $f(\xi) = F(x, \xi y - V)$ for $\xi \in \mathbb{R}$. Since

$$f(0) = F(x, y - V), \quad \lim_{\xi \to \infty} f(\xi) = +\infty,$$

the equation

$$F(x, \xi y - V) = 1 \tag{5.4.2}$$

has a unique solution $\xi \in \mathbb{R}$. For $y = y_0$ in (5.4.0), comparing (5.4.1) with (5.4.2) yields

$$\xi = F(x, W_x). \tag{5.4.3}$$

Define the function $\widetilde{F} : TM \to [0, +\infty)$ by

$$\widetilde{F}(x, y) := \begin{cases} 1/\xi, & \text{if } F(x, y) = 1, \\ F(x, y)\widetilde{F}\left(x, \frac{y}{F(x,y)}\right), & \text{other case.} \end{cases} \tag{5.4.4}$$

Clearly, for any $\lambda > 0$, we have $\widetilde{F}(x, \lambda y) = \lambda \widetilde{F}(x, y)$. Thus, $\widetilde{F} = \widetilde{F}(x, y)$ is a Finsler function on M. Moreover, by (5.4.1) and (5.4.4), we have

$$\widetilde{F}(x, W_x) = \widetilde{F}(x, F(x, W_x)y_0) = F(x, W_x)\widetilde{F}(x, y_0) = \frac{F(x, W_x)}{F(x, W_x)} = 1. \tag{5.4.5}$$

It implies that the length of the velocity vector W_x generated by the combined force is constant with respect to $\widetilde{F}$.

By virtue of (5.4.1), (5.4.3) and (5.4.4), one can see that $\widetilde{F}$ satisfies

$$F\left(x, \frac{y}{\widetilde{F}(x,y)} - V\right) = 1. \tag{5.4.6}$$

Let $C : [a, b] \to M$ be the parametrization of a piecewise smooth oriented curve on M such that the velocity vector $\dot{C}(t) = W_{C(t)}$. Then, by (5.4.5), the time $b - a$ for which the object travels along $C(t)$ is equal to

$$b - a = \int_a^b dt = \int_a^b \widetilde{F}(C(t), W_{C(t)})dt = L_{\widetilde{F}}(C).$$

Here the right hand side $L_{\widetilde{F}}(C)$ denotes the length of the curve $C(t)$ with respect to the metric $\widetilde{F}$. This means that under the effect of the external force $-V$, the shortest path curve from a point p to another q on (M, F) is not the geodesic, but is the geodesic with respect to the Finsler metric $\widetilde{F}$.

Given a Finsler metric F and a vector field V, we can define a new Finsler metric $\widetilde{F}$ by (5.4.6). This is the *navigation* in Finsler geometry.

Proposition 5.3. *Let $F(x, y)$ be a Finsler metric in an n-dimensional manifold M, $V = V^i(x)\frac{\partial}{\partial x^i}$ be any vector field satisfying $F(x, -V_x) < 1$. If $\widetilde{F}(x, y)$ is the Finsler metric given by the navigation (5.4.6), then the Busemann-Hausdorff volume forms of $F(x, y)$ and $\widetilde{F}(x, y)$ are the same, i.e.,*

$$dV_F = dV_{\widetilde{F}}.$$

Proof. Fix a basis $\{e_i\}$ in $T_x M$ and let $V_x = v^i e_i$. Put

$$\mathcal{U}_F := \{(y^i) \in \mathbb{R}^n | F(x, y^i e_i) < 1\},$$
$$\mathcal{U}_{\widetilde{F}} := \{(y^i) \in \mathbb{R}^n | \widetilde{F}(x, y^i e_i) < 1\}.$$

From the definition of $\widetilde{F}$ it follows that

$$\mathcal{U}_{\widetilde{F}} = \mathcal{U}_F + (v^i).$$

Since shifting does not change the Euclidean volume, $\mathrm{Vol}(\mathcal{U}_F) = \mathrm{Vol}(\mathcal{U}_{\widetilde{F}})$. This implies that (Chapter 4, §4.1)

$$\sigma_{B(\widetilde{F})}(x) = \sigma_{B(F)}(x).$$

The proof is completed. $\qquad\qquad\qquad\qquad\qquad\qquad\qquad\qquad\qquad\square$

Example 5.5. Let $\phi = \phi(y)$ be a Minkowski norm in $\mathbb{R}^n$ (see Chapter 2, §2.1, after Example 2.1). Put

$$\mathcal{U} := \{y \in \mathbb{R}^n | \phi(y) < 1\}.$$

Let $F(x, y) = \phi(y)$ where $y \in T_x\mathcal{U} \cong \mathcal{U}$. Take $V_x = -x$ where $x \in \mathcal{U}$. Thus, $F(x, y)$ is a Minkowski norm in $\mathbb{R}^n$, where V is a radius vector field toward the origin. Observe that

$$F(x, -V_x) = \phi(x) < 1, \quad x \in \mathcal{U}.$$

For a non-zero vector $y \in T_x\mathcal{U} \setminus \{0\} \cong \mathbb{R}^n \setminus \{0\}$, define $\Theta = \Theta(x, y) > 0$ by

$$F\left(x, \frac{y}{\Theta(x, y)} - V_x\right) = 1. \tag{5.4.7}$$

The metric $\Theta(x, y)$ can also be defined by the following (see Figure 5.2)

$$z := x + \frac{y}{\Theta(x, y)} \in \partial\mathcal{U}.$$

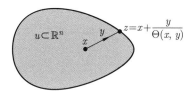

Figure 5.2

The equation (5.4.7) can be written as

$$\Theta(x, y) = \phi(y + \Theta(x, y)x). \tag{5.4.8}$$

Differentiating (5.4.8) with respect to x^k and y^k respectively, one obtains

$$\begin{aligned}
\left(1 - \phi_{w^i}(w)x^i\right)\Theta_{x^k}(x, y) &= \phi_{w^k}(w)\Theta(x, y), \\
\left(1 - \phi_{w^i}(w)x^i\right)\Theta_{y^k}(x, y) &= \phi_{w^k}(w),
\end{aligned} \tag{5.4.9}$$

where $w^i = y^i + \Theta(x, y)x^i$. It follows from (5.4.9) that

$$\Theta_{x^k} = \Theta\Theta_{y^k}. \tag{5.4.10}$$

The above argument was given by T. Okada ([90]). Particularly, if $\phi = |y|$ is the standard Euclidean norm on $\mathbb{R}^n$, then $\mathcal{U} = B^n(1)$ is the unit ball in $\mathbb{R}^n$. In this case, $\Theta = F$ is the Funk metric as defined in (2.1.4). Hence, any Finsler metric $\Theta(x, y)$ satisfying (5.4.10) is also called a *Funk metric*.

Example 5.6. Let $h(x,y) = \sqrt{h_{ij}(x)y^iy^j}$ be a Riemannian metric on M, $V = v^i(x)\frac{\partial}{\partial x^i}$ be any vector field satisfying $h(x, -V_x) = \sqrt{h_{ij}(x)v^iv^j} < 1$. By navigation, one can define a Finsler metric $F = F(x,y)$ by (5.4.6), i.e.,

$$h\left(x, \frac{y}{F} - V\right) = \sqrt{h_{ij}\left(\frac{y^i}{F} - V\right)\left(\frac{y^j}{F} - V\right)} = 1. \qquad (5.4.11)$$

Solving (5.4.11) for F, one obtains

$$F(x,y) = \alpha + \beta = \sqrt{a_{ij}(x)y^iy^j} + b_i(x)y^i,$$

where

$$a_{ij} = \frac{(1 - h_{pq}v^pv^q)h_{ij} + h_{ip}h_{jq}v^pv^q}{(1 - h_{pq}v^pv^q)^2},$$

$$b_i = -\frac{h_{ip}v^p}{1 - h_{pq}v^pv^q}. \qquad (5.4.12)$$

It is easy to see that

$$\|\beta\|_\alpha = \sqrt{a^{ij}b_ib_j} = \sqrt{h_{ij}v^iv^j} = h(x, -V_x) < 1.$$

Thus, F is a Randers metric.

Conversely, every Randers metric $F = \alpha + \beta$ on a manifold M can be constructed from a Riemannian metric h and a vector field V on M by navigation. In fact, for $\alpha = \sqrt{a_{ij}(x)y^iy^j}$, $\beta = b_i(x)y^i$, h and v are given by

$$h_{ij} := (1 - \|\beta\|^2)(a_{ij} - b_ib_j), \quad v^i := -\frac{a^{ij}b_j}{1 - \|\beta\|^2}. \qquad (5.4.13)$$

Then F is given by (5.4.11) for $h(x,y) = \sqrt{h_{ij}(x)y^iy^j}$ and $V = v^i(x)\frac{\partial}{\partial x^i}$. Moreover, $\|\beta\|_\alpha < 1$.

Concretely, let $B^n \subset \mathbb{R}^n$ be the standard Euclidean ball and let

$$h := \frac{\sqrt{1 - |a|^2}}{1 + \langle a, x\rangle}\sqrt{|y|^2 - \frac{2\langle a, y\rangle\langle x, y\rangle}{1 + \langle a, x\rangle} - \frac{(1 - |x|^2)\langle a, y\rangle^2}{(1 + \langle a, x\rangle)^2}},$$

$$V := -\frac{1 + \langle a, x\rangle}{1 - |a|^2}(x + a), \qquad (5.4.14)$$

where $y \in T_xB^n \cong \mathbb{R}^n$, $a \in \mathbb{R}^n$ is a constant vector with $|a| < 1$. By (5.4.11) one obtains

$$F = \frac{\sqrt{|y|^2 - (|x|^2|y|^2 - \langle x, y\rangle^2)}}{1 - |x|^2} + \frac{\langle x, y\rangle}{1 - |x|^2} + \frac{\langle a, y\rangle}{1 + \langle a, x\rangle}. \qquad (5.4.15)$$

When $a = 0$, (5.4.15) is just the Funk metric on B^n given as in (2.1.4).

5.4.2 Randers metrics and navigation

By Example 5.6, any Randers metric $F = \alpha + \beta$ can be determined by a Riemannian metric $h = \sqrt{h_{ij}y^i y^j}$ and a vector field $V = v^i \frac{\partial}{\partial x^i}$ by means of the navigation (5.4.11). According to (5.4.12), F can be expressed by

$$F = \frac{\sqrt{\lambda h^2 + V_0^2}}{\lambda} - \frac{V_0}{\lambda}, \qquad (5.4.16)$$

where

$$V_0 = v_i y^i = h_{ij} v^j y^i, \quad \lambda = 1 - \|V\|_h^2 = 1 - h_{ij} v^i v^j.$$

Let

$$\phi(s) := \sqrt{1 + s^2} - s, \quad \alpha := \frac{h}{\sqrt{\lambda}}, \quad \beta := \frac{V_0}{\lambda}.$$

F may be expressed as

$$F = \alpha \phi(s), \quad s = \frac{\beta}{\alpha}.$$

Thus, by using the notation of (4.3.4) and the formula (2.4.3), a direct computation gives spray coefficients G^i of F

$$G^i = G_\alpha^i - \alpha \phi s^i_{\ 0} + \frac{1}{2(1 + b^2)\phi}(2\alpha \phi s_0 + r_{00})\left(\phi b^i - \frac{y^i}{\alpha}\right). \qquad (5.4.17)$$

It is easy to check that

$$1 + b^2 = \frac{1}{\lambda}, \quad h^2 - 2FV_0 = \lambda F^2. \qquad (5.4.18)$$

We write

$$\widetilde{r}_{ij} := \frac{1}{2}(v_{i|j} + v_{j|i}), \quad \widetilde{s}_{ij} := \frac{1}{2}(v_{i|j} - v_{j|i}),$$
$$\widetilde{r}_j := v^i \widetilde{r}_{ij}, \quad \widetilde{r} := \widetilde{r}_j v^j, \quad \widetilde{s}_j := v^i \widetilde{s}_{ij}, \qquad (5.4.19)$$

where "|" denotes the covariant differentiation with respect to h. Here and from now on, we will lift up subscripts and drop down superscripts by using h^{ij} and h_{ij}. For example, $v_i = h_{ij} v^j$, $\widetilde{s}^i_{\ j} = h^{ik} \widetilde{s}_{kj}$, etc. Noting that $\widetilde{s}_j v^j = 0$, we have

$$\lambda_{|i} = -2(\widetilde{r}_i + \widetilde{s}_i).$$

Thus, there is a relation between spray coefficients G_α^i of α and that G_h^i of h as follows:

$$G_\alpha^i = G_h^i + \frac{1}{\lambda}(\widetilde{r}_0 + \widetilde{s}_0)y^i - \frac{1}{2\lambda}(\widetilde{r}^i + \widetilde{s}^i)h^2,$$

where $\widetilde{r}_0 = \widetilde{r}_i y^i$, $\widetilde{s}_0 = \widetilde{s}_i y^i$. Set $\widetilde{r}_{00} := \widetilde{r}_{ij} y^i y^j$. It follows from the above and (5.4.17) that

$$r_{00} = \frac{1}{\lambda}\widetilde{r}_{00} + \frac{1}{\lambda^2}\widetilde{r}h^2,$$

$$s^i_0 = \widetilde{s}^i_0 + \frac{1}{\lambda}\{(\widetilde{r}_0 + \widetilde{s}_0)v^i - (\widetilde{r}^i + \widetilde{s}^i)V_0\},$$

$$s_0 = \frac{1}{\lambda}\widetilde{s}_0 + \frac{1}{\lambda^2}\{(\widetilde{r}_0 + \widetilde{s}_0)(1 - \lambda) - \widetilde{r}V_0\},$$

$$G^i = G^i_h - F\widetilde{s}^i_0 - \frac{1}{2}F^2(\widetilde{r}^i + \widetilde{s}^i) + \frac{1}{2}\left(\frac{y^i}{F} - v^i\right)(2F\widetilde{r}_0 - \widetilde{r}_{00} - F^2\widetilde{r}). \quad (5.4.20)$$

(5.4.20) was firstly obtained by C. Robles ([98]).

Theorem 5.10. *Let $F = \alpha + \beta$ be a Randers metric constructed from a Riemannian metric $h = \sqrt{h_{ij}y^i y^j}$ and a vector field $V = v^i\frac{\partial}{\partial x^i}$ by virtue of the navigation (5.4.16). Then F has isotropic $\mathbf{S}$-curvature $\mathbf{S} = (n+1)c(x)F$ if and only if V satisfies*

$$\widetilde{r}_{ij} = -2c(x)h_{ij}, \quad (5.4.21)$$

i.e.,

$$v_{i|j} + v_{j|i} = -4c(x)h_{ij}. \quad (5.4.21')$$

Proof. From (5.4.20) it follows that

$$\frac{\partial G^s}{\partial y^s} = \frac{\partial G^s_h}{\partial y^s} + \frac{n+1}{2F}(2F\widetilde{r}_0 - \widetilde{r}_{00} - F^2\widetilde{r}).$$

Denote by $dV_F = \sigma_F dx^1 \wedge \cdots \wedge dx^n$ and $dV_h = \sigma_h dx^1 \wedge \cdots \wedge dx^n$ the Busemann-Hausdorff volume forms with respect to F and h, respectively. By Proposition 5.3, we see that $\sigma_F = \sigma_h$. Since h is Riemannian, then

$$\frac{\partial G^s_h}{\partial y^s} = y^s \frac{\partial(\ln\sigma_h)}{\partial x^s}.$$

By means of (4.2.5), from the above two formulas we have

$$\mathbf{S} = \frac{n+1}{2F}(2F\widetilde{r}_0 - \widetilde{r}_{00} - F^2\widetilde{r}). \quad (5.4.22)$$

Let

$$\xi^i := y^i - F(x,y)v^i.$$

Since $\|V\|_h < 1$, the vector $\xi := \xi^i\frac{\partial}{\partial x^i} \in T_xM$ is arbitrary. By (5.4.18), it is easy to see that

$$h_{ij}\xi^i\xi^j = h^2 - 2FV_0 + (1 - \lambda)F^2 = F^2. \quad (5.4.22')$$

Combining (5.4.22') with (5.4.22) yields

$$\mathbf{S} = -\frac{n+1}{2}\frac{\widetilde{r}_{ij}\xi^i\xi^j}{h_{ij}\xi^i\xi^j}F.$$

This completes the proof of Theorem 5.10. $\square$

Now assume that h has constant sectional curvature $K_h = \mu$. Thus, h is locally isometric to $h_\mu = \sqrt{h_{ij}(x)y^i y^j}$:

$$h_\mu = \frac{\sqrt{|y|^2 + \mu(|x|^2|y|^2 - \langle x, y\rangle^2)}}{1 + \mu|x|^2}, \quad y \in T_x B^n(r_\mu) \cong \mathbb{R}^n, \qquad (5.4.23)$$

where $r_\mu = +\infty$ for $\mu \geq 0$; $r_\mu = \pi/\sqrt{-\mu}$ for $\mu < 0$. The components h_{ij} of h_μ and its inverse h^{ij} are

$$h_{ij} = \frac{\delta^i_j}{1 + \mu|x|^2} - \frac{\mu x^i x^j}{(1 + \mu|x|^2)^2}, \quad h^{ij} = (1 + \mu|x|^2)\{\delta^i_j + \mu x^i x^j\}.$$

Proposition 5.4. *Let $h = h_\mu$ be given by (5.4.23), and V a vector field defined on the Euclidean ball $B^n(r_\mu)$. If $V = v^i \frac{\partial}{\partial x^i}$ satisfies (5.4.21), where $c(x) = c$ is a constant, then*

$$V = \begin{cases} -2cx + xQ + b, & \text{for } \mu = 0, \\ xQ + b + \mu\langle b, x\rangle x, & \text{for } \mu \neq 0, \end{cases} \qquad (5.4.24)$$

where Q is a skew-symmetric matrix, $b \in \mathbb{R}^n$ is a constant vector. Moreover, $c = 0$ when $\mu \neq 0$. Conversely, if V is a vector field satisfying (5.4.24), then V satisfies (5.4.21) with $c(x) = c = \text{const.}$, where $c = 0$ when $\mu \neq 0$.

Proof. Assume that $c(x) = c = \text{const.}$ Covariant differentiating (5.4.21') yields that

$$v_{i|j|k} + v_{j|i|k} = 0.$$

Permutating the indices i, j, k and adding algebraically these formulas, one can obtain from the Ricci identity that

$$v_{i|j|k} = -v_s \overline{R}_k{}^s{}_{ij}, \qquad (5.4.25)$$

where $\overline{R}_k{}^s{}_{ij}$ denotes the Riemannian curvature tensor of h. Since h has constant sectional curvature $K_h = \mu$,

$$\overline{R}_k{}^s{}_{ij} = \mu(\delta^s_i h_{jk} - \delta^s_j h_{ik}), \qquad (5.4.26)$$

from which it follows that $\overline{R}_k{}^s{}_{ij}$ is covariant constant, namely, $\overline{R}_k{}^s{}_{ij|l} = 0$. Covariant differentiating (5.4.25) yields that

$$v_{i|j|k|l} = -v_{s|l}\overline{R}_k{}^s{}_{ij}.$$

Permutating the indices k and l and using the Ricci identity, we have $v_{i|j|k|l} - v_{i|j|l|k} = v_{s|j}\overline{R}_i{}^s{}_{kl} + v_{i|s}\overline{R}_j{}^s{}_{kl}$, from which and (5.4.21') it follows that

$$4c\overline{R}_{ijkl} + v_{s|j}\overline{R}_i{}^s{}_{kl} - v_{s|i}\overline{R}_j{}^s{}_{kl} + v_{s|l}\overline{R}_k{}^s{}_{ij} - v_{s|k}\overline{R}_l{}^s{}_{ij} = 0.$$

Substituting (5.4.26) into the above formula and using (5.4.21'), one obtains that

$$2c\mu(h_{ik}h_{jl} - h_{il}h_{jk}) = 0,$$

which implies that

$$c\mu = 0.$$

Hence, $c = 0$ when $\mu \neq 0$. In the following, we consider two cases respectively.

Case (i): $\mu = 0$. Suppose that $u_i := v_i + 2cx^i$. Then (5.4.21) is reduced as

$$\frac{\partial u_i}{\partial x^j} + \frac{\partial u_j}{\partial x^i} = 0.$$

Solving the equation yields that

$$u_i = x^j q_j^i + b^i,$$

where $Q = (q_j^i)$ is a skew-symmetric matrix, $b = (b^i) \in \mathbb{R}^n$ is a constant vector. We then obtain

$$V = -2cx + xQ + b.$$

Case (ii): $\mu \neq 0$. In this case, we have $c = 0$ and (5.4.21) is reduced as

$$v_{i|j} + v_{j|i} = 0.$$

This is the equation of the Killing vector field in the Riemannian space of constant curvature. By the known classical method (or see [166]), we can solve the equation as follows.

By (5.4.23), the coefficients of the Levi-Civita connection for h_μ are

$${}^h\Gamma^i_{jk} = -\mu \frac{x^j \delta^i_k + x^k \delta^i_j}{1 + \mu|x|^2},$$

from which it follows that

$$v_{i|j} = \frac{\partial v_i}{\partial x^j} + \mu \frac{x^i v_j + x^j v_i}{1 + \mu|x|^2}.$$

Thus, the equation of the Killing vector field is

$$\frac{\partial v_i}{\partial x^j} + \frac{\partial v_j}{\partial x^i} + 2\mu \frac{x^i v_j + x^j v_i}{1 + \mu|x|^2} = 0.$$

Let $u_i := (1 + \mu|x|^2)v_i$. The above equation is reduced as

$$\frac{\partial u_i}{\partial x^j} + \frac{\partial u_j}{\partial x^i} = 0.$$

As similar as the case (i), we obtain

$$u_i = x^j q_j^i + b^i,$$

where $Q = (q_j^i)$ is a skew-symmetric matrix, $b = (b^i) \in \mathbb{R}^n$ is a constant vector. Thus,

$$v_i = (1 + \mu |x|^2)^{-1}(x^j q_j^i + b^i).$$

By $v^i = h^{ij} v_j$, we obtain finally

$$v^i = x^j q_j^i + b^i + \mu \langle b, x \rangle x^i.$$

Conversely, it is obvious. Proposition 5.4 is proved. $\qquad\Box$

Theorem 5.11. *Let $F = \alpha + \beta$ be a Randers metric constructed from a Riemannian metric $h = \sqrt{h_{ij} y^i y^j}$ and a vector field $V = v^i \frac{\partial}{\partial x^i}$ by the navigation (5.4.16). Then F has constant flag curvature if and only if h and V satisfy the following: at any point $p \in M$ there exists a local coordinate system (x^i) such that $x^i(p) = 0$, h can be expressed by (5.4.23), and V is given by (5.4.24). In this case the flag curvature of F is $K = \mu - c^2$, and $\mathbf{S}$-curvature is $\mathbf{S} = (n+1)cF$.*

Proof. Let F be a Randers metric given by (5.4.16).

We prove the necessity firstly. If F has constant flag curvature, then F has constant Ricci curvature. According to Theorem 5.12 in §5.4.3 below, V satisfies (5.4.21). So, it follows from Theorem 5.10 that F has constant $\mathbf{S}$-curvature. By Proposition 5.1 we conclude $K = \sigma = \text{const.}$

Thus, (5.4.20) is reduced as

$$G^i = G_h^i + Q^i, \quad Q^i := -F\widetilde{s}_0^i - \frac{1}{2} F^2 \widetilde{s}^i + cF y^i. \qquad (5.4.27)$$

By (3.3.15), a direct computation gives

$$R^i{}_j = \overline{R}_p{}^i{}_{jq} \xi^p \xi^q - F_{y^j} \overline{R}_p{}^i{}_{sq} \xi^p \xi^q v^s - c^2 (F^2 \delta^i_j - F F_{y^j} y^i), \qquad (5.4.28)$$

where $\xi^i = y^i - F v^i$, $\overline{R}_p{}^i{}_{jq}$ is the Riemannian curvature tensor with respect to h.

Put $\widetilde{h} := h(x, \xi) = \sqrt{h_{pq} \xi^p \xi^q} = \sqrt{\xi_k \xi^k}$ and $\widetilde{V}_0 := v_i \xi^i$. From (5.4.22′) we see that $\widetilde{h} = F$. Hence,

$$y^i = \xi^i + \widetilde{h} v^i,$$

and

$$\lambda \widetilde{h} = \lambda F = \sqrt{\lambda h^2 + V_0^2} - V_0$$

$$= \sqrt{\lambda h^2 + V_0^2} - v_i(\xi^i + \widetilde{h} v^i) = \sqrt{\lambda h^2 + V_0^2} - \widetilde{V}_0 - \widetilde{h}(1 - \lambda),$$

which is just

$$\sqrt{\lambda h^2 + V_0^2} = \widetilde{h} + \widetilde{V}_0.$$

It follows from the above that

$$F_{y^j} = \frac{\xi_j}{\widetilde{h} + \widetilde{V}_0},$$

$$F^2 \delta_j^i - F F_{y^j} y^i = \widetilde{h}^2 \delta_j^i - \xi_j \xi^i - \frac{1}{\widetilde{h} + \widetilde{V}_0} \xi_j (\widetilde{h}^2 \delta_p^i - \xi_p \xi^i) v^p.$$

Let $\widetilde{R}^i{}_j = \overline{R}_p{}^i{}_{jq} \xi^p \xi^q$ and $\mu := \sigma + c^2$. From (5.4.28) we get

$$R^i{}_j - (\mu - c^2)(F^2 \delta_j^i - F F_{y^j} y^i)$$
$$= \widetilde{R}^i{}_j - \mu(\widetilde{h}^2 \delta_j^i - \xi_j \xi^i) - \frac{\xi_j}{\widetilde{h} + \widetilde{V}_0} \left\{ \widetilde{R}^i{}_p - \mu(\widetilde{h}^2 \delta_p^i - \xi_p \xi^i) \right\} v^p.$$
$$(5.4.29)$$

Since F has constant flag curvature σ, i.e., $R^i{}_j = (\mu - c^2)(F^2 \delta_j^i - F F_{y^j} y^i)$ (see (5.2.1′)), we have from (5.4.29)

$$\widetilde{R}^i{}_j - \mu(\widetilde{h}^2 \delta_j^i - \xi_j \xi^i) - \frac{\xi_j}{\widetilde{h} + \widetilde{V}_0} \left\{ \widetilde{R}^i{}_p - \mu(\widetilde{h}^2 \delta_p^i - \xi_p \xi^i) \right\} v^p = 0.$$

It follows that

$$\widetilde{R}^i{}_j = \mu(\widetilde{h}^2 \delta_j^i - \xi_j \xi^i). \tag{5.4.30}$$

This implies that h has constant sectional curvature $K_h = \mu = \sigma + c^2$. Thus, the necessity follows from Proposition 5.4.

The sufficiency follows directly from Proposition 5.4. Theorem 5.11 is proved. □

5.4.3 Ricci curvature and Einstein metrics

Definition 5.4. Let (M, F) be an n-dimensional Finsler manifold. F is called an *Einstein metric* if there is a scalar function $K = K(x)$ in M such that the Ricci curvature of F satisfies

$$Ric = (n - 1)K(x)F^2. \tag{5.4.31}$$

The *Ricci tensor* of F is defined as

$$Ric_{ij} := \left[\frac{1}{2} Ric \right]_{y^i y^j} = \frac{1}{2} [R^s{}_s]_{y^i y^j}.$$

We see from the above that F is Einsteinian if and only if
$$Ric_{ij} = (n-1)K(x)g_{ij}.$$
Thus, if F is Riemannian, the Finsler-Einstein metric is usual Einstein metric. Definition 5.4 was introduced firstly by Akbar-Zadeh ([6]), who would like to show the Finsler-Einstein metric is a critical point of the Einstein-Hilbert functional as in the Riemannian case. Unfortunately, the Euler-Lagrange equation deduced by Akbar-Zadeh may be wrong. A correct computation is given in [32] (see §11.3 below).

By Definition 5.4, if an n-dimensional Finsler metric F has constant flag curvature K, then its Ricci curvature is $Ric = (n-1)KF^2$, which implies that it is Einsteinian.

Theorem 5.12 ([13]). *Let* $F = \alpha + \beta$ *be a Randers metric constructed from a Riemannian metric* $h = \sqrt{h_{ij}y^iy^j}$ *and a vector field* $V = v^i\frac{\partial}{\partial x^i}$ *by the navigation (5.4.16). Then* F *is an Einstein metric satisfying (5.4.31) if and only if there is a constant* c *such that*

(i) h is a Riemann-Einstein metric with the Ricci curvature $^hRic = (n-1)\left(K(x) + c^2\right)$,

(ii) V is an infinitesimal homothetic vector field with respect to h, i.e., $\tilde{r}_{ij} = -2ch_{ij}$.

To prove the theorem we need the following lemmas.

Lemma 5.3. *$F = \alpha + \beta$ is Einsteinian if and only if equations (5.4.34), (5.4.37) and (5.4.38) below are satisfied.*

Proof. We use the notations (4.3.4) for the Randers metric $F = \alpha + \beta$. By a direct computation, we can see that the Ricci curvature of F is given by
$$Ric = {}^\alpha Ric + 2\alpha s^m_{0,m} - 2t_{00} - \alpha^2 t^m_m$$
$$+ (n-1)\left\{\frac{3(r_{00} - 2s_0\alpha)^2}{4(\alpha+\beta)^2} + \frac{4\alpha[q_{00} - t_0\alpha] - [r_{00,0} - 2s_{0,0}\alpha]}{2(\alpha+\beta)}\right\},$$
where
$$t_{ij} := s_{im}s^m_j, \quad t_j := b^i t_{ij}, \quad q_{ij} := r_i{}^m s_{mj},$$
$^\alpha Ric$ denotes the Ricci curvature with respect to the Riemannian metric α, "," denotes the covariant differential with respect to α, and the subscript "0" denotes the contraction with y^i.

It follows that F satisfies (5.4.31) if and only if
$$4(\alpha+\beta)^2\{^\alpha Ric + 2\alpha s^m_{0,m} - 2t_{00} - \alpha^2 t^m_m\} + (n-1)\{3(r_{00} - 2s_0\alpha)^2$$
$$+ 8\alpha[q_{00} - t_0\alpha](\alpha+\beta) - (r_{00,0} - 2s_{0,0}\alpha)(\alpha+\beta) - 4K(\alpha+\beta)^4\} = 0.$$

Distinguishing between the rational part and irrational part in the above, we obtain

$$4(\alpha^2 + \beta^2)\{{}^\alpha Ric - 2t_{00} - \alpha^2 t^m_{\ m}\} + 16\alpha^2\beta s^m_{\ 0,m}$$
$$+ (n-1)\{3(r^2_{00} + 4s^2_0\alpha^2) + 4s_{0,0}\alpha^2 - 2r_{00,0}\beta \tag{5.4.32}$$
$$+ 8\alpha^2(q_{00} - t_0\beta) - 4K(\alpha^4 + 6\alpha^2\beta^2 + \beta^4)\} = 0,$$

$$8\beta\{{}^\alpha Ric - 2t_{00} - \alpha^2 t^m_{\ m}\} + 8(\alpha^2 + \beta^2)s^m_{\ 0,m}$$
$$+ (n-1)\{-12r_{00}s_0 - 2r_{00,0} + 4s_{0,0}\beta + 8q_{00}\alpha \tag{5.4.33}$$
$$- 8t_0\alpha^2 - 16K(\alpha^2 + \beta^2)\beta\} = 0.$$

Multiplying (5.4.33) by β and then subtracting (5.4.32) yield that

$$4(\alpha^2 - \beta^2)\{{}^\alpha Ric - 2t_{00} - \alpha^2 t^m_{\ m}\}$$
$$+ 4(n-1)(\alpha^2 - \beta^2)\{3s^2_0 + s_{0;0} + 2q_{00} - K(\alpha^2 + 3\beta^2)\}$$
$$= -3(n-1)(r_{00} + 2s_0\beta)^2.$$

Since $\| \beta \|_\alpha < 1$ and the polynomial $\alpha^2 - \beta^2$ is irreducible, there is a function $c = c(x)$ such that

$$r_{00} + 2s_0\beta = 2c(\alpha^2 - \beta^2), \tag{5.4.34}$$

$${}^\alpha Ric - 2t_{00} - \alpha^2 t^m_{\ m} + \{3s^2_0 + s_{0;0} + 2q_{00} - K(\alpha^2 + 3\beta^2)\}$$
$$+ 3(n-1)c^2(\alpha^2 - \beta^2) = 0. \tag{5.4.35}$$

Multiplying (5.4.35) by 8β and then subtracting (5.4.33) yield that

$$8(\alpha^2 - \beta^2)s^m_{\ 0,m} = 2(n-1)\{6(r_{00} + 2s_0\beta)s_0 + r_{00,0}$$
$$+ 2s_{0,0}\beta + 4q_{00}\beta + 4t_0\beta \tag{5.4.36}$$
$$+ [4K\beta + 12c^2\beta](\alpha^2 - \beta^2)\}.$$

By using (5.4.34) one can get

$$q_{00} = -s_0 - 2cs_0\beta - t_0\beta.$$

Differentiating (5.4.34) yields

$$r_{00,0} + 2s_{0,0}\beta = 4s^2_0\beta + 8cs_0\beta^2 + \{2c_0 - 4cs_0 - 8c^2\beta\}(\alpha^2 - \beta^2).$$

Substituting the above into (5.4.36) yields that

$$s^m_{\ 0,m} = (n-1)\{(K + c^2)\beta + 2cs_0 + t_0 + \frac{1}{2}c_0\}. \tag{5.4.37}$$

Substituting (5.4.37) into (5.4.35), we obtain

$${}^\alpha Ric = (n-1)\{(K - 3c^2)\alpha^2 + (K + c^2)\beta^2 - s_{0,0} - s^2_0 - \beta c_0\}$$
$$+ 2t_{00} + \alpha^2 t^m_{\ m}. \tag{5.4.38}$$

Thus, $F = \alpha + \beta$ satisfies (5.4.31) if and only if (5.4.34), (5.4.37) and (5.4.38) are satisfied. □

Lemma 5.4. *Under the hypothesis of (5.4.34) and (5.4.38), the condition (5.4.37) is equivalent to that c is constant.*

Proof. By the Ricci identity we have

$$b_{i,j,k} - b_{i,k,j} = b^{s\ \alpha}R_{isjk},$$
$$-b_{k,i,j} + b_{k,j,i} = b^{s\ \alpha}R_{ksji},$$
$$b_{j,k,i} - b_{j,i,k} = b^{s\ \alpha}R_{jski}.$$

Adding the above three equations and noting $b_{i,j} + b_{j,i} = 2r_{ij}$, one can get

$$s_{ij,k} = -b^{s\ \alpha}R_{ksij} + r_{ik,j} - r_{jk,i},$$

i.e.,

$$s^i{}_{0,i} = b^i\,(^{\alpha}Ric)_{i0} + r^i{}_{i,0} - r^i{}_{0,i}. \tag{5.4.39}$$

On the other hand, by means of (5.4.34) we have

$$b^i s_{i,0} = (b^i s_i)_{,0} - b^i_{,0} s_i \xlongequal{(5.4.34)} -t_0 + s^i s_i \beta - 2cs_0,$$

$$b^i s_{0,i} = b^i (b^k s_{kj})_{,i} y^j = b^i b_{k,i} s^k_j y^j + b^i b^k s_{kj,i} y^j$$
$$\xlongequal{(5.4.34)} (1 - b^2) 2cs_0 - (1 + b^2)t_0 + b^i b^k r_{ik,0} - b^i b^k r_{0k,i},$$

$$b^i b^k r_{ik,0} - b^i b^k r_{0k,i} \xlongequal{(5.4.34)} -2b^2 (s_k s^k \beta - 2cs_0 - t_0) + b^2 b^i s_{0,i}$$
$$+ 2cb^2 (2c\beta + s_0)(1 - b^2) - 4cb^2 (s_0 + 2c\beta)(1 - b^2)$$
$$+ 2cb^2 [-(1 + b^2)s_0 + 2c(1 - b^2)\beta] + \beta(1 + b^2)s^m s_m$$
$$+ 2c_0(1 - b^2)b^2 - 2c_k b^k \beta(1 - b^2).$$

It follows from these that

$$b^i s_{0,i} = 2cs_0 - s_k s^k_0 + s^m s_m \beta + 2c_0 b^2 - 2c_i b^i \beta.$$

From (5.4.38) one can easily deduce

$$b^i\,(^{\alpha}Ric)_{i0} = (n-1)\left\{ \beta(K - 3c^2 + Kb^2 + c^2 b^2) - \frac{1}{2}c_0 b^2 - \frac{1}{2}b^i s_{i,0}\right.$$
$$\left. - \frac{1}{2}b^i s_{0,i} - \frac{1}{2}\beta c_{,i} b^i \right\} + 2t_0 + \beta t^m{}_m.$$

Then we obtain

$$b^i\,(^{\alpha}Ric)_{i0} = (n-1)\left\{ \beta(K - 3c^2 + Kb^2 + c^2 b^2) - \frac{3}{2}c_0 b^2\right.$$
$$\left. + \frac{1}{2}s_i s^i{}_0 - s^m s_m \beta + \frac{1}{2}t_0 + \frac{1}{2}\beta c_i b^i \right\} + 2t_0 + \beta t^m{}_m. \tag{5.4.40}$$

By virtue of (5.4.34) we have

$$r^i{}_{i,0} \overset{(5.4.34)}{=\!=\!=\!=} 2c_0(n - b^2) - 4c(1 - b^2)(s_0 + 2c\beta), \qquad (5.4.41)$$

$$r^i{}_{0,i} \overset{(5.4.34)}{=\!=\!=\!=} -\beta s^i{}_{,i} + s^i s_i\beta + t_0 - b^i s_{0,i} + 2cs_0(2b^2 - n)$$
$$- 4c^2\beta(n - 2b^2 + 1) + 2c_0 - 2c_i b^i\beta.$$

Since

$$s^i{}_{,i} = (b_i s^{ij})_{,j} = s_{ij}s^{ij} - b^i s^j{}_{i,j}$$
$$\overset{(5.4.37)}{=\!=\!=\!=} s_{ij}s^{ij} - (n-1)(K + c^2)b^2 + (n-1)s^m s_m - (n-1)\frac{c_{,i}}{2}b^i,$$

we obtain

$$r^i{}_{0,i} = 2c_0 - 2\beta c_i b^i - 4c^2\beta(n - 2b^2 + 1) + 2cs_0(2b^2 - n)$$
$$- s^m{}_{,m}\beta + s^m s_m\beta + t_0 - s_{0,m}b^m. \qquad (5.4.42)$$

It follows from (5.4.37) that

$$s^i{}_{,i} = (b_i s^{ij})_{,j} = s_{ij}s^{ij} - b^i s^j{}_{i,j}$$
$$\overset{(5.4.37)}{=\!=\!=\!=} s_{ij}s^{ij} - (n-1)(K + c^2)b^2 + (n-1)s^m s_m - (n-1)\frac{c_{,i}}{2}b^i.$$

Substituting it into (5.4.42) yields that

$$r^i{}_{0,i} = -\beta s^{ij}s_{ij} + (n-1)\beta(K + c^2)b^2 - (n-1)s^m s_m\beta$$
$$+ \frac{n-1}{2}\beta c_i b^i + 2s^i s_{i0} + 2cs_0(2b^2 - n - 1) \qquad (5.4.43)$$
$$- 4c^2\beta(n - 2b^2 + 1) + 2c_0(1 - b^2).$$

Inserting (5.4.40), (5.4.41) and (5.4.43) into (5.4.39) yields that

$$s^i{}_{0,i} = (n-1)\left\{(K + c^2)\beta + t_0 + 2cs_0 + 2c_0 - \frac{3}{2}c_0 b^2\right\}.$$

Comparing it with (5.4.37), one can see

$$\frac{3}{2}(1 - b^2)c_0 = 0.$$

This implies that $c_0 = 0$, i.e., $c =$ constant, since $b^2 < 1$.

Conversely, if $c =$ constant, we have

$$s_{i,j} = (b^k s_{ki})_{,j} = b^k{}_{,j}s_{ki} + b^k s_{ki,j} = b^k{}_{,j}s_{ki} + b^k(b^s{}^\alpha R_{jski} + r_{jk,i} - r_{ji,k}).$$
$$s^j{}_{,j} = -t^j{}_j + (n-1)s^j s_j - (n-1)b^2(K + c^2).$$

It follows from (5.4.34), (5.4.38) and the above that

$$s^m{}_{0,m} \overset{(5.4.39)}{=\!=\!=\!=} b^i\,(^\alpha Ric)_{i0} + r^i{}_{i,0} - r^i{}_{0,i} = (n-1)\{(K + c^2)\beta + 2cs_0 + t_0\}.$$

$\square$

Proof of Theorem 5.12. By Lemmas 5.3 and 5.4, a Randers metric $F = \alpha + \beta$ is Einstein if and only if there exists a constant c such that (5.4.34) and (5.4.38) hold. We now express (5.4.34) and (5.4.38) using the navigation.

According to Theorem 4.1, the equation (5.4.34) is equal to that $\mathbf{S} = (n+1)cF$ with a constant c, i.e., F has constant isotropic $\mathbf{S}$-curvature. From Theorem 5.10 it follows that the second condition (ii) of Theorem 5.12 is satisfied. In the following, we are going to check the first condition (i) of Theorem 5.12.

Under the hypothesis of (ii) of Theorem 5.12, by using (5.4.16)-(5.4.20), from $^{\alpha}G^i = ^h G^i + \theta^i$ we have

$$\theta^i = \frac{1}{\lambda}(-2cV_0 + \tilde{s}_0)y^i - \left(\frac{1}{2\lambda}h^2 + \frac{1}{\lambda^2}V_0^2\right)\tilde{s}^i + \frac{1}{\lambda}V_0\tilde{s}^i{}_0.$$

Again,

$$^{\alpha}R^i{}_k = ^h R^i{}_k + 2\theta^i{}_{|k} - y^m(\theta^i{}_{|m})._{.k} + 2\theta^m\theta^i{}_{.m.k} - \theta^i{}_{.m}\theta^m{}_{.k}.$$

A straightforward computation gives

$$
\begin{aligned}
^{\alpha}Ric = {}^h Ric &+ \frac{4}{\lambda^2}(-2cV_0 + \tilde{s}_0)^2 + \frac{2}{\lambda}(4c^2h^2 - {}^h R_{p00q}v^pv^q)\\
&- \left(\frac{2}{\lambda^2}h^2 + \frac{8}{\lambda^3}V_0^2\right)\tilde{s}^m\tilde{s}_m + \frac{8}{\lambda^2}V_0\tilde{s}^m\tilde{s}_{m0}\\
&+ \left(\frac{1}{\lambda}h^2 + \frac{2}{\lambda^2}V_0^2\right)(\tilde{s}^k{}_p\tilde{s}^p{}_k + {}^h R_p{}^k{}_{kq}v^pv^q) + \frac{2}{\lambda}V_0\,{}^h R_0{}^k{}_{kq}v^q\\
&- \frac{2(n+1)}{\lambda^2}(-2cV_0 + \tilde{s}_0)^2 - \frac{n+1}{\lambda}(4c^2h^2 - \tilde{s}_{0p}\tilde{s}^p{}_0 - {}^h R_{p00q}v^pv^q)\\
&+ \frac{2(n+1)}{\lambda^2}(-2cV_0 + \tilde{s}_0)^2 - \frac{4(n+1)}{\lambda^2}cV_0\tilde{s}_0\\
&- \frac{2(n+1)}{\lambda^2}\left(\frac{1}{2}h^2 + \frac{1}{\lambda}V_0^2\right)\tilde{s}^m\tilde{s}_m + \frac{2(n+1)}{\lambda^2}V_0\tilde{s}^m\tilde{s}_{m0}\\
&- \frac{(n+3)}{\lambda^2}(-2cV_0 + \tilde{s}_0)^2 + \frac{2}{\lambda^2}(h^2 + \frac{4}{\lambda}V_0^2)\tilde{s}^m\tilde{s}_m\\
&- 4V_0(-2c\tilde{s}_0 + 2\tilde{s}^m\tilde{s}_{m0}) - \frac{2}{\lambda^2}\tilde{s}_0^2 - \frac{1}{\lambda^2}V_0^2\tilde{s}^m{}_k\tilde{s}^k{}_m\\
= {}^h Ric &- (n+1)\frac{\tilde{s}_0^2}{\lambda^2} - (n-1)\frac{4}{\lambda^2}c^2V_0^2 - (n+1)\left(\frac{h^2}{\lambda^2} + \frac{2V_0^2}{\lambda^3}\right)\tilde{s}^m\tilde{s}_m\\
&- (n-1)\frac{4}{\lambda}c^2h^2 + \left(\frac{h^2}{\lambda} + \frac{V_0^2}{\lambda^2}\right)\tilde{t}^m{}_m + (n-1)\frac{1}{\lambda}{}^h R_{pijq}v^pv^qy^iy^j\\
&+ \frac{2(n+1)V_0}{\lambda^2}\tilde{s}_m\tilde{s}^m{}_0 + \frac{(n+1)}{\lambda}\tilde{s}_{0m}\tilde{s}^{m0}
\end{aligned}
$$

$$+ \left(\frac{h^2}{\lambda} + \frac{2V_0^2}{\lambda^2} \right) {}^h R_p{}^i{}_{iq} v^p v^q + \frac{2V_0}{\lambda} {}^h R_p{}^i{}_{iq} y^p v^q. \tag{5.4.44}$$

Here the following formulas have been used

$$\tilde{r}_{ij} = -2ch_{ij}, \quad \tilde{r}_i = -2cv_i, \quad \tilde{r} = -2c(1-\lambda),$$

$$\lambda_{|k} = 4cv_k - 2\tilde{s}_k, \quad \lambda_{|0} = 4cV_0 - 2\tilde{s}_0, \quad s_i = \frac{1}{\lambda}\tilde{s}_i,$$

$$V_{0|k} = -2cy_k - \tilde{s}_{k0}, \tag{5.4.45}$$

$$\tilde{s}^i{}_{|k} = 2c\tilde{s}^i{}_k - \tilde{s}^i{}_m \tilde{s}^m{}_k - v^p v^q {}^h R_p{}^i{}_{kq},$$

$$\tilde{s}^i{}_{0|k} = y^p v^q {}^h R_p{}^i{}_{kq}.$$

On the other hand, the curvature equation (5.4.38) is reduced as

$$\begin{aligned}
{}^\alpha Ric &= (n-1)\left\{ (\sigma - 3c^2)\left(\frac{1}{\lambda}h^2 + \frac{1}{\lambda^2}V_0^2 \right) + (\sigma + c^2)\frac{1}{\lambda^2}V_0^2 - \frac{1}{\lambda}\tilde{s}_{0|0} \right.\\
&\quad \left. - \left(\frac{1}{\lambda^2}h^2 + \frac{2}{\lambda^3}V_0^2 \right)\tilde{s}^m\tilde{s}_m + \frac{2}{\lambda^2}\tilde{s}^m\tilde{s}_{m0}V_0 - \frac{1}{\lambda^2}\tilde{s}_0^2 \right\} + 2\frac{1}{\lambda}\tilde{t}_{00} - \frac{2}{\lambda^2}\tilde{s}_0^2 \\
&\quad + \frac{4}{\lambda^2}\tilde{s}^m\tilde{s}_{m0}V_0 - \frac{2}{\lambda^3}V_0^2\tilde{s}^m\tilde{s}_m + \left(\frac{1}{\lambda}h^2 + \frac{1}{\lambda^2}V_0^2 \right)\left(\tilde{t}^m{}_m - \frac{2}{\lambda}\tilde{s}^m\tilde{s}_m \right) \\
&= (n-1)\left\{ (\sigma - 3c^2)\frac{h^2}{\lambda} + (\sigma - c^2)\frac{2V_0^2}{\lambda^2} \right\} + \left(\frac{h^2}{\lambda} + \frac{V_0^2}{\lambda^2} \right)\tilde{t}^m{}_m \\
&\quad - (n+1)\left(\frac{h^2}{\lambda^2} + \frac{2V_0^2}{\lambda^3} \right)\tilde{s}^m\tilde{s}_m + \frac{(n+1)}{\lambda}\tilde{s}_{0m}\tilde{s}^{m0} + \frac{2(n+1)V_0}{\lambda^2}\tilde{s}_m\tilde{s}^m{}_0 \\
&\quad - (n+1)\frac{\tilde{s}_0^2}{\lambda^2} + (n-1)\frac{1}{\lambda}{}^h R_{pijq}v^p v^q y^i y^j,
\end{aligned} \tag{5.4.46}$$

where the following relations have been used

$$\alpha^2 = \frac{1}{\lambda}h^2 + \frac{1}{\lambda^2}V_0^2, \quad \beta = -\frac{1}{\lambda}V_0,$$

$$s_0 = \frac{1}{\lambda}\tilde{s}_0, \quad s_{0,0} = \frac{1}{\lambda}\tilde{s}_{0|0} - \frac{2}{\lambda^2}V_0\tilde{s}^m\tilde{s}_{m0} + \left(\frac{1}{\lambda^2}h^2 + \frac{2}{\lambda^3}V_0^2 \right)\tilde{s}^m\tilde{s}_m,$$

$$\tilde{s}_{0|0} = -{}^h R_{ijkl}v^i v^l y^j y^k,$$

$$t_{00} = \frac{1}{\lambda}\tilde{t}_{00} - \frac{1}{\lambda^2}\tilde{s}_0^2 + \frac{2}{\lambda^2}\tilde{s}^m\tilde{s}_{m0}V_0 - \frac{1}{\lambda^3}V_0^2\tilde{s}^m\tilde{s}_m,$$

$$t^m{}_m = \tilde{t}^m{}_m - \frac{2}{\lambda}\tilde{s}^m\tilde{s}_m.$$

Since

$$s^m{}_0 = a^{mj}s_{jk}y^k = -\tilde{s}^m{}_0 + \frac{1}{\lambda}V_0\tilde{s}^m, \quad s^m{}_{0,j} = s^m{}_{0|j} + s^p{}_0\theta^m{}_{y^p y^j} - s^m{}_p\theta^p{}_{y^j},$$

we get

$$s^m_{0,m} = s^m_{0|m} + s^p_0 \theta^m_{y^p y^m} - s^m_p \theta^p_{y^m}$$

$$\overset{(5.4.45)}{=\!=\!=\!=} -^h R^k_{0\ kq} v^q + \frac{2c(n-1)}{\lambda} \widetilde{s}_0 - \frac{n-1}{\lambda} \widetilde{s}^m \widetilde{s}_{m0}$$

$$+ \frac{n-1}{\lambda^2} V_0 \widetilde{s}^m \widetilde{s}_m - \frac{1}{\lambda} V^h_0 R^k_{p\ kq} v^p v^q.$$

On the other hand, from (5.4.37) it follows that

$$s^m_{0,m} = (n-1)\{(K+c^2)\beta + 2cs_0 + t_0\}$$

$$\overset{(5.4.45)}{=\!=\!=\!=} (n-1)\left\{ -(K+c^2)\frac{V_0}{\lambda} + 2c\widetilde{s}_0 - \widetilde{t}_0 \right.$$

$$\left. - \frac{1-\lambda}{\lambda} \widetilde{s}^m \widetilde{s}_{m0} + \frac{1}{\lambda^2} V_0 \widetilde{s}^m \widetilde{s}_m \right\}.$$

Comparing with these on $s^m_{0,m}$ yields that

$$\lambda\,^h R^k_{0\ kq} v^q + {}^h R^k_{p\ kq} v^p v^q V_0 = (n-1)(K+c^2)V_0.$$

Differentiating the above with respect to y^p and contracting with v^p, one can get

$$^h R^k_{p\ kq} v^p v^q = (n-1)(K+c^2)(1-\lambda),$$

and

$$^h R^k_{0\ kq} v^q = (n-1)(K+c^2)V_0.$$

Substituting these into (5.4.44) and (5.4.46) respectively, and comparing with two expressions of $^\alpha Ric$, we obtain finally

$$^h Ric = (n-1)(K+c^2)h^2.$$

Therefore, Theorem 5.12 is proved completely. $\qquad\square$

As is well known, a Riemann-Einstein metric has constant Ricci curvature for $n \geq 3$. Combining Example 5.5 and Theorem 5.12, we obtain directly

Corollary 5.2. *For any Einstein-Randers metric with $n \geq 3$, $K(x)$ in (5.4.31) must be constant.*

Remark. We do not know whether Corollary 5.2 is true for general Finsler metrics. In other words, is $K(x)$ in (5.4.31) constant for general Finsler-Einstein metrics with $n \geq 3$? Please see Chapter 10 below for further details.

Proposition 5.5. *Let F be a three-dimensional Randers metric. Then F is Einsteinian if and only if F has constant flag curvature.*

Proof. The sufficiency is obvious. We now prove the necessity. Let F be an Einstein-Randers metric. From Theorem 5.12 it follows that the Riemannian metric h is a 3-dimensional Einstein metric, so that h is of constant curvature (cf. [169]). Thus, h and V can be expressed respectively by (5.4.23) and (5.4.24). According to Theorem 5.11, we conclude that F has constant flag curvature. □

Exercises

5.1 Prove (5.1.7) and (5.1.9) in detail.

5.2 Prove Theorem 5.3 in detail.

5.3 Prove Proposition 5.2 in detail.

5.4 Prove Lemma 5.1 in detail.

5.5 Let a be constant. Prove the following Finsler metric F has constant flag curvature a:

$$F = \frac{\sqrt{|y|^2 + a(|x|^2|y|^2 - \langle x, y\rangle^2)}}{1 + a|x|^2}, \quad y \in T_x\mathbb{B}^n(r_a) \equiv \mathbb{R}^n,$$

where $r_a = 1/\sqrt{-a}$ for $a < 0$; and $r_a = +\infty$ for $a \geq 0$.

5.6 Prove the sufficiency of Theorem 5.11 in detail.

5.7 Let V^3 be a 3-dimensional real vector space, $V^3 \otimes \mathbb{C}$ its complexification (a complex vector space). Let $\{\mathbf{b}_1, \mathbf{b}_2, \mathbf{b}_3\}$ be a base of V^3. Take a quadratic form Q on $V^3 \otimes \mathbb{C}$:

$$Q(\mathbf{u}, \mathbf{v}) := e^{i\alpha}u^1v^1 + e^{i\beta}u^2v^2 + e^{-i\alpha}u^3v^3,$$

where $i = \sqrt{-1}$, $\mathbf{u} = u^i\mathbf{b}_i$, $\mathbf{v} = v^i\mathbf{b}_i$, $\alpha, \beta \in \mathbb{R}$. Let $[X] := \{tX | t > 0\}$ for $X \in V^3 \setminus \{0\}$. Then $\mathbf{S}^2 := \{[X] | X \in V^3 \setminus \{0\}\}$ is diffeomorphic to the standard sphere $\mathbb{S}^2$ in $\mathbb{R}^3$. For $Y \in V^3 \setminus \{0\}$, denote by $[X, Y] \in T_{[X]}\mathbf{S}^2$ the tangent vector of the curve $c(t) := [X + tY]$ at $t = 0$. Define the function $F : T\mathbf{S}^2 \to \mathbb{R}$ by

$$F([X, Y]) := \text{Re}\left\{\sqrt{\frac{Q(X, X)Q(Y, Y) - Q(X, Y)^2}{Q(X, X)^2}} - i\frac{Q(X, Y)}{Q(X, X)}\right\},$$

where $\text{Re}\{\cdot\}$ denotes the real part of a complex number. Clearly, F is well-defined. Then F is a Finsler metric on $\mathbf{S}^2$ when $|\beta| \leq \alpha < \frac{\pi}{2}$. Prove that such a metric F has constant flag curvature $K_F = 1$ (see [23], [11], [103]).

5.8 Let $F = \alpha + \beta$ be a Randers metric in M, where β is a Killing form with constant length with respect to α. Prove that F has constant flag curvature $a > 0$ if and only if in a local orthonormal base at any point $x \in M$, $\alpha = \sqrt{\Sigma_i (y^i)^2}$ and $\beta = b_i y^i$ satisfy the following:

$$\sum_s b_{s|i} b_{s|j} = a(||\beta||_\alpha^2 \delta_{ij} - b_i b_j),$$

$$
^\alpha R^i_k = a\Big\{[(1 - ||\beta||_\alpha^2)\alpha^2 + \beta^2]\delta^i_k + \alpha^2 b_i b_k
$$
$$
- (1 - ||\beta||_\alpha^2) y^i y^k - \beta(b_k y^i + b_i y^k)\Big\} - 3(b_{i|s} y^s)(b_{k|p} y^p),
$$

where $^\alpha R^i_k$ denotes the Ricci curvature of α (cf. [103], [149]).

PART II
Further Studies

Chapter 6

Projective Changes

6.1 The projective equivalence

It is the famous Hilbert's fourth problem to study and characterize metric functions (not necessary regularity) on an open subset in $\mathbb{R}^n$ such that straight lines are geodesics. Hilbert's fourth problem in the regular case is just to characterize Finsler metrics with such a property. In Finsler geometry, projectively flat Finsler metrics are very important. We begin with projectively equivalent Finsler metrics.

6.1.1 Projective equivalence

Let F and $\overline{F}$ be two Finsler metrics on a differentiable manifold M. F and $\overline{F}$ are said to be *projectively equivalent*, or *projectively related*, if geodesics of (M, F) and $(M, \overline{F})$ are identical as oriented curves in the same orientation. More precisely, if $\overline{\gamma}(\overline{t})$ is a geodesic of $\overline{F}$, there is a parameter change $\overline{t}(t)$ $(d\overline{t}/dt > 0)$ preserving the curve orientation, such that $\gamma(t) = \overline{\gamma}(\overline{t}(t))$ is a geodesic of F, and vice versa.

Let F and $\overline{F}$ be two projectively equivalent Finsler metrics. For $y \in T_xM \setminus \{0\}$, let $\gamma(t)$ be a geodesic of F with $\gamma(0) = x$ and $\dot{\gamma}(0) = y$. There is a parameter change $\overline{t} = \overline{t}(t)$ $(d\overline{t}/dt > 0)$, with $\overline{t}(0) = 0$ and $\dot{\overline{t}}(0) = 1$, such that $\overline{\gamma}(\overline{t}) = \gamma(t)$ is a geodesic of $\overline{F}$ with $\overline{\gamma}(0) = x$ and $\dot{\overline{\gamma}}(0) = y$. Let G^i and $\overline{G}^i$ be the geodesic coefficients of F and $\overline{F}$, respectively. By the geodesic equation (Chapter 2, §2.4), we have

$$2G^i(x, y) = -\ddot{\gamma}^i(0) = -\ddot{\overline{\gamma}}^i(0) - \ddot{\overline{t}}(0)\dot{\overline{\gamma}}^i(0) = 2\overline{G}^i(x, y) - \ddot{\overline{t}}(0)y^i.$$

It follows that $P := \frac{1}{2}\ddot{\overline{t}}(0)$ depends only on (x, y), i.e., $P = P(x, y)$ is a function of $(x, y) \in TM$. Moreover, $P(x, y)$ satisfies

$$P(x, \lambda y) = \lambda P(x, y), \quad \lambda > 0.$$

We get

$$\overline{G}^i(x,y) = G^i(x,y) + P(x,y)y^i. \qquad (6.1.1)$$

On the other hand, if the geodesic coefficients of F and $\overline{F}$ satisfy (6.1.1), then F and $\overline{F}$ are projectively equivalent. The change of Finsler metrics satisfying (6.1.1) is called a *projective change*. The function $P(x,y)$ is called a *projective factor*. Sprays $\overline{\mathbf{G}}$ and $\mathbf{G}$ satisfying (6.1.1) are said to be *projectively equivalent*.

Let $\{\omega^i, \omega^{n+i}\}$ be a local coframe field on $T^*(TM_0)$, $\overline{F}$ be a function defined on TM_0. For the Chern connection ∇ on (M, F), we have (Chapter 3, §3.3)

$$\nabla \overline{F} = d\overline{F} = \overline{F}_{|i}\omega^i + \overline{F}_{;i}\omega^{n+i},$$

$$\nabla \overline{F}_{|i} = d\overline{F}_{|i} - \overline{F}_{|j}\omega_i^j = \overline{F}_{|i|j}\omega^j + \overline{F}_{|i;j}\omega^{n+j}.$$

In a local coordinate system, $\omega^i = dx^i$, $\omega^{n+i} = \delta y^i = dy^i + N_j^i dx^j$. Then

$$\overline{F}_{|i} = \overline{F}_{x^i} - N_i^k \overline{F}_{y^k}, \quad \overline{F}_{;i} = \overline{F}_{y^i} \quad \overline{F}_{|i;j} = [\overline{F}_{|i}]_{y^j}.$$

So it holds that

$$\overline{F}_{x^k}y^k = \overline{F}_{|k}y^k + 2G^l\overline{F}_{y^l},$$

$$\overline{F}_{x^k y^j}y^k - \overline{F}_{x^j} = \overline{F}_{|k;j}y^k - \overline{F}_{|j} + 2G^l\overline{F}_{y^l y^j}.$$

With the geodesic equation (2.4.3) and the above formulas, a direct computation gives

$$\overline{G}^i = G^i + Py^i + Q^i,$$

where

$$P(x,y) = \frac{\overline{F}_{|i}y^i}{2\overline{F}}, \quad Q^i = \frac{1}{2}\overline{F}\overline{g}^{ij}\{\overline{F}_{|k;j}y^k - \overline{F}_{|j}\}.$$

Hence $\overline{G}^i = G^i + Py^i$ if and only if $Q^i = 0$. Therefor, we get the following

Theorem 6.1 (A. Rapcsák [97]). *Finsler metrics F and $\overline{F}$ are projectively equivalent if and only if*

$$\overline{F}_{|k;j}y^k - \overline{F}_{|j} = 0. \qquad (6.1.2)$$

Example 6.1. Let $F(x,y)$ be a Finsler metric, $\beta = b_i(x)y^i$ be a 1-form. Consider the Finsler metric $\overline{F} = F + \beta$. One can get

$$d\beta = \frac{1}{2}\left(\frac{\partial b_j}{\partial x^i} - \frac{\partial b_i}{\partial x^j}\right)dx^i \wedge dx^j,$$

$$\overline{F}_{|k;j}y^k - \overline{F}_{|j} = \beta_{|k;j}y^k - \beta_{|j} = \left(\frac{\partial b_j}{\partial x^k} - \frac{\partial b_k}{\partial x^j}\right)y^k.$$

By Theorem 6.1, F and $\overline{F} = F + \beta$ are projectively equivalent if and only if $d\beta = 0$, i.e., β is *closed*.

6.1.2 Projective invariants

Suppose that Finsler metrics $\overline{F}$ and F are projectively equivalent. Denote by $\overline{R}^i{}_j$ and $R^i{}_j$ the Riemannian curvatures of $\overline{F}$ and F respectively. By (3.3.15) and (6.1.1), a direct computation shows

$$\overline{R}^i{}_j = R^i{}_j + \Xi\delta^i_j + \nu_j y^i, \qquad (6.1.3)$$

where

$$\Xi := P^2 - P_{|k}y^k, \quad \nu_j := 3(P_{|j} - PP_{;j}) + \Xi_{;j}. \qquad (6.1.4)$$

Noticing $\Xi(x, \lambda y) = \lambda^2 \Xi(x, y)$, $\nu_i(x, \lambda y) = \lambda\nu_i(x, y)$ and using the notations in (3.3.9'), (6.1.3) can be rewritten as

$$\overline{\mathbf{R}}_y(v) = \mathbf{R}_y(v) + \Xi_y v + \nu_y(v)y, \quad \forall v \in T_x M, \qquad (6.1.3')$$

where $\nu_y(v) = \nu_i(y)v^i$, $v = v^i \frac{\partial}{\partial x^i}$.

It follows from (3.2.13) and (6.1.3) that

$$\overline{Ric} = Ric + (n-1)\Xi. \qquad (6.1.5)$$

As the Weyl projective curvature tensor in Riemann geometry, the *Weyl projective curvature tensor* of a Finsler metric F is defined by

$$\mathbf{W} := W^i{}_j \frac{\partial}{\partial x^i} \otimes dx^j, \quad W^i{}_j := A^i{}_j - \frac{1}{n+1}\frac{\partial A^s{}_j}{\partial y^s}y^i, \quad A^i{}_j := R^i{}_j - \frac{Ric}{n-1}\delta^i_j. \qquad (6.1.6)$$

Hence it holds that

$$\mathbf{W}_y(y) = W^i{}_j y^j = 0, \quad \text{tr}\, \mathbf{W}_y = W^s{}_s = 0.$$

By (6.1.3), (6.1.5) and (6.1.6), we can obtain

$$\overline{A}^i{}_j = A^i{}_j + \nu_j y^i. \qquad (6.1.7)$$

Differentiating (6.1.7) gives

$$\frac{\partial \overline{A}^s{}_j}{\partial y^s} = \frac{\partial A^s{}_j}{\partial y^s} + (n+1)\nu_j.$$

Plugging it back into (6.1.7) yields that

$$\overline{W}^i{}_j = \overline{A}^i{}_j - \frac{1}{n+1}\frac{\partial \overline{A}^s{}_j}{\partial y^s}y^i = A^i{}_j - \frac{1}{n+1}\frac{\partial A^s{}_j}{\partial y^s}y^i = W^i{}_j.$$

Thus, we have the following

Proposition 6.1. *The Weyl projective curvature tensor defined by (6.1.6) is a projective invariant.*

The *Berwald curvature* of a Finsler metric F is defined by

$$\mathbf{B} := B^i{}_{jkl} \frac{\partial}{\partial x^i} \otimes dx^j \otimes dx^k \otimes dx^l, \quad B^i{}_{jkl} := \frac{\partial^3 G^i}{\partial y^j \partial y^k \partial y^l}. \qquad (6.1.8)$$

Obviously, $B^i{}_{jkl}$ is symmetric in j, k and l. According to (4.2.6), the mean Berwald curvature is

$$E_{ij} = \frac{1}{2} B^s{}_{ijs} = \frac{1}{2} \left[\frac{\partial G^s}{\partial y^s} \right]_{y^i y^j}.$$

Now we define a new tensor of a Finsler metric F using $B^i{}_{jkl}$ and E_{ij}. The *Douglas curvature tensor* of F is defined by

$$\mathbf{D} := D^i{}_{jkl} \frac{\partial}{\partial x^i} \otimes dx^j \otimes dx^k \otimes dx^l,$$
$$D^i{}_{jkl} := B^i{}_{jkl} - \frac{2}{n+1} \{ E_{jk}\delta^i_l + E_{kl}\delta^i_j + E_{lj}\delta^i_k + E_{jk;l}y^i \}. \qquad (6.1.9)$$

Substituting (6.1.8) and (4.2.6) into (6.1.9) yields that

$$D^i{}_{jkl} = \frac{\partial^3}{\partial y^j \partial y^k \partial y^l} \left(G^i - \frac{1}{n+1} \frac{\partial G^s}{\partial y^s} y^i \right). \qquad (6.1.10)$$

So the Douglas curvature tensor are fully symmetric, and

$$\mathbf{D}_y(u, v, y) = 0, \quad \operatorname{tr} \mathbf{D}_y(u, v) := \frac{1}{2} D^s{}_{jks} u^j v^k = 0, \quad u, v \in T_x M.$$

A Finsler metric with vanishing Douglas curvature is called a *Douglas metric*. Obviously, Berwald metrics are Douglas metrics. In particular, Riemannian metrics are Douglas metrics. Hence, the Douglas curvature tensor does not appear in Riemannian geometry.

For projectively equivalent Finsler metrics $\overline{F}$ and F, the function $P(x, y)$ in (6.1.1) is positively homogeneous of degree one in y. From (6.1.10) one can easily verify that (as an exercise)

$$\overline{\mathbf{D}} = \mathbf{D}.$$

Proposition 6.2. *The Douglas curvature tensor defined by (6.1.9) is a projective invariant.*

If F is flat, the spray of F is flat by Definition 5.3. From the geodesic equation (2.4.2) it follows that all geodesics are lines (i.e., the equation is linear) in a suitable coordinate system. We give the following definition.

Definition 6.1. A Finsler metric $F(x, y)$ defined on an open set $U \subset \mathbb{R}^n$ is called to be *projectively flat* if its geodesics are lines in U. A Finsler manifold (M, F) is called to be *locally projectively flat* if for any point of (M, F), there is an open neighbourhood of that point in which all geodesics are lines.

The importance of the Weyl projective curvature tensor and the Douglas curvature tensor lies in the following

Theorem 6.2 (J. Douglas). *An n-dimensional* $(n \geq 3)$ *Finsler manifold* (M, F) *is locally projectively flat if and only if* $\mathbf{W} = \mathbf{D} = 0$.

Sketch of the proof. The necessity is obvious. We now prove the sufficiency. Since $\mathbf{D} = 0$, the *projective spray* defined by $\Pi^i := G^i - \frac{1}{n+1}\frac{\partial G^s}{\partial y^s}y^i$ is affine. O. Veblen and J. M. Thomas proved in 1926 that any affine projective spray with $\mathbf{W} = 0$ must be locally projectively flat (refer to [107], §13.5). This proves our theorem here.

By (3.2.16) and (6.1.6), it holds for a Riemannian metric $g = g_{ij}(x)y^iy^j$ that

$$A^i_{\ j} = \left(R_k{}^i{}_{jl} - \frac{1}{n-1}\delta^i_j S_{kl} \right) y^k y^l,$$

$$W^i_{\ j} = \left\{ R_k{}^i{}_{jl} - \frac{1}{n-1}(\delta^i_j S_{kl} - \delta^i_l S_{jk}) \right\} y^k y^l,$$

where S_{kl} are the components of the Ricci tensor of g. Set

$$W_j{}^i{}_{kl} := \frac{1}{3}\left\{ \frac{\partial^2 W^i{}_k}{\partial y^j y^l} - \frac{\partial^2 W^i{}_l}{\partial y^j y^k} \right\} = R_j{}^i{}_{kl} - \frac{1}{n-1}\left(\delta^i_k S_{jl} - \delta^i_l S_{jk} \right). \quad (6.1.11)$$

They are the components of the Weyl projective curvature tensor in Riemann geometry ([169]). Clearly, for a Riemannian metric g, $W_j{}^i{}_{kl} = 0$ if and only if g is of constant curvature. The following theorem is a direct corollary of Theorem 6.2.

Theorem 6.3 (E. Beltrami). *An n-dimensional* $(n \geq 3)$ *Riemannian manifold* (M, g) *is locally projectively flat if and only if it is of constant curvature.*

From (6.1.9) it follows that $\mathbf{B} = \mathbf{D}$ if $\mathbf{E} = 0$. Conversely, if $\mathbf{B} = \mathbf{D}$, then

$$E_{ij} = \frac{1}{2}B^s{}_{ijs} = \frac{1}{2}D^s{}_{ijs} = 0, \quad \text{i.e.,} \quad \mathbf{E} = 0.$$

A spray $\mathbf{G}$ with $\mathbf{E} = 0$ (resp. $\mathbf{B} = 0$) is called a *mean Berwald spray* (resp. *Berwald spray*) (compare with Example 2.2 in Chapter 2, §2.3). Summarized as above, we have the following

Proposition 6.3. *Any Finsler spray on a manifold M is projectively equivalent to a mean Berwald spray. Moreover, a Finsler spray is projectively equivalent to a Berwald spray if and only if* $\mathbf{D} = 0$.

Proof. Take a volume form $d\mu = \sigma(x)dx^1 \wedge \cdots \wedge dx^n$ on the manifold (M, F). Denote by $\mathbf{S}$ the $\mathbf{S}$-curvature of $(M, F, d\mu)$. Let $\mathbf{G}$ be the spray of F. Set

$$\widetilde{\mathbf{G}} := \mathbf{G} - \frac{\mathbf{S}}{n+1}\mathbf{Y}, \quad \mathbf{Y} := y^i \frac{\partial}{\partial y^i}. \tag{6.1.12}$$

In a local coordinate system,

$$\widetilde{G}^i = G^i - \frac{\mathbf{S}}{n+1}y^i.$$

Differentiating the above equation yields

$$\frac{\partial \widetilde{G}^i}{\partial y^j} = \frac{\partial G^i}{\partial y^j} - \frac{1}{n+1}\frac{\partial \mathbf{S}}{\partial y^j}y^i - \frac{\mathbf{S}}{n+1}\delta^i_j. \tag{6.1.13}$$

Since $\mathbf{S}$ is homogenous in y, i.e., $\frac{\partial \mathbf{S}}{\partial y^k}y^k = \mathbf{S}$, we get from (6.1.13)

$$\frac{\partial \widetilde{G}^k}{\partial y^k} = \frac{\partial G^k}{\partial y^k} - \mathbf{S}.$$

In virtue of (4.2.5), it holds that

$$\widetilde{\mathbf{S}} = \frac{\partial \widetilde{G}^k}{\partial y^k} - y^k \frac{\partial \ln\sigma}{\partial x^k} = \frac{\partial G^k}{\partial y^k} - y^k \frac{\partial \ln\sigma}{\partial x^k} - \mathbf{S} = \mathbf{0}.$$

By (4.2.6), it is easy to see $\widetilde{\mathbf{E}} = 0$.

(6.1.12) implies that sprays $\widetilde{\mathbf{G}}$ and $\mathbf{G}$ are projectively equivalent. It shows the first part of the proposition. The second part of the proposition follows from (6.1.9) directly. $\quad\square$

Lemma 6.1. *Let (M, F) be an n-dimensional Finsler manifold. The Weyl projective curvature tensor of F vanishes if and only if F of scalar flag curvature.*

Proof. Denote by $R := Ric/(n-1)$. By (6.1.6), the Weyl projective curvature tensor can be written as

$$W^i{}_j = R^i{}_j - R\delta^i_j - \zeta_j y^i, \quad \zeta_j := \frac{1}{n+1}\frac{\partial}{\partial y^s}\left(R^s{}_j - R\delta^s_j\right). \tag{6.1.14}$$

By using (3.1.15) and noting that spray coefficients G^i are homogeneous of degree 2 in y, it is easy to verify that $y^k R^i{}_k = 0$ (as an exercise). Since $R^i{}_j$ is homogeneous of degree 2, we get

$$\zeta_k y^k = \frac{y^k}{n+1}\frac{\partial}{\partial y^s}\left(R^s{}_k - R\delta^s_k\right) = \frac{1}{n+1}(-R^s{}_s - 2R) = -R. \tag{6.1.15}$$

We now prove the necessity. If $W^i{}_j = 0$, it follows from (6.1.14) that

$$R^i{}_j = R\delta^i_j + \zeta_j y^i, \quad R_{ij} = Rg_{ij} - \zeta_j y_i, \quad (6.1.16)$$

where $y_i := g_{ij}y^j$. Since both R_{ij} and g_{ij} are symmetric, it holds from $(6.1.16)_2$ that

$$\zeta_j y_i = \zeta_i y_j.$$

Contracting it with y^i and using (6.1.15) and $y^i y_i = F^2$, we obtain

$$\zeta_j = -\frac{R}{F^2} y_j. \quad (6.1.17)$$

Substituting it into $(6.1.16)_1$ yields

$$R^i{}_j = R\left(\delta^i_j - F^{-2}y^i y_j\right).$$

Comparing with (5.2.1'), one can see that F is a Finsler metric with scalar flag curvature.

Now we turn to the proof of the sufficiency. Suppose F of scalar flag curvature, i.e., (5.2.1') holds. Contracting i with j shows

$$K = \frac{R^s{}_s}{n-1} = \frac{Ric}{n-1} = R.$$

Therefore

$$R^i{}_j = R(\delta^i_j - F^{-2}y^i y_j) = R\delta^i_j + \zeta_j y^i, \quad (6.1.18)$$

where ζ_j is defined by (6.1.17). By the homogeneity of ζ_j, a direct computation gives

$$\frac{1}{n+1}\frac{\partial}{\partial y^s}(R^s{}_j - R\delta^s_j) = \frac{1}{n+1}\frac{\partial}{\partial y^s}(\zeta_j y^s) = \zeta_j.$$

Substituting it into (6.1.18) and noting (6.1.14), we obtain $W^i{}_j = 0$. $\square$

Remark. When $n \geq 3$ and F is Riemannian, Lemma 6.1 implies that F has constant sectional curvature if and only if it is projectively flat. This is just the Beltrami theorem.

6.2 Projectively flat metrics

6.2.1 Projectively flat metrics

Let (M, F) be a projectively flat Finsler manifold. From Theorem 6.1 (exchanging roles of $\overline{F}$ and F), we have

$$G^i = Py^i, \quad P = \frac{F_{x^k}y^k}{2F}, \quad F_{x^k y^i}y^k = F_{x^i}. \quad (6.2.1)$$

By (6.1.3), the Riemannian curvature is

$$R^i_{\ j} = \Xi\delta^i_j + \nu_j y^i, \quad \Xi := P^2 - P_{x^k}y^k, \quad \nu_j := 3(P_{x^j} - PP_{y^j}) + \Xi_{y^j}. \quad (6.2.1')$$

$$\mathbf{R}_y(v) = \Xi_y v + \nu_y(v)y, \quad v \in T_x M.$$

Using this and (2.1.11), we get

$$0 = \langle \mathbf{R}_y(v), y \rangle_y = \Xi_y \langle v, y \rangle_y + \nu_y(v)F^2(y),$$

from which it follows that

$$\nu_y(v) = -\frac{\Xi_y}{F^2(y)} \langle v, y \rangle_y.$$

Thus,

$$R^i_{\ j} = \Xi\delta^i_j + \nu_j y^i = \Xi\{\delta^i_j - [\ln F]_{y^j} y^i\},$$

$$K(y) := \frac{\Xi_y}{F^2(y)} = \frac{P^2 - P_{x^k}y^k}{F^2}, \quad y, v \in T_x M. \qquad (6.2.2)$$

Comparing it with (5.2.1) yields the following

Proposition 6.4. *Projectively flat Finsler metrics must have scalar flag curvature.*

Remark. When $n \geq 3$, this proposition can be shown directly by Theorem 6.2 and Lemma 6.1.

We now consider locally projectively flat Randers metric $F = \alpha + \beta$, where $\alpha = \sqrt{a_{ij}(x)y^i y^j}$ is a Riemannian metric and $\beta = b_i(x)y^i$ is a 1-form. We have the following

Theorem 6.4. *A Randers metric $F = \alpha + \beta$ of dimension n $(n \geq 3)$ is locally projectively flat if and only if α is a Riemannian metric of constant curvature and β is closed.*

Proof. We first prove the necessity. Let $F = \alpha + \beta$ be locally projectively flat. By (6.2.1), there is a scalar function $\widetilde{P}$ such that in a local coordinate system $G^i = \widetilde{P}y^i$. Using the notation in §4.3.2, by (4.3.5) we obtain

$$G^i_\alpha + Py^i + Q^i = G^i = \widetilde{P}y^i. \qquad (6.2.3)$$

It follows that

$$\frac{\partial G^k_\alpha}{\partial y^k} + (n+1)P = (n+1)\widetilde{P}$$

since

$$\frac{\partial Q^k}{\partial y^k} = \alpha^{-1} y_k s^k{}_0 + \alpha s^k{}_k = 0.$$

Thus, by (6.2.3) we obtain

$$\alpha s^i{}_0 = Q^i = \frac{1}{n+1} \frac{\partial G_\alpha^k}{\partial y^k} y^i - G_\alpha^i.$$

Since the right hand side of the above identity is homogeneous of degree 2 in $y \in T_x M$, both sides are equal to zero, i.e.,

$$s^i{}_0 = 0, \quad G_\alpha^i = \frac{1}{n+1} \frac{\partial G_\alpha^k}{\partial y^k} y^i.$$

The first equation means that β is closed. The second one shows that α is locally projectively flat. By the Beltrami's theorem 6.3, α is a Riemannian metric of constant curvature.

The sufficiency is obvious. □

Remark. In [108] it has been proved that a Randers metric $F = \alpha + \beta$ is both projectively flat and of constant flag curvature if and only if it is either locally Minkowskian or isometric to the generalized Funk metric $F = c(\alpha + \beta)$ defined on the open unit ball $B^n \subset \mathbb{R}^n$, where $c > 0$ is a constant and

$$\alpha := \frac{\sqrt{(1 - |x|^2)|y|^2 + \langle x, y \rangle^2}}{1 - |x|^2}, \tag{6.2.4}$$

$$\beta := \pm \left\{ \frac{\langle x, y \rangle}{1 - |x|^2} + \frac{\langle a, y \rangle}{1 + \langle a, x \rangle} \right\} \tag{6.2.5}$$

with a constant vector $a \in \mathbb{R}^n$ ($|a| < 1$).

Example 6.2. Consider the Riemannian metric

$$\alpha_\mu := \frac{\sqrt{|y|^2 + \mu(|x|^2 |y|^2 - \langle x, y \rangle^2)}}{1 + \mu |x|^2}, \quad y \in T_x(B^n(r_\mu)) \cong \mathbb{R}^n,$$

where $r_\mu = 1/\sqrt{-\mu}$ for $\mu < 0$, and $r_\mu = +\infty$ for $\mu \geq 0$. It is easy to verify that α_μ has constant sectional curvature $K = \mu$. Thus

$$G_\alpha^i = -\frac{\mu \langle x, y \rangle}{1 + \mu |x|^2} y^i,$$

i.e., α_μ is projectively flat on $B^n(r_\mu)$.

Define a Finsler metric on the open unit ball $B^n(1) \subset \mathbb{R}^n$ as follows

$$F = \frac{\sqrt{(1 - |x|^2)|y|^2 + \langle x, y \rangle^2} + \langle x, y \rangle}{1 - |x|^2} + \frac{\langle a, y \rangle}{1 + \langle a, x \rangle},$$

where $a \in \mathbb{R}^n$ is a constant vector with $|a| < 1$. In virtue of (4.3.5), a direct computation shows that the spray coefficients of F satisfy that $G^i = Py^i$, where

$$P = \frac{1}{2} \left\{ \frac{\sqrt{(1 - |x|^2)|y|^2 + \langle x, y \rangle^2} + \langle x, y \rangle}{1 - |x|^2} - \frac{\langle a, y \rangle}{1 + \langle a, x \rangle} \right\}.$$

Thus F is projectively flat. Moreover, we have

$$P_{x^k} y^k = \frac{1}{2} \left\{ \frac{(\sqrt{(1 - |x|^2)|y|^2 + \langle x, y \rangle^2} + \langle x, y \rangle)^2}{(1 - |x|^2)^2} + \frac{\langle a, y \rangle^2}{(1 + \langle a, x \rangle)^2} \right\}.$$

By (6.2.2) we see that F is of constant flag curvature $K = -1/4$.

6.2.2   Projectively flat metrics with constant flag curvature

In this section, we are going to discuss projectively that (α, β)-metrics of constant flag curvature.

Lemma 6.2. *Let $F(x, y)$ be a Finsler metric defined on an open set $U \subset \mathbb{R}^n$. Then F is a projectively flat metric with constant flag curvature $K = c$ if and only if there is a positively homogeneous function $P(x, y)$ of degree one in y on $TU \cong U \times \mathbb{R}^n$ such that*

$$\begin{aligned} F_{x^i} &= (PF)_{y^i}, \\ P_{x^i} &= PP_{y^i} - cFF_{y^i}, \end{aligned} \tag{6.2.6}$$

where $P = \frac{1}{2F} F_{x^k} y^k$ is the projective factor of F and $P^2 - PP_{x^k} y^k = cF^2$.

Proof. If F is projectively flat, then (6.2.1) holds. Thus,

$$(PF)_{y^i} = \frac{1}{2}(F_{x^k} y^k)_{y^i} = \frac{1}{2}(F_{x^k y^i} y^k + F_{x^i}) = F_{x^i},$$

which is the first equation of (6.2.6).

Suppose that F has constant flag curvature $K = c$. Comparing (6.2.1′) with (6.2.2) yields that

$$cF^2 = \Xi, \quad 3(P_{x^j} - PP_{y^j}) + \Xi_{y^j} = \nu_j = -cF^2[\ln F]_{y^j}.$$

Substituting the first equation of the above into the second one, we obtain the second equation of (6.2.6).

Conversely, if (6.2.6) is satisfied, with the homogeneity of $P(x, y)$, we have

$$F_{x^k y^i} y^k = (PF)_{y^k y^i} y^k = (PF)_{y^i} = F_{x^i},$$

$$\frac{1}{2F} F_{x^k} y^k = \frac{1}{2F} (PF)_{y^k} y^k = P.$$

Comparing these with (6.2.1) (cf. Theorem 6.1) shows that F is projectively flat with the projective factor $P(x, y)$. Contracting the second equation of (6.2.6) with y^i, we get

$$\Xi = P^2 - P_{x^k} y^k = cF^2.$$

Comparing it with (6.2.2) yields that F has constant flag curvature $K = c$. $\square$

Theorem 6.5 ([73]). *An (α, β)-metric $F(x, y) = \alpha\phi(s)$ with $s = \frac{\beta}{\alpha}$ defined on the open set $U \subset \mathbb{R}^n$ is projectively flat metric with constant flag curvature if and only if it is one of the following:*

(i) *α is a projectively flat metric and β is parallel with respect to α;*
(ii) *$F = \sqrt{\alpha^2 + k\beta^2} + \epsilon\beta$ is projectively flat with constant flag curvature $K < 0$, where k and $\epsilon \neq 0$ are constants;*
(iii) *$F = \frac{(\sqrt{\alpha^2 + k\beta^2} + \epsilon\beta)^2}{\sqrt{\alpha^2 + k\beta^2}}$ is a projectively flat metric with constant curvature $K = 0$, where k and $\epsilon \neq 0$ are constants.*

Remark. In case (i), $F = \alpha\phi(\beta/\alpha)$ is a projectively flat Berwald metric. If the flag curvature K is constant, then F is a Riemannian metric with $K \neq 0$ or F is a local Minkowski metric. (See [87] for details.) The Finsler metric in case (ii) is of Randers type, i.e., $F = \bar{\alpha} + \bar{\beta}$, where $\bar{\alpha} := \sqrt{\alpha^2 + k\beta^2}$, $\bar{\beta} := \epsilon\beta$. One can refer to the Remark of Theorem 6.4. The Finsler metric in case (iii) may be expressed as $F = (\tilde{\alpha} + \tilde{\beta})^2/\tilde{\alpha}$, where $\tilde{\alpha} := \sqrt{\alpha^2 + k\beta^2}$, $\tilde{\beta} := \epsilon\beta$. In [119] and [85], it was proved that the non-Minkowskian projectively flat metric $F = (\tilde{\alpha} + \tilde{\beta})^2/\tilde{\alpha}$ has vanishing flag curvature if and only if F is isometric to the Finsler metric $F = c(\tilde{\alpha} + \tilde{\beta})^2/\tilde{\alpha}$ defined on the unit open ball $B^n \subset \mathbb{R}^n$ after rescaling x, where c is a constant, $\tilde{\alpha} = \lambda\alpha$, $\tilde{\beta} = \lambda\beta$, α and β are determined by (6.2.4) and (6.2.5) respectively, and

$$\lambda(x) := \frac{(1 + \langle a, x \rangle)^2}{1 - |x|^2}.$$

To prove Theorem 6.5, we need some preliminaries. Let G_α^i be the geodesic coefficients of α is given by

$$G_\alpha^i = \frac{a^{il}}{4} \left\{ [\alpha^2]_{x^k y^l} y^k - [\alpha^2]_{x^l} \right\},$$

where $(a^{ij}) := (a_{ij})^{-1}$. By (2.4.3), the geodesic coefficients G^i of $F = \alpha\phi(\beta/\alpha)$ are given by

$$G^i = G_\alpha^i + \alpha Q s^i{}_0 + \alpha^{-1} \Theta \left(-2\alpha Q s_0 + r_{00} \right) y^i + \Psi \left(-2\alpha Q s_0 + r_{00} \right) b^i. \quad (6.2.7)$$

Here we have already used the notations in (4.3.4) and

$$Q = \frac{\phi'}{\phi - s\phi'},$$

$$\Theta = \frac{\phi - s\phi'}{2\big((\phi - s\phi') + (b^2 - s^2)\phi''\big)} \cdot \frac{\phi'}{\phi} - s\Psi, \qquad (6.2.8)$$

$$\Psi = \frac{1}{2} \frac{\phi''}{(\phi - s\phi') + (b^2 - s^2)\phi''}.$$

In virtue of (6.2.7), if α is projectively flat $(G_\alpha^i = \xi y^i)$ and β is parallel with respect to α $(r_{ij} = 0, s_{ij} = 0)$, then $G^i = G_\alpha^i = \xi y^i$. If $K \neq 0$, by Numata's theorem ([87]), F is Riemannian. If $K = 0$, F is locally Minkowskian.

On the other hand, by using Lemma 6.2, the second author has proved the following result.

Theorem 6.6 ([113]). *Let $F = \alpha\phi(s)$ with $s = \beta/\alpha$ be an (α, β)-metric defined on an open subset $\mathcal{U}$ in n-dimensional Euclidean space, where $\alpha = \sqrt{a_{ij}(x)y^i y^j}$, $\beta = b_i(x)y^i \neq 0$. Set $b = \|\beta_x\|_\alpha$. Suppose the following conditions hold: (a) β is not parallel with respect to α, (b) F is not of Randers type, and (c) $db \neq 0$ everywhere or $b = $ constant on $\mathcal{U}$. Then $F = \alpha\phi(s)$ is projectively flat if and only if $\phi = \phi(s)$ satisfies*

$$\big\{1 + (k_1 + k_2 s^2)s^2 + k_3 s^2\big\}\phi''(s) = (k_1 + k_2 s^2)\big\{\phi(s) - s\phi'(s)\big\}, \quad (6.2.9)$$

$$b_{i,j} = 2\tau\big\{(1 + k_1 b^2)a_{ij} + (k_2 b^2 + k_3)b_i b_j\big\}, \qquad (6.2.10)$$

$$G_\alpha^i = \xi y^i - \tau\big(k_1 \alpha^2 + k_2 \beta^2\big)b^i, \qquad (6.2.11)$$

where $b_{i,j}$ is the covariant differential of β with respect to α, $\tau = \tau(x)$ is a scalar function defined on $\mathcal{U}$, $\xi = \xi(x, y)$ is homogeneous in y of degree one, k_1, k_2 and k_3 are constants.

Notice that if $\phi = \phi(s)$ satisfies (6.2.9), $k_2 = k_3 = 0$ and $\phi(0) = 1$, then $\phi = a_1 s + \sqrt{1 + k_1 s}$, where a_1 is a constant. Hence, $F = \alpha\phi(\beta/\alpha)$ is of Randers type. This case is excluded in Theorem 6.6.

Remark. The condition (c) in the theorem is not essential. Actually, if db has isolated zero points, it can be proved that the big bracket on the right hand side of (6.2.10) is non-zero at the isolated zero point of db. We can use the continuity method to determine the function $\tau(x)$ in (6.2.10).

More generally, we can prove the following

Lemma 6.3. *If the function* $\phi = \phi(s)$ *satisfies (6.2.9),* $k_2 = k_1 k_3$ *and* $\phi(0) = 1$*, then* $\phi(s) = a_1 s + \sqrt{1 + k_1 s^2}$*, where* a_1 *is a constant.*

Proof. Substituting $k_2 = k_1 k_3$ into (6.2.9) yields that

$$(1 + k_1 s^2)(1 + k_3 s^2)\phi''(s) = k_1(1 + k_3 s^2)\Big\{\phi(s) - s\phi'(s)\Big\}.$$

Clearly, $1 + k_3 s^2 \neq 0$ as $s \to 0$. Hence

$$(1 + k_1 s^2)\phi''(s) = k_1\Big\{\phi(s) - s\phi'(s)\Big\}.$$

The general solution of the above equation is $\phi = c_1 s + c_2 \sqrt{1 + k_1 s^2}$. □

The following lemma is evident.

Lemma 6.4. *If (6.2.9) admits* $k_2 = k_1 k_3 + \frac{6}{25}(k_1 - k_3)^2$*, then*

$$\phi = a_1 s + \sqrt{1 + \frac{1}{5}(3k_1 + 2k_3)s^2} + \frac{\frac{1}{5}(k_1 - k_3)s^2}{\sqrt{1 + \frac{1}{5}(3k_1 + 2k_3)s^2}}.$$

The solution of (6.2.9) depends only on $a_1 = \phi'(0)$ (it will be assumed always that $\phi(0) = 1$). If coefficients of s^k ($k \geq 2$) in the Taylor expansion of $\phi(s)$ at $s = 0$ may be determined by k_1, k_2 and k_3 uniquely, then we have the following

Lemma 6.5 ([73]). *Let*

$$\phi(s) = 1 + a_1 s + a_2 s^2 + a_3 s^3 + a_4 s^4 + a_5 s^5 + a_6 s^6 + a_7 s^7 + a_8 s^8 + o(s^8)$$

satisfy (6.2.9). Then we have

$$a_3 = 0, \quad a_5 = 0, \quad a_7 = 0,$$

and

$$a_2 = \frac{k_1}{2},$$

$$a_4 = \frac{1}{12}(k_2 - k_1 k_3) - \frac{1}{8}k_1^2,$$

$$a_6 = -\frac{11}{120}\left(k_1 + \frac{4}{11}k_3\right)(k_2 - k_1 k_3) + \frac{1}{16}k_1^3$$

$$a_8 = \frac{1}{56}(k_2 - k_1 k_3)\left(\frac{61}{12}k_1^2 + k_3^2\right) - \frac{5}{224}k_2^2 + \frac{31}{336}k_1 k_2 k_3$$

$$- \frac{47}{672}k_1^2 k_3^2 - \frac{5}{128}k_1^4.$$

Actually, for any solution $\phi(s)$ of (6.2.9), $\phi(s) - \phi'(0)s$ is an even function of s.

Proof of Theorem 6.5. The proof will be divided into the following two lemmas. Firstly, we claim that the flag curvature $K = 0$. Then, we determine the expression of ϕ.

Lemma 6.6. *Let $F = \alpha\phi(s)$ with $s = \beta/\alpha$ be an (α, β)-metric defined on $\mathcal{U} \subset \mathbb{R}^n$ $(n \geq 3)$, where $\alpha = \sqrt{a_{ij}y^iy^j}$ and $\beta = b_iy^i \neq 0$. Set $b = \|\beta_x\|_\alpha$. Suppose F is not of Randers type and $db \neq 0$ everywhere or b is a constant on $\mathcal{U}$. Then the flag curvature $K = 0$ if F is a projectively flat metric with constant flag curvature K.*

Proof. If β is parallel with respect to α, then we have

$$G^i = G^i_\alpha. \tag{6.2.12}$$

Since F is projectively flat, i.e.,

$$G^i = \theta y^i,$$

we have from (6.2.12)

$$G^i_\alpha = \theta y^i.$$

Thus, α is projectively flat and θ is a 1-form. By the Beltrami theorem, the sectional curvature of α is a constant, denoted by κ,

$$\frac{\theta^2 - \theta_{x^k} y^k}{\alpha^2} = \kappa.$$

On the other hand, the flag curvature of F is

$$K = \frac{\theta^2 - \theta_{x^k} y^k}{F^2} = \kappa \frac{\alpha^2}{F^2}.$$

If $K \neq 0$, then

$$F^2 = \frac{\kappa}{K} \alpha^2,$$

i.e., F is Riemannian, which is excluded by the assumption. Hence, the flag curvature $K = 0$.

If β is not parallel with respect to α, then, by Theorem 6.6, ϕ, α and β satisfy (6.2.9), (6.2.10) and (6.2.11) respectively. It is easy to see that

$$s_{ij} = 0,$$

$$r_{00} = 2\tau\left\{1 + (k_1 + k_2s^2)b^2 + k_3s^2\right\}\alpha^2,$$

$$\Psi = \frac{k_1 + k_2s^2}{2[1 + (k_1 + k_2s^2)b^2 + k_3s^2]},$$

$$\Theta = \frac{1 + (k_1 + k_2s^2)s^2 + k_3s^2}{2[1 + (k_1 + k_2s^2)b^2 + k_3s^2]} \frac{\phi'}{\phi} - s\Psi.$$

By (6.2.7), the spray coefficients are

$$G^i = Py^i, \quad P = \xi + \tau\alpha\Xi(s),$$

where $\xi = \xi_i y^i$, $\tau = \tau(x)$ and

$$\Xi := (1 + (k_1 + k_2 s^2)s^2 + k_3 s^2)\frac{\phi'}{\phi} - (k_1 + k_2 s^2)s.$$

It follows from equations (6.2.10) and (6.2.11) that

$$\alpha_{x^m} y^m = 2\alpha\left\{\xi - \tau\alpha(k_1 + k_2 s^2)s\right\},$$

$$s_{x^m} y^m = 2\tau\alpha\left\{1 + (k_1 + k_2 s^2)s^2 + k_3 s^2\right\}.$$

By using the above equations and (6.2.2), one can get

$$K\alpha^2\phi^2 = \xi^2 - \xi_{x_m} y^m + \tau^2\alpha^2\Xi - \alpha\tau_{x_m} y^m\Xi + 2\tau^2\alpha^2\Gamma, \qquad (6.2.13)$$

where

$$\Gamma := (k_1 + k_2 s^2)s\Xi - \left\{1 + (k_1 + k_2 s^2)s^2 + k_3 s^2\right\}\Xi_s.$$

Noticing that Ξ and ϕ in (6.2.13) are functions of $s = \beta/\alpha$, we can take the following coordinate transformation $(s, y^a) \to (y^i)$:

$$y^1 = \frac{s}{\sqrt{b^2 - s^2}}\overline{\alpha}, \quad y^a = y^a, \quad a = 2, \cdots, n, \quad \overline{\alpha} := \sqrt{\sum_{a=2}^{n}(y^a)^2}. \quad (6.2.14)$$

Then

$$\alpha = \frac{b}{\sqrt{b^2 - s^2}}\overline{\alpha}, \quad \beta = \frac{bs}{\sqrt{b^2 - s^2}}\overline{\alpha}, \qquad (6.2.15)$$

and

$$\xi = \frac{s\xi_1}{\sqrt{b^2 - s^2}}\overline{\alpha} + \overline{\xi}_0, \quad \tau_{x^m} y^m = \frac{s\tau_1}{\sqrt{b^2 - s^2}}\overline{\alpha} + \overline{\tau}_0,$$

where $\overline{\xi}_0 := \xi_a y^a$, $\overline{\tau}_0 := \tau_{x^a} y^a$. Put

$$\xi_{ij} := \frac{1}{2}\left(\frac{\partial\xi_i}{\partial x^j} + \frac{\partial\xi_j}{\partial x^i}\right).$$

We have

$$\xi_{x^m} y^m = \xi_{ij} y^i y^j = \frac{s^2\xi_{11}}{b^2 - s^2}\overline{\alpha}^2 + \frac{2s\overline{\xi}_{10}}{\sqrt{b^2 - s^2}}\overline{\alpha} + \overline{\xi}_{00},$$

where $\bar{\xi}_{10} := \xi_{1a}y^a$, $\bar{\xi}_{00} := \xi_{ab}y^ay^b$. By the above equations and (6.2.13), one can get

$$\frac{Kb^2}{b^2-s^2}\bar{\alpha}^2\phi^2 = \frac{1}{\sqrt{b^2-s^2}}\left\{2s\xi_1\bar{\xi}_0 - 2s\bar{\xi}_{10} - \bar{\tau}_0 b\Xi\right\}\bar{\alpha} + \bar{\xi}_0^2 - \bar{\xi}_{00}$$

$$+\frac{1}{b^2-s^2}\left\{s^2(\xi_1^2-\xi_{11}) + \tau^2b^2\Xi^2 - \tau_1 bs\Xi + 2\tau^2b^2\Gamma\right\}\bar{\alpha}^2,$$

which is equivalent to the following two equations

$$2s(\xi_1\bar{\xi}_0 - \bar{\xi}_{10}) - \bar{\tau}_0 b\Xi = 0, \tag{6.2.16}$$

$$\frac{1}{b^2-s^2}\left\{s^2(\xi_1^2-\xi_{11}) + \tau^2b^2\Xi^2 - \tau_1 bs\Xi + 2\tau^2b^2\Gamma - Kb^2\phi^2\right\}\bar{\alpha}^2 + \bar{\xi}_0^2 - \bar{\xi}_{00} = 0. \tag{6.2.17}$$

It follows from (6.2.16) that $\bar{\tau}_0 = 0$ and $\xi_1\bar{\xi}_0 - \bar{\xi}_{10} = 0$. We get from (6.2.17) that

$$s^2\mu + \tau^2b^2\Xi^2 - \tau_1 bs\Xi + 2\tau^2b^2\Gamma - Kb^2\phi^2 + \delta(b^2-s^2) = 0, \tag{6.2.18}$$

$$\bar{\xi}_0^2 - \bar{\xi}_{00} = \delta\bar{\alpha}^2, \tag{6.2.19}$$

where $\mu := \xi_1^2 - \xi_{11}$ and δ is a constant independent of s. Substituting Ξ and Γ into (6.2.18) yields that

$$\left\{4(1 + (k_1 + k_2s^2)s^2 + k_3s^2)\tau^2b^2k_2s^2 + s^2\mu + (b^2-s^2)\delta\right.$$

$$\left. - ((k_1 + k_2s^2)\tau^2b^2 - \tau_1 b)s^2(k_1 + k_2s^2)\right\} + \left\{-s\tau_1 b\right.$$

$$\left. - 2\tau^2b^2(s(k_1 + k_2s^2) + 2s^3k_2 + 2k_3s)\right\}(1 + (k_1 + k_2s^2)s^2 + k_3s^2)\phi'\phi(s)$$

$$+ 3\tau^2b^2(1 + (k_1 + k_2s^2)s^2 + k_3s^2)^2(\phi')^2 - Kb^2\phi^4 = 0. \tag{6.2.20}$$

By Lemma 6.5, ϕ can be written as

$$\phi = 1 + a_1s + a_2s^2 + a_4s^4 + a_6s^6 + a_8s^8 + o(s^8),$$

where a_2, a_4, a_6 and a_8 are given in Lemma 6.5. Substituting the above Taylor expression into (6.2.20) and comparing the coefficients of s^k ($k = 0, 1, 2$), one can see that

$$\delta = K - 3\tau^2a_1^2,$$

$$\tau_1 a_1 = 2b(2(k_1 - k_3) - 3a_1^2)\tau^2a_1 - 2ba_1K,$$

and

$$\mu = \left[(2a_2 + 3a_1^2)b^2 + 1\right]K$$

$$- \left[4(k_2 - k_1k_3) + 3(2k_3 - k_1)a_1^2 + 3a_1^4\right]\tau^2b^2 - 3\tau^2a_1^2.$$

Inserting these into (6.2.20) yields that

$$\left\{ -\phi^4 + (3s^2 a_1^2 - 2k_2 s^4 - k_1 s^2 + 1)\phi^2 + 2D(s)s\phi'\phi \right\} K$$

$$- 3\left\{ a_1^4 s^2 + (1 + 2k_3 s^2 + k_1 s^2 + 2k_2 s^4)a_1^2 - (k_1 + k_2 s^2)^2 s^2 \right\}\tau^2 \phi^2$$

$$+ 6\left\{ sa_1^2 - s(k_1 + k_2 s^2) \right\} D(s)\tau^2 \phi'\phi + 3\tau^2 D(s)^2 \phi'^2 = 0,$$

$$(6.2.21)$$

where $D(s) = 1 + (k_1 + k_2 s^2)s^2 + k_3 s^2$. Plugging the Taylor expression of ϕ into (6.2.21), we can obtain

$$2a_1 \left\{ \left[a_1^2 - (k_1 - k_3) \right] K + \left[-3a_1^4 + 3(k_1 - k_3)a_1^2 - 2(k_2 - k_1 k_3) \right]\tau^2 \right\} s^3$$

$$+ \left\{ \left[2a_1^4 - 2(k_1 - k_3)a_1^2 - \frac{3}{2}(k_2 - k_1 k_3) \right] K \right.$$

$$\left. - 3a_1^2 \left[a_1^4 - (k_1 - k_3)^2 + \frac{3}{2}(k_2 - k_1 k_3) \right]\tau^2 \right\} s^4$$

$$+ a_1 \left\{ \left[k_1 a_1^2 - k_1(k_1 - k_3) - 2(k_2 - k_1 k_3) \right] K + \left[-3k_1 a_1^4 \right.\right.$$

$$\left.\left. + (-4(k_2 - k_1 k_3) + 3k_1(k_1 - k_3))a_1^2 + \frac{2}{5}(3k_1 - 8k_3)(k_2 - k_1 k_3) \right]\tau^2 \right\} s^5$$

$$- \frac{1}{6}(k_2 - k_1 k_3)\left\{ \left[3a_1^2 + 2(k_1 - k_3) \right] K + \left[3a_1^4 - 8(k_2 - k_1 k_3) \right]\tau^2 \right\} s^6$$

$$+ o(s^7) = 0.$$

$$(6.2.22)$$

Since F is not of Randers type, it follows from Lemma 6.3 that $k_2 - k_1 k_3 \neq 0$.

If $a_1 = 0$, (6.2.22) is reduced to

$$9(k_2 - k_1 k_3)Ks^4 + 2(k_2 - k_1 k_3)\left\{ (k_1 - k_3)K - 4(k_2 - k_1 k_3)\tau^2 \right\} s^6 - 6o(s^7) = 0.$$

Hence, $(k_2 - k_1 k_3)K = 0$ and $K = 0$.

If $a_1 \neq 0$, it follows from (6.2.22) that

$$\left[a_1^2 - (k_1 - k_3) \right] K + \left[-3a_1^4 + 3(k_1 - k_3)a_1^2 - 2(k_2 - k_1 k_3) \right]\tau^2 = 0, \quad (6.2.23)$$

$$\left[2a_1^4 - 2(k_1 - k_3)a_1^2 - \frac{3}{2}(k_2 - k_1 k_3) \right] K$$

$$- 3a_1^2 \left[a_1^4 - (k_1 - k_3)^2 + \frac{3}{2}(k_2 - k_1 k_3) \right]\tau^2 = 0, \quad (6.2.24)$$

$$\left[k_1 a_1^2 - k_1(k_1 - k_3) - 2(k_2 - k_1 k_3) \right] K$$

$$+ \left\{ \frac{2}{5}(3k_1 - 8k_3)(k_2 - k_1 k_3) + [-4(k_2 - k_1 k_3) \right.$$

$$\left. + 3k_1(k_1 - k_3)]a_1^2 - 3k_1 a_1^4 \right\}\tau^2 = 0, \quad (6.2.25)$$

$$\left[3a_1^2 + 2(k_1 - k_3)\right]K + \left[3a_1^4 - 8(k_2 - k_1k_3)\right]\tau^2 = 0. \tag{6.2.26}$$

Computing $(6.2.23) \times k_1 - (6.2.25)$ gives

$$2(k_2 - k_1k_3)K + 4(k_2 - k_1k_3)\left\{a_1^2 - \frac{4}{5}(k_1 - k_3)\right\} = 0.$$

Noticing $k_2 - k_1k_3 \neq 0$, we have

$$K = 2\left\{-a_1^2 + \frac{4}{5}(k_1 - k_3)\right\}\tau^2. \tag{6.2.27}$$

It follows from $(6.2.23) \times 4 - (6.2.26)$ that

$$\left\{a_1^2 - 6(k_1 - k_3)\right\}K + 3a_1^2\left\{-5a_1^2 + 4(k_1 - k_3)\right\}\tau^2 = 0. \tag{6.2.28}$$

Inserting (6.2.27) into (6.2.28) yields $a_1^2 = \frac{4}{5}(k_1 - k_3)$ or $a_1^2 = \frac{12}{17}(k_1 - k_3)$.
If $a_1^2 = \frac{4}{5}(k_1 - k_3)$, then $K = 0$ by (6.2.27).
If $a_1^2 = \frac{12}{17}(k_1 - k_3)$, then $K = \frac{4}{15}a_1^2\tau^2$. By (6.2.23) and (6.2.24), we get respectively

$$(k_2 - k_1k_3)K = \frac{41}{72}a_1^4 K,$$

$$(k_2 - k_1k_3)K = \frac{2015}{3528}a_1^4 K.$$

Hence, $K = 0$ for $k_2 - k_1k_3 \neq 0$. $\qquad\square$

Using Lemma 6.6, one can determine the expression of ϕ under the condition $K = 0$.

Lemma 6.7. *Let $F = \alpha\phi(s)$ with $s = \beta/\alpha$ be an (α, β)-metric defined on an open set $\mathcal{U} \subset \mathbb{R}^n$ $(n \geq 3)$, where $\alpha = \sqrt{a_{ij}y^iy^j}$ and $\beta = b_iy^i \neq 0$. Set $b = \|\beta_x\|_\alpha$. Suppose that F is not of Randers type, β is not parallel with respect to α, and $db \neq 0$ everywhere or b is constant on $\mathcal{U}$. If F is a projectively flat metric with zero flag curvature, then*

$$\phi = \frac{(\sqrt{1 + ks^2} + \epsilon s)^2}{\sqrt{1 + ks^2}},$$

where $k = \frac{1}{5}(3k_1 + 2k_3)$, $\epsilon = \pm\frac{1}{\sqrt{5}}\sqrt{k_1 - k_3}$.

Proof. By the assumption $K = 0$, (6.2.21) can be reduced to

$$\left\{-a_1^4s^2 - (1 + 2k_3s^2 + k_1s^2 + 2k_2s^4)a_1^2 + (k_1 + k_2s^2)^2s^2\right\}\tau^2\phi^2$$
$$+ 2\left\{sa_1^2 - s(k_1 + k_2s^2)\right\}D(s)\tau^2\phi'\phi + \tau^2 D(s)^2\phi'^2 = 0, \tag{6.2.29}$$

Since β is not parallel with respect to α, $\tau \neq 0$ by means of (6.2.10). On putting $f = \frac{\phi'}{\phi}$, (6.2.29) becomes

$$\left\{ -a_1^4 s^2 - (1 + 2k_3 s^2 + k_1 s^2 + 2k_2 s^4)a_1^2 + (k_1 + k_2 s^2)^2 s^2 \right\}$$
$$+ 2\left\{ sa_1^2 - s(k_1 + k_2 s^2) \right\} D(s)\tau^2 f + D(s)^2 f^2 = 0, \tag{6.2.30}$$

which is a quadratic equation with respect to f. Thus,

$$f(s) = \frac{k_2 s^3 + (k_1 - a_1^2)s \pm \sqrt{a_1^2 + (-a_1^2 k_1 + 2a_1^4 + 2k_3 a_1^2)s^2}}{k_2 s^4 + (k_1 + k_3)s^2 + 1}. \tag{6.2.31}$$

On the other hand, $\phi(s)$ satisfies (6.2.9) so that f satisfies

$$f' = \frac{k_1 + k_2 s^2}{D(s)}(1 - sf) - f^2. \tag{6.2.32}$$

It should hold that $a_1 \neq 0$. In fact, if $a_1 = 0$, one can get from (6.2.30) that

$$f = \frac{s(k_1 + k_2 s^2)}{D(s)}.$$

Substituting it into (6.2.32) yields that

$$2s^2 \frac{k_1 k_3 - k_2}{D(s)} = 0.$$

Thus, $k_2 = k_1 k_3$. By Lemma 6.3, F is of Randers type, which contradicts to the assumption of Lemma 6.7.

We then have from (6.2.32)

$$3a_1^4 - 3(k_1 - k_3)a_1^2 + 2(k_2 - k_1 k_3)$$
$$\pm \frac{a_1^2}{\sqrt{\Delta}}\left\{ -4a_1^4 + 6(k_1 - k_3)a_1^2 - 2(k_1 - k_3)^2 - (k_2 - k_1 k_3) \right\} = 0,$$

where $\Delta := a_1^2 - 2a_1^2(k_1/2 - k_3 - a_1^2)s^2$. Thus,

$$3a_1^4 - 3(k_1 - k_3)a_1^2 + 2(k_2 - k_1 k_3) = 0,$$
$$2a_1^4 - 3(k_1 - k_3)a_1^2 + (k_1 - k_3)^2 + \frac{1}{2}(k_2 - k_1 k_3) = 0.$$

It follows from these that either
(i) $a_1^2 = k_1 - k_3$ and $k_2 = k_1 k_3$, or
(ii) $a_1^2 = \frac{4}{5}(k_1 - k_3)$ and $k_2 = \frac{6}{25}(k_1 - k_3)^2 + k_1 k_3$.
In case (i), we get from Lemma 6.3

$$\phi = a_1 s + \sqrt{1 + s^2 k_1}.$$

Hence, F is of Randers type, which is impossible by the assumption of Lemma 6.7.

In case (ii), one can obtain from Lemma 6.4

$$\phi = a_1 s + \sqrt{1 + \frac{1}{5}(3k_1 + 2k_3)s^2} + \frac{\frac{1}{5}(k_1 - k_3)s^2}{\sqrt{1 + \frac{1}{5}(3k_1 + 2k_3)s^2}}.$$

Since $(a_1)^2 = \frac{4}{5}(k_1 - k_3)$, then

$$\phi = \frac{(\sqrt{1 + ks^2} + \epsilon s)^2}{\sqrt{1 + ks^2}},$$

where

$$\epsilon := \pm \frac{1}{\sqrt{5}}(k_1 - k_3), \qquad k := \frac{1}{5}(3k_1 + 2k_3). \qquad \square$$

Combining Lemma 6.6 with Lemma 6.7 completes the proof of Theorem 6.5. $\qquad \square$

Remark. Recently, B. L. Li has completed the classification of projectively flat Finsler metrics with constant flag curvature ([68]).

6.3 Projectively flat metrics with almost isotropic S-curvature

6.3.1 Randers metrics with almost isotropic S-curvature

Proposition 6.5. *Let $F = \alpha + \beta$ be a non-Riemannian projectively flat metric on an n-dimensional manifold M. If F has constant Ricci curvature $Ric = (n-1)\lambda F^2$, then $\lambda \leq 0$. If $\lambda = 0$, F is a locally Minkowskian metric. If $\lambda = -1/4$, F is given by (6.2.4) and (6.2.5). In this case*

$$K = -\frac{1}{4}, \quad \mathbf{S} = \pm\frac{1}{2}(n+1)F.$$

Proof. According to Theorem 6.4, we can assume that α is a Riemannian metric with constant sectional curvature $K_\alpha = \mu$ and β is a closed 1-form. Let $\Phi = b_{i,j}y^i y^j$ and $\Psi = b_{i,j,k}y^i y^j y^k$ be homogeneous forms, where "," denotes the covariant differential with respect to α. By (4.3.5), the spray coefficients of F are

$$G^i = G^i_\alpha + Py^i, \quad P = \frac{r_{00}}{2F} = \frac{\Phi}{2F}.$$

Substituting it into (3.3.15) yields that

$$R^i{}_j = \overline{R}^i{}_j + \left[3\left(\frac{\Phi}{2F}\right)^2 - \frac{\Psi}{2F}\right]\left\{\delta^i_j - \frac{y^i F_{y^j}}{F}\right\} + \nu_j y^i, \qquad (6.3.1)$$

where $\overline{R}{}^{i}{}_{j}$ is the curvature of α,

$$\nu_j := \frac{1}{F}(b_{i,k,j} - b_{i,j,k})y^i y^k. \tag{6.3.2}$$

By the assumption, F has constant Ricci curvature. It follows from (6.3.1) that

$$\mu\alpha^2 + 3\left(\frac{\Phi}{2F}\right)^2 - \frac{\Psi}{2F} = \lambda F^2,$$

i.e.,

$$\mu\alpha^2(\alpha + \beta)^2 + \frac{3}{4}\Phi^2 - \frac{1}{2}\Psi(\alpha + \beta) = \lambda(\alpha + \beta)^4,$$

which is equivalent to the following two equations

$$\frac{3}{4}\Phi^2 = \frac{1}{2}\beta\Psi + (\lambda - \mu)\alpha^4 + (6\lambda - \mu)\alpha^2\beta^2 + \lambda\beta^4, \tag{6.3.3}$$

$$\frac{1}{2}\Psi = 2(\mu - 2\lambda)\alpha^2\beta - 4\lambda\beta^3. \tag{6.3.4}$$

Plugging (6.3.4) into (6.3.3) yields

$$\frac{3}{4}\Phi^2 = (\lambda - \mu)\alpha^4 + (2\lambda + \mu)\alpha^2\beta^2 - 3\lambda\beta^3. \tag{6.3.5}$$

Differentiating the both sides of (6.3.5), one can get

$$\frac{3}{2}\Phi b_{i,j,k}y^i y^j = 2(2\lambda + \mu)\alpha^2\beta b_{i,k}y^i - 12\lambda\beta^3 b_{i,k}y^k.$$

Contracting the above with y^k, we obtain

$$\frac{3}{2}\Phi\Psi = 2\{(2\lambda + \mu)\alpha^2 - 6\lambda\beta^2\}\Phi\beta.$$

Substituting (6.3.4) into it, one may get

$$(\mu - 4\lambda)\Phi\alpha^2\beta = 0.$$

We claim that $\mu = 4\lambda$. In fact, if it is not true, the above implies $\Phi\beta = 0$. Thus, Φ vanishes identically on $U = \{x \in M | \beta \neq 0\}$, i.e., β is parallel with respect to α. Thus, $\Psi = 0$. It follows from (6.3.4) that $\mu = 4\lambda = 0$, which is a contradiction.

Substituting $\mu = 4\lambda$ into (6.3.5) gives

$$\Phi^2 = -4\lambda(\alpha^2 - \beta^2)^2,$$

which implies $\lambda \leq 0$. Put $c := \pm\sqrt{-\lambda}$. The above becomes $\Phi = 2c(\alpha^2 - \beta^2)$. Since $s_{ij} = 0$, we have $\Phi = e_{00}$. Thus

$$e_{00} = 2c(\alpha^2 - \beta^2). \tag{6.3.6}$$

In the following we give the expression of β by means of (6.3.6).

If $\lambda = 0$, then $c = 0$, $\mu = 4\lambda = 0$ and α is flat. By (6.3.6), $e_{00} = 0$. Since β is closed, then $b_{i,j} = 0$, i.e., β is parallel with respect to α. Thus, $G^i(x,y) = G^i_\alpha(x,y)$ is a quadratic form in y. Hence F is a flat Berwald metric. By Theorem 5.6, F is locally Minkowskian.

Suppose $\lambda = -c^2 < 0$. In this case α has constant negative curvature $\mu = -4c^2$. Without loss of generality (take a homothetic transformation if necessary), one can assume that $\mu = -1$ ($c = \pm 1/2$), i.e., $\lambda = -1/4$. Then $\alpha = \alpha_{-1}$ can be expressed as

$$\alpha_{-1} = \frac{\sqrt{|y|^2 - (|x|^2|y|^2 - \langle x,y \rangle^2)}}{1 - |x|^2}, \quad y \in T_x B^n(1) \cong \mathbb{R}^n.$$

From (6.3.6) we get

$$b_{i,j} = \pm(a_{ij} - b_i b_j). \tag{6.3.7}$$

Thus, $\beta = b_i y^i$ can be expressed as a gradient form

$$\beta = \pm\frac{\langle x,y \rangle}{1 - |x|^2} \pm \frac{df_x(y)}{f(x)},$$

where $f(x) > 0$ is a scalar function defined on $B^n(1)$. By (6.3.7) it follows that $f_{x^i x^j} = 0$, which implies that f is a linear function

$$f = \delta(1 + \langle a,x \rangle), \quad \delta > 0, \quad a \in \mathbb{R}^n \text{ is a constant vector.}$$

Hence

$$\beta = \pm\frac{\langle x,y \rangle}{1 - |x|^2} \pm \frac{\langle a,y \rangle}{1 + \langle a,x \rangle}, \quad y \in T_x B^n(1) \cong \mathbb{R}^n. \qquad \square$$

Theorem 6.7 ([26]). *Let $F = \alpha + \beta$ be a locally projectively flat metric on an n-dimensional manifold M. If F has almost isotropic $\mathbf{S}$-curvature, i.e., (4.3.1) holds, where η is a closed 1-form, then the flag curvature K of F can be expressed as*

$$\begin{aligned} K &= \frac{3c_{x^k}(x)y^k}{F(x,y)} + 3c^2(x) + \mu \\ &= \frac{3}{4}\{\mu + 4c^2(x)\}\frac{F(x,-y)}{F(x,y)} + \frac{\mu}{4}, \end{aligned} \tag{6.3.8}$$

where $c_{x^k} = \partial c(x)/\partial x^k$, μ is a real constant. Moreover,

(i) If $\mu + 4c^2(x) = 0$, then $c(x) = c$ is a constant and the flag curvature is $K = -c^2$. In this case $F = \alpha + \beta$ is either locally Minkowskian or locally isometric to the metric (2.1.3) up to a homothetic factor ($c = \pm\frac{1}{2}$).

(ii) If $\mu + 4c^2(x) \neq 0$, then $F = \alpha + \beta$ can be locally expressed as

$$\alpha \cong \alpha_\mu, \quad \beta = -\frac{2c_{x^k}y^k}{\mu + 4c^2(x)}, \tag{6.3.9}$$

where α_μ is given in Example 6.2, $c(x) = c_\mu(x)$ is given by

$$c_\mu(x) = \begin{cases} (\lambda + \langle a, x \rangle)\sqrt{\dfrac{\mu}{\pm(1 + \mu|x|^2) - (\lambda + \langle a, x \rangle)^2}}, & \text{for } \mu \neq 0, \\ \dfrac{\pm 1}{2\sqrt{\lambda + 2\langle a, x \rangle + |x|^2}}, & \text{for } \mu = 0, \end{cases} \tag{6.3.10}$$

where $a \in \mathbb{R}^n$ is a constant vector, λ is a constant.

Proof. Let $\alpha = \sqrt{a_{ij}y^iy^j}$ and $\beta = b_iy^i$. Write $\Phi = e_{00}$ and Ψ as in the proof of Proposition 6.5. By Theorem 4.1, we have

$$\Phi = e_{00} = 2c(\alpha^2 - \beta^2) = 2c(\alpha - \beta)F. \tag{6.3.11}$$

Noting that $\alpha_{,k} = 0$, $\Phi = \beta_{,k}y^k$ and $\Psi = \Phi_{,k}y^k$, from (6.3.11) we see

$$\begin{aligned} \Psi &= 2c_{,k}y^k(\alpha^2 - \beta^2) - 4c\beta\beta_{,k}y^k \\ &= 2c_{x^k}y^k(\alpha^2 - \beta^2) - 4c\Phi\beta \\ &= 2c_{x^k}y^k(\alpha^2 - \beta^2) - 8c^2\beta(\alpha^2 - \beta^2) \\ &= 2(c_{x^k}y^k - 4c^2\beta)(\alpha - \beta)F. \end{aligned}$$

It follows from (6.3.1) and the above that

$$\begin{aligned} KF^2 &= \mu\alpha^2 + 3\left(\frac{\Phi}{2F}\right)^2 - \frac{\Psi}{2F} \\ &= \mu\alpha^2 + 3c^2(\alpha - \beta)^2 - (c_{x^k}y^k - 4c^2\beta)(\alpha - \beta). \end{aligned} \tag{6.3.12}$$

On the other hand, a projectively flat metric must have scalar flag curvature. From Proposition 5.1, the flag curvature K of F can be expressed as

$$K = \frac{3c_{x^k}y^k}{F} + \sigma(x).$$

Substituting it into (6.3.12) yields that

$$\{2c_{x^k}y^k + (\sigma + c^2)\beta\}(2\alpha + \beta) + \{\sigma - 3c^2 - \mu\}\alpha^2 = 0,$$

from which it follows that

$$\begin{aligned} 2c_{x^k}y^k + (\sigma + c^2)\beta &= 0, \\ \sigma - 3c^2 - \mu &= 0. \end{aligned} \tag{6.3.13}$$

From the second formula of (6.3.13) we get $\sigma = 3c^2 + \mu$, inserting which into the first one of (6.3.13) yields that

$$(\mu + 4c^2)\beta = -2c_{x^k}y^k. \tag{6.3.14}$$

Substituting $\sigma = 3c^2 + \mu$ into the expression of the flag curvature K, one can get the first formula of (6.3.8). By using (6.3.14) again, we obtain the second formula of (6.3.8). This proves the first part of the theorem.

Case (i): $\mu + 4c^2(x) = 0$. So, c is constant. Thus (6.3.8) implies

$$K = 3c^2 + \mu = -c^2.$$

By Proposition 6.5, the theorem is proved.

Case (ii): $\mu + 4c^2(x) \neq 0$. By (6.3.14),

$$\beta = -\frac{2c_{x^k}y^k}{\mu + 4c^2}. \tag{6.3.15}$$

Since β is an exact form, it follows from (6.3.11) and (6.3.15) that

$$c_{,i,j} = -c(\mu + 4c^2)a_{ij} + \frac{12cc_{,i}c_{,j}}{\mu + 4c^2},$$

where "," denotes the covariant differential with respect to α. In a suitable local coordinate system the above equation can be rewritten as

$$
\begin{aligned}
c_{x^i x^j} &+ \frac{\mu(x^i c_{x^j} + x^j c_{x^i})}{1 + \mu|x|^2} \\
&= -c(\mu + 4c^2)\left\{\frac{\delta_{ij}}{1 + \mu|x|^2} - \frac{\mu x^i x^j}{(1 + \mu|x|^2)^2}\right\} + \frac{12cc_{x^i}c_{x^j}}{\mu + 4c^2}.
\end{aligned} \tag{6.3.16}
$$

To solve $c = c(x)$ from (6.3.16), we put

$$\varphi := \begin{cases} \dfrac{2c\sqrt{1 + \mu|x|^2}}{\sqrt{\pm(\mu + 4c^2)}}, & \text{when } \mu \neq 0, \\[2mm] c^{-2}, & \text{when } \mu = 0, \end{cases} \tag{6.3.17}$$

where sign $\pm$ is chosen such that the inequality $\pm(\mu + 4c^2) > 0$ holds. Then (6.3.16) is equivalent to

$$\varphi_{x^i x^j} = \begin{cases} 0, & \text{when } \mu \neq 0, \\ 8\delta_{ij}, & \text{when } \mu = 0. \end{cases}$$

Solving the equation yields

$$\varphi = \begin{cases} \lambda + \langle a, x\rangle, & \text{when } \mu \neq 0, \\ 4(\lambda + 2\langle a, x\rangle + |x|^2), & \text{when } \mu = 0, \end{cases}$$

where $a \in \mathbb{R}^n$ is a constant vector and λ is a constant. Substituting it into (6.3.17) yields (6.3.10). Theorem 6.7 is proved completely. $\square$

6.3.2 Projectively flat metrics with almost isotropic S-curvature

In this section, we shall study more general projectively flat metrics.

Theorem 6.8 ([28]). *Let $F = F(x, y)$ be a projectively flat Finsler metric defined on $U \subset \mathbb{R}^n$. Suppose that F has almost isotropy $\mathbf{S}$-curvature, i.e., (4.3.1) holds, where $c = c(x)$ is a scalar function, $\eta = \eta_i dx^i$ is a closed 1-form. Then, F must be one of the following:*

(i) If $K \neq -c^2(x) + \frac{c_{x^k} y^k}{F(x,y)}$ on U everywhere, then $F = \alpha + \beta$ is a Randers metric defined on U as in Theorem 6.7 (ii).

(ii) If $K = -c^2(x) + \frac{c_{x^k} y^k}{F(x,y)}$, then $c(x) = c$ is a constant, and F is either locally Minkowskian (c=0) or F can be expressed up to a homothetic factor as

$$F = \begin{cases} \Theta(x, y) + \dfrac{\langle a, y \rangle}{1 + \langle a, x \rangle}, & c = \dfrac{1}{2}, \\[3mm] \Theta(x, -y) - \dfrac{\langle a, y \rangle}{1 + \langle a, x \rangle}, & c = -\dfrac{1}{2}, \end{cases} \tag{6.3.18}$$

where $a \in \mathbb{R}^n$ is a constant vector $\Theta = \Theta(x, y)$ is the Funk metric defined by (2.1.4).

Proof. Since $F(x, y)$ is projectively flat, the spray coefficients G^i can be expressed as (6.2.1). The flag curvature K is given by (6.2.2). By the assumption and (4.2.5), the $\mathbf{S}$-curvature is

$$\mathbf{S} = (n+1)\{cF + \eta\} = \frac{\partial G^s}{\partial y^s} - y^s \frac{\partial (\ln \sigma_F)}{\partial y^s} = (n+1)P - y^s \frac{\partial (\ln \sigma_F)}{\partial x^s}. \tag{6.3.19}$$

Since $\eta = \eta(x, y)$ is closed, then η is locally expressed as $h_{x^i} y^i$ where $h = h(x)$ is a scalar function. It follows form (6.3.19) that

$$P = cF + d\varphi, \tag{6.3.20}$$

where $\varphi := h(x) + \frac{1}{n+1} \ln(\sigma_F(x))$. By means of (6.3.20) and the second formula of (6.2.1), we have

$$F_{x^s} y^s = 2FP = 2F\{cF + \varphi_{x^s} y^s\}. \tag{6.3.21}$$

Substituting (6.3.20) and (6.3.21) into (6.2.2) yields

$$\begin{aligned} K &= \frac{1}{F^2} \left\{ (cF + \varphi_{x^s} y^s)^2 - c_{x^s} y^s F - cF_{x^s} y^s - \varphi_{x^i x^j} y^i y^j \right\} \\ &= \frac{1}{F^2} \left\{ -c^2 F^2 - c_{x^s} y^s F + (\varphi_{x^i} \varphi_{x^j} - \varphi_{x^i x^j}) y^i y^j \right\}. \end{aligned} \tag{6.3.22}$$

On the other hand, since F of scalar flag curvature, by Proposition 5.1, it shows that

$$K = 3\frac{c_{x^s}y^s}{F} + \sigma, \tag{6.3.23}$$

where $\sigma = \sigma(x)$ is a scalar function. Comparing it with (6.3.22) yields

$$(\sigma + c^2)F^2 + 4c_{x^s}y^s F - (\varphi_{x^i}\varphi_{x^j} - \varphi_{x^i x^j})y^i y^j = 0. \tag{6.3.24}$$

Now we discuss two cases separately.

(i) $K \neq -c^2(x) + \frac{c_{x^k}y^k}{F(x,y)}$ on U everywhere. By (6.3.23), at any point $x \in U$ there is a non-zero $y \in T_x M$ such that

$$\sigma(x) + c^2(x) + \frac{2c_{x^s}y^s}{F(x,y)} \neq 0.$$

We claim that $\sigma(x) + c^2(x) \neq 0$ on U everywhere. In fact, if it is not, there would be a point $x_0 \in U$ such that $\sigma(x_0) + c^2(x_0) = 0$. Substituting it into the above yields that $dc \neq 0$ at point x_0. Thus, at the point x_0, (6.3.24) may be reduced as

$$4c_{x^s}(x_0)y^s F(x_0, y) - (\varphi_{x^i}(x_0)\varphi_{x^j}(x_0) - \varphi_{x^i x^j}(x_0))y^i y^j = 0.$$

This gives rise to the so called the *Kropina metric* $\phi := F(x_0, y)$, which is singular at some direction $y \in T_x M$. Such a metric is eliminated from our consideration. So, the claim holds.

We now solve the quadratic equation (6.3.24) with respect to F and obtain

$$F = \frac{\sqrt{(\sigma + c^2)(\varphi_{x^i}\varphi_{x^j} - \varphi_{x^i x^j})y^i y^j + 4(c_{x^s}y^s)^2} - 2c_{x^s}y^s}{\sigma + c^2}.$$

This is a Randers metric $F = \alpha + \beta$. By Theorem 4.1, the **S**-curvature is isotropic, i.e., $\eta = 0$. Since F is projectively flat, then α has constant curvature $K_\alpha = \mu$, and β is closed. By Theorem 6.7, the flag curvature is given in (6.3.23), where $\sigma = 3c^2(x) + \mu$ (refer to (6.3.8)). The inequality $\sigma(x) + c^2(x) \neq 0$ is equivalent to $\mu + 4c^2(x) \neq 0$. Hence $F = \alpha + \beta$ is given by Theorem 6.7 (ii).

(ii) Suppose that $K = -c^2(x) + \frac{c_{x^k}y^k}{F(x,y)}$. By (6.3.23), we have

$$\sigma(x) + c^2(x) + \frac{2c_{x^s}y^s}{F} \equiv 0,$$

which implies that $c(x) = c$ is a constant, so that $\sigma(x) = -c^2$ is a constant too. Thus, the flag curvature $K = -c^2$ is a constant. (6.3.24) can be reduced to

$$\varphi_{x^i x^j} - \varphi_{x^i}\varphi_{x^j} = 0.$$

Solving the equation gives

$$\varphi = -\ln(1 + \langle a, x \rangle) + C,$$

where $a \in \mathbb{R}^n$ is a constant vector and C is a constant.

If $c = 0$, then $K = -c^2 = 0$. The projective factor $P = d\varphi$ is a 1-form by means of (6.3.20). Thus the spray coefficients $G^i = Py^i$ are quadratic in $y \in T_x U$ and F is a Berwald metric. Hence, F is locally Minkowskian in virtue of Theorem 5.6.

If $c \neq 0$, then $K = -c^2 < 0$. Set

$$\Psi := P + cF = 2cF + d\varphi.$$

We have

$$F = \frac{1}{2c}\{\Psi(x, y) - d\varphi\} = \frac{1}{2c}\left\{\Psi(x, y) + \frac{\langle a, y \rangle}{1 + \langle a, x \rangle}\right\}.$$

By using Lemma 6.2, we have

$$F_{x^k} = (PF)_{y^k}, \quad P_{x^k} = PP_{y^k} + c^2 FF_{y^k}.$$

Thus

$$\begin{aligned}
\Psi_{x^i} &= P_{x^i} + cF_{x^i} \\
&= PP_{y^i} + c^2 FF_{y^i} + c(PF)_{y^i} \\
&= (P + cF)\{P_{y^i} + cF_{y^i}\} = \Psi\Psi_{y^i}.
\end{aligned}$$

Since c might be negative, Ψ may have negative sign as a is sufficiently small. In fact, when $x \to 0$, $\Psi(0, y) = 2cF(0, y) - \langle a, y \rangle$ is negative when $c < 0$ and $a \to 0$. So, we introduce the following function

$$\Theta := \begin{cases} \Psi(x, y), & \text{when } c > 0, \\ -\Psi(x, -y), & \text{when } c < 0. \end{cases}$$

Then $\Theta = \Theta(x, y)$ satisfies

$$\Theta_{x^i} = \Theta\Theta_{y^i}.$$

Hence Θ is a Funk metric (see Chapter 5, §5.4.1, Example 5.4). Taking $c = \pm\frac{1}{2}$, we obtain (6.3.18). □

6.4 Some special projectively equivalent Finsler metrics

6.4.1 Projectively equivalent Randers metrics

In this section, we study the projective equivalence between Randers metrics. Any two positively definite metric spaces are called to be projectively equivalent (§6.1) if there is a diffeomorphism between them such that the pull back metric is projectively equivalent to the origin one. In Riemann geometry, any two Riemannian metrics of dimension n $(n \geq 3)$ with constant sectional curvature are always locally projectively equivalent according to the Beltrami theorem (Theorem 6.3).

Let M be an n-dimensional differentiable manifold, $F = \alpha + \beta$ and $\overline{F} = \overline{\alpha} + \overline{\beta}$ be two Randers metrics on M. We assume that α and $\lambda\overline{\alpha}$ coincide either everywhere or nowhere, where $\lambda = \lambda(x) > 0$ is a scalar function on M.

Denote by G^i and $\overline{G}^i$ the geodesic coefficients of F and $\overline{F}$ respectively in the same local coordinate system. If F is projectively equivalent to $\overline{F}$, then they satisfy the following

$$G^i = \overline{G}^i + Py^i,$$

where $P = P(x, y)$ is homogeneous in y. Let D and $\overline{D}$ be the Douglas tensors of F and $\overline{F}$ respectively.

Lemma 6.8. *Given $F = \alpha + \beta$ and $\overline{F} = \overline{\alpha} + \overline{\beta}$, $D = \overline{D}$ if and only if one of the following holds:*
(i) β and $\overline{\beta}$ are closed; or
(ii) β and $\overline{\beta}$ are not closed, and $\alpha = \lambda(x)\overline{\alpha}$, $s_{ij} = \lambda\overline{s}_{ij}$, where $\lambda = \lambda(x) > 0$ is a scalar function on M.

Proof. Let $G^i = G^i(x, y)$ and $\overline{G}^i = \overline{G}^i(x, y)$ be the spray coefficients of F and $\overline{F}$ respectively in the same local coordinate system, and $G^i_\alpha = G^i_\alpha(x, y)$ and $\overline{G}^i_{\overline{\alpha}} = \overline{G}^i_{\overline{\alpha}}(x, y)$ be geodesic coefficients of α and $\overline{\alpha}$ respectively. From (6.2.7) we get

$$G^i = G^i_\alpha + \alpha s^i_0 + \frac{-2\alpha s_0 + r_{00}}{2(\alpha + \beta)} y^i,$$
$$\overline{G}^i = \overline{G}^i_{\overline{\alpha}} + \overline{\alpha}\overline{s}^i_0 + \frac{-2\overline{\alpha}\overline{s}_0 + \overline{r}_{00}}{2(\overline{\alpha} + \overline{\beta})} y^i,$$

$$(6.4.1)$$

where we have used the notations of (4.3.4).

Put $\widetilde{G}^i = G^i_\alpha + \alpha s^i_o$. Obviously, $\widetilde{G}^i$ and G^i are projectively equivalent, so that they have the same Douglas tensors, i.e., $D = \widetilde{D}$, where $\widetilde{D}$ denotes the Douglas tensor of $\widetilde{G}^i$. We will compute D^i_{jkl} by $\widetilde{G}^i$. Set $Q^i = \alpha s^i_o$. We then have

$$\frac{\partial Q^m}{\partial y^m} = \frac{y_m}{\alpha} s^m_o + \alpha s^m_m = 0.$$

By the definition of Douglas tensor,

$$D^i_{jkl} = \widetilde{D}^i_{jkl} = \widehat{D}^i_{jkl} + \frac{\partial^3 Q^i}{\partial y^j \partial y^k \partial y^l},$$

where $\widehat{D}$ denotes the Douglas tensor of α. Since α is a Riemannian metric, $\widehat{D}^i_{jkl} = 0$. Hence

$$D^i_{jkl} = \frac{\partial^3 Q^i}{\partial y^j \partial y^k \partial y^l}.$$

Similarly,

$$\overline{D}^i_{jkl} = \frac{\partial^3 \overline{Q}^i}{\partial y^j \partial y^k \partial y^l},$$

where $\overline{Q}^i = \overline{\alpha} s^i_0$. Suppose that $Q^i = \overline{Q}^i + P^i$, where P^i is homogenous of degree 2 in y. We have

$$\frac{\partial^3 Q^i}{\partial y^j \partial y^k \partial y^l} = \frac{\partial^3 \overline{Q}^i}{\partial y^j \partial y^k \partial y^l} + \frac{\partial^3 P^i}{\partial y^j \partial y^k \partial y^l}.$$

Since $D = \overline{D}$, then

$$\frac{\partial^3 P^i}{\partial y^j \partial y^k \partial y^l} = 0,$$

which holds if and only if $P^i = H^i_{ik}(x) y^j y^k$. Hence

$$\alpha s^i_0 = \overline{\alpha} s^i_0 + H^i_{ik}(x) y^j y^k.$$

Replacing y by $-y$ yields

$$-\alpha s^i_0 = -\overline{\alpha} s^i_0 + H^i_{ik}(x) y^j y^k,$$

which implies

$$\alpha s^i_0 = \overline{\alpha} s^i_0.$$

We then see that only one of the following holds:
(i) β and $\overline{\beta}$ are all closed, and $s^i_0 = \overline{s}^i_0 = 0$; or
(ii) β and $\overline{\beta}$ are not closed, and $\alpha = \lambda(x)\overline{\alpha}$, where $\lambda = \lambda(x) > 0$ is a scalar function on M. In this case we have $s^i_0 = \frac{\overline{s}^i_0}{\lambda}$, i.e. $s_{ij} = \lambda \overline{s}_{ij}$. $\qquad \square$

Theorem 6.9 ([127]). *The Randers metrics $F = \alpha + \beta$ and $\overline{F} = \overline{\alpha} + \overline{\beta}$ are projectively equivalent if and only if one of the following holds:*
(i) β and $\overline{\beta}$ are closed, and α is projectively equivalent to $\overline{\alpha}$; or
(ii) β and $\overline{\beta}$ are not closed, $\alpha = \lambda\overline{\alpha}$ with a positive constant λ, and $\beta - \lambda\overline{\beta}$ is closed.

Proof. We prove the necessity firstly. Since F and $\overline{F}$ are projectively equivalent, $D = \overline{D}$. By Lemma 6.11, we need only to consider the following two cases.

Case (i): β and $\overline{\beta}$ are closed, $s_{ij} = \overline{s}_{ij} = 0$. From (6.4.1) we have

$$G^i = G^i_\alpha + \frac{r_{00}}{2(\alpha + \beta)} y^i.$$

Thus

$$\overline{F}_{;k} := \frac{\partial \overline{F}}{\partial x^k} - \frac{\partial G^l_\alpha}{\partial y^k}\frac{\partial \overline{F}}{\partial y^l} - \left\{ \frac{\partial P}{\partial y^k} y^l + P\delta^l_k \right\} \frac{\partial \overline{F}}{\partial y^l}$$

$$= \overline{F}_{|k} - \left\{ \frac{\partial P}{\partial y^k} y^l + P\delta^l_k \right\} \frac{\partial \overline{F}}{\partial y^l},$$

where $\overline{F}_{|k} := \frac{\partial \overline{F}}{\partial x^k} - \frac{\partial G^l_\alpha}{\partial y^k}\frac{\partial \overline{F}}{\partial y^l}$ is the covariant derivative of $\overline{F}$ with respect to α, and $P = \frac{r_{00}}{2(\alpha+\beta)} y^i$.

By Theorem 6.1 and the projective equivalence between F and $\overline{F}$, we have

$$\frac{\partial \overline{F}_{;k}}{\partial y^l} y^k - \overline{F}_{;l}$$

$$= \frac{\partial \overline{F}_{|k}}{\partial y^l} y^k - \overline{F}_{|l} - \left\{ \frac{\partial P}{\partial y^l} y^m + P\delta^m_l \right\} \frac{\partial \overline{F}}{\partial y^m} + \left\{ \frac{\partial P}{\partial y^l} y^m + P\delta^m_l \right\} \frac{\partial \overline{F}}{\partial y^m}$$

$$= \frac{\partial \overline{F}_{|k}}{\partial y^l} y^k - \overline{F}_{|l} = 0.$$

Hence, $\overline{F}$ is projectively equivalent to α. Moreover, $\overline{\alpha}$ is projectively equivalent to α.

Case (ii): Both β and $\overline{\beta}$ are not closed. Moreover, $\alpha = \lambda(x)\overline{\alpha}$, $s^i_0 = \frac{1}{\lambda(x)}\overline{s}^i_o$, so that $\alpha s^i_0 = \overline{\alpha}\overline{s}^i_0$. Since $\overline{F}$ and F are projectively equivalent, then $G^i = \overline{G}^i + Py^i$, where $P = P(x, y)$ is homogenous in y. It follows from (6.4.1) that

$$G^i_\alpha = \overline{G}^i_{\overline{\alpha}} + (P - P_1 + P_2)y^i, \qquad (6.4.2)$$

where $P_1 = \frac{-2\alpha s_0 + r_{00}}{2(\alpha+\beta)}$, $P_2 = \frac{-2\overline{\alpha}\overline{s}_0 + \overline{r}_{00}}{2(\overline{\alpha}+\overline{\beta})}$.

It follows from $\alpha = \lambda(x)\overline{\alpha}$ that

$$G_\alpha^i = \frac{1}{4}a^{il}\{[\alpha^2]_{x^k y^l}y^k - [\alpha^2]_{x^l}\}$$

$$= \frac{1}{4\lambda^2}\overline{a}^{il}\{[\lambda^2\overline{\alpha}^2]_{x^k y^l}y^k - [\lambda^2\overline{\alpha}^2]_{x^l}\}$$

$$= \frac{1}{4\lambda^2}\overline{a}^{il}\{\lambda^2[\overline{\alpha}^2]_{x^k y^l}y^k + 4\lambda\lambda_{x^k}y^k\overline{y}_l - \lambda^2[\overline{\alpha}^2]_{x^l} - 2\lambda\lambda_{x^l}[\overline{\alpha}^2]\}$$

$$= G_{\overline{\alpha}}^i + \frac{1}{2\lambda}\{2\lambda_o y^i - \lambda_{x^l}\overline{a}^{il}[\overline{\alpha}^2]\}.$$

Comparing it with (6.4.2) yields

$$\lambda_{x^l}\overline{a}^{il}[\overline{\alpha}^2] = 0.$$

Contracting the above with $\overline{a}_{ij}$, one can get $\lambda_{x^j}\overline{\alpha}^2 = 0$. Since $\overline{\alpha} \neq 0$, then $\lambda_{x^j} = 0$. Thus, λ is a positive constant and $\overline{G}_{\overline{\alpha}}^i = G_\alpha^i$. By $s_{ij} = \lambda\overline{s}_{ij}$, we see that $\beta - \lambda\overline{\beta}$ is closed.

Now we prove the sufficiency. In Case (i), $s_0^i = \overline{s}_0^i = 0$ since β and $\overline{\beta}$ are closed. The first equation of (6.4.1) implies that F and α are projectively equivalent. The second equation of (6.4.1) shows $\overline{F}$ and $\overline{\alpha}$ are projectively equivalent. Since α and $\overline{\alpha}$ are projectively equivalent, F and $\overline{F}$ are projectively equivalent.

Consider Case (ii). $\overline{G}_{\overline{\alpha}}^i = G_\alpha^i$ since $\alpha = \lambda\overline{\alpha}$ with a positive constant λ. Thus, $\overline{\alpha}$ and α are projectively equivalent. Since $\beta - \lambda\overline{\beta}$ is closed, then $s_{ij} = \lambda\overline{s}_{ij}$. Hence, $\alpha s_o^i = \overline{\alpha s}_0^i$. By (6.4.1), we obtain $G^i = \overline{G}^i + Py^i$. Thus, $\overline{F}$ and F are projectively equivalent. $\square$

From the proof of Theorem 6.9 and Lemma 6.11, we have obtained the following

Theorem 6.10 ([127]). *Randers metrics $F = \alpha + \beta$ and $\overline{F} = \overline{\alpha} + \overline{\beta}$ are projectively equivalent if and only if they have the same Douglas tensor and Riemannian metrics α and $\overline{\alpha}$ are projectively equivalent.*

According to this theorem and the curvature properties of a Finsler metric (see Chapter 5), we can conclude the following corollaries. The proof may refer to [127] and so is omitted here.

Corollary 6.1. *Let $F = \alpha + \beta$ be a Randers metric with constant flag curvature. The metric $\overline{F} = \overline{\alpha} + \overline{\beta}$ is chosen such that $\alpha \neq \lambda(x)\overline{\alpha}$. Then F is projectively equivalent to $\overline{F}$ if and only if both of them are projectively flat and α has non-positive constant curvature.*

Corollary 6.2. *Let $F = \alpha + \beta$ be an Einstein-Randers metric. The metric $\overline{F} = \overline{\alpha} + \overline{\beta}$ is chosen such that $\alpha \neq \lambda(x)\overline{\alpha}$. If F is projectively equivalent to $\overline{F}$, then both α and $\overline{\alpha}$ are the Riemannian Einstein metrics. Moreover, α has non-positive scalar curvature and F has non-positive Ricci curvature.*

6.4.2   The projective equivalence of (α, β)-metrics

Firstly, we prove the following

Lemma 6.9'. *Let $H^i = H^i(x, y)$ be homogeneous functions of degree 2 with respect to y. They satisfy*

$$\frac{\partial^3}{\partial y^j \partial y^k \partial y^l}\left(H^i - \frac{1}{n+1}H_{y^m}^m y^i\right) = 0 \qquad (*)$$

if and only if there exist scalar functions $\Gamma_{kl}^i = \Gamma_{kl}^i(x)$ on M such that

$$H^i y^j - H^j y^i = \frac{1}{2}(\Gamma_{kl}^i y^j - \Gamma_{kl}^j y^i)y^k y^l. \qquad (**)$$

Proof. $(*)$ implies $(**)$: If $(*)$ holds, then there exist scalar functions $\Gamma_{kl}^i = \Gamma_{kl}^i(x)$ on M such that

$$H^i - \frac{1}{n+1}H_{y^m}^m y^i = \frac{1}{2}\Gamma_{kl}^i y^k y^l,$$

which implies $(**)$ immediately.

$(**)$ implies $(*)$: Differentiating $(**)$ with respect to y^p, y^q, y^h, y^r yields that

$$(H_{pqhr}^i y^j + H_{pqh}^i \delta_r^j + H_{pqr}^i \delta_h^j) - (H_{pqhr}^j y^i + H_{pqh}^j \delta_r^i + H_{pqr}^j \delta_h^i)$$
$$+ (H_{phr}^i \delta_q^j - H_{phr}^j \delta_q^i) + (H_{qhr}^i \delta_p^j - H_{qhr}^j \delta_p^i) = 0,$$

where $H_{pqhr}^i := H_{y^p y^q y^h y^r}^i, \cdots$, etc. Contracting the above equation with respect to j and h and by the homogeneity of H^i, we obtain

$$(n+1)H_{pqr}^i - (H_{prm}^m \delta_q^i + H_{qrm}^m \delta_p^i + H_{pqm}^m \delta_r^i + H_{pqrm}^m y^i) = 0,$$

which is equivalent to the equation $(*)$. $\qquad\square$

We now give the necessary and sufficient condition that two (α, β)-metrics have the same Douglas tensor.

Consider an (α, β)-metric $F = \alpha\phi(\beta/\alpha)$. By (6.2.7) and (6.2.8), one can get

$$\alpha Q(s_0^i y^j - s_0^j y^i) + \Psi(-2Q\alpha s_0 + r_{00})(b^i y^j - b^j y^i)$$
$$= \frac{1}{2}(G_{kl}^i y^j - G_{kl}^j y^i)y^k y^l, \qquad (6.4.3)$$

where $G_{kl}^i(x) = \Gamma_{kl}^i(x) - \frac{\partial^2 G_\alpha^i}{\partial y^k \partial y^l}$.

Lemma 6.9 ([42]). *Two Finsler metrics* $F = \alpha\phi(\beta/\alpha)$ *and* $\overline{F} = \overline{\alpha}\overline{\phi}(\overline{\beta}/\overline{\alpha})$ *have the same Douglas tensor if and only if*

$$\alpha Q(s_0^i y^j - s_0^j y^i) + \Psi(-2Q\alpha s_0 + r_{00})(b^i y^j - b^j y^i)$$

$$- \left\{ \overline{\alpha}\overline{Q}(\overline{s}_0^i y^j - \overline{s}_0^j y^i) + \overline{\Psi}(-2\overline{Q}\overline{\alpha}\overline{s}_0 + \overline{r}_{00})(\overline{b}^i y^j - \overline{b}^j y^i) \right\} \qquad (6.4.4)$$

$$= \frac{1}{2}(G_{kl}^i y^j - G_{kl}^j y^i) y^k y^l,$$

where $G_{kl}^i = \Gamma_{kl}^i(x) - \frac{\partial^2 G_\alpha^i}{\partial y^k \partial y^l}$.

Proof. Write $H^i := G^i - \overline{G}^i$, where G^i and $\overline{G}^i$ denote the spray coefficients of F and $\overline{F}$, respectively. It is clear that $H^i = H^i(x, y)$ are homogeneous functions of degree 2 with respect to y. By Lemma 6.9′ and the definition of Douglas tensor, F and $\overline{F}$ have the same Douglas tensor if and only if H^i satisfy the equation $(**)$. Thus, the equation (6.4.4) follows from $(**)$ immediately. $\qquad\square$

Lemma 6.10 ([42]). *If* ϕ *satisfies* $\frac{Q(s)-Q(0)}{s} = k$ $(= \text{const.})$, *then* $\phi = Ce^{\int_0^s \frac{\phi'(0)+kt}{1+\phi'(0)t+kt^2} dt}$, *where* $C > 0$ *is a positive constant.*

Proof. Noting that $Q(0) = \phi'(0)$, it is easy to verify the lemma directly. $\quad\square$

Lemma 6.11 ([42]). *For* $n \geq 3$, *let* $F = \alpha\phi(\beta/\alpha)$ *be an* (α, β)-*metric with* $\phi \neq Ce^{\int_0^s \frac{\phi'(0)+kt}{1+\phi'(0)t+kt^2} dt}$, *where* $C > 0$ *and* k *are constants. Let* $\overline{F} = \overline{\alpha} + \overline{\beta}$ *be a Randers metric, where* α *and* $\overline{\alpha}$ *are conformal Riemannian metrics,* β *and* $\overline{\beta}$ *are non-zero 1-forms. Then* F *and* $\overline{F}$ *have the same Douglas tensor if and only if both* F *and* $\overline{F}$ *are Douglas metrics.*

Proof. The sufficiency is obvious. We need only to prove the necessity. Suppose that F and $\overline{F}$ have the same Douglas tensor. For the Randers metric $\overline{F}$ we have $\overline{Q} = 1$ and $\overline{\Psi} = 0$. Then (6.4.4) simplifies to

$$\alpha Q(s_0^i y^j - s_0^j y^i) + \Psi(-2Q\alpha s_0 + r_{00})(b^i y^j - b^j y^i) - \overline{\alpha}(\overline{s}_0^i y^j - \overline{s}_0^j y^i)$$

$$= \frac{1}{2}(G_{kl}^i y^j - G_{kl}^j y^i) y^k y^l.$$

Since α and $\overline{\alpha}$ are conformal, there is a positive function $\lambda(x)$ defined on M such that $\overline{\alpha} = \lambda(x)\alpha$. Hence

$$\alpha Q(s_0^i y^j - s_0^j y^i) + \Psi(-2Q\alpha s_0 + r_{00})(b^i y^j - b^j y^i) - \lambda(x)\alpha(\overline{s}_0^i y^j - \overline{s}_0^j y^i)$$

$$= \frac{1}{2}(G_{kl}^i y^j - G_{kl}^j y^i) y^k y^l. \qquad (6.4.5)$$

At arbitrary point $x \in M$ we take a coordinate transformation $(s, y^a) \rightarrow (y^i)$ on $T_x M$ as follows

$$y^1 = \frac{s}{\sqrt{b^2 - s^2}} \widetilde{\alpha}, \quad y^a = y^a, \quad 2 \leq a \leq n, \quad 1 \leq i \leq n,$$

where $\widetilde{\alpha} = \sqrt{\sum_{a=2}^n (y^a)^2}$. Then

$$\alpha = \frac{b}{\sqrt{b^2 - s^2}} \widetilde{\alpha}, \quad \beta = \frac{bs}{\sqrt{b^2 - s^2}} \widetilde{\alpha}.$$

Thus, (6.4.5) can be simplified by the transformation. Put $\widetilde{s}_0^a := s_b^a y^b$, $\widetilde{\overline{s}}_0^a := \overline{s}_b^a y^b$, $\widetilde{G}_{10}^a := G_{1b}^a y^b$.

For $i = a, j = b$, (6.4.5) gives

$$
bQ(\widetilde{s}_0^a y^b - \widetilde{s}_0^b y^a) - \lambda b(\widetilde{\overline{s}}_0^a y^b - \widetilde{\overline{s}}_0^b y^a)
$$
$$
= \frac{s}{2} \{ (\widetilde{G}_{10}^b + \widetilde{G}_{01}^b) y^a - (\widetilde{G}_{10}^a + \widetilde{G}_{01}^a) y^b) \}
\tag{6.4.6}
$$

and

$$
bs\widetilde{\alpha}^2 Q(s_1^a y^b - s_1^b y^a) - \lambda bs\widetilde{\alpha}^2 (\overline{s}_1^a y^b - \overline{s}_1^b y^a)
$$
$$
= \frac{1}{2} \{ (\widetilde{G}_{00}^a y^b - \widetilde{G}_{00}^b y^a)(b^2 - s^2) + s^2 \widetilde{\alpha}^2 (G_{11}^a y^b - G_{11}^b y^a) \}.
\tag{6.4.7}
$$

Setting $s \rightarrow 0$ in (6.4.7) yields

$$\widetilde{G}_{00}^a y^b - \widetilde{G}_{00}^b y^a = 0.$$

Substituting it into (6.4.7), we obtain

$$bQ(s_1^a y^b - s_1^b y^a) - \lambda b(\overline{s}_1^a y^b - \overline{s}_1^b y^a) = \frac{1}{2} s(G_{11}^a y^b - G_{11}^b y^a). \tag{6.4.8}$$

Putting $s = 0$ in (6.4.8), one gets

$$bQ(0)(s_1^a y^b - s_1^b y^a) = \lambda b(\overline{s}_1^a y^b - \overline{s}_1^b y^a). \tag{6.4.9}$$

Substituting it into (6.4.8) yields that

$$b(Q(s) - Q(0))(s_1^a y^b - s_1^b y^a) = \frac{1}{2} s(G_{11}^a y^b - G_{11}^b y^a).$$

If $(Q(s) - Q(0))/s \neq$ const., then we have

$$s_1^a y^b - s_1^b y^a = 0.$$

Hence, $s_1^a = 0$. Inserting $s_1^a y^b - s_1^b y^a = 0$ into (6.4.9), we obtain

$$\overline{s}_1^a y^b - \overline{s}_1^b y^a = 0,$$

which implies that $\overline{s}_1^a = 0$.

Set $s = 0$ in (6.4.6). We have

$$bQ(0)(\widetilde{s}_0^a y^b - \widetilde{s}_0^b y^a) = \lambda b(\overline{\widetilde{s}}_0^a y^b - \overline{\widetilde{s}}_0^b y^a). \tag{6.4.10}$$

Substituting (6.4.10) into (6.4.6) yields that

$$b(Q(s) - Q(0))(\widetilde{s}_0^a y^b - \widetilde{s}_0^b y^a) = \frac{s}{2}\{(\widetilde{G}_{10}^b + \widetilde{G}_{01}^b)y^a - (\widetilde{G}_{10}^a + \widetilde{G}_{01}^a)y^b)\}.$$

If $(Q(s) - Q(0))/s \neq$ const., then

$$\widetilde{s}_0^a y^b - \widetilde{s}_0^b y^a = 0.$$

Hence, $s_c^a \delta_d^b - s_c^b \delta_d^a = 0$. Taking the trace of b and d, one can gets $(n-2)s_c^a = 0$. Since $n \geq 3$, we have $s_c^a = 0$. Inserting it into (6.4.10) yields that $\overline{\widetilde{s}}_0^a y^b - \overline{\widetilde{s}}_0^b y^a = 0$. Similarly, we can obtain $\overline{s}_c^a = 0$.

We have proved that $\overline{s}_j^i = 0$, i.e., $\overline{\beta}$ is a closed 1-form. Therefore, both $\overline{F}$ and F are Douglas metrics. $\qquad\square$

Recall that a Finsler metric is of Randers type if it is an (α, β)-metric in the form $F = \sqrt{\alpha^2 + c\beta^2} + \epsilon\beta$, where c and ϵ are constants. We have the following

Theorem 6.11 ([42]). *Let $F = \alpha\phi(\beta/\alpha)$ be an (α, β)-metric with dimension $n \geq 3$ satisfying (i) β is not parallel with respect to α; (ii) either $db \neq 0$ everywhere or b is a constant; (iii) F is not of Randers type and $\phi \neq Ce^{\int_0^s \frac{\phi'(0)+kt}{1+\phi'(0)t+kt^2}\,dt}$, where $C > 0$ and k are constant. Let $\overline{F} = \overline{\alpha} + \overline{\beta}$ be a Randers metric, where α and $\overline{\alpha}$ are conformal Riemannian metrics, β and $\overline{\beta}$ are non-zero 1-forms. Then F and $\overline{F}$ are projectively equivalent if and only if there is a local coordinate system such that*

$$(1 + (k_1 + k_2 s^2)s^2 + k_3 s^2)\phi'' = (k_1 + k_2 s^2)(\phi - s\phi'), \tag{6.4.11}$$

$$\begin{cases} G_\alpha^i = G_{\overline{\alpha}}^i + \xi y^i - \tau(k_1\alpha^2 + k_2\beta^2)b^i, \\ b_{i|j} = 2\tau[(1 + k_1 b^2)\alpha_{ij} + (k_2 b^2 + k_3)b_i b_j], \\ d\overline{\beta} = 0, \end{cases} \tag{6.4.12}$$

where $b^i := a^{ij}b_j$, $b := \|\beta\|_\alpha$, $b_{i|j}$ is the covariant derivative of β with respect to α, $\tau = \tau(x)$ is a scalar function on M, ξ is a 1-form on M, k_1, k_2, k_3 are constants.

Proof. If F and $\overline{F}$ are projectively equivalent, they have the same Douglas tensor. By Lemma 6.14, they are Douglas metrics. It is well known that a Randers metric $\overline{F} = \overline{\alpha} + \overline{\beta}$ is Douglasian if and only if $d\overline{\beta} = 0$. It was proved in [72] that an (α, β)-metric $F = \alpha + \beta$ satisfying the hypothesis of the theorem is Douglas metric if and only if (6.4.11) and (6.4.12)$_2$ hold. Substituting (6.4.11) and (6.4.12)$_2$ into (6.2.7), one can easily get (6.4.12)$_1$ by a result in [97].

Conversely, inserting (6.4.11)-(6.4.12) into (6.2.7), one can see that F and $\overline{F}$ are projectively equivalent. □

6.4.3 The projective equivalence of quadratic (α, β)-metrics

In this section we give the necessary and sufficient condition that a quadratic (α, β)-metric $F = \frac{(\alpha+\beta)^2}{\alpha}$ and a Randers metric $\overline{F} = \overline{\alpha} + \overline{\beta}$ are projectively equivalent. The Riemannian metrics α and $\overline{\alpha}$ in Theorem 6.10 are conformal, which will not be required here.

The geodesic coefficients of a quadratic (α, β)-metric are given by (6.2.7), where

$$\Theta = \frac{1-2s}{1+2b^2-3s^2}, \quad Q = \frac{2}{1-s}, \quad \Psi = \frac{1}{1+2b^2-3s^2}. \qquad (6.2.8')$$

Then (6.2.7) may be rewritten as

$$G^i = \widehat{G}^i + \Theta\{-2Q\alpha s_0 + r_{00}\}\alpha^{-1}y^i,$$

where $\widehat{G}^i := G_\alpha^i + \alpha Q s_0^i + \Psi\{-2Q\alpha s_0 + r_{00}\}b^i$. Obviously, G^i and $\widehat{G}^i$ are projectively equivalent and have the same Douglas tensor.

On putting

$$T^i := \alpha Q s_0^i + \Psi\{-2Q\alpha s_0 + r_{00}\}b^i, \qquad (6.4.13)$$

we have $\widehat{G}^i = G_\alpha^i + T^i$. Since G^i and $\widehat{G}^i$ have the same Douglas tensor, then

$$D_{jkl}^i = \widehat{D}_{jkl}^i$$

$$= \frac{\partial^3}{\partial y^j \partial y^k \partial y^l}\left(G_\alpha^i - \frac{1}{n+1}\frac{\partial G_\alpha^m}{\partial y^m}y^i + T^i - \frac{1}{n+1}\frac{\partial T^m}{\partial y^m}y^i\right) \quad (6.4.14)$$

$$= \frac{\partial^3}{\partial y^j \partial y^k \partial y^l}\left(T^i - \frac{1}{n+1}\frac{\partial T^m}{\partial y^m}y^i\right).$$

Set $y_i := a_{il}y^l$. It is easy to see $\alpha_{y^k} = \alpha^{-1}y_k$, $(s)_{y^k} = \alpha^{-2}(b_k\alpha - sy_k)$. Moreover,

$$[\alpha Q s_0^m]_{y^m} = \alpha^{-1}y_m Q s_0^m + \alpha^{-2}Q'[b_m\alpha^2 - \beta y_m]s_0^m = Q's_0,$$

and

$$y^m = \Psi'\alpha^{-1}(b^2 - s^2)[r_{00} - 2Q\alpha s_0]$$
$$+ 2\Psi[r_0 - Q'(b^2 - s^2)s_0 - Qss_0],$$

where $r_j := b^i r_{ij}$, $r_0 = r_i y^i$. By (6.4.13), it follows that

$$T^m_{y^m} = Q' s_0 + \Psi' \alpha^{-1} (b^2 - s^2)[r_{00} - 2Q\alpha s_0]$$
$$+ 2\Psi[r_0 - Q'(b^2 - s^2)s_0 - Qss_0].$$

(6.4.15)

Suppose that (α, β)-metrics F and $\overline{F}$ have the same Douglas tensor, i.e., $D^i_{jkl} = \overline{D}^i_{jkl}$. By (6.1.10) and (6.4.14), we obtain

$$\frac{\partial^3}{\partial y^j \partial y^k \partial y^l} \left(T^i - \overline{T}^i - \frac{1}{n+1}(T^m_{y^m} - \overline{T}^m_{y^m})y^i \right) = 0.$$

Thus, there is a function $H^i_{jk} := H^i_{jk}(x)$ such that

$$T^i - \overline{T}^i - \frac{1}{n+1}(T^m_{y^m} - \overline{T}^m_{y^m})y^i = H^i_{00},$$

(6.4.16)

where $H^i_{00} := H^i_{jk} y^j y^k$, T^i and $T^m_{y^m}$ are given by (6.4.13) and (6.4.15).

Lemma 6.12 ([42]). *A quadratic (α, β)-metric $F = \frac{(\alpha+\beta)^2}{\alpha}$ and a Randers metric $\overline{F} = \overline{\alpha} + \overline{\beta}$ have the same Douglas tensor if and only if both F and $\overline{F}$ are Douglas metrics.*

Proof. The sufficiency is obvious. We now prove the necessity. If F and $\overline{F}$ have the same Douglas tensor, then (6.4.16) holds. Substituting $(6.2.8')$ into (6.4.16) yields that

$$\frac{A^i \alpha^6 + B^i \alpha^5 + C^i \alpha^4 + D^i \alpha^3 + E^i \alpha^2 + F^i \alpha + H^i}{I\alpha^5 + J\alpha^4 + K\alpha^3 + L\alpha^2 + M\alpha + N} - \overline{\alpha} s^i_0 = H^i_{00}, \quad (6.4.17)$$

where

$$A^i = -2(1 + 2b^2)[2b^i s_0 - (1 + 2b^2)s^i_0],$$
$$B^i = (1 + 2b^2)[b^i r_{00} - 2\lambda y^i(r_0 + s_0)],$$
$$C^i = -\beta[(1 + 2b^2)(b^i r_{00} + 12\beta s^i_0 - 2\lambda y^i r_0)$$
$$- 2(6\beta b^i + \lambda y^i + 14\lambda y^i b^2)s_0],$$
$$D^i = -3\beta[b^i r_{00}\beta + 2\lambda y^i(b^2 r_{00} - \beta r_0 - \beta s_0)],$$
$$E^i = 3\beta^2[6\beta^2 s^i_0 + \beta b^i r_{00} + 2\lambda y^i(b^2 r_{00} - \beta r_0 - 5\beta s_0)],$$
$$F^i = 6\lambda y^i \beta^3 r_{00}, \quad H^i = -6\lambda y^i \beta^4 r_{00},$$
$$I = -(1 + 2b^2)^2, \quad J = \beta(1 + 2b^2)^2, \quad K = 6\beta^2(1 + 2b^2),$$
$$L = -6\beta^3(1 + 2b^2), \quad M = -9\beta^4, \quad N = 9\beta^5.$$

(6.4.17) is equivalent to

$$A^i \alpha^6 + B^i \alpha^5 + C^i \alpha^4 + D^i \alpha^3 + E^i \alpha^2 + F^i \alpha + H^i$$
$$= (I\alpha^5 + J\alpha^4 + K\alpha^3 + L\alpha^2 + M\alpha + N)(H^i_{00} + \overline{\alpha} s^i_0).$$

(6.4.18)

Replacing y^i in (6.4.18) by $-y^i$ and then adding with (6.4.18), we obtain

$$\alpha(B^i\alpha^4 + D^i\alpha^2 + F^i)$$
$$= \alpha H^i_{00}(I\alpha^4 + K\alpha^2 + M) + \overline{\alpha}\overline{s}^i_0(J\alpha^4 + L\alpha^2 + N). \tag{6.4.19}$$

(6.4.19) implies that $\overline{\alpha}\overline{s}^i_0 N$ has a divisor α.

If $\overline{\alpha} \neq \mu(x)\alpha$, then $\overline{s}^i_0 N = 9\beta^5\overline{s}^i_0$ has the divisor α. Note that β^2 can not be divisible by α. It follows that $\beta\overline{s}^i_0$ includes the divisor α^2. Thus, for any index i, there is a scalar function $\tau^i = \tau^i(x)$ such that $\beta\overline{s}^i_0 = \tau^i\alpha^2$. It is equivalent to

$$b_j\overline{s}^i_k + b_k\overline{s}^i_j = 2\tau^i\alpha_{jk}. \tag{6.4.20}$$

If $n \geq 3$ and $\tau^i \neq 0$, then

$$2 \geq \operatorname{rank}(b_j\overline{s}^i_k) + \operatorname{rank}(b_k\overline{s}^i_j)$$
$$\geq \operatorname{rank}(b_j\overline{s}^i_k + b_k\overline{s}^i_j)$$
$$= \operatorname{rank}(2\tau^i\alpha_{jk}) \geq 3,$$

which is a contradiction. Hence, $\tau^i = 0$. From (6.4.20) it follows that $\beta\overline{s}^i_0 = 0$. Since $\beta \neq 0$, we have $\overline{s}^i_0 = 0$, i.e., $\overline{\beta}$ is closed. Hence, F and $\overline{F}$ are Douglas metrics.

If $\overline{\alpha} = \mu(x)\alpha$, then F and $\overline{F}$ are Douglas metrics by the Lemma 6.11. $\square$

As similar to the proof of Theorem 6.10, noting that $F = (\alpha + \beta)^2/\alpha$ with $k_1 = 2, k_2 = 0, k_3 = -3$, we can obtain the following

Theorem 6.12 ([42]). *For $n \geq 3$, let $F = \frac{(\alpha+\beta)^2}{\alpha}$ be a quadratic (α, β)-metric and $\overline{F} = \overline{\alpha}+\overline{\beta}$ be a Randers metric on the manifold M, where α and $\overline{\alpha}$ are Riemannian metrics, $\beta = b_iy^i$ and $\overline{\beta}$ are non-zero 1-forms. Then F and $\overline{F}$ are projectively equivalent if and only if there is a local coordinate system such that*

$$G^i_\alpha = G^i_{\overline{\alpha}} + \xi y^i - \tau\alpha^2 b^i,$$
$$b_{i|j} = \tau[(1 + 2b^2)\alpha_{ij} - 3b_ib_j],$$
$$d\overline{\beta} = 0,$$

where $b^i := a^{ij}b_j$, $b := \|\beta\|_\alpha$, $b_{i|j}$ is covariant derivative of β with respect to α, $\tau = \tau(x)$ is a scalar function on M, and ξ is a 1-form on M.

Exercises

6.1 Prove that a Riemannian metric α is locally projectively flat if and only if the projective curvature tensor W of α vanishes identically, so that α has constant curvature.

6.2 Prove that two Finsler metrics have the same Douglas tensor if they are projectively equivalent.

6.3 Prove that $y^k R^i{}_k = 0$ and (6.1.15) by (3.3.15).

6.4 Prove that the condition (c) in Theorem 6.6 is not essential, i.e., the big bracket on the right hand side of (6.2.10) cannot be zero at the isolated points of $db = 0$.

6.5 Prove that a locally projectively flat Randers metric with constant flag curvature must be either local Minkowskian or a general Funk metric (refer to [108]).

6.6 Compute the expression (6.2.7) of the spray coefficients of an (α, β)-metric.

6.7 Let $F = \alpha + \frac{\beta^2}{\alpha}$ be an n-dimensional ($n \geq 3$) Finsler metric, where α is a Riemannian metric and β is a 1-form. Set $b := ||\beta||_\alpha \neq 0$. Prove that F is a Douglas metric if and only if $d\beta = 0$, $r_{00} = \tau\{(1+2b^2)\alpha^2 - 3\beta^2\}$.

6.8 Let $F = \alpha + \varepsilon\beta + \kappa\frac{\beta^2}{\alpha}$, where α is a Riemannian metric, β is a 1-form and ε, κ ($\neq 0$) are constants. Assume that $b := ||\beta||_\alpha < 1$. Prove that F is a Finsler metric if and only if $s := \frac{\beta}{\alpha}$ satisfies

$$|s| \leq b, \quad 1 + \varepsilon s + \kappa s^2 > 0, \quad 1 + 2\kappa b^2 - 3\kappa s^2 > 0.$$

6.9 Let φ be defined by (6.3.17). Prove that (6.3.16) can be reduced to

$$\varphi_{x^i x^j} = \begin{cases} 0, & \text{when } \mu \neq 0, \\ 8\delta_{ij}, & \text{when } \mu = 0, \end{cases}$$

and solve the equation in detail.

Chapter 7

Comparison Theorems

7.1 Volume comparison theorems for Finsler manifolds

Volume comparison theorems in Riemannian geometry were given by P. Günthet ([52]) and R. L. Bishop ([21]) in 1960s. Later, they are applied widely in global differential geometry and geometric analysis. Because of complexity, such comparison theorems in Finsler geometry were open until the end of last century, which were studied by the second author of this book in [105]. In this section we shall establish volume comparison theorems for Finsler manifolds with a volume measure $d\mu$.

7.1.1 The Jacobian of the exponential map

Let (M, F) be a forward complete Finsler manifold of dimension n, and $\{y^i\}$ be the coordinates on T_pM at a fixed point $p \in M$. The induced Riemannian metric of F on T_pM is

$$g_p(y) := g_{ij}(p, y)dy^i \otimes dy^j.$$

There is an induced $(n-1)$-dimensional Riemannian metric $\dot{g}_p$ from g_p on the indicatrix $S_pM = \{y \in T_pM | F(p, y) = 1\}$. The Riemannian volume form on $(S_pM, \dot{g}_p)$ is denoted by $d\nu_p$. For any $y \in S_pM$, we have (see §4.1.2)

$$d\nu_p(y) = \sqrt{\det(g_{ij}(p, y))}\sum_{i=1}(-1)^{i-1}y^i dy^1 \wedge \cdots \widehat{dy^i} \cdots \wedge dy^n.$$

Let $(\bar{r}, \bar{y})$ be the *polar coordinate system* on $(T_pM \setminus \{0\}, F(p, \cdot))$, i.e., for any $v \in T_pM \setminus \{0\}$,

$$\bar{r}(v) := F(p, v), \quad \bar{y}(v) := v/\bar{r}(v) \in S_pM.$$

We then have (see §2.4.3)

$$g_p = d\bar{r} \otimes d\bar{r} + \bar{r}^2 \dot{g}_p, \quad \dot{g}_p = \dot{g}_{\alpha\beta} d\bar{\theta}^\alpha \otimes d\bar{\theta}^\beta, \quad 1 \leq \alpha, \beta, \cdots \leq n-1,$$

where $\{\bar{\theta}^\alpha\}$ is the spherical coordinates on $S_p M$. Thus,

$$d\nu_p = \sqrt{\det(\dot{g}_{\alpha\beta})} d\bar{\Theta}, \quad d\bar{\Theta} = d\bar{\theta}^1 \wedge \cdots \wedge d\bar{\theta}^{n-1}.$$

For any $y \in S_p M$, denote by i_y the cut value of y:

$$i_y := \sup\{r | \exp_p(ty), 0 < t < r, \text{ is injective}\}.$$

The injective radius i_p at p and the injective radius i_M of M are defined respectively by

$$i_p := \inf_{y \in S_p M} i_y, \quad i_M := \inf_{p \in M} i_p.$$

The cut locus of p is defined by

$$\text{Cut}_p := \{\exp_p(i_y y) | y \in S_p M\}.$$

Set $\mathcal{D}_p := M - \text{Cut}_p$. Clearly, $\mathcal{D}_p - \{p\}$ is the maximal homeomorphic domain of $\exp_p$. Thus, $M = \mathcal{D}_p \sqcup \text{Cut}_p$ ([10, 104]). The pole coordinate system of $\mathcal{D}_p - \{p\}$ is denoted by (r, y), i.e., for any $q \in \mathcal{D}_p$, $r(q) = \bar{r} \circ \exp_p^{-1}(q)$, $y(q) = \bar{y} \circ \exp_p^{-1}(q)$. More precisely,

$$\frac{\partial}{\partial \theta^\alpha}\Big|_{(r,y)} = (\exp_p)_{*ry}\left(r\frac{\partial}{\partial\bar{\theta}^\alpha}\right),$$

$$\frac{\partial}{\partial r}\Big|_{(r,y)} = (\exp_p)_{*ry}y, \tag{7.1.1}$$

where $\theta^\alpha(q) := \bar{\theta}^\alpha \circ \bar{y} \circ \exp_p^{-1}(q) = \bar{\theta}^\alpha \circ y(q)$.

Given a volume form $d\mu$ on M, we have $d\mu|_{(r,y)} = \sigma_p(r,y)dr \wedge d\Theta$ in the pole coordinate system, where $d\Theta = d\theta^1 \wedge \cdots \wedge d\theta^{n-1}$. It follows that

$$d\mu|_{(r,y)} = \sigma_p(r,y)dr \wedge d\Theta$$
$$= \left(\frac{\sigma_p(r,y)}{\sqrt{\det \dot{g}_p(y)}}\right) dr \wedge \left(\sqrt{\det \dot{g}_p(y)}d\Theta\right)$$
$$= \left(\frac{\sigma_p(r,y)}{\sqrt{\det \dot{g}_p(y)}}\right) dr \wedge d\nu_p(y)$$
$$=: \hat{\sigma}_p(r,y)dr \wedge d\nu_p(y),$$

where

$$\hat{\sigma}_p(r,y) := \frac{\sigma_p(r,y)}{\sqrt{\det \dot{g}_p(y)}}.$$

Thus,

$$d\mu|_{(r,y)} = \widehat{\sigma}_p(r,y)dr \wedge d\nu_p(y) = (\exp_p^{-1*})\left(\widehat{\sigma}_p(\overline{r},\overline{y})d\overline{r} \wedge d\nu_p(\overline{y})\right). \quad (7.1.2)$$

Similarly, we can define the distortion and **S**-curvature (Chapter 4, §4.2) for the volume measure $d\mu$ on Finsler manifold (M, F).

Lemma 7.1. *Let τ be the distortion of $(M, F, d\mu)$. Then*

$$\lim_{r \to 0^+} \frac{\widehat{\sigma}_p(r,y)}{\mathfrak{s}_k^{n-1}(r)} = e^{-\tau(y)},$$

where

$$\mathfrak{s}_k(t) := \begin{cases} \dfrac{1}{\sqrt{k}}\sin(\sqrt{k}t), & k > 0, \\ t, & k = 0, \\ \dfrac{1}{\sqrt{-k}}\sinh(\sqrt{-k}t), & k < 0. \end{cases} \quad (7.1.3)$$

Proof. It follows from the definition of the distortion that

$$\widehat{\sigma}_p(r,y) = \frac{\sigma(r,y)}{\sqrt{\det \dot{g}_p(y)}}$$

$$= \frac{\sigma(r,y)}{\sqrt{\det g(\exp_p(ry), \frac{\partial}{\partial r})}} \frac{\sqrt{\det g(\exp_p(ry), \frac{\partial}{\partial r})}}{\sqrt{\det \dot{g}_p(y)}}$$

$$= e^{-\tau\left((\exp_p)_{*ry}y\right)} \frac{\sqrt{\det g(\exp_p(ry), \frac{\partial}{\partial r})}}{\sqrt{\det \dot{g}_p(y)}},$$

where $\det g(\exp_p(ry), \frac{\partial}{\partial r})$ is the determinate of $g_{ij}(\exp_p(ry), \frac{\partial}{\partial r})$ (in the pole coordinate system). By the Gauss lemma (cf. [10], p.140), we have $g_{\frac{\partial}{\partial r}}(\frac{\partial}{\partial r}, \frac{\partial}{\partial r}) = 1$ and $g_{\frac{\partial}{\partial r}}(\frac{\partial}{\partial r}, \frac{\partial}{\partial \theta^\alpha}) = 0$. Hence,

$$\sqrt{\det\left[g\left(\exp_p(ry), \frac{\partial}{\partial r}\right)\right]}$$

$$= \sqrt{\det\left[g_{\frac{\partial}{\partial r}}\left(\frac{\partial}{\partial \theta^\alpha}, \frac{\partial}{\partial \theta^\beta}\right)\right]}$$

$$= r^{n-1}\sqrt{\det\left[g_{\frac{\partial}{\partial r}}\left((\exp_p)_{*ry}\frac{\partial}{\partial \overline{\theta}^\alpha}, (\exp_p)_{*ry}\frac{\partial}{\partial \overline{\theta}^\beta}\right)\right]}.$$

On the other hand, $\frac{\partial}{\partial r}|_{(r,y)} = (\exp_p)_{*ry}y$, from which it follows that $\lim_{r \to 0^+} \frac{\widehat{\sigma}_p(r,y)}{\mathfrak{s}_k^{n-1}(r)} = e^{-\tau(y)}.$ $\square$

Fixing a point $p \in M$ and a tangent vector $y \in S_p M$, we can define an inner product $\langle \cdot, \cdot \rangle := g_y(\cdot, \cdot)$ on $T_p M$. Denote by $y^\perp$ the orthogonal supplement of $\mathbb{R}y$ in $(T_p M, \langle \cdot, \cdot \rangle)$, i.e., $T_p M = \mathbb{R}y \oplus y^\perp$. Let $\gamma_y(t)$ be a geodesic with constant velocity satisfying that $\gamma_y(0) = p$ and $\dot{\gamma}_y(0) = y$, and $P_{t;y}$ be a parallel displacement from $\gamma_y(0)$ to $\gamma_y(t)$ along γ_y with respect to the Chern connection ∇ (see §3.3.1 in Chapter 3).

Set $T = \dot{\gamma}_y(t)$ for $0 \le t < c_y$. Write $R_T := R_T(\cdot, T)T$ and

$$\mathcal{R}(t, y) := P_{t;y}^{-1} \circ R_T \circ P_{t;y} : y^\perp \to y^\perp.$$

Let $\mathcal{A}(t, y)$ be the solution of the following system of ordinary differential equations in the matrix (linear transformation) form on $y^\perp$:

$$\begin{cases} \mathcal{A}'' + \mathcal{R}(t, y)\mathcal{A} = 0, \\ \mathcal{A}(0, y) = 0, \\ \mathcal{A}'(0, y) = \mathcal{I}, \end{cases} \qquad (7.1.4)$$

where $\mathcal{A}' = \frac{d}{dt}\mathcal{A}$, and $\mathcal{I}$ is the identity matrix.

For any $0 \le t_1 \le t_2$, let $P_{t_1 \to t_2; y}$ be the parallel displacement from $\gamma_y(t_1)$ to $\gamma_y(t_2)$ along γ_y. We then have for any vector $V(t) \in y^\perp$

$$\begin{aligned} \nabla_T^T (P_{t;y} V(t)) &= \lim_{s \to t^-} \frac{P_{s \to t; y}(P_{s;y} V(s)) - P_{t;y} V(t)}{s - t} \\ &= \lim_{s \to t^-} \frac{P_{t;y} V(s) - P_{t;y} V(t)}{s - t} \\ &= P_{t;y} V'(t). \end{aligned}$$

Thus, the above system of ordinary differential equations can be reduced as

$$\begin{cases} \nabla_T^T \nabla_T^T (P_{t;y}\mathcal{A}X) + R_T(P_{t;y}\mathcal{A}X, T)T = 0, \quad \forall X \in y^\perp, \\ (P_{t;y}\mathcal{A}(t, y)X)|_{t=0} = 0, \\ \nabla_T^T (P_{t;y}\mathcal{A}(t, y)X)|_{t=0} = X. \end{cases}$$

We then have

$$P_{t;y}\mathcal{A}(t, y)X = (\exp_p)_{*ty} tX.$$

Consider arbitrary two bases $\{e_\alpha\}$ and $\{E_\alpha\}$ on $y^\perp$ and a non-singular linear transformation $\mathcal{P} : y^\perp \to y^\perp$. Set $E_\alpha = H_\alpha^\beta e_\beta$, $\mathcal{P}e_\alpha = \mathcal{P}_\alpha^\beta e_\beta$ and $\mathcal{P}E_\alpha = \widetilde{\mathcal{P}}_\alpha^\beta E_\beta$. We have $H_\alpha^\beta \mathcal{P}_\beta^\delta (H^{-1})_\delta^\gamma = \widetilde{\mathcal{P}}_\alpha^\gamma$ and $\det(\widetilde{\mathcal{P}}_\alpha^\beta) = \det(\mathcal{P}_\alpha^\beta)$. Thus, one can define

$$\det \mathcal{A}(t, y) := \det(\mathcal{A}(t, y)_a^\beta)$$

for any $y \in S_p M$ and $0 \le t < c_y$, where $\mathcal{A}(t, y)e_\alpha = \mathcal{A}(t, y)_\alpha^\beta e_\beta$ and $\{e_\alpha\}$ is a basis of $y^\perp$.

Let $(\bar{r}, \bar{y})$ and (r, y) be polar coordinate systems of on $T_p M \setminus \{p\}$ and $\mathcal{D}_p \setminus \{p\}$ respectively, and $\{\bar{\theta}^\alpha\}$ be a local coordinate system on $S_p M$. For any $q \in \mathcal{D}_p \setminus \{p\}$, we can define $\theta^\alpha(q) := \bar{\theta}^\alpha \circ y(q)$. From (7.1.1) we have

$$P_{r;y} \circ \mathcal{A}(r,y) \frac{\partial}{\partial \bar{\theta}^\alpha} = (\exp_p)_{*ry} r \frac{\partial}{\partial \bar{\theta}^\alpha} = \frac{\partial}{\partial \theta^\alpha}.$$

Define

$$\mathcal{A}(r,y) \frac{\partial}{\partial \bar{\theta}^\alpha} =: \mathcal{A}(r,y)_\alpha^\beta \frac{\partial}{\partial \bar{\theta}^\beta}, \quad \det \mathcal{A}(r,y) := \det \mathcal{A}(r,y)_\alpha^\beta.$$

For any $X, Y \in T_p M$, it holds that

$$g_{\frac{\partial}{\partial r}}(P_{r;y} X, P_{r;y} Y) = g_{\dot{\gamma}_y(r)}(P_{r;y} X, P_{r;y} Y) = g_y(X, Y).$$

Thus,

$$\det[(g_{\frac{\partial}{\partial r}})_{ij}] = \det[(g_{\frac{\partial}{\partial r}})_{\alpha\beta}]$$

$$= \det\left[g_{\frac{\partial}{\partial r}}\left(P_{r,y} \circ \mathcal{A}(r,y) \frac{\partial}{\partial \bar{\theta}^\alpha}, P_{r,y} \circ \mathcal{A}(r,y) \frac{\partial}{\partial \bar{\theta}^\beta} \right) \right]$$

$$= \det\left[g_y\left(\mathcal{A}(r,y) \frac{\partial}{\partial \bar{\theta}^\alpha}, \mathcal{A}(r,y) \frac{\partial}{\partial \bar{\theta}^\beta} \right) \right]$$

$$= \det\left[\mathcal{A}(r,y)_\alpha^\delta \mathcal{A}(r,y)_\beta^\eta g_y\left(\frac{\partial}{\partial \bar{\theta}^\delta}, \frac{\partial}{\partial \bar{\theta}^\sigma} \right) \right]$$

$$= (\det \mathcal{A}(r,y))^2 \det \dot{g}_p(y).$$

In other words,

$$\sqrt{\frac{\det g(\exp_p(ry), \frac{\partial}{\partial r})}{\det \dot{g}_p(y)}} = \det \mathcal{A}(r,y). \tag{7.1.5}$$

Thus, by the proof of Lemma 7.1, we have

$$\lim_{r \to 0^+} \frac{\det \mathcal{A}(r,y)}{r^{n-1}} = 1. \tag{7.1.5'}$$

Set $\mathcal{A} = \mathcal{A}(t, y)$ for convenience. Recall that $\langle \cdot, \cdot \rangle = g_y(\cdot, \cdot)$ is an inner product on $T_p M$. Let $\mathcal{A}^*$ be the adjoint linear transformation of $\mathcal{A}$ on $(y^\perp, \langle \cdot, \cdot \rangle)$, i.e., $\langle \mathcal{A}(X), Y \rangle = \langle X, \mathcal{A}^*(Y) \rangle$ for any $X, Y \in y^\perp$. It is easy to verify that $\mathcal{A}^* \mathcal{A}$ is self-adjoint and $\det \mathcal{A}^* = \det \mathcal{A}$.

Lemma 7.2. *(i)* $\mathcal{A}'^* \mathcal{A} = \mathcal{A}^* \mathcal{A}'$.
(ii) $\mathcal{A}' \mathcal{A}^{-1}$ *is self-adjoint for any* $0 < t < c_y$.

Proof. Let $J_X = (\exp_p)_{*ty} tX = P_{t;y} \mathcal{A} X$ and $J_Y = (\exp_p)_{*ty} tY = P_{t;y} \mathcal{A} Y$ for any X, $Y \in y^\perp$. By the Lagrange identity (cf. [10], Exercise 5.4.6, p.135), we can get

$$
\begin{aligned}
0 &= g_T(\nabla_T^T J_X, J_Y) - g_T(J_X, \nabla_T^T J_Y) \\
&= g_T(P_{t;y} \mathcal{A}' X, P_{t;y} \mathcal{A} Y) - g_T(P_{t;y} \mathcal{A} X, P_{t;y} \mathcal{A}' Y) \\
&= g_y(\mathcal{A}' X, \mathcal{A} Y) - g_y(\mathcal{A} X, \mathcal{A}' Y) \\
&= g_y(X, (\mathcal{A}'^* \mathcal{A} - \mathcal{A}^* \mathcal{A}')(Y)),
\end{aligned}
$$

which implies $\mathcal{A}'^* \mathcal{A} = \mathcal{A}^* \mathcal{A}'$.

It follows from (i) that $0 = \langle X, (\mathcal{A}^{-1})^* [\mathcal{A}'^* \mathcal{A} - \mathcal{A}^* \mathcal{A}'] \mathcal{A}^{-1} Y \rangle$, which means

$$
\langle X, (\mathcal{A}' \mathcal{A}^{-1})^* Y \rangle = \langle X, \mathcal{A}' \mathcal{A}^{-1} Y \rangle. \qquad \square
$$

7.1.2 Distance function and comparison theorems

The distance function from a point $p \in M$ on an n-dimensional Finsler manifold (M, F) is defined by $r(\cdot) := d_F(p, \cdot)$, where $d_F(p, \cdot)$ is the distance induced by the Finsler metric F (Chapter 2, §2.1). Just as similar to the Riemannian case ([169]), we have the Laplacian comparison theorems for the distance function on the Finsler manifold.

Theorem 7.1. *Let $(M, F, d\mu)$ be an n-dimensional forward complete Finsler manifold, $r(\cdot)$ the distance function from a point $p \in M$.*

(i) If the Ricci curvature of (M, F) satisfies $Ric \geq (n-1)k$ for a constant k, then

$$
\triangle r|_x + \mathbf{S}(\nabla r)|_x \leq (n-1) \frac{\mathfrak{s}_k'(r)}{\mathfrak{s}_k(r)}, \quad \forall x \in \mathcal{D}_p \setminus \{p\};
$$

(ii) If the flag curvature of (M, F) satisfies $\mathbf{K} \leq k$, then

$$
\triangle r|_x + \mathbf{S}(\nabla r)|_x \geq (n-1) \frac{\mathfrak{s}_k'(r)}{\mathfrak{s}_k(r)}, \quad \forall x \in (\mathcal{D}_p \setminus \{p\}) \cap B_p^+ \left(\frac{\pi}{\sqrt{k}} \right),
$$

where $\mathfrak{s}_k$ is defined by (7.1.3), $\mathbf{S}$ is the $\mathbf{S}$-curvature associated with $d\mu$, and $\frac{\pi}{\sqrt{k}}$ means $+\infty$ for $k \leq 0$.

Proof. Recall that the definition of the Hessian of a function on (M, F) (§5.1.2). For any point $x \in \mathcal{D}_p \setminus \{p\}$, set $T := \nabla r$. We then have

$$
H(r)(u, v) = \langle \nabla_u^T \nabla r, v \rangle_{g_T}, \quad \forall u, v \in T_x M.
$$

Let $\gamma : [0, r(p)] \to M$ be a normal minimal geodesic from p to x, we have $\dot{\gamma}(r(x)) = \nabla r|_x = T|_x$ (see §5.1.2). Let $\{J_\alpha\}$ ($\alpha = 1, \cdots, n-1$) be Jacobi fields along $\gamma(t)$ satisfying $J_\alpha(0) = 0$ and $J_\alpha(r(x)) = e_\alpha$, where $\{e_\alpha, T\}$ is an orthonormal basis on $T_x M$ with respect to g_T. Thus, at the point x, we have

$$tr_{g_T} H(r) = g_T^{ij} H(r)(e_i, e_j) = \sum_\alpha H(r)(J_\alpha, J_\alpha)|_x = \sum_\alpha \langle \nabla_{J_\alpha}^T T, J_\alpha \rangle_{g_T}$$

$$= \sum_\alpha \langle \nabla_T^T J_\alpha, J_\alpha \rangle_{g_T} = \sum_\alpha I(J_\alpha, J_\alpha), \tag{$*$}$$

where $I(\cdot, \cdot)$ is the index form along γ (§5.1.2). Let $E_\alpha(t)$ be the parallel vector fields along γ with $E_\alpha(r(x)) = e_\alpha$. Then $\{E_\alpha\}$ are orthogonal with respect to g_T.

We now prove *the case (i) of Theorem 7.1*. Set $W_\alpha(t) = \frac{\mathfrak{s}_k(t)}{\mathfrak{s}_k(r(x))} E_\alpha(t)$. It is obvious that $W_\alpha(0) = J_\alpha(0) = 0$, $W_\alpha(r(x)) = J_\alpha(r(x)) = e_\alpha$. By the index Lemma (§5.1.2), $I(W_\alpha, W_\alpha) \geq I(J_\alpha, J_\alpha)$. It follows from $(*)$ and the condition of (i) that

$$tr_{g_T} H(r) \leq \sum_\alpha I(W_\alpha, W_\alpha)$$

$$= \frac{1}{\mathfrak{s}_k^2(r(x))} \int_0^{r(x)} \left[\sum_\alpha g_T(\nabla_T W_\alpha, \nabla_T W_\alpha) - \mathfrak{s}_k^2(t) Ric(T) \right] dt$$

$$\leq \frac{(n-1)}{\mathfrak{s}_k^2(r(x))} \int_0^{r(x)} [(\mathfrak{s}_k'(t))^2 - k\mathfrak{s}_k^2(t)] dt = (n-1) \frac{\mathfrak{s}_k'(r(x))}{\mathfrak{s}_k(r(x))}.$$

Thus, (i) follows from Lemma 5.1 (§5.1.2) immediately.

We now prove *the case (ii) of Theorem 7.1*. By using the notations as in (i), we get from the Jacobi equation that $g_T(J_\alpha, T) = 0$. Setting $J_\alpha(t) = \varphi_\alpha^\beta(t) E_\beta(t)$, we have $\varphi_\alpha^\beta(0) = 0$, $\varphi_\alpha^\beta(r(x)) = \delta_\alpha^\beta$ $(\alpha, \beta = 1, \cdots, n-1)$.

Let $(\widetilde{M}, \widetilde{F})$ be an n-dimensional simply connected forward complete Finsler manifold with constant flag curvature k. Take a point $\widetilde{p} \in \widetilde{M}$ and a geodesic $\widetilde{\gamma} : [0, r(x)] \to \widetilde{M}$ from $\widetilde{p}$. There is no conjugate points of $\widetilde{p}$ along $\widetilde{\gamma}$ since $r(x) < \frac{\pi}{\sqrt{k}}$. Let $\{\widetilde{E}_\alpha, \widetilde{T}\}$ be the parallel vector fields along $\widetilde{\gamma}$, which become an orthonormal frame field with respect to $\widetilde{g}_{\widetilde{T}}$, where $\widetilde{T} = \dot{\widetilde{\gamma}}$. Set $V_\alpha(t) = \varphi_\alpha^\beta(t) \widetilde{E}_\beta(t)$, $X_\alpha(t) = \frac{\mathfrak{s}_k(t)}{\mathfrak{s}_k(r(x))} \widetilde{E}_\alpha(t)$. Since the flag curvature of (M, F) is $K \leq k$, then $I(V_\alpha, V_\alpha) \leq I(J_\alpha, J_\alpha)$ according to Lemma 9.5.1 of [10] (p.242). Since X_α is a Jacobi field, $I(X_\alpha, X_\alpha) \leq I(V_\alpha, V_\alpha)$ by the index Lemma (§5.1.2). We then obtain from (∗)

$$tr_{g_T} H(r) = \sum_\alpha I(J_\alpha, J_\alpha) \geq \sum_\alpha I(V_\alpha, V_\alpha)$$

$$\geq \sum_\alpha I(X_\alpha, X_\alpha) = (n-1) \frac{\mathfrak{s}'_k(r(x))}{\mathfrak{s}_k(r(x))}.$$

Thus, (ii) follows from Lemma 5.1 (§5.1.2) directly.   □

Lemma 7.3. *Let (M^n, F) be a Finsler manifold of dimension n. If there is a unit vector $y \in S_pM$ such that the flag curvature $\mathbf{K}(y; \cdot) \equiv k$, then*

$$R_y(X, y)y = k(X - g_y(y, X)y)$$

for any $X \in T_pM$.

Proof. By the definition of the flag curvature, we have

$$R_y(y, X, y, X) = -k \left(g_y(X, X) - g_y^2(y, X) \right).$$

Let $\{e_i\}$ be an orthonormal basis with $e_n = y$ on T_pM with respect to g_y. The above equation then can be reduced as

$$[R_{ninj}(y) + k \left(g_{ij}(y) - g_{ni}(y)g_{nj}(y) \right)] X^i X^j = 0.$$

Since X is arbitrary and $R_{ninj} = R_{njni}$, we may differentiate the above equation with respect to X^l and obtain

$$[R_{inln}(y) + k(g_{il}(y) - g_{ni}(y)g_{nl}(y))]X^i = 0.$$

Thus, we have

$$\begin{aligned}
0 &= g^{ls}(y)[R_{inln}(y) + k(g_{il}(y) - g_{ni}(y)g_{nl}(y))]X^i e_s \\
&= [-R_{n\,in}^{s} + k(\delta_i^s - g_{ni}\delta_n^s)]X^i e_s \\
&= -R_y(X, y)y + k(X - g_y(y, X)y).
\end{aligned}$$ □

Lemma 7.4 (M. Gromov). *Let $f(t)$ and $g(t)$ be two positive functions defined on $[0, \infty)$. If f/g is decreasing with respect to t, then*

$$\int_0^x f dt \Big/ \int_0^x g dt$$

is decreasing with respect to x.

Proof. For $x_1 < x_2$, it holds that

$$\int_0^{x_1} f dt \int_0^{x_2} g dt = \int_0^{x_1} f dt \left(\int_0^{x_1} g dt + \int_{x_1}^{x_2} g dt \right),$$

$$\int_0^{x_2} f dt \int_0^{x_1} g dt = \left(\int_0^{x_1} f dt + \int_{x_1}^{x_2} f dt \right) \int_0^{x_1} g dt.$$

In order to prove

$$\int_0^{x_1} f dt \int_0^{x_2} g dt \geq \int_0^{x_2} f dt \int_0^{x_1} g dt,$$

we just need to prove

$$\int_0^{x_1} f dt \int_{x_1}^{x_2} g dt \geq \int_{x_1}^{x_2} f dt \int_0^{x_1} g dt.$$

Let $f = gh$. Since h is decreasing, we have

$$\int_0^{x_1} f dt \int_{x_1}^{x_2} g dt = \int_0^{x_1} g h dt \int_{x_1}^{x_2} g dt \geq h(x_1) \int_0^{x_1} g dt \int_{x_1}^{x_2} g dt$$

$$\geq \int_0^{x_1} g dt \int_{x_1}^{x_2} h g dt = \int_{x_1}^{x_2} f dt \int_0^{x_1} g dt. \qquad \square$$

7.1.3 Volume comparison theorems

For convenience we denote by $\gamma_y(t)$ the geodesic with constant velocity satisfying $\dot\gamma_y(0) = y$. By Lemma 7.1, we have the following comparison theorem for any volume form $d\mu$.

Theorem 7.2 ([132]). *Let $(M, F, d\mu)$ be n-dimensional forward complete Finsler manifold with*

$$Ric \geq (n-1)k,$$

where k is a real constant. Then the function

$$\mathcal{P}(r) = \frac{\mathcal{F}(r,y)}{\mathfrak{s}_k^{n-1}(r)}$$

is monotonically decreasing in r and converges to 1 (as $r \to 0^+$), where (r,y) is a polar coordinate system on $\mathcal{D}_p \setminus \{p\}$ for a point $p \in M$,

$$\mathcal{F}(r,y) := e^{\tau(\dot\gamma_y(r))} \widehat\sigma_p(r,y) = \sqrt{\frac{\det g(\exp_p(ry), \frac{\partial}{\partial r})}{\det \dot g_p(y)}}. \qquad (7.1.6)$$

Hence,

$$Vol_\mu(B^+(p,r)) \leq \mathcal{V}_{p,k,n}(r) \quad \text{for any } r > 0, \qquad (7.1.7)$$

where

$$\mathcal{V}_{p,k,n}(r) := \left(\int_{S_p M} d\nu_p(y) \right) \cdot \left(\int_0^r e^{-\tau(\dot\gamma_y(t))} \mathfrak{s}_k^{n-1}(t) dt \right), \qquad (7.1.8)$$

and $d\nu_p(y)$, $\mathfrak{s}_k(t)$ are defined by (7.1.2), (7.1.3) respectively. In particular, the equality for some $r_0 > 0$ holds in (7.1.7) if and only if for each $y \in S_p M$

$$\mathbf{K}(\dot\gamma_y(t); \cdot) \equiv k, \quad 0 \leq t \leq r_0 \leq \mathfrak{i}_p.$$

In this case,

$$g\left(\frac{\partial}{\partial r}\Big|_{(r,y)} \right) = dr \otimes dr + \mathfrak{s}_k^2(r) \dot{g}_p(y), \quad 0 < r < r_0,$$

where $\dot{g}_p$ is a Riemannian metric on $S_p M$ (see §7.1.1).

Proof. Recall that (7.1.2) $d\mu|_{(r,y)} = \hat\sigma_p(r,y) dr \wedge d\nu_p(y)$. By the definition of divergence,

$$(\Delta r) d\mu = \text{div}(\nabla r) d\mu = d(\nabla r \rfloor d\mu) = d\hat\sigma_p \wedge d\nu_p(y) = \frac{\partial \hat\sigma_p(r,y)}{\partial r} dr \wedge d\nu_p(y).$$

Hence $\Delta r = \frac{\partial}{\partial r} \log \hat\sigma_p(r,y)$. Theorem 7.1 now yields that

$$\Delta r + S(\nabla r) \leq \frac{\partial}{\partial r} \log[\mathfrak{s}_k(r)]^{n-1}.$$

Thus, for any $y \in S_p M$,

$$\frac{\partial}{\partial r} \left(\frac{\hat\sigma_p(r,y)}{e^{-\tau(\dot\gamma_y(r))} \mathfrak{s}_k^{n-1}(r)} \right) \leq 0, \quad \text{for} \quad 0 < r < \mathfrak{i}_y. \qquad (7.1.9)$$

Lemma 7.1 together with (7.1.9) yields $\hat\sigma_p(r,y) \leq e^{-\tau(\dot\gamma_y(r))} \mathfrak{s}_k^{n-1}(r)$, for $0 < r < \mathfrak{i}_y$. Thus, for any $r > 0$,

$$\text{Vol}_\mu(B^+(p,r)) \leq \int_{S_p M} d\nu_p(y) \int_0^{\min\{r,\mathfrak{i}_y\}} e^{-\tau(\dot\gamma_y(r))} \mathfrak{s}_k^{n-1}(r) dr$$

$$\leq \int_{S_p M} d\nu_p(y) \int_0^r e^{-\tau(\dot\gamma_y(r))} \mathfrak{s}_k^{n-1}(r) dr \qquad (7.1.10)$$

$$= \mathcal{V}_{p,k,n}(r).$$

If the equality in (7.1.10) holds for some $r_0 > 0$, then $r_0 \leq \mathfrak{i}_p$ and the equality in (7.1.9) holds. By Lemma 7.1 again, we have

$$e^{-\tau(\dot\gamma_y(r))} \sqrt{\frac{\det g(\exp_p(ry), \frac{\partial}{\partial r})}{\det \dot{g}_p(y)}} = \hat\sigma_p(r,y) = e^{-\tau(\dot\gamma_y(r))} \mathfrak{s}_k^{n-1}(r)$$

for each $y \in S_p M$ and $0 < r < r_0$. It follows from (7.1.5) that

$$\det \mathcal{A}(r, y) = \sqrt{\frac{\det g(\exp_p(ry), \frac{\partial}{\partial r})}{\det \dot{g}_p(y)}} = (\mathfrak{s}_k(r))^{n-1} \qquad (7.1.11)$$

for any $y \in S_p M$ and $0 < r < r_0$.

Set $\mathcal{B} := \mathcal{A}^* \mathcal{A}$. For $t \in (0, c_y)$, let $\{e_\alpha\}$ be a g_y-orthonormal basis for $y^\perp$, which are the eigenvectors of $\mathcal{B}(t, y)$. Denote by $\{\lambda_\alpha\}$ the eigenvalues, i.e., $\mathcal{B}(t, y)e_\alpha = \lambda_\alpha e_\alpha$. Then $\mathcal{B}^{-1} e_\alpha = \lambda_\alpha^{-1} e_\alpha$. Hence,

$$\frac{(\det \mathcal{B})'}{\det \mathcal{B}} = \mathrm{tr}(\mathcal{B}' \mathcal{B}^{-1}) = \sum_{\alpha,\beta} \mathcal{B}'^{\beta}_{\alpha} (\mathcal{B}^{-1})^{\alpha}_{\beta} = \sum_\alpha (\mathcal{B}')^{\alpha}_{\alpha} \lambda_\alpha^{-1}.$$

Put $J_\alpha(t) := (\exp_p)_{*ty} t e_\alpha$. Then

$$\lambda_\alpha = g_y(\mathcal{B} e_\alpha, e_\alpha) = g_y(\mathcal{A}^* \mathcal{A} e_\alpha, e_\alpha)$$
$$= g_y(\mathcal{A} e_\alpha, \mathcal{A} e_\alpha) = g_T(P_{t;y} \mathcal{A} e_\alpha, P_{t;y} \mathcal{A} e_\alpha) = g_T(J_\alpha, J_\alpha).$$

It is easy to check that $(\mathcal{A}^*(t, y))' = (\mathcal{A}'(t, y))^*$. Hence,

$$\mathcal{B}'^{\alpha}_{\alpha} = \sum_\alpha g_y(\mathcal{B}' e_\alpha, e_\alpha)$$

$$= \sum_\alpha [g_y((\mathcal{A}')^* \mathcal{A} e_\alpha, e_\alpha) + g_y(\mathcal{A}^* \mathcal{A}' e_\alpha, e_\alpha)]$$

$$= 2 g_y(\mathcal{A}' e_\alpha, \mathcal{A} e_\alpha) = 2 g_T(\nabla_T^T J_\alpha, J_\alpha).$$

Thus,

$$\frac{(\det \mathcal{A})'}{\det \mathcal{A}} = \frac{(\det \mathcal{B})'}{2 \det \mathcal{B}} = \sum_\alpha \frac{g_T(\nabla_T^T J_\alpha, J_\alpha)}{g_T(J_\alpha, J_\alpha)}.$$

Fix s with $0 < s < c_y$. Let $\{E_\alpha\}$ denote $n-1$ parallel vector fields along γ_y such that $g_T(E_\alpha, T) = 0$ and $E_\alpha(s) = \frac{J_\alpha}{\|J_\alpha\|}(s)$, where $\|\cdot\| := \sqrt{g_T(\cdot, \cdot)}$.

Now set $V_\alpha(t) = \frac{\mathfrak{s}_k(t)}{\mathfrak{s}_k(s)} E_\alpha(t)$. Since $Ric \geq (n-1)k$, we have

$$\frac{(\det \mathcal{A})'(s, y)}{\det \mathcal{A}(s, y)} = \sum_\alpha \frac{g_T(\nabla_T^T J_\alpha(s), J_\alpha(s))}{g_T(J_\alpha(s), J_\alpha(s))} = \sum_\alpha \frac{I(J_\alpha, J_\alpha)}{g_T(J_\alpha(s), J_\alpha(s))}$$

$$\leq \sum_\alpha \frac{I(\|J_\alpha(s)\| V_\alpha, \|J_\alpha(s)\| V_\alpha)}{g_T(J_\alpha, J_\alpha)} = \sum_\alpha I(V_\alpha, V_\alpha)$$

$$= \frac{1}{\mathfrak{s}_k^2(s)} \int_0^s [(n-1)(\mathfrak{s}_k'(s))^2 - Ric(T)(\mathfrak{s}_k(s))^2] dt$$

$$\leq \frac{1}{\mathfrak{s}_k^2(s)} \int_0^s [(n-1)(\mathfrak{s}_k'(s))^2 - (n-1)k(\mathfrak{s}_k(s))^2] dt$$

$$= (n-1)\frac{\mathfrak{s}_k'(s)}{\mathfrak{s}_k(s)},$$

which implies that $\det \mathcal{A}(t, y) \leq (\mathfrak{s}_k(t))^{n-1}$.

The above argument together with (7.1.11) implies that if a Jacobi field $J(t)$ satisfies $J(0) = 0$ and $g_T(J, T) = 0$, then

$$J(t) = \mathfrak{s}_k(t) E(t), \quad 0 \leq t < c_y,$$

where $E(t)$ is a parallel vector field along γ_y. Hence, for $0 \leq t \leq r_0 \leq \mathfrak{i}_p$, we have

$$\mathbf{K}(\dot{\gamma}_y(t); \cdot) \equiv k.$$

In particular,

$$g_{\alpha\beta}(\nabla r|_{(r,y)}) = g_{\nabla r}\left(\frac{\partial}{\partial\theta^\alpha}, \frac{\partial}{\partial\theta^\beta}\right)$$

$$= g_{P_{r;y}y}\left(P_{r;y}\mathcal{A}(r; y)\frac{\partial}{\partial\overline{\theta}^\alpha}, P_{r;y}\mathcal{A}(r; y)\frac{\partial}{\partial\overline{\theta}^\beta}\right)$$

$$= g_y\left(\mathcal{A}(r; y)\frac{\partial}{\partial\overline{\theta}^\alpha}, \mathcal{A}(r; y)\frac{\partial}{\partial\overline{\theta}^\beta}\right)$$

$$= [\mathfrak{s}_k(t)]^2 \dot{g}_{\alpha\beta}(y).$$

Hence,

$$g\left(\frac{\partial}{\partial r}\bigg|_{(r,y)}\right) = dr \otimes dr + \mathfrak{s}_k^2(r)\dot{g}_p(y), \quad 0 < r < r_0.$$

Suppose that for each $y \in S_p M$,

$$\mathbf{K}(\dot{\gamma}_y(t); \cdot) \equiv k, \quad 0 \leq t \leq r_0 \leq \mathfrak{i}_p.$$

We now show

$$\mathrm{Vol}_\mu(B^+(p, r)) = \mathcal{V}_{p,k,n}(r) \quad \text{for any} \quad 0 < r \leq r_0.$$

Given $y \in S_p M$, set $T = \dot{\gamma}_y(t)$. Let $J(t)$ be a Jacobi field along $\gamma_y(t)$ such that $J(0) = 0$ and $g_T(J, T) = 0$. Since $\mathbf{K}(T; \cdot) = k$, $\nabla_T^T \nabla_T^T J + kJ = 0$. Hence, $\mathfrak{i}_y \leq \frac{\pi}{\sqrt{k}}$ and $J(t) = \mathfrak{s}_k(t) E(t)$, where $E(t)$ is a parallel field along $\gamma_y(t)$.

Let (r, y) (or (r, θ)) be the polar coordinate system with respect to p. It follows from (7.1.1) that $\frac{\partial}{\partial\theta^\alpha}$ is a Jacobi field and

$$\lim_{r \to 0^+} \frac{1}{r}\frac{\partial}{\partial\theta^\alpha}\bigg|_{(r,y)} = \frac{\partial}{\partial\overline{\theta}^\alpha}\bigg|_y.$$

Hence,

$$\frac{\partial}{\partial\theta^\alpha}\bigg|_{(t,y)} = \mathfrak{s}_k(t) E_\alpha(t),$$

where $E_\alpha(t)$ is a parallel field along $\gamma_y(t)$ satisfying $E_\alpha(0) = \frac{\partial}{\partial \theta^\alpha}\big|_y$.
Since $\frac{\partial}{\partial r}\big|_{(t,y)} = \dot{\gamma}_y(t) = T$, then

$$\sqrt{\det\left[g\left(\exp_p(ty), \frac{\partial}{\partial r} \right) \right]} = \mathfrak{s}_k^{n-1}(t)\sqrt{\det g_T(E_\alpha, E_\beta)} = \mathfrak{s}_k^{n-1}(t)\sqrt{\det \dot{g}_p(y)}.$$

By the definition of the distortion, we deduce

$$\frac{d}{dt}\log\sqrt{\det\left[g\left(\exp_p(ty), \frac{\partial}{\partial r} \right) \right]} = \frac{d}{dt}\log\widehat{\sigma}_p(t,y) + \frac{d}{dt}\tau(\dot{\gamma}_y(t)).$$

From above two formulas it follows that

$$\frac{d}{dt}\log\widehat{\sigma}_p(t,y) = \frac{d}{dt}\log[e^{-\tau(\dot{\gamma}_y(t))}\mathfrak{s}_k^{n-1}(t)].$$

By Lemma 7.1, we have

$$\frac{\widehat{\sigma}_p(t,y)}{e^{-\tau(\dot{\gamma}_y(t))}\mathfrak{s}_k^{n-1}(t)} = \lim_{\varepsilon \to 0^+} \frac{\widehat{\sigma}_p(\varepsilon,y)}{e^{-\tau(y)}\mathfrak{s}_k^{n-1}(\varepsilon)} = 1.$$

Hence, $\mu(B^+(p,r)) = \mathcal{V}_{p,k,n}(r)$, for any $0 < r \le \mathfrak{i}_p$. Since $g_{\frac{\partial}{\partial r}}(\frac{\partial}{\partial r}, \frac{\partial}{\partial \theta^\alpha}) = 0$, then

$$g\left(\frac{\partial}{\partial r}\bigg|_{(r,y)} \right) = dr \otimes dr + \mathfrak{s}_k^2(r)\dot{g}_p(y), \quad 0 < r < \mathfrak{i}_y. \qquad \square$$

Put

$$\pi^* = \pi^*(k) := \begin{cases} \pi/\sqrt{k}, & \text{for } k > 0, \\ +\infty, & \text{for } k \le 0. \end{cases}$$

By using the similar argument as in Theorem 7.2, one can show the following

Theorem 7.3 ([132]). *Let $(M, F, d\mu)$ be a forward complete Finsler n-manifold. Suppose that the flag curvature of F satisfies*

$$\mathbf{K} \le k$$

for a real constant k. Then the function

$$\mathcal{P}(r) = \frac{\mathcal{F}(r,y)}{\mathfrak{s}_k^{n-1}(r)}$$

is monotonically increasing in r and converges to 1 (as $r \to 0^+$). Therefore,

$$\text{Vol}_\mu(B^+(p,r)) \ge \mathcal{V}_{p,k,n}(r) \qquad (7.1.12)$$

for any $0 < r \le \min\{\mathfrak{i}_p, \pi^*\}$, where the equality holds for some $r_0 > 0$ if and only if for each $y \in S_p M$,

$$\mathbf{K}(\dot{\gamma}_y(t); \cdot) \equiv k, \quad 0 \le t \le r_0 \le \min\{\mathfrak{i}_p, \pi^*\}.$$

In this case,

$$g\left(\frac{\partial}{\partial r}\bigg|_{(r,y)} \right) = dr \otimes dr + \mathfrak{s}_k^2(r)\dot{g}_p(y), \quad 0 < r < r_0,$$

where (r, y) is a polar coordinate system with respect to p.

Remark. If Finsler manifolds in Theorems 7.2 and 7.3 are Riemannian manifolds (M, g), then $\dot{g}_p$ is the standard metric of the Euclidean sphere. When the equality in (7.1.7) (resp. (7.1.12)) holds,

$$g = dr \otimes dr + \mathfrak{s}_k^2(r)\dot{g}_p$$

in a polar coordinate system (r, y) with respect to p. This means the metric sphere $B_p(r)$ in (M, g) is isometric to the metric sphere with radius r in the space form of constant curvature k. Hence, Theorems 7.2 and 7.3 imply volume comparison theorems in Riemannian geometry (cf. [169], §4.3).

Recall that $\mathbf{S}(\dot{\gamma}_y(t)) = \frac{d}{dt}\tau(\gamma_y(t))$. Hence, by Theorem 7.1 and Lemma 7.4, we can obtain the following relative volume comparison theorems.

Corollary 7.1. *Let $(M, F, d\mu)$ be a forward complete Finsler n-manifold.*
(i) If $Ric \geq (n-1)k$ and $a \leq \tau \leq b$, then

$$\frac{\mathrm{Vol}_\mu(B^+(p,r))}{\mathrm{Vol}_\mu(B^+(p,R))} \geq e^{a-b} \frac{\int_0^r \mathfrak{s}_k^{n-1}(t)dt}{\int_0^R \mathfrak{s}_k^{n-1}(t)dt}$$

for any $0 < r \leq R < \pi^*$.
(ii) If $Ric \geq (n-1)k$ and $\mathbf{S} \geq (n-1)h$, then the function

$$\mathcal{P}_1(r) = \frac{\mathrm{Vol}_\mu(B^+(p,r))}{\mathcal{V}_{p,k,h,n}(r)}$$

is monotonically decreasing in r and converges to 1 (as $r \to 0^+$), where

$$\mathcal{V}_{p,k,h,n}(r) = \int_{S_pM} e^{-\tau(y)}d\nu_p(y) \int_0^r (e^{-ht}\mathfrak{s}_k(t))^{n-1}dt.$$

Proof. (i) Since $Ric \geq (n-1)k$, Theorem 7.2 together with Lemma 7.4 implies that

$$\frac{\int_0^r \widehat{\sigma}_p(t,y)dt}{\int_0^r e^{-\tau(\dot{\gamma}_y(t))}\mathfrak{s}_k(t)dt}$$

is a decreasing function. Hence, for any $0 < r \leq R < \pi^*$, we have

$$\frac{\int_0^{\min\{i_y,R\}} \widehat{\sigma}_p(t,y)dt}{\int_0^R e^{-b}\mathfrak{s}_k(t)dt} \leq \frac{\int_0^{\min\{i_y,R\}} \widehat{\sigma}_p(t,y)dt}{\int_0^{\min\{i_y,R\}} e^{-\tau(\dot{\gamma}_y(t))}\mathfrak{s}_k(t)dt}$$

$$\leq \frac{\int_0^{\min\{i_y,r\}} \widehat{\sigma}_p(t,y)dt}{\int_0^{\min\{i_y,r\}} e^{-\tau(\dot{\gamma}_y(t))}\mathfrak{s}_k(t)dt} \leq \frac{\int_0^{\min\{i_y,r\}} \widehat{\sigma}_p(t,y)dt}{\int_0^r e^{-a}\mathfrak{s}_k(t)dt}.$$

Then

$$\frac{\text{Vol}_\mu(B^+(p,R))}{e^{-b}\int_0^R \mathfrak{s}_k(t)dt} = \frac{\int_{S_pM} d\nu_p(y)\int_0^{\min\{i_y,R\}} \widehat{\sigma}_p(t,y)dt}{\int_0^R e^{-b}\mathfrak{s}_k(t)dt}$$

$$\leq \frac{\int_{S_pM} d\nu_p(y)\int_0^{\min\{i_y,r\}} \widehat{\sigma}_p(t,y)dt}{\int_0^r e^{-a}\mathfrak{s}_k(t)dt} = \frac{\text{Vol}_\mu(B^+(p,r))}{e^{-a}\int_0^r \mathfrak{s}_k(t)dt}.$$

(ii) It follows from Theorem 7.1 that

$$\frac{\partial}{\partial r}\log\widehat{\sigma}_p(r,y) \leq \frac{\partial}{\partial r}\log[e^{-hr}\mathfrak{s}_k(r)]^{n-1}.$$

Hence,

$$\frac{\partial}{\partial r}\left(\frac{\widehat{\sigma}_p(r,y)}{[e^{-hr}\mathfrak{s}_k(r)]^{n-1}}\right) \leq 0.$$

Let $D(r) := \{y \in S_pM : r < i_y\}$. Clearly, for any $0 < r \leq R < +\infty$, $D(R) \subset D(r)$. Thus, for any $0 < r \leq R < +\infty$,

$$\frac{\int_{D(R)} \widehat{\sigma}_p(R,y)d\nu_p(y)}{[e^{-hR}\mathfrak{s}_k(R)]^{n-1}} \leq \frac{\int_{D(r)} \widehat{\sigma}_p(r,y)d\nu_p(y)}{[e^{-hr}\mathfrak{s}_k(r)]^{n-1}}.$$

Lemma 7.4 now implies that

$$\frac{\int_0^r dt \int_{D(t)} \widehat{\sigma}_p(t,y)d\nu_p(y)}{\int_0^r [e^{-ht}\mathfrak{s}_k(t)]^{n-1}dt} = \frac{\left(\int_{S_pM} e^{-\tau(y)}d\nu_p(y)\right)\cdot\text{Vol}_\mu(B_p^+(r))}{\mathcal{V}_{p,k,h,n}(r)}$$

is a decreasing function. Then

$$\mathcal{P}_1(r) = \frac{\text{Vol}_\mu(B^+(p,r))}{\mathcal{V}_{p,k,h,n}(r)}$$

is monotonically decreasing in r.

It is easy to see that $D(r) = S_pM$ if $r < i_p$. Lemma 7.1 now implies that

$$\lim_{r\to 0^+}\frac{\text{Vol}_\mu(B^+(p,r))}{\mathcal{V}_{p,k,h,n}(r)} = \lim_{r\to 0^+}\frac{\int_0^r dt \int_{S_pM} \widehat{\sigma}_p(t,y)d\nu_p(y)}{\int_{S_pM} e^{-\tau(y)}d\nu_p(y)\cdot\int_0^r [e^{-ht}\mathfrak{s}_k(t)]^{n-1}dt}$$

$$= \lim_{r\to 0^+}\frac{\int_{S_pM} \widehat{\sigma}_p(r,y)d\nu_p(y)}{\int_{S_pM} e^{-\tau(y)}d\nu_p(y)\cdot[e^{-hr}\mathfrak{s}_k(r)]^{n-1}}$$

$$= \frac{\lim_{r\to 0^+}\int_{S_pM} \frac{\widehat{\sigma}_p(r,y)}{[e^{-hr}\mathfrak{s}_k(r)]^{n-1}}d\nu_p(y)}{\int_{S_pM} e^{-\tau(y)}d\nu_p(y)}$$

$$= 1. \qquad\qquad \square$$

For the Busemann-Hausdorff measure, Corollary 7.1 is an improvement of volume comparison theorems in [103, 143].

We now generalize Corollary 7.1 further. One can refer to [157] for the Riemannian case. We introduce the following notations firstly.

Let $(M, F, d\mu)$ be an n-dimensional forward complete Finsler manifold. For a point $p \in M$, let $\Gamma \subseteq S_p M$ be a measurable set. For $0 \le r < R < \infty$, we define

$$A_{r,R}^{\Gamma}(p) := \{x \in M \,|\, r \le d(p, x) \le R, \text{there is a minimal geodesic } \gamma$$
$$\text{from } p \text{ to } x \text{ such that } \gamma(0) \in \Gamma\}.$$

Obviously, $A_{r,R}^{\Gamma}(p) = B_p^+(R) \backslash B_p^+(r)$ for $\Gamma = S_p M$. Define

$$\text{Vol}_\mu(A_{r,R}^{\Gamma}(p, k, h)) := \int_r^R dt \int_\Gamma e^{-\tau(y)} [\mathfrak{s}_k(t) e^{-ht}]^{n-1} d\nu_p(y).$$

Remark. The geometric meaning of $\text{Vol}_\mu(A_{r,R}^{\Gamma}(p, k, h))$ is as follows. Let $\widetilde{F}$ be another Finsler metric on M such that $(M, \widetilde{F})$ is a forward complete Finsler manifold, on which any point $p \in M$ satisfies following:

(1) $\widetilde{g}_{ij}(p, y) = g_{ij}(p, y)$, where $\widetilde{g}_{ij}$ and g_{ij} are fundamental tensors of $\widetilde{F}$ and F respectively. Hence, $\{y \in T_p M \,|\, F(p, y) = 1\} = \{y \in T_p M \,|\, \widetilde{F}(p, y) = 1\} = S_p M$;

(2) For any $y \in S_p M$, it holds that

$$K(\dot{\widetilde{\gamma}}_y(t); \cdot) \equiv k, \quad \mathbf{S}(\dot{\widetilde{\gamma}}_y(t)) \equiv (n - 1)h, \quad 0 \le t < i_y,$$

where $\widetilde{\gamma}_y(t)$ is the normal geodesic on $(M, \widetilde{F})$ with $\dot{\widetilde{\gamma}}_y(0) = y$;

(3) When $k > 0$, $\widetilde{i}_y = \widetilde{i}_p$ for any $y \in S_p M$, where $\widetilde{i}_y$ and $\widetilde{i}_p$ are the cut locus and the injective radius of (p, y) on $(M, \widetilde{F})$, respectively.

Let $A_{r,R}^{\Gamma}(p, k, h)$ be the similar set in $(M, \widetilde{F})$ corresponding to $A_{r,R}^{\Gamma}(p)$, i.e.,

$$A_{r,R}^{\Gamma}(p, k, h) := \{x \in (M, \widetilde{F}) \,|\, r \le d(p, x) \le R, \text{there is a minimal}$$
$$\text{geodesic } \widetilde{\gamma} \text{ from } p \text{ to } x \text{ such that } \widetilde{\gamma}(0) \in \Gamma\}.$$

Consider a pole coordinate system (r, y) on $(M, \widetilde{F})$ with respect to p. From the proof of Theorem 7.2 we have

$$d\mu|_{(r,y)} = e^{-\tau(y)} [\mathfrak{s}_k(t) e^{-ht}]^{n-1} d\nu_p(y),$$

i.e.,

$$\text{Vol}_\mu(A_{r,R}^{\Gamma}(p, k, h)) = \int_r^R dt \int_\Gamma e^{-\tau(y)} [\mathfrak{s}_k(t) e^{-ht}]^{n-1} d\nu_p(y).$$

If (M, F) is a Riemannian manifold, then $S_p M = \mathbb{S}^{n-1}$ and $\tau(y) \equiv 0$. So, $A_{r,R}^{\Gamma}(p, k, h)$ may be viewed as the set in the space form with constant sectional curvature k corresponding to $A_{r,R}^{\Gamma}(p)$.

We now need the following

Lemma 7.5. *Let (M, F) be n-dimensional Finsler manifold and $p \in M$. We then have*

$$\int_{S_pM} e^{-\tau_B(y)} d\nu_p(y) = c_{n-1}, \quad \int_{S_pM} e^{\tau_H(y)} d\nu_p(y) = c_{n-1},$$

where $c_{n-1} := \mathrm{Vol}(\mathbb{S}^{n-1})$ denotes the volume of the Euclidean $(n-1)$-sphere.

Proof. Let $\{U; x^i\}$ be a local coordinate neighborhood about p, and (x^i, y^i) denote the local coordinates of TM on U. Recall that

$$d\nu_p(y) = \sqrt{\det g_{ij}(p, y)} \cdot \left(\sum_{j=1}^{n} (-1)^{j-1} y^j dy^1 \wedge \cdots \wedge \widehat{dy^j} \cdots \wedge dy^n \right).$$

Let $d\mu_B = \sigma_B dx^1 \wedge \cdots \wedge dx^n$, where

$$\sigma_B(p) = \frac{\mathrm{Vol}(\mathbb{B}^n)}{\mathrm{Vol}\{y \in T_pM : F(p, y) < 1\}}.$$

Thus,

$$\int_{S_pM} e^{-\tau_B(y)} d\nu_p(y) = \sigma_B(p) \int_{S_pM} \left(\sum_{j=1}^{n} (-1)^{j-1} y^j dy^1 \wedge \cdots \wedge \widehat{dy^j} \cdots \wedge dy^n \right)$$

$$= \sigma_B(p) \mathrm{Vol}(S_pM).$$

By [10] (applying Stocks' theorem), we have $\mathrm{Vol}(S_pM) = n\mathrm{Vol}\{y \in T_pM : F(p, y) < 1\}$. Hence

$$\int_{S_pM} e^{-\tau_B(y)} d\nu_p(y) = n\mathrm{Vol}(\mathbb{B}^n) = c_{n-1}.$$

Let $d\mu_H = \sigma_H dx^1 \wedge \cdots \wedge dx^n$, where (see §4.1.2)

$$\sigma_H(p) = \frac{1}{c_{n-1}} \int_{S_pM} \sqrt{\det g_{ij}(p, y)} d\nu_p(y).$$

We then have

$$\int_{S_pM} e^{\tau_H(y)} d\nu_p(y) = \frac{1}{\sigma_H(p)} \int_{S_pM} \sqrt{\det g_{ij}(p, y)} d\nu_p(y)$$

$$= c_{n-1}. \qquad \square$$

Lemma 7.6 ([157]). *Let f, g be two positive functions defined on $[0, \infty)$. If f/g is monotonically decreasing, then for any $R > r \geq 0, S > s \geq 0, r \geq s, R \geq S$,*

$$\frac{\int_r^R f(t) dt}{\int_r^R g(t) dt} \leq \frac{\int_s^S f(t) dt}{\int_s^S g(t) dt}.$$

By using Lemma 7.6, we obtain the following

Theorem 7.4. *Let $(M, F, d\mu)$ be an n-dimensional forward complete Finsler manifold with*

$$Ric \geq (n-1)k \quad and \quad \mathbf{S} \geq (n-1)h$$

for real constants k and h. Let $\Gamma \subseteq S_p M$ be a measurable set. For any $R > r \geq 0$, $S > s \geq 0$, $r \geq s$, $R \geq S$, it holds that

$$\frac{\mathrm{Vol}_\mu(A^\Gamma_{r,R}(p))}{\mathrm{Vol}_\mu(A^\Gamma_{r,R}(p,k,h))} \leq \frac{\mathrm{Vol}_\mu(A^\Gamma_{s,S}(p))}{\mathrm{Vol}_\mu(A^\Gamma_{s,S}(p,k,h))}. \tag{7.1.13}$$

Proof. Firstly we have

$$A^\Gamma_{r,R}(p) = \int_r^R dt \int_{D(t)\cap\Gamma} \widehat{\sigma}(t,y) d\nu_p(y),$$

$$A^\Gamma_{r,R}(p,k,h) = \int_r^R dt \int_\Gamma e^{-\tau(y)}[\mathfrak{s}_k(t)e^{-ht}]^{n-1} d\nu_p(y)$$

$$= \int_\Gamma e^{-\tau(y)} d\nu_p(y) \int_r^R [\mathfrak{s}_k(t)e^{-ht}]^{n-1} dt.$$

By (7.1.9), it is easy to see that

$$\frac{\int_{D(R)\cap\Gamma} \widehat{\sigma}_p(R,y) d\nu_p(y)}{[e^{-hR}\mathfrak{s}_k(R)]^{n-1}} \leq \frac{\int_{D(r)\cap\Gamma} \widehat{\sigma}_p(r,y) d\nu_p(y)}{[e^{-hr}\mathfrak{s}_k(r)]^{n-1}},$$

which implies that

$$\frac{\int_{D(t)\cap\Gamma} \widehat{\sigma}_p(t,y) d\nu_p(y)}{[e^{-ht}\mathfrak{s}_k(t)]^{n-1}}$$

is monotonically decreasing in t. It follows from Lemma 7.6 that

$$\frac{\int_r^R dt \int_{D(t)\cap\Gamma} \widehat{\sigma}_p(t,y) d\nu_p(y)}{\int_r^R [e^{-ht}\mathfrak{s}_k(t)]^{n-1} dt} \leq \frac{\int_s^S dt \int_{D(t)\cap\Gamma} \widehat{\sigma}_p(t,y) d\nu_p(y)}{\int_s^S [e^{-ht}\mathfrak{s}_k(t)]^{n-1} dt}.$$

Hence, the inequality (7.1.13) holds. $\qquad\square$

7.2 Berger-Kazdan comparison theorems

7.2.1 The Kazdan inequality

Let (M, F) be a forward complete n-dimensional Finsler manifold. Fix a point $p \in M$ and a tangent vector $y \in S_p M$. Recall the Jacobi differential equation (7.1.4) in §7.1.1. For any $0 < s < t < c_y$, let $\mathcal{C}_s(t, y)$ be the solution of the following Jacobi equation on $y^{\perp}$

$$
\begin{cases}
\mathcal{C}_s'' + \mathcal{R}(t, y)\mathcal{C}_s = 0, \\
\mathcal{C}_s(s, y) = 0, \\
\mathcal{C}_s'(s, y) = \mathcal{I}.
\end{cases}
$$

Thus, $\det \mathcal{C}_s(t, y) = \det \mathcal{A}(t - s, \dot{\gamma}_y(s))$ for any $t \geq s$. We have the following

Lemma 7.7. *Given any $y \in S_p M$, we have for any $0 < s < t < c_y$*

$$
\mathcal{C}_s(t, y) = \mathcal{A}(t, y) \left(\int_s^t (\mathcal{A}^* \mathcal{A})^{-1}(r, y) dr \right) \mathcal{A}^*(s, y),
$$

$$
[\det \mathcal{C}_s(t, y)]^{\frac{1}{n-1}} \tag{7.2.1}
$$

$$
\geq [\det \mathcal{A}(t, y)]^{\frac{1}{n-1}} [\det \mathcal{A}(s, y)]^{\frac{1}{n-1}} \int_s^t \frac{1}{(\det \mathcal{A}(r, y))^{\frac{2}{n-1}}} dr,
$$

where the equality holds if and only if $\mathcal{A}(t, y) = [\det \mathcal{A}(t, y)]^{\frac{1}{n-1}} \mathcal{I}$.

Proof. A direct computation yields that $\mathcal{C}_s(s, y) = 0$, $\mathcal{C}_s'(s, y) = \mathcal{I}$ and

$$
\mathcal{C}_s'(t, y) = \mathcal{A}'(t, y) \left(\int_s^t (\mathcal{A}^* \mathcal{A})^{-1}(r, y) dr \right) \mathcal{A}^*(s, y) + (\mathcal{A}^{-1})^*(t, y)\mathcal{A}^*(s, y).
$$

Noting that $\mathcal{A}$ satisfies (7.1.4), we have

$$
\begin{aligned}
\mathcal{C}_s''(t, y) = {}& \mathcal{A}''(t, y) \left(\int_s^t (\mathcal{A}^* \mathcal{A})^{-1}(r, y) dr \right) \mathcal{A}^*(s, y) \\
& + \mathcal{A}'(t, y)(\mathcal{A}^* \mathcal{A})^{-1}(t, y)\mathcal{A}^*(s, y) + [(\mathcal{A}^{-1})^*]'(t, y)\mathcal{A}^*(s, y) \\
= {}& -\mathcal{R}(t, y)\mathcal{C}_s(t, y) + [\mathcal{A}'(t, y)\mathcal{A}^{-1}(t, y)][(\mathcal{A}^{-1})^*(t, y)\mathcal{A}^*(s, y)] \\
& - (\mathcal{A}^{-1}\mathcal{A}'\mathcal{A}^{-1})^*(t, y)\mathcal{A}^*(s, y).
\end{aligned}
$$

Since $\mathcal{A}'\mathcal{A}^{-1}$ is self adjoint (Lemma 7.2), then it follows from the above identity that

$$
\mathcal{C}_s''(t, y) + \mathcal{R}(t, y)\mathcal{C}_s(t, y) = 0.
$$

In the following, we shall prove the second inequality of (7.2.1). The proof will be separated in three steps.

Step one. We recall firstly the following Jensen inequality (cf. [25], p.237):

Let $\mathfrak{D}$ be the convex set determined by a positively definite self-adjoint linear transformation in a linear space V, $f = f(B)$ be a strongly convex function defined on $\mathfrak{D}$, and $d\nu$ be the positive measure on $\mathbb{R}$. For any $B : [a, b] \to \mathfrak{D}$ we then have

$$f\left(\frac{1}{\nu((a,b))}\int_a^b B(t)d\nu(t)\right) \le \frac{1}{\nu((a,b))}\int_a^b f(B(t))d\nu(t), \qquad (7.2.2)$$

where the equality holds if and only if $B(t)$ is a constant on $[a, b]$.

We now put

$$f(D) = (\det D)^{-1}, \quad \phi(t) = (\det \mathcal{A}(t,y))^{1/(n-1)},$$
$$D(t) = \phi^2(t)(\mathcal{A}^*\mathcal{A})^{-1}(t), \quad d\nu(t) = \phi^{-2}(t)dt$$

for any $D : [a, b] \to \mathfrak{D}$. We will prove $f(D)$ is strictly convex. Restricting f to any line $D(t) \subset \mathfrak{D}$, i.e., $D''(t) = 0$, we get

$$\frac{d}{dt}f(D(t)) = -(\det D)^{-2}(\det D)' = -(\det D)^{-1}\mathrm{tr}(D^{-1}D),$$

$$\begin{aligned}
\frac{d^2}{dt^2}f(D(t)) &= -\frac{d}{dt}(\det D)^{-1}\mathrm{tr}(D^{-1}D') \\
&= -\left[\frac{d}{dt}(\det D)^{-1}\right]\cdot\mathrm{tr}(D^{-1}D') - (\det D)^{-1}\frac{d}{dt}\mathrm{tr}(D^{-1}D') \\
&= (\det D)^{-1}[\mathrm{tr}(D^{-1}D')]^2 - (\det D)^{-1}[\mathrm{tr}((D^{-1})'D') + \mathrm{tr}(D^{-1}D'')] \\
&= (\det D)^{-1}\{[\mathrm{tr}(D^{-1}D')]^2 + \mathrm{tr}[(D^{-1}D')^2]\}.
\end{aligned}$$

Since $D^* = D \subset \mathfrak{D}$, then $(D')^* = (D^*)' = D'$, i.e., D' is self adjoint. Define the inner product $\mathfrak{S}(X, Y) := \langle DX, Y\rangle$, where $\langle\ ,\ \rangle$ is the inner product on V. Thus, the inner product $\mathfrak{S}$ is positively definite and satisfies

$$\begin{aligned}
\mathfrak{S}(D^{-1}D'X, Y) &= \langle DD^{-1}D'X, Y\rangle = \langle D'X, Y\rangle \\
&= \langle X, D'Y\rangle = \mathfrak{S}(X, D^{-1}D'Y),
\end{aligned}$$

i.e., $D^{-1}D'$ is self adjoint with respect to $\mathfrak{S}$. Hence, it can be reduced (by a linear transformation) to a diagonal matrix Λ. Thus, $\mathrm{tr}[(D^{-1}D')^2] = \mathrm{tr}(\Lambda^2) \ge 0$.

In conclusion, we have

$$\frac{d^2}{dt^2}f(D(t)) \ge 0,$$

where the equality holds if and only if $D' \equiv 0$.

Step two. Clearly, $D(t)$, $0 < t < c_y$, defined on $(y^\perp, \langle\cdot,\cdot\rangle)$ is self adjoint. Noticing that $\det \mathcal{A}^* = \det \mathcal{A}$ and using Jensen's inequality (7.2.2), we have

$$\nu((s,t))^n \le \det\left(\int_s^t D(r)d\nu(r)\right)\cdot\int_s^t \frac{1}{\det D(r)}d\nu(r).$$

Thus, $\det D(r) = \phi^{2(n-1)}(r) (\det \mathcal{A})^{-2}(r) = 1$ and

$$\left(\int_s^t \phi^2(r)dr \right)^{n-1} \leq \det \left(\int_s^t (\mathcal{A}^*\mathcal{A})^{-1}(r)dr \right).$$

Applying it to $\mathcal{C}_s(t,y)$ and using the first equality in (7.2.1), we have

$$\det \mathcal{C}_s(t,y) = \det \mathcal{A}(t) \det \left(\int_s^t (\mathcal{A}^*\mathcal{A})^{-1}(r)dr \right) \det \mathcal{A}^*(s)$$

$$\geq \det \mathcal{A}(t) \left(\int_s^t \phi^2(r)dr \right)^{n-1} \det \mathcal{A}^*(s)$$

$$= \left(\phi(t)\phi(s) \int_s^t \phi^2(r)dr \right)^{n-1}.$$

Step three. Consider the equality case in the above expression. By the first step, it is easy to see that the above equality holds if and only if

$$0 = \frac{d}{dt}D(t) = \frac{d}{dt}(\phi^2(t)(\mathcal{A}^*\mathcal{A})^{-1}(t)).$$

Hence, there is a constant $a \neq 0$ such that $\phi^2(t)\mathcal{I} = a\mathcal{A}^*(t)\mathcal{A}(t)$. Differentiating it with respect to t and using the Lemma 7.2, we get $\phi\phi'\mathcal{I} = a\mathcal{A}^*\mathcal{A}'$. Thus,

$$a\mathcal{A}' = \phi\phi'(\mathcal{A}^*)^{-1} = a\frac{\phi'}{\phi}\mathcal{A},$$

i.e., $\mathcal{A}(t,y) = \phi(t)\mathcal{I}$, $0 < t < c_y$. This completes the proof of the lemma. $\square$

Given $\lambda > 0$, let $\mathcal{S}$ be the following function set:

$$\mathcal{S} = \{\varphi \in C([0,\pi/\lambda]) |\; \varphi(x) = x^\alpha(\pi/\lambda - x)^\beta \psi(x),$$
$$\text{where } 0 \leq \alpha, \beta < 2, \; \psi \in C([0,\pi/\lambda]), \text{ satisfying } \psi|_{[0,\pi/\lambda]} > 0\}.$$

Define that

$$F(\varphi) := \int_0^{\pi/\lambda} dt \int_t^{\pi/\lambda} dr \int_t^r \frac{\varphi(t)\varphi(r)}{\varphi^2(s)}\rho(r-t)ds, \qquad (7.2.3)$$

where $\rho \in C([0,\pi/\lambda])$ is a non-negative function.

Theorem 7.5 (J. L. Kazdan). *If $\rho(\pi/\lambda - t) = \rho(t)$ for any $0 \leq t \leq \pi/\lambda$, then we have $F(\varphi) \geq F(\sin\circ\lambda)$, where $\sin\circ\lambda(x) := \sin(\lambda x)$.*

Proof. Without loss of generality, we can assume $\lambda = 1$. Otherwise, we may choose the transformations $\bar{t} = \lambda t$, $\bar{x} = \lambda x$ and $\bar{y} = \lambda y$.

Write φ as $\varphi(x) = \sin x \exp u(x)$, where $u \in C([0, \pi])$. Then $F(\varphi)$ can be expressed by

$$J(u) = \int_\Omega \exp[u(x) + u(y) - 2u(t)]d\mu(x, y, t),$$

where Ω be the integral domain of $F(\varphi)$ in $\mathbb{R}^3$ and

$$d\mu(x, y, t) = \frac{\sin x \sin y}{\sin^2 t}\rho(y - x)dtdydx.$$

We now need only to prove that

$$J(u) \geq J(0). \tag{7.2.4}$$

Since exp is convex, by the Jensen's inequality (7.2.2), we have

$$J(u) \geq \mu(\Omega) \exp[(\mu(\Omega)^{-1}K(u))], \tag{7.2.5}$$

where

$$K(u) = \int_\Omega [u(x) + u(y) - 2u(t)]d\mu(x, y, t). \tag{7.2.6}$$

If $u = $ constant, then the inequality in (7.2.5) becomes an equality. Since $\mu(\Omega) = J(0)$, the theorem follows from that $K(u) = 0$ for any $u \in C([0, \pi])$. Thus, we need only to prove the following lemma.

Lemma 7.8 ([19]). $K(u) = 0$ *for any* $u \in C([0, \pi])$ *if and only if* $\rho(\pi - t) = \rho(t)$, $0 \leq t \leq \pi$.

Proof. We shall compute three terms in (7.2.6) in details. Since

$$\int_x^y \sin^{-2} tdt = \frac{\sin(y - x)}{\sin x \sin y},$$

we have

$$\int_\Omega u(x)d\mu(x, y, t) = \int_0^\pi u(x)dx \int_x^\pi \sin(y - x)\rho(y - x)dy, \tag{7.2.7}$$

$$\int_\Omega u(y)d\mu(x, y, t) = \int_0^\pi u(y)dy \int_0^y \sin(y - x)\rho(y - x)dx. \tag{7.2.8}$$

Set $y - x = \pi - s$ in (7.2.7). By exchanging the integral order on x and y in (7.2.8) and putting $x - y = s$, we have

$$\int_\Omega [u(x) + u(y)]d\mu(x, y, t) = \int_0^\pi u(x)a(x)dx, \tag{7.2.9}$$

where

$$a(x) = \int_0^x \sin s \cdot \rho(s)ds + \int_x^\pi \sin s \cdot \rho(\pi - s)ds.$$

Exchanging the integral order in the last term of (7.2.6) yields that

$$\int_\Omega u(t)d\mu(x, y, t) = \int_0^\pi u(t)b(t)\sin^{-2}tdt, \qquad (7.2.10)$$

where

$$b(t) = \int_0^t \sin x dx \int_t^\pi \sin y \cdot \rho(y - x)dy.$$

It follows from (7.2.9) and (7.2.10) that

$$K(u) = \int_0^\pi u(t)f(t)\sin^{-2}tdt,$$

where

$$f(t) = \sin^2 ta(t) - 2b(t). \qquad (7.2.11)$$

Thus, in order to prove $K(u) = 0$ for all u under consideration, we need only to prove $f(t) = 0$. Since $f(0) = 0$, we want to prove $f'(t) = 0$.

Note that

$$b'(t) = \sin t \left[\int_t^\pi \sin y \cdot \rho(y - t)dy - \int_0^t \sin x \cdot \rho(t - x)dx \right].$$

We set $y - t = \pi - s$ in the first integral and $t - x = s$ in the second integral. Then we obtain

$$b'(t) = \sin t \left[\int_t^\pi \sin(s - t)\rho(\pi - s)ds + \int_0^t \sin(s - t)\rho(s)ds \right]. \qquad (7.2.12)$$

By means of (7.2.11), (7.2.12) and the expression of $a(t)$, a direct computation gives rise to

$$f'(t) = \sin^2 t \left[\sin t \cdot h(t) + 2\int_0^t \cos s \cdot h(s)ds - 2c \right], \qquad (7.2.13)$$

where

$$h(s) = \rho(s) - \rho(\pi - s),$$

$$c = \int_0^\pi \cos t \cdot \rho(t)dt = \int_0^{\pi/2} \cos t \cdot h(t)dt.$$

It follows from (7.2.13) that $f'(t) = 0$ if $h(t) = 0$. This shows the sufficient condition.

To prove the necessity, we set

$$g(t) = \sin t \cdot h(t) + 2 \int_0^t \cos s \cdot h(s)ds - 2c.$$

Thus, $g(t) = 0$ is equivalent to $f'(t) = 0$. Since

$$g'(t) = \sin t \cdot h'(t) + 3\cos t \cdot h(t) = \sin^{-2} t \frac{d}{dt}[\sin^3 t \cdot h(t)],$$

$g'(t) = 0$ implies that $h(t) = $ constant $\cdot \sin^{-3} t$. Noting that $h(\pi/2) = 0$, we have $h(t) = 0$. Hence, this shows the necessary condition. $\square$

Proof. In conclusion, Theorem 7.5 has been proved. $\square$

7.2.2   The rigidity of reversible Finsler manifolds

In this section, we are going to show the following

Theorem 7.6 ([61])**.** *Let (M, F) be an n-dimensional forward complete reversible Finsler manifold. If $\mathbf{K} \equiv 1$ and $\mathbf{S}_B \equiv 0$, then F is a Riemannian metric of constant curvature and the universal covering of (M, F) is isometric to a Euclidean sphere $\mathbb{S}^n$.*

Remark. The assumption on reversibility in the theorem can not be removed. Example 5.2 (§5.2.2) implies that there is a class of the non-reversible Randers metrics with positive constant flag curvature and vanishing $\mathbf{S}_B$-curvature.

Before proving Theorem 7.6, some preliminaries are requisite.

Let Vol_B be the Busemann-Hausdorff volume, $c_n := \mathrm{Vol}\,(\mathbb{S}^n)$ be the Euclidean volume of $\mathbb{S}^n$ and $\gamma_y(t)$ be a geodesic of constant velocity satisfying $\dot{\gamma}_y(0) = y$.

Lemma 7.9. *Let (M, F) be an n-dimensional, simply-connected, forward complete and reversible Finsler manifold with $K = 1$. If its $\mathbf{S}$-curvature with respect to the Busemann-Hausdorff volume measure vanishes identically and its diameter equals π, then $\mathrm{Vol}_B(M) = c_n$.*

Proof. Under the hypothesis of the lemma, by [104], for any point $x \in M$ there is a unique point $x' \in M$ such that $d(x, x') = \pi$ and x' is the cut locus of x. Thus, $\mathbf{i}_x = \pi$ and $B_x^+(\pi) = M \setminus \{x'\}$. It follows from the volume comparison theorem that $\mathrm{Vol}_B(M) = c_n$ immediately. $\square$

Let (x^i, y^i) be the local coordinate system of TM. The induced volume form dV_{SM} on $SM \subset TM$ can be written by (refer to §4.1.2 and §4.3.3)

$$
\begin{aligned}
dV_{SM} =& \frac{1}{(n-1)!} \omega \wedge (d\omega)^{n-1} \\
=& \det(g_{ij}(x,y)) \left(\sum (-1)^{i-1} y^i dy^1 \wedge \cdots \wedge \widehat{dy^i} \wedge \cdots \wedge dy^n \right) \\
& \wedge dx^1 \wedge \cdots \wedge dx^n \\
=& \sqrt{\det g_{ij}(x,y)} \cdot d\nu_x(y) \wedge dx^1 \wedge \cdots \wedge dx^n,
\end{aligned}
$$

where $\omega = \left(\frac{\partial F}{\partial y^i} dx^i \right)\Big|_{SM}$ is the restriction of the Hilbert form to SM.

Theorem 7.7 ([44]). *Let (M, F) be an n-dimensional compact reversible Finsler manifold, then*

$$
V_{SM} \le c_{n-1} \cdot \mathrm{Vol}_B(M),
$$

where the equality holds if and only if F is Riemannian.

In other words, for any compact reversible Finsler manifold, the Holmes-Thompson volume is not larger than the Busemann-Hausdorff volume.

Proof. Let $B_x := \{ y \in T_x M \cong \mathbb{R}^n : F(x, y) < 1 \}$ and $\overline{B}_x$ be its closure. The Euclidean volume of $\overline{B}_x$ is

$$
\mathrm{Vol}(\overline{B}_x) = \int_{B_x} dy, \quad dy := dy^1 \wedge \cdots \wedge dy^n.
$$

On the other hand, by the Legendre transformation, the dual norm F^* on the dual space $T_x^* M$ (refer to §3.4.1) determines a dual sphere $\overline{B}_x^*$, whose Euclidean volume is given by (cf. [10], p.414)

$$
\mathrm{Vol}(\overline{B}_x^*) = \int_{B_x} \det(g_{ij}) dy.
$$

Since (M, F) is reversible, by the Blaschke-Santaló's inequality of the convex body (cf. [10], p.403-414), we have

$$
\left[\mathrm{Vol}(\overline{B}_x^*) \right]^{\frac{1}{2}} \left[\mathrm{Vol}(\overline{B}_x) \right]^{\frac{1}{2}} \le \mathrm{Vol}(\mathbb{B}),
$$

where $\mathrm{Vol}(\mathbb{B})$ is the standard volume of the Euclidean ball. Moreover, the equality holds if and only if $F(y)$ at the point x is a norm induced from the Euclidean inner product. Hence,

$$
\int_{B_x} \det(g_{ij}) dy \le \frac{\mathrm{Vol}(\mathbb{B})^2}{\mathrm{Vol}(B_x)} = \frac{c_{n-1} \mathrm{Vol}(\mathbb{B})}{n \mathrm{Vol}(B_x)}, \tag{7.2.14}
$$

where the equality holds if and only if F is a norm induced from a Euclidean inner product on the tangent space at x.

A direct computation on $\overline{B}_x$ (cf. [10], p.417) yields

$$d \left[\det(g_{ij}) \sum (-1)^{i-1} y^i dy^1 \wedge \cdots \wedge \widehat{dy^i} \wedge \cdots \wedge dy^n \right] = n \det(g_{ij}) dy.$$

Applying the Stokes formula, we get

$$\int_{S_x M} \det(g_{ij}) \left(\sum (-1)^{i-1} y^i dy^1 \wedge \cdots \wedge \widehat{dy^i} \wedge \cdots \wedge dy^n \right) = n \int_{B_x} \det(g_{ij}) dy.$$

Then by the above inequality and (7.2.14), we have

$$\begin{aligned}
V_{SM} &= \int_{SM} \det(g_{ij}) \left(\sum (-1)^{i-1} y^i dy^1 \wedge \cdots \wedge \widehat{dy^i} \wedge \cdots \wedge dy^n \right) \\
&\quad \wedge dx^1 \wedge \cdots \wedge dx^n \\
&= \int_M dx \int_{S_x M} \det(g_{ij}) \left(\sum (-1)^{i-1} y^i dy^1 \wedge \cdots \wedge \widehat{dy^i} \wedge \cdots \wedge dy^n \right) \\
&= n \int_M dx \int_{B_x} \det(g_{ij}) dy \\
&\leq c_{n-1} \cdot \int_M \frac{\text{Vol}(\mathbb{B})}{\text{Vol}(B_x)} dx = c_{n-1} \text{Vol}_B(M),
\end{aligned}$$

where the equality holds if and only if F is a norm induced from a Euclidean inner product on the tangent space at every point x, i.e., F is Riemannian. $\qquad \square$

Theorem 7.8. *Let (M, F) be an n-dimensional forward complete Finsler manifold, whose geodesics are all closed with the length 2π. Then the ratio*

$$i(M) = \frac{V_{SM}}{V_{U\mathbb{S}^n}}$$

is an integer, where $\mathbb{S}^n$ is the standard Euclidean unit sphere, $U\mathbb{S}^n$ denotes the unit sphere bundle on $\mathbb{S}^n$.

Proof. Since orbits (geodesics) of the geodesic flow are cycled with period 2π, the geodesic flow on SM defines a point-free action $S^1 = \mathbb{R}/\mathbb{Z}-$. The orbits are just the closed geodesics with length 2π. Thus, the orbit space SM/S^1 can be viewed as a $2(n-1)$-dimensional manifold CM consisting of closed geodesics on M. The nature projection $p : SM \to CM$, $y \mapsto \gamma_y(t)$ ($\gamma_y(t)$ is the geodesic with the initial vector y) forms a principle bundle with the structure group S^1. By [93], the Ω defined by $p^*\Omega = i^*(d\omega/2\pi) = d\omega/2\pi$ (ω is the Hilbert form) is a symplectic form on CM.

By the Fubini's theorem of fibrations (cf. [140]), we get

$$V_{SM} = \int_{SM} \frac{1}{(n-1)!} \omega \wedge (d\omega)^{n-1}$$

$$= \frac{1}{(n-1)!} \int_{SM} \omega \wedge p^*(2\pi\Omega)^{n-1}$$

$$= \frac{(2\pi)^{n-1}}{(n-1)!} \int_{x \in CM} \left(\int_{p^{-1}(x)} \omega \right) \Omega^{n-1}.$$

Put

$$j(M) := \int_{CM} \Omega^{n-1}.$$

Then $j(M)$ is a topological invariant of the principle bundle $p : SM \to CM$. In virtue of the discussion in [140] (cf. [140], §3), $j(M)$ is even. Let $i(M) := \frac{1}{2}j(M)$. Since $\int_{p^{-1}(x)} \omega = 2\pi$, we have

$$V_{SM} = \frac{(2\pi)^n}{(n-1)!} \int_{CM} \Omega^{n-1} = \frac{(2\pi)^n}{(n-1)!} 2 \cdot i(M).$$

Noting

$$2 \cdot \frac{(2\pi)^n}{(n-1)!} = c_{n-1}c_n = V_{U\mathbb{S}^n},$$

we get the conclusion of the theorem. □

Remark. Under the same hypothesis as in Theorem 7.8, $i(M) = 1$ if M is homeomorphic to a sphere. This is proved in [140] and [148].

Proof of Theorem 7.6. By the assumption, M and its universal cover $\widetilde{M}$ are n-dimensional Finsler manifolds with flag curvature $K = 1$. By Bonnet-Myers Theorem (§5.1.2), they all are compact. All geodesics of them are closed with length 2π. Moreover, $\widetilde{M}$ is diffeomorphic to a sphere ([104]). It follows from Theorem 7.8 that $i(M) = 1$, $V_{S\widetilde{M}} = V_{U\mathbb{S}^n}$.

Since $\mathbf{K} = 1, \mathbf{S}_B = 0$, we have from Lemma 7.9 that $\mathrm{Vol}_B(\widetilde{M}) = c_n$. By Theorem 7.7, we get

$$V_{U\mathbb{S}^n} = c_{n-1} \cdot c_n$$

$$= c_{n-1} \cdot \mathrm{Vol}_B(\widetilde{M})$$

$$\geq V_{S\widetilde{M}} = V_{U\mathbb{S}^n},$$

Thus, $V_{S\widetilde{M}} = c_{n-1} \cdot \mathrm{Vol}_B(\widetilde{M})$. By Theorem 7.7, one can see that $(\widetilde{M}, F)$ is Riemannian and isometric to $\mathbb{S}^n$. Hence, F is a Riemannian metric of constant curvature. □

As an application of Theorem 7.6, we generalize the maximal radius theorem to the Finsler case.

Corollary 7.2 ([61]). *Let (M, F) be an n-dimensional complete reversible Finsler manifold. If $Ric(M) \geq n-1$, $\mathbf{S}_B \equiv 0$, $\operatorname{diam}(M) = \pi$, then (M, F) is isometric to the standard Euclidean unit sphere $\mathbb{S}^n$.*

Proof. Since $\operatorname{diam}(M) = \pi$, there are two points $x_1, x_2 \in M$ such that $d_F(x_1, x_2) = \pi$. By Corollary 7.1 to Theorem 7.2, we have

$$\frac{\operatorname{Vol}_B B^+_{x_1}(\pi/2)}{V_{1,0,n}(\pi/2)} \geq \frac{\operatorname{Vol}_B B^+_{x_1}(\pi)}{V_{1,0,n}(\pi)} = \frac{\operatorname{Vol}_B(M)}{V_{1,0,n}(\pi)}.$$

So,

$$\operatorname{Vol}_B B^+_{x_1}(\pi/2) \geq \operatorname{Vol}_B(M)/2.$$

By the same reason, we have

$$\operatorname{Vol}_B B^+_{x_2}(\pi/2) \geq \operatorname{Vol}_B(M)/2.$$

Since $B^+_{x_1}(\pi/2) \cap B^+_{x_2}(\pi/2) = \emptyset$,

$$\operatorname{Vol}_B(M) \geq \operatorname{Vol}_B \left(B^+_{x_1}(\pi/2) \cup B^+_{x_2}(\pi/2) \right)$$
$$= \operatorname{Vol}_B B^+_{x_1}(\pi/2) + \operatorname{Vol}_B B^+_{x_2}(\pi/2) \geq \operatorname{Vol}_B(M).$$

Thus, we get

$$\operatorname{Vol}_B B^+_{x_1}(\pi/2) = \operatorname{Vol}_B B^+_{x_2}(\pi/2) = \operatorname{Vol}_B(M)/2.$$

Define now

$$\mathcal{P}_{x_1}(r) = \frac{\operatorname{Vol}_B(B^+_{x_1}(r))}{\operatorname{Vol}_{1,0,n}(r)}, \quad \mathcal{P}_{x_2}(r) = \frac{\operatorname{Vol}_B(B^+_{x_2}(r))}{\operatorname{Vol}_{1,0,n}(r)}.$$

From the above discussion we obtain

$$\mathcal{P}_{x_1}(r) = \mathcal{P}_{x_1}(\pi), \quad \mathcal{P}_{x_2}(\pi - r) \geq \mathcal{P}_{x_2}(\pi/2) = \mathcal{P}_{x_1}(\pi/2), \quad r \in [\pi/2, \pi].$$

Since F is reversible, it holds for $r \in [\pi/2, \pi]$ that

$$\operatorname{Vol}_B(M) \geq \operatorname{Vol}_B(B^+_{x_1}(r)) + \operatorname{Vol}_B(B^+_{x_2}(\pi - r))$$
$$\geq \mathcal{P}_{x_1}(\pi/2) \left[\operatorname{Vol}_{1,0,n}(r) + \operatorname{Vol}_{1,0,n}(\pi - r) \right]$$
$$= \mathcal{P}_{x_1}(\pi/2) \cdot \operatorname{Vol}_{1,0,n}(\pi) = \operatorname{Vol}_B(M),$$

which implies that

$$\mathcal{P}_{x_2}(\pi - r) = \mathcal{P}_{x_2}(\pi/2) = \mathcal{P}_{x_1}(\pi/2), \quad r \in [\pi/2, \pi].$$

Noting that $\mathcal{P}_{x_2}(0) = \mathcal{P}_{x_1}(0) = 1$, one can see that

$$1 = \mathcal{P}_{x_2}(\pi - r) = \mathcal{P}_{x_1}(r), \ r \in [\pi/2, \pi].$$

Exchanging positions of x_1 and x_2 in the above proof yields that

$$\mathcal{P}_{x_1}(r) = \mathcal{P}_{x_2}(r) = 1, \quad r \in [0, \pi],$$

i.e., $\mathrm{Vol}_B(M) = \mathrm{Vol}_{1,0,n}(\pi) = c_n$.

In virtue of the equality in Theorem 7.2, the flag curvature of (M, F) at the point x_1 (or x_2) is 1. To prove that the flag curvature of (M, F) equals 1 identically, we need to prove that for any $p \in M$, there is a point $q \in M$ such that $d_F(p, q) = \pi$. We now use reductio ad absurdum. If not, there is a positive number ε such that $B_p^+(\pi - \varepsilon) = M$. Hence

$$\frac{\mathrm{Vol}_B B_p^+(\pi - \varepsilon)}{V_{1,0,n}(\pi - \varepsilon)} = \frac{\mathrm{Vol}_B(M)}{V_{1,0,n}(\pi - \varepsilon)} = \frac{V_{1,0,n}(\pi)}{V_{1,0,n}(\pi - \varepsilon)} > 1.$$

On the other hand, by Corollary 7.1 to Theorem 7.2, one obtains

$$1 = \lim_{r \to 0^+} \frac{\mathrm{Vol}_B B_p^+(r)}{V_{1,0,n}(r)} \geq \frac{\mathrm{Vol}_B B_p^+(\pi - \varepsilon)}{V_{1,0,n}(\pi - \varepsilon)} = \frac{V_{1,0,n}(\pi)}{V_{1,0,n}(\pi - \varepsilon)} > 1,$$

which is a contradiction. Hence, the flag curvature $K \equiv 1$. In virtue of Theorem 7.6, the corollary is proved completely. $\qquad\square$

7.2.3 The Berger-Kazdan comparison theorem

Let (M, F) be an n-dimensional Finsler manifold, and the local coordinate system of TM be (x^i, y^i). For a fixed point $x \in M$, let (r, y) be the polar coordinate system on $\mathcal{D}_x \setminus \{x\}$ (§7.1.1). Set

$$\sqrt{g(x, r, y)} := \sqrt{\frac{\det g(\exp_x(ry), \frac{\partial}{\partial r})}{\det \dot{g}_x(y)}} = \det \mathcal{A}(r, y)$$

for convenience.

We now prove the following Berger-Kazdan comparison theorem.

Theorem 7.9 ([132]). *Let (M, F) be an n-dimensional compact Finsler manifold with the reversibility λ. Define $\mathbf{S}_B^M := \max_{y \in SM} \mathbf{S}_B(y)$ and $\mathbf{S}_H^M := \max_{y \in SM} \mathbf{S}_H(y)$. If $\mathfrak{i}_M = \pi$, then the volume $\mathrm{Vol}_B(M)$ of M with respect to the Busemann-Hausdorff measure satisfies*

$$\mathrm{Vol}_B(M) \geq \frac{c_n}{\lambda^n} e^{-\frac{\pi}{\lambda}(|\mathbf{S}_B^M| + |\mathbf{S}_H^M|)}, \tag{7.2.15}$$

where $\mathbf{S}_B$ and $\mathbf{S}_H$ are the $\mathbf{S}$-curvatures with respect to Busemann-Hausdorff measure and Holmes-Thompson measure, respectively. If (M, F) is reversible, i.e., $\lambda = 1$, then the equality holds in (7.2.15) if and only if (M, F) is isometric to the standard Euclidean unit sphere $\mathbb{S}^n$.

Proof. Let $\gamma_y(t)$ be the geodesic with initial vector $\dot{\gamma}_y(0) = y$ ($F(y) = 1$) for a unit vector $y \in SM$. Since $i_M = \pi$ and the reversibility is λ for $r \in [0, \pi/2]$, we have

$$B^+ \left(\gamma_y(0), \frac{r}{\lambda} \right) \cap B^+ \left(\gamma_y(\pi), \frac{\pi - r}{\lambda} \right) = \emptyset.$$

Hence

$$\text{Vol}_B(M) \geq \text{Vol}_B \left(B^+ \left(\gamma_y(0), \frac{r}{\lambda} \right) \right) + \text{Vol}_B \left(B^+ \left(\gamma_y(\pi), \frac{\pi - r}{\lambda} \right) \right).$$

Observe that

$$\int_{SM} \text{Vol}_B \left(B^+(\pi_1(y), r) \right) dV_{SM}$$

$$= \int_M d\mu_H(x) \int_{S_x M} \text{Vol}_B \left(B^+(x, r) \right) e^{\tau_H(y)} d\nu_x(y)$$

$$= c_{n-1} \int_M \text{Vol}_B \left(B^+(x, r) \right) d\mu_H(x)$$

$$= c_{n-1} \int_M d\mu_H(x) \int_0^r dt \int_{S_x M} \widehat{\sigma}_{Bx}(t, y) d\nu_x(y)$$

$$= c_{n-1} \int_M d\mu_H(x) \int_0^r dt \int_{S_x M} \frac{\sigma_{Bx}(t, y)}{\sqrt{\det \dot{g}_x(y)}} d\nu_x(y)$$

$$= c_{n-1} \int_M d\mu_H(x) \int_0^r dt \int_{S_x M} \sqrt{g(x, t, y)} e^{-\tau_B((\exp_x)_* t_y y)} d\nu_x(y).$$

For any $y \in SM$ we denote by $\varphi_t(y)$ the geodesic flow on SM with $\varphi_0(y) = y$. It is obvious that $\mathfrak{p} \circ \varphi_t(y) = \gamma_y(t)$, where $\mathfrak{p} : SM \to M$ is the bundle projection. Since $\varphi_t : SM \to SM$ is a diffeomorphism, we have from Proposition 4.7 (§4.3.3)

$$\int_{SM} \text{Vol}_B \left(B^+ \left(\gamma_y(\pi), \frac{\pi - r}{\lambda} \right) \right) dV_{SM}(y)$$

$$= \int_{SM} \text{Vol}_B \left(B^+ \left(\mathfrak{p} \circ \varphi_\pi(y), \frac{\pi - r}{\lambda} \right) \right) dV_{SM}(y)$$

$$= \int_{\varphi_\pi^{-1} \circ \varphi_\pi(SM)} \text{Vol}_B \left(B^+ \left(\mathfrak{p} \circ \varphi_\pi(y), \frac{\pi - r}{\lambda} \right) \right) dV_{SM}(y)$$

$$= \int_{\varphi_\pi(SM)} (\varphi_\pi^{-1})^* \left[\text{Vol}_B \left(B^+ \left(\mathfrak{p} \circ \varphi_\pi(y), \frac{\pi - r}{\lambda} \right) \right) dV_{SM}(y) \right]$$

$$= \int_{\varphi_\pi(SM)} \text{Vol}_B \left(B^+ \left(\mathfrak{p} \circ \varphi_\pi(y), \frac{\pi - r}{\lambda} \right) \right) dV_{SM}(\varphi_\pi(y))$$

$$= \int_{SM} \text{Vol}_B \left(B^+ \left(\mathfrak{p}(y), \frac{\pi - r}{\lambda} \right) \right) dV_{SM}(y).$$

By the definition of dV_{SM} (or Lemma 7.5), $\mathrm{Vol}(SM) = c_{n-1}\mathrm{Vol}_H(M)$, where $\mathrm{Vol}_H(M)$ is the volume of M with respect to the Holmes-Thompson measure. We obtain

$$c_{n-1}\mathrm{Vol}_H(M)\mathrm{Vol}_B(M) = \int_{SM} \mathrm{Vol}_B(M)dV_{SM}(y)$$

$$\geq \int_{SM} \left[\mathrm{Vol}_B\left(B^+\left(\gamma_y(0),\frac{r}{\lambda}\right)\right) + \mathrm{Vol}_B\left(B^+\left(\gamma_y(\pi),\frac{\pi-r}{\lambda}\right)\right)\right]dV_{SM}(y)$$

$$= \int_{SM} \left[\mathrm{Vol}_B\left(B^+\left(\mathfrak{p}(y),\frac{r}{\lambda}\right)\right) + \mathrm{Vol}_B\left(B^+\left(\mathfrak{p}(y),\frac{\pi-r}{\lambda}\right)\right)\right]dV_{SM}(y)$$

$$= c_{n-1}\int_M d\mu_H(x)\int_{S_x M} d\nu_x(y)\left[\left(\int_0^{r/\lambda} + \int_0^{\frac{\pi-r}{\lambda}}\right)D(x,t,y)dt\right],$$

where $D(x,t,y) := \sqrt{g(x,t,y)}e^{-\tau_B(\varphi_t(y))}$. Thus,

$$\frac{\pi}{2}\mathrm{Vol}_H(M)\mathrm{Vol}_B(M)$$

$$\geq \int_M d\mu_H(x)\int_{S_x M} d\nu_x(y)\int_0^{\pi/2}\left[\left(\int_0^{r/\lambda} + \int_0^{\frac{\pi-r}{\lambda}}\right)D(x,t,y)dt\right]dr.$$

Exchanging the integral order yields that

$$\int_0^{\pi/2} dr\int_0^{r/\lambda} D(x,t,y)dt = \int_0^{\frac{\pi}{2\lambda}} dt\int_{t\lambda}^{\pi/2} D(x,t,y)dr$$

$$= \int_0^{\frac{\pi}{2\lambda}} (\pi/2 - t\lambda)D(x,t,y)dt,$$

$$\int_0^{\pi/2} dr\int_0^{\frac{\pi-r}{\lambda}} D(x,t,y)dt$$

$$= \int_0^{\frac{\pi}{2\lambda}} dt\int_0^{\pi/2} D(x,t,y)dr + \int_{\frac{\pi}{2\lambda}}^{\pi/\lambda} dt\int_0^{\pi-\lambda t} D(x,t,y)dr$$

$$= \int_0^{\frac{\pi}{2\lambda}} \frac{\pi}{2}D(x,t,y)dt + \int_{\frac{\pi}{2\lambda}}^{\pi/\lambda} (\pi - \lambda t)D(x,t,y)dt.$$

Hence,

$$\int_0^{\pi/2}\left[\int_0^{r/\lambda} + \int_0^{\frac{\pi-r}{\lambda}} D(x,t,y)dt\right]dr = \int_0^{\frac{\pi}{\lambda}} (\pi - \lambda t)D(x,t,y)dt.$$

Thus, we obtain

$$\frac{\pi}{2}\mathrm{Vol}_H(M)\mathrm{Vol}_B(M)$$

$$\geq \int_M d\mu_H(x) \int_{S_xM} d\nu_x(y) \int_0^{\frac{\pi}{\lambda}} (\pi - \lambda t)D(x,t,y)dt$$

$$= \lambda \int_M d\mu_H(x) \int_{S_xM} d\nu_x(y) \int_0^{\frac{\pi}{\lambda}} dt \int_0^{\frac{\pi}{\lambda}-t} D(x,t,y)dr$$

$$= \lambda \int_0^{\frac{\pi}{\lambda}} dt \int_0^{\frac{\pi}{\lambda}-t} dr \int_{SM} e^{-\tau_H(y)}D(x,t,y)dV_{SM}(y)$$

$$= \lambda \int_0^{\frac{\pi}{\lambda}} dt \int_0^{\frac{\pi}{\lambda}-t} dr \int_{SM} e^{-\tau_H(\varphi_r(y))}D(\mathfrak{p}(\varphi_r(y)),t,\varphi_r(y))dV_{SM}(y)$$

$$= \lambda \int_0^{\frac{\pi}{\lambda}} dt \int_0^{\frac{\pi}{\lambda}-t} dr \int_{SM} e^{-[\tau_H(\varphi_r(y))+\tau_{BH}(\varphi_{t+r}(y))]}$$
$$\cdot \sqrt{g(\mathfrak{p}(\varphi_r(y)),t,\varphi_r(y))}dV_{SM}(y).$$

By the definition of the **S**-curvature, we have

$$\tau_H(\varphi_r(y)) \leq \tau_H(y) + \frac{\pi}{\lambda}|\mathbf{S}_H^M|, \quad \tau_B(\varphi_{t+r}(y)) \leq \tau_B(y) + \frac{\pi}{\lambda}|\mathbf{S}_B^M|.$$

Putting $\Lambda = e^{-\frac{\pi}{\lambda}(|\mathbf{S}_B^M|+|\mathbf{S}_H^M|)}$, one can see that

$$\frac{\pi}{2\lambda}\mathrm{Vol}_H(M)\mathrm{Vol}_B(M)$$

$$\geq \Lambda \int_0^{\frac{\pi}{\lambda}} dt \int_0^{\frac{\pi}{\lambda}-t} dr \int_{SM} e^{-[\tau_H(y)+\tau_B(y)]}\sqrt{g(\mathfrak{p}(\varphi_r(y)),t,\varphi_r(y))}dV_{SM}(y)$$

$$= \Lambda \int_M d\mu_H(x) \int_{S_xM} e^{-\tau_B(y)}d\nu_x(y) \int_0^{\frac{\pi}{\lambda}} dt \int_0^{\frac{\pi}{\lambda}-t} \sqrt{g(\mathfrak{p}(\varphi_r(y)),t,\varphi_r(y))}dr$$

$$= \Lambda \int_M d\mu_H(x) \int_{S_xM} e^{-\tau_B(y)}d\nu_x(y) \int_0^{\frac{\pi}{\lambda}} dr \int_0^{\frac{\pi}{\lambda}-r} \sqrt{g(\mathfrak{p}(\varphi_r(y)),t,\varphi_r(y))}dt$$

$$= \Lambda \int_M d\mu_H(x) \int_{S_xM} e^{-\tau_B(y)}d\nu_x(y) \int_0^{\frac{\pi}{\lambda}} dr \int_r^{\frac{\pi}{\lambda}} \sqrt{g(\mathfrak{p}(\varphi_r(y)),t-r,\varphi_r(y))}dt.$$

The Hölder inequality together with Lemma 7.7 and Theorem 7.4 yields that

$$\int_0^{\frac{\pi}{\lambda}} dr \int_r^{\frac{\pi}{\lambda}} \sqrt{g(\mathfrak{p}(\varphi_r(y)), t - r, \varphi_r(y))} dt$$

$$\geq \frac{\left[\int_0^{\frac{\pi}{\lambda}} dr \int_r^{\frac{\pi}{\lambda}} \sqrt{g(\mathfrak{p}(\varphi_r(y)), t - r, \varphi_r(y))}^{\frac{1}{n-1}} \sin^{n-2}(\lambda(t - r)) dt \right]^{n-1}}{\left[\int_0^{\frac{\pi}{\lambda}} dr \int_r^{\frac{\pi}{\lambda}} \sin^{n-1}(\lambda(t - r)) dt \right]^{n-2}}$$

$$\geq \frac{\left[\int_0^{\frac{\pi}{\lambda}} dr \int_r^{\frac{\pi}{\lambda}} dt \int_r^t \frac{\sqrt{g(x,t,y)}^{\frac{1}{n-1}} \sqrt{g(x,s,y)}^{\frac{1}{n-1}}}{\sqrt{g(x,l,y)}^{\frac{2}{n-1}}} \sin^{n-2}(\lambda(t - r)) dl \right]^{n-1}}{\left[\int_0^{\frac{\pi}{\lambda}} dr \int_r^{\frac{\pi}{\lambda}} \sin^{n-1}(\lambda(t - r)) dt \right]^{n-2}}$$

$$\geq \frac{1}{\lambda^{n-1}} \int_0^{\frac{\pi}{\lambda}} dr \int_r^{\frac{\pi}{\lambda}} \sin^{n-1}(\lambda(t - r)) dt$$

$$= \frac{1}{\lambda^{n+1}} \int_0^{\pi} dr \int_r^{\pi} \sin^{n-1}(t - r) dt = \frac{\pi c_n}{2 c_{n-1} \lambda^{n+1}}.$$

Then it follows from Lemma 7.5 that

$$\text{Vol}_H(M) \text{Vol}_B(M) \geq \frac{c_n \Lambda}{c_{n-1} \lambda^n} \int_M d\mu_H(x) \int_{S_x M} e^{-\tau_B(y)} d\nu_x(y)$$

$$= \frac{c_n \Lambda}{\lambda^n} \text{Vol}_H(M),$$

i.e.,

$$\text{Vol}_B(M) \geq \frac{c_n \Lambda}{\lambda^n}.$$

We now consider the case that $\lambda = 1$ and the equality of (7.2.15) holds. By the above discussion, for any $y \in SM$, $0 \leq t \leq \pi$ and $0 \leq r \leq \pi - t$, we have

$$\tau_H(\varphi_r(y)) + \tau_B(\varphi_{t+r}(y)) = \tau_H(y) + \tau_B(y) + \pi(|\mathbf{S}_B^M| + |\mathbf{S}_H^M|).$$

Since (M, F) is reversible, $\mathbf{S}_B^M \geq 0$, $\mathbf{S}_H^M \geq 0$ and

$$\tau_H(y) + \tau_B(y) + r\mathbf{S}_H^M + (t + r)\mathbf{S}_B^M \geq \tau_H(\varphi_r(y)) + \tau_B(\varphi_{t+r}(y)),$$

which implies that $\mathbf{S}_H^M = \mathbf{S}_B^M = 0$. Now assume that there is a $y \in SM$ such that $\mathbf{S}_H(y) < 0$. We then have $\mathbf{S}_H(-y) = -\mathbf{S}_H(y) > 0$, which is a contradiction. Hence, $\mathbf{S}_H = \mathbf{S}_B = 0$.

By Lemma 7.7 and the condition that the equality holds in the Hölder inequality, for any $y \in SM$, $0 \leq t \leq \pi$ and $0 \leq r \leq \pi - t$, we have

$$\begin{cases} \sqrt{g(\mathfrak{p}(\varphi_r(y)), t - r, \varphi_r(y))} = \sin^{n-1}(t - r), \\ \mathcal{A}(t, y) = \sqrt{g(x, t, y)}^{\frac{1}{n-1}} \mathcal{I}, \end{cases}$$

i.e., $\mathcal{A}(t, y) = \sin t \cdot \mathcal{I}$. It means that $\mathcal{R}(t, y) = \mathcal{I}$ for any $0 \leq t \leq \pi$. Putting $t \to 0^+$ yields that

$$R_y = R_y(\cdot, y)y = \mathcal{I} : y^\perp \to y^\perp,$$

i.e., $K \equiv 1$.

Thus, we have proved that (M, F) is an n-dimensional compact reversible Finsler manifold with $K \equiv 1$ and $\mathbf{S}_B \equiv 0$. By Theorem 7.5, F is Riemannian and the universal covering of M is $\mathbb{S}^n$. Since $\mathrm{Vol}_B(M) = c_n$, then (M, F) is isometric to $\mathbb{S}^n$. □

Remark. In the Riemannian case, the **S**-curvature vanishes identically, i.e., $\mathbf{S}_B^M = \mathbf{S}_H^M = 0$. Moreover, $\lambda = 1$. Hence, the above theorem is just the Berger-Kazdan comparison theorem in Riemannian geometry ([19, 25]).

Exercises

7.1   Let (M, F) be a Finsler manifold. Fix a point $x \in M$ and $y \in T_x M \setminus \{0\}$, let $r := F(x, y)$. Suppose that the exponential map $\exp_x y$ is defined. Let T be the tangent vector of the (radial) geodesic $\exp_x(ty)$ $(0 \leq t \leq 1)$. For any $t \in (0, 1]$ and any vector V in the tangent space of (geodesic) hypersurface $S_x(tr)$, prove (Gauss Lemma):

$$g_T(\exp_{x*} V, T) = \langle \exp_{x*} V, T \rangle_{g_T} = 0.$$

7.2   Prove Lemma 7.6 and further discuss the equality in (7.1.13).

7.3   Prove Jensen's inequality (7.2.2).

7.4   For a ball $\overline{B}_x := \{y \in T_x M | F(x, y) \leq 1\}$ in Finsler manifold (M, F), prove the following equality:

$$d\left[\det(g_{ij}) \sum (-1)^{i-1} y^i dy^1 \wedge \cdots \wedge \widehat{dy^i} \wedge \cdots \wedge dy^n \right] = n \det(g_{ij}) dy.$$

7.5   Let $(\mathbb{R}^n, F)$ be the n-dimensional $(n \geq 3)$ Minkowski space. Prove (Brickell) that if the curvature of the Riemannian metric $\widehat{g} := g_{ij}(y) dy^i \otimes dy^j$ vanishes identically on $\mathbb{R}^n \setminus \{0\}$, then F must be the norm of an inner product on $\mathbb{R}^n$ ([17]).

Chapter 8

Fundamental Groups of Finsler Manifolds

8.1 Fundamental groups of Finsler manifolds

8.1.1 Fundamental groups and covering spaces

Let M be an n-dimensional differential manifold and fix a point $p \in M$. A continuous curve $\gamma(t)$ $(0 \le t \le 1)$ on M is called a *loop* at p if $\gamma(0) = \gamma(1) = p$. We denote the class of all such loops by

$$\Gamma(p) = \Big\{ \gamma(t) \subset M \mid 0 \le t \le 1, \ \gamma(0) = \gamma(1) = p, \ \gamma(t) \ \text{continuous} \Big\}.$$

Let $\gamma_1(t), \gamma_2(t) \in \Gamma(p)$, we can define the product operator $*$ as follows

$$\gamma_1 * \gamma_2(t) := \begin{cases} \gamma_1(2t), & \text{if } 0 \le t \le \dfrac{1}{2}, \\ \gamma_2[2(1-t)], & \text{if } \dfrac{1}{2} \le t \le 1. \end{cases}$$

It is obvious that $\gamma_1 * \gamma_2(t) \in \Gamma(p)$. Denote by $1 \in \Gamma(p)$ the constant curve and by $[\gamma]$ the class of all loops homotopic to γ. It is easy to verify that if $[\gamma_1] = [\gamma_1']$ and $[\gamma_2] = [\gamma_2']$, then $[\gamma_1 * \gamma_2] = [\gamma_1' * \gamma_2']$. If $\gamma^{-1}(t) = \gamma(1-t)$, then $[\gamma_1 * \gamma^{-1}] = 1$ and $[1 * \gamma] = [\gamma]$. Thus the operation $[\gamma_1] * [\gamma_2] = [\gamma_1 * \gamma_2]$ is well-defined. Then, the set $\{[\gamma] \mid \gamma \in \Gamma(p)\}$ with operation $*$ becomes a group. Its unit is 1 and the inverse of $[\gamma]$ is given by $[\gamma]^{-1} = [\gamma^{-1}]$. This group is called the *fundamental group* of M at p, denoted by $\pi_1(p)$.

If M is connected, $q \in M$ is another point, then $\pi_1(p)$ is isomorphic to $\pi_1(q)$. In fact, let σ is an arbitrary curve from q to p, then $[\sigma * \gamma * \sigma^{-1}] \in \pi_1(q)$ for any $[\gamma] \in \pi_1(p)$, thus the map $[\gamma] \to [\sigma * \gamma * \sigma^{-1}]$ is an isomorphism. For this reason, for connected manifold M, we simply denote by $\pi(M)$ the fundamental group, without mentioning the point. It is also called the first homotopy group.

Let M and $\widetilde{M}$ be connected n-dimensional manifold and $\psi : \widetilde{M} \to M$ a continuous map. If ψ is an onto map and for every point $p \in M$, there exists an open neighborhood U of $p \in M$, such that $\psi^{-1}(U)$ is union of disjoint open subsets in $\widetilde{M}$ with each homeomorphic to U, then $\widetilde{M}$ is called the *universal covering space* of M, and ψ is called the *covering map*. Such U is called an admissible neighborhood on M.

When $\widetilde{M}$ is simply connected, $\widetilde{M}$ is called the *universal covering space* of M. First we have the following

Proposition 8.1. *Let (M, F) be a forward complete Finsler manifold and $p \in M$ a fixed point. Then, every homotopy class of a loop at p contains a closed geodesic with shortest length among all loops in the class.*

Proof. Let γ be the homotopy class of loops at p, $c_i \in [\gamma]$ a sequence of loops such that

$$|\gamma| = \lim_{i \to \infty} L(c_i),$$

here $|\gamma| := \inf_{c \in [\gamma]} L(c)$. Clearly, $\{c_i\}$ is contained in a compact subset $K \subset M$. Since K is compact, its injectivity radius $i_K > 0$. Hence, for any pair of points $x_1, x_2 \in K$, there is a minimizing geodesic from x_1 to x_2, as long as $d(x_1, x_2) < i_K$.

There is a positive integer N such that for each i, there are at most N points $x_i^k \in c_i$ with $x_i^1 = p = x_i^N$ satisfying

$$d(x_i^k, x_i^{k+1}) \le L(c_i^k) \le \frac{1}{2} i_k, \quad k = 1, \cdots, N,$$

where c_i^k denotes the arc of c_i from x_i^k to x_i^{k+1}. Let σ_i^k denote the minimizing geodesic from x_i^k to x_i^{k+1}. Then $\sigma_i := U_{k=1}^N \sigma_i^k$ is a piecewise smooth geodesic loop consisting of σ_i^k. Clearly, σ_i is homotopy equivalent to c_i, and

$$L(\sigma_i) \le L(c_i).$$

Then

$$|\gamma| = \lim_{i \to \infty} L(\sigma_i).$$

Taking a subsequence if necessary, we may assume that for all i, c_i consists of N smooth geodesic segments c_i^k ($k = 1, \cdots, N$).

For a fixed k, let

$$\lim_{i \to \infty} x_i^k = x^k, \quad \lim_{i \to \infty} x_i^{k+1} = x^{k+1}.$$

Let σ^k a minimizing geodesic from x^k to x^{k+1}. Then we must have

$$\lim_{i \to \infty} L(c_i^k) = L(\sigma^k).$$

Let $\sigma := \cup_{k=1}^{N}\sigma^k$. Then σ is a piecewise smooth geodesic loop at p and

$$L(\sigma) = \sum_{k=1}^{N} \lim_{i\to\infty} L(\sigma_i^k) = \lim_{i\to\infty} L(\sigma_i) = |\gamma|.$$

By the ODE theory for geodesics, σ is actually a globally smooth geodesic (cf. [10], p.215). Thus, σ is a minimal closed geodesic. This completes the proof. $\qquad\square$

Let (M, F) be a connected Finsler manifold and $\psi : \widetilde{M} \to M$ the universal covering of M. We may define a Finsler metric on $\widetilde{M}$ such that ψ becomes an isometry. To do so, it is enough to define

$$\widetilde{F}(\widetilde{x}, \widetilde{y}) := F(\psi(\widetilde{x}), \psi(\widetilde{y})), \quad \forall \widetilde{x} \in \widetilde{M}, \ \widetilde{y} \in T_{\widetilde{x}}\widetilde{M}.$$

Assume that there is a homeomorphism $\varsigma : \widetilde{M} \to \widetilde{M}$ such that $\psi \circ \varsigma = \psi$, where $\psi : \widetilde{M} \to M$ is the universal covering. Then ς is called a *deck transformation* of $(\widetilde{M}, \psi)$. Let $p \in M$ and $\widetilde{p} \in \widetilde{M}$ with $p = \psi(\widetilde{p})$. For any $\alpha \in \pi_1(M, p)$, let $\gamma : [0, 1] \to M$ be a representative of α. γ has a unique lift $\widetilde{\gamma}$ with $\widetilde{\gamma}(0) = \widetilde{p}$. Define $\widetilde{\alpha p} = \widetilde{\gamma}(1)$. One can show that it is well-defined. In this sense, $\pi_1(M)$ can be viewed as the *universal transformation group* of $\widetilde{M}$. Hence, γ is a local isometric map of $\widetilde{M}$. The *conjugate class* of γ is the set $\{\gamma'\gamma\gamma'^{-1}|\gamma' \in \pi_1(M)\}$. The conjugate class of $\gamma = 1$ is just $\{1\}$.

Proposition 8.2. *Let (M, F) be a forward complete Finsler manifold, $\psi : \widetilde{M} \to M$ be a cover. Then $(\widetilde{M}, \psi^*F)$ is forward complete too.*

Proof. Let $\widetilde{\gamma}(t)$, $a \leq t < b$, be a forward maximal geodesic in $\widetilde{M}$. Without loss of generality, we may assume that it is normal. If $b \neq \infty$, take an increasing sequence of t_i in $[a, b)$, convergent to b. Let $\gamma := \psi \circ \widetilde{\gamma}$. Then γ is a unit speed geodesic in M. Since for $i \leq j$, $d_M(\gamma(t_i), \gamma(t_j)) = d_{\widetilde{M}}(\widetilde{\gamma}(t_i), \widetilde{\gamma}(t_j)) \leq t_j - t_i$, where d_M and $d_{\widetilde{M}}$ denotes the distance on M and $\widetilde{M}$, respectively, we see that $\{\gamma(t_i)\}$ is a forward Cauchy sequence. Thus, $\{\gamma(t_i)\}$ converges to a point $x \in M$. We define $\gamma(b) := x$. By the ODE theory, $\gamma(t)$ can be defined in a neighborhood of $t = b$. Then using the homotopy lifting theorem ([22]), γ has a unique lift $\widetilde{\gamma}_0$, satisfying $\widetilde{\gamma}_0(t) = \widetilde{\gamma}(t)$ for $t \in [a, b)$. Since $\psi : \widetilde{M} \to M$ is a covering map, $\widetilde{\gamma}_0$ is a geodesic too. This is a contradiction. Thus $b = \infty$. $\qquad\square$

The following proposition is obvious.

Proposition 8.3. *Let (M, F) be a forward complete Finsler manifold of finite reversibility number λ and $\psi : \widetilde{M} \to M$ be a covering map. Then ψ^*F has the same reversibility number λ.*

8.1.2   Algebraic norms and geometric norms

Definition 8.1. Let G be a finitely generated group, $S = \{g_i\}$ a set of generators. For each $g \in G$, define $\|g\|_{alg}$ as the shortest length of g represented by g_i and g_i^{-1}. Then for each i, $\|g_i\|_{alg} = 1$. $\| \cdot \|_{alg} : G \to \mathbb{R}^+$ is a norm on G and it satisfies

(i) $\|g\|_{alg} = 0$ holds if and only if $g = 1$;
(ii) $\|gh\|_{alg} \leq \|g\|_{alg} + \|h\|_{alg}$;
(iii) $\|g^{-1}\|_{alg} = \|g\|_{alg}$.

We call $\| \cdot \|_{alg}$ the *algebraic norm* associated with S.

Proposition 8.4. *Let G be a finitely generated group. Then all the algebraic norms of finite generating sets associated with G are equivalent.*

Proof. We may assume that $G \neq \{1\}$, otherwise the proposition is obvious. Take two finite generating sets of G, S_1 and S_2. Denote by $\| \cdot \|_i$ ($i = 1, 2$) denote the corresponding algebraic norms. Let $S_1 = \{g_i\}_{i=1}^n$, $C_1 := \max_{g \in S_1} \|g\|_2$. For any $g \in G$, let $\|g\|_1 = \Lambda$. Then g can expressed by Λ elements in S_1 and S_1^{-1}, where $S_1^{-1} := \{g_i^{-1}\}_{i=1}^n$. Let $g = g_{i_1}^{\pm} \cdots g_{i_\Lambda}^{\pm}$, $g_{i_\alpha} \in S_1$, $1 \leq \alpha \leq \Lambda$. Then

$$\|g\|_2 = \|g_{i_1}^{\pm} \cdots g_{i_\Lambda}^{\pm}\|_2 \leq \sum_{\alpha=1}^{\Lambda} \|g_{i_\alpha}^{\pm}\|_2 = \sum_{\alpha=1}^{\Lambda} C_1 = C_1 \|g\|_1.$$

Making S_1 and S_2 switched, we obtain

$$\|g\|_1 \leq C2 \|g\|_2, \quad \forall g \in G,$$

where $C_2 := \max_{g \in S_2} \|g\|_1 < \infty$. Since $G \neq \{1\}$, we have $C_i > 0$, $i = 1, 2$. The proposition follows from the above two inequalities. $\square$

Let G and S be as in Definition 8.1. Define the *counting function* associated with S, $N(r)$, by

$$N(r) := \sharp\Big\{ g \in G : \|g\|_{alg} \leq r \Big\}.$$

If there is a number $a > 1$ such that $N(r) \geq a^r$, then G is said to be *of exponential growth*. This is equivalent to (see [23, 72]):

$$\limsup_{r \to \infty} \frac{\log N(r)}{r} = \lim_{r \to \infty} \frac{N(r)}{r} > 0.$$

If $N(r) \leq Cr^n$, where C is a constant, then G is said to be *of polynomial growth of order n*.

Remark. According to [25, 78], the growth order is independent of the choice of a particular generating set, namely, keeping the exponential growth or polynomial growth invariant.

Definition 8.2. Let G be a finitely generated group and S its generating set. Let $N(r)$ denote the counting function associated with S. The entropy of S is defined by

$$h(S) = \liminf_{r \to \infty} \frac{\log(N(r))}{r}.$$

The entropy of G, $h(G)$, is defined to be the infimum of the entropies of all generating sets.

$$h(G) := \inf_S \{h(S)\}.$$

Remark. It has been indicated in [25, 78] that the limit $\lim_{r \to \infty} N(r)^{1/r}$ must exist. Thus the limit $h(S) = \lim_{r \to \infty} \frac{\log(N(r))}{r}$. For a free group Γ generated by k elements, $h(\Gamma) = \log(2k - 1)$. If Γ is a finitely generated group and there are p ($p < k$) relations among generators, then $h(\Gamma) \geq \log(2(k - p) - 1)$ (see [51], pp. 281-282, or [99]).

Definition 8.3. Let (M, F) be a forward complete Finsler manifold, and $\psi : \widetilde{M} \to M$ be the universal covering. For any point $p \in M$ and any $\alpha \in \pi_1(M)$, the geometric norm associated with p is defined by

$$\|\alpha\|_{geo} := d_{\widetilde{M}}(\widetilde{p}, \alpha\widetilde{p}),$$

where $\widetilde{p}$ is an arbitrary point in the fiber $\pi^{-1}(p)$.

It is easy to verify that the geometric norm satisfies the triangle inequality since $\pi_1(M)$ acts on $\widetilde{M}$ isometrically.

Proposition 8.5 ([130]). *For $\alpha \in \pi_1(M, p)$, the geometric norm $\|\alpha\|_{geo}$ is equal to the length of the shortest loop in α, and the shortest loop must be a geodesic.*

Proof. As shown early, we have

$$L_{\psi * F}(\widetilde{\gamma}) = \int_a^b F(\dot{\widetilde{\gamma}})dt, \quad d_{\widetilde{M}}(\widetilde{p}, \alpha\widetilde{p}) = \inf L_{\psi * F}(\widetilde{\gamma}),$$

where the infimum is taken over all Lipschitz continuous curves $\widetilde{\gamma} : [a, b] \to \widetilde{M}$, $\widetilde{\gamma}(a) = \widetilde{p}$, $\widetilde{\gamma}(b) = \alpha\widetilde{p}$.

Since (M, F) is forward complete, $(\widetilde{M}, \psi * F)$ is forward complete too (see Proposition 8.2). Then there is a globally minimizing geodesic $\widetilde{\gamma}$ from $\widetilde{p}$ to $\alpha\widetilde{p}$ such that $d_{\widetilde{M}}(\widetilde{p}, \alpha\widetilde{p}) = L_{\psi * F}(\widetilde{\gamma})$. Let $\gamma := \psi \circ \widetilde{\gamma}$. γ is a geodesic in

M with $L_F(\gamma) = L_{\psi*F}(\widetilde{\gamma})$. Since $\widetilde{M}$ is the universal cover of M, $\gamma \in \alpha$. We may assert that γ is the loop with shortest length in α. In fact, if not, then there is a Lipschitz continuous loop $\xi \in \alpha$ such that $L_F(\xi) < L_F(\gamma)$ (we may assume that ξ is a closed geodesic, cf. Proposition 8.1). But $\xi : [a, b] \to M$ has a unique lift $\widetilde{\xi}$ with $\widetilde{\xi}(a) = \widetilde{p}$, $\widetilde{\xi}(b) = \alpha\widetilde{p}$, and $L_F(\xi) = L_{\psi*F}(\widetilde{\xi})$. This implies that $L_{\psi*F}(\widetilde{\gamma}) > L_{\psi*F}(\widetilde{\xi})$, a contradiction. $\qquad\square$

Proposition 8.6. *Let (M, F) be a compact Finsler manifold with reversibility number λ and diameter d. Then, for any $p \in M$, the fundamental group $\pi_1(M, p)$ can be generated by finitely many classes $\alpha \in \pi_1(M, p)$ with $\|\alpha\|_{geo} \leq (1+\lambda)d$. All algebraic norm associated with a finite generator set and the geometric norm associated with a point in M are equivalent.*

Proof. (i) First notice that for any uniform bounded sequence of curves $\{\gamma_i : [a, b] \to M\}$, there is a convergent subsequence. In fact, the compactness implies that the reversibility number λ of (M, F) is bounded. Let d denote the induced distance on (M, F). Let $\bar{d}(x_1, x_2) := \frac{1}{2}(d(x_1, x_2) + d(x_2, x_1))$. Then, the reversible $\bar{d}$ is topologically equivalent to d. This can be proved by applying Arzelà-Ascoli Theorem ([7], Theorem 2.5.14) to the reversible metric space $(M.\bar{d})$.

(ii) Second, for arbitrary point $p \in M$ and arbitrary positive number r, there exist only finitely many homotopy classes $\alpha \in \pi_1(M, p)$ such that $\|\alpha\|_{geo} < r$. Then if not true, then there is an infinite sequence of classes $\{\alpha_i\}_{i=1}^\infty$ such that $\|\alpha_i\|_{geo} < r_0$ for some $r_0 > 0$. For each i, by Proposition 7.1, there exists a loop $\gamma_i \in \alpha_i$ with $L_F(\gamma_i) = \|\alpha\|_{geo}$. Without loss of generality, we may assume that all γ_i are defined on the unit interval $I = [0, 1]$. Let λ_d denote the reversibility number of the metric d induced by F. Then $\lambda_d \leq \lambda < \infty$. By the above argument, we may assume that $\{\gamma_i\}$ is convergent. Hence, there is a continuous curve $\gamma : I \to M$ such that for any $\epsilon > 0$, there is $N = N(\epsilon)$ such that $d(\gamma(t), \gamma_i(t)) < \epsilon$, $\forall t \in I$, $i > N$. Let i_M be the injectivity radius of M and $\epsilon = i_m/2$. Then there is a positive number $N = N(\epsilon)$ such that $\gamma_i \simeq \gamma$ rel $\{0, 1\}$ for $i > N$, namely, they are homotopy equivalent with fixed endpoints. Therefore, for any $i, j > N$, $\alpha_i = \alpha_j$, a contradiction.

(iii) For each $\alpha \in \pi_1(M, p)$, let $\gamma : [0, 1] \to M$ be a loop representing it. For any $\epsilon > 0$, partition $[0, 1]$ as $\{t_i\}_{i=0}^k$ such that $0 = t_0 < t_1 < \cdots < t_k = 1$ and $L_F(\gamma|_{[t_i, t_{i+1}]}) < \epsilon$. Since M is compact, for each i, there is a minimizing geodesic c_{t_i} from p to $\gamma(t_i)$. Then γ is homotopy equivalent to the loop $c_{t_i}\gamma|_{[t_i, t_{i+1}]}c_{t_{i+1}}^{-1}$. Thus we obtain a generating set for

$\pi_1(M,p)$, each generator has length less than $(1+\lambda)d+\epsilon$. By (ii), the set of classes in $\pi_1(M,p)$ with length $< (1+\lambda)d+\epsilon$ is finite. For a sufficiently small ϵ, by (ii) again, one can see that there is no class $\alpha \in \pi_1(M,p)$ with $(1+\lambda)d < \|\alpha\|_{geo} < (1+\lambda)d+\epsilon$. This proves the first statement in the proposition.

(iv) By Proposition 8.4, we just need to show that the geometric norm at p is equivalent to some algebraic norm. Let $\psi : \widetilde{M} \to M$ be the universal covering, $\widetilde{p}$ be an arbitrary point in $\psi^{-1}(p)$. Let S be the set of elements in $\pi_1(M,p)$ with geometric norm not greater than $(2+\lambda)d$. By (iii), it is the generating set of $\pi_1(M,p)$. Let $\|\cdot\|_{alg}$ denote the algebraic norm associated with S. The for each $\alpha \in \pi_1(M,p)$, with $\|\alpha\|_{alg} = m$, $\alpha = \prod_{i=1}^{m} \gamma_i$, where $\gamma_i \in S \cup S^{-1}$, $S^{-1} := \{\gamma^{-1} : \gamma \in S\}$. Since $\pi_1(M,p)$ acts on $\widetilde{M}$ isometrically, we have

$$\|\alpha\|_{geo} = d_{\widetilde{M}}(\widetilde{p}, \alpha\widetilde{p}) = d_{\widetilde{M}}\left(\widetilde{p}, \prod_{i=1}^{m}\gamma_i\widetilde{p}\right) = d_{\widetilde{M}}\left(\gamma_1^{-1}\widetilde{p}, \prod_{i=2}^{m}\gamma_i\widetilde{p}\right)$$

$$\leq d_{\widetilde{M}}(\gamma_1^{-1}\widetilde{p}, \widetilde{p}) + d_{\widetilde{M}}\left(\widetilde{p}, \prod_{i=2}^{m}\gamma_i\widetilde{p}\right)$$

$$= d_{\widetilde{M}}(\widetilde{p}, \gamma_1\widetilde{p}) + d_{\widetilde{M}}\left(\widetilde{p}, \prod_{i=2}^{m}\gamma_i\widetilde{p}\right) \leq \sum_{i=1}^{m} d_{\widetilde{M}}(\widetilde{p}, \gamma_i\widetilde{p})$$

$$= \sum_{i=1}^{m}\|\gamma_i\|_{geo} \leq (2+\lambda)dm = (2+\lambda)d\|\alpha\|_{alg}.$$

Conversely, for any $\alpha \in \pi_1(M,p)$, there is a normal geodesic $\widetilde{\gamma}$ from $\widetilde{p}$ to $\alpha\widetilde{p}$ such that $L_{\psi*F}(\widetilde{\gamma}) = \|\alpha\|_{geo}$. Let $k = d^{-1}\|\alpha\|_{geo}$. Then $k \in \mathbb{N}$ and $kd \leq \|\alpha\|_{geo} < (k+1)d$. Then $\widetilde{p} = \widetilde{\gamma}(0), \widetilde{g}(d), \cdots, \widetilde{g}(kd)$, each pair of consecutive points has distance of d. Since d is the diameter, for each $i \leq k$, there is an element $\beta_i \in \pi_1(M,p)$ such that $d_{\widetilde{M}}(\widetilde{\gamma}(id), \beta_i\widetilde{p}) \leq d$. In particular, one may take $\beta_0 = 1$. By the triangle inequality, we obtain

$$d_{\widetilde{M}}(\beta_i\widetilde{p}, \beta_{i+1}\widetilde{p}) \leq d_{\widetilde{M}}(\beta_i\widetilde{p}, \widetilde{g}(id)) + d_{\widetilde{M}}(\widetilde{g}(id), \widetilde{g}((i+1)d))$$
$$+ d_{\widetilde{M}}(\widetilde{g}((i+1)d), \beta_{i+1}\widetilde{p}) \leq (2+\lambda)d.$$

Thus $\beta_i^{-1}\beta_{i+1} \in S$. Similarly, using $d_{\widetilde{M}}(\widetilde{g}(kd), \alpha\widetilde{p}) \leq d$ and triangle inequality, we get $\|\beta_{k-1}^{-1}\alpha\|_{geo} = d_{\widetilde{M}}(\beta_{k-1}\widetilde{p}, \alpha\widetilde{p}) \leq (2+\lambda)d$, namely, $\beta_{k-1}^{-1}\alpha \in S$. Since $\alpha = (\beta_0^{-1}\beta_1)(\beta_1^{-1}\beta_2)\cdots(\beta_{k-1}^{-1}\alpha)$, where $\beta_0 = 1$, we have $\|\alpha\|_{alg} \leq k \leq d^{-1}\|\alpha\|_{geo}$. Then

$$d\|\cdot\|_{alg} \leq \|\cdot\|_{geo} \leq (2+\lambda)d\|\cdot\|_{alg}. \qquad \square$$

Now we recall the concept of fundamental domain (see [25]).

Definition 8.4. Let $f : \widetilde{M} \to M$ be a covering, with deck transformation group Γ. We say $\Omega \subset \widetilde{M}$ is a fundamental domain of the covering if
(1) $\gamma(\Omega) \cap \Omega = \emptyset$, for all $\gamma \in \Gamma - \{1\}$,
(2) $f(\overline{\Omega}) = M$.

Since Γ acts transitively on the fibers $f^{-1}(p)$ for each $p \in M$, then $f(\overline{\Omega}) = M$ is equivalent to $\cup_{\gamma \in \Gamma}\gamma(\overline{\Omega}) = \widetilde{M}$ and $f|_{\gamma(\Omega)} : \gamma(\Omega) \to f(\Omega)$ is a homeomorphism, for each $\gamma \in \Gamma$.

Supposing that (M, F) is a forward complete Finsler manifold, one can construct a fundamental domain by cut loci. Let $p \in M$ and $\widetilde{p}$ be any point in $f^{-1}(p)$. Since $(\widetilde{M}, f^*F)$ is forward complete, $f_* : T_{\widetilde{p}}\widetilde{M} \to T_pM$ is linear isometry and for each $\widetilde{X} \in T_{\widetilde{p}}\widetilde{M}$, one has $\exp_p(f_*\widetilde{X}) = f(\exp_{\widetilde{p}}\widetilde{X})$. Let $\mathcal{D}_p := M - Cut_p$ and $D_p := \exp_p^{-1}(\mathcal{D}_p)$. Then for each $p \in M$, one has

$$p \mapsto D_p \subset T_pM \mapsto f_*|_{\widetilde{p}}^{-1}(D_p) \subset T_{\widetilde{p}}\widetilde{M} \mapsto \exp_{\widetilde{p}}(f_*|_{\widetilde{p}}^{-1}(D_p)) =: \Omega_p.$$

Now we show Ω_p is a fundamental domain. From the above definition, it suffices to show $\gamma(\Omega_p) \cap \Omega_p = \emptyset$, for all $\gamma \in \Gamma - \{1\}$. If there exists γ such that $z \in \gamma(\Omega_p) \cap \Omega_p$ (i.e., $z, \gamma^{-1}z \in \Omega_p$), then one can find y_1, y_2 in $f_*|_{\widetilde{p}}^{-1}(D_p)$ such that $\exp_{\widetilde{p}}(y_1) = z$ and $\exp_{\widetilde{p}}(y_2) = \gamma^{-1}z$. Since $\exp_p(f_*y_1) = f(z) = \exp_p(f_*y_2)$ and $f_*y_1, f_*y_2 \in D_p$, then $f_*y_1 = f_*y_2$ and $y_1 = y_2$. That is $\gamma = 1$.

Let d denote the diameter of M. Then one has $\text{diam}(\Omega_p) \le d$.

Lemma 8.1 ([130]). *Let $(M, F, d\mu)$ be a forward complete Finsler n-manifold and $f : \widetilde{M} \to M$ be the universal cover. Given any point $p \in M$ and any subgroup Λ (of $\pi_1(M)$) with a finite generating set G, let $N(\cdot)$ be the counting function of Λ associated with G. Then there exist positive number $\eta = \eta(p, G)$ and $\epsilon = \epsilon(p)$ such that*

$$N(r) \le \frac{\mu(B^+(\widetilde{p}, \eta r + \epsilon))}{\mu(B^+(\widetilde{p}, \epsilon))} \qquad (8.1.1)$$

for all $r > 0$, where $\widetilde{p}$ is any point in the fiber $f^{-1}(p)$, and $\mu(B^+(\widetilde{p}, s))$ denotes the volume of the forward geodesic ball with radius s centered at $\widetilde{p}$ with respect to $f^*d\mu$.

Proof. Let $\| \cdot \|_{geo}$ denote the geometric norm associated with p. Put $G = \{\alpha_i\}_1^l$ and $\eta = \max_{1 \le i \le l} \|\alpha_i\|_{geo}$. It follows from the triangle inequality that the forward ball $\overline{B^+(\widetilde{p}, \eta r)}$ contains at least $N(r)$ distinct points of the orbit $\Lambda\widetilde{p}$. Since $\pi_1(M)$ acts properly discontinuously on $\widetilde{M}$, then there exists $\epsilon > 0$ such that the forward balls $B^+(\alpha\widetilde{p}, \epsilon) = \alpha(B^+(\widetilde{p}, \epsilon))$ disjoint for all $\alpha \in \pi_1(M)$. Therefore the forward ball $\overline{B^+(\widetilde{p}, \eta r + \epsilon)}$ contains at least $N(r)$ disjoint set $\alpha(B^+(\widetilde{p}, \epsilon))$, that is, (8.1.1) holds. $\qquad\square$

8.1.3 Growth of fundamental groups

We now can prove the following theorem which generalizes the results in ([104], Corollary 1.5) and see [78], Theorem 1).

Theorem 8.1 ([130]). *Let (M, F) be a forward complete Finsler n-manifold with $Ric \geq (n-1)k_1 \geq 0$ and $\mathbf{S} \geq (n-1)k_2 \geq 0$ for some constants k_1 and k_2. Then any finitely generated subgroup of $\pi_1(M)$ has polynomial growth of degree n.*

Proof. Let Λ denote any subgroup of $\pi_1(M)$ with a finite generating set G. Let $\widetilde{p}$, η and $N(\cdot)$ be defined as in the above lemma. Using Lemma 8.1, we have

$$
\begin{aligned}
N(r) &\leq \frac{\mu(B^+(\widetilde{p}, \eta r + \epsilon))}{\mu(B^+(\widetilde{p}, \epsilon))} \leq \int_0^{\eta r + \epsilon} (e^{-k_2 t} t)^{n-1} dt \left(\int_0^{\epsilon} (e^{-k_2 t} t)^{n-1} dt \right)^{-1} \\
&\leq \int_0^{\eta r + \epsilon} t^{n-1} dt \left(\int_0^{\epsilon} t^{n-1} dt \right)^{-1} \leq \left(\frac{\eta + \epsilon}{\epsilon} \right)^n r^n.
\end{aligned}
$$

The third inequality follows from Lemma 7.4 (see §7.1.2). $\qquad\square$

Let (M, F) be a compact Finsler manifold and $f : \widetilde{M} \to M$ be the universal cover. We can always choose a compact subset $E \subset \widetilde{M}$ such that $\cup_{\gamma \in \pi_1(M)} \gamma(E) = \widetilde{M}$. For example, $E = \overline{\Omega}$, where Ω is a fundamental domain constructed as before.

Note that $\{\gamma(E) : \gamma \in \pi_1(M)\}$ is a locally finite cover of $\widetilde{M}$ by compact subsets. For if not, there would exist $\widetilde{p} \in E \subset \widetilde{M}$ and $r > 0$ such that $\overline{B^+(\widetilde{p}, r)}$ contains points from infinitely many distinct $\gamma(E)$. Let d denote the diameter of E. Then $\overline{B^+(\widetilde{p}, r + d)}$ contains infinitely many distinct $\gamma(E)$ and (therefore) $\{\gamma(\widetilde{p})\}$ has a convergent subsequence, which is a contradiction. Now define

$$\Gamma_E := \{\gamma \in \pi_1(M) : \gamma(E) \cap E \neq \emptyset\}.$$

Then, from above, Γ_E is finite.

Define

$$\nu := \inf_{\gamma \in \pi_1(M) - \Gamma_E} d(E, \gamma(E)).$$

Then $\nu > 0$. If not, there would be two sequences $\{a_n\}$, $\{b_n\}$ in E and a sequence $\{\gamma_n\}$ in $\pi_1(M) - \Gamma_E$ such that $\gamma_n \neq \gamma_m$ for $n \neq m$, and $d(a_n, \gamma_n(b_n)) \to 0$, as $n \to \infty$. Since E is compact, there exist convergent subsequences of $\{a_n\}$ and $\{b_n\}$. Without loss of generality, we can suppose $\{a_n\}$ and $\{b_n\}$ converges themselves to a, b respectively. Hence, we have $\gamma_n(b_n) \to a$. Since γ is isometric for each $\gamma \in \pi_1(M)$, then $d(\gamma_n^{-1}(a), b_n) = d(a, \gamma_n(b_n)) \to 0$, which implies that $\gamma_n^{-1}(a) \to b$. But this contradicts the proper discontinuity of the action of $\pi_1(M)$ on $\widetilde{M}$.

Lemma 8.2. *Let Γ_E and ν be defined as above. Then we have*
(1) Γ_E is a finite generating set of $\pi_1(M)$.
(2) For each $\gamma \in \pi_1(M)$ and any two points $x, y \in E$,

$$\|\gamma\|_{alg} \leq \left\lceil \frac{d(y, \gamma(x))}{\nu} \right\rceil + 1,$$

where $\| \cdot \|_{alg}$ is the algebra norm associated with Γ_E.

Proof. For any $\gamma \in \pi_1(M)$ and any two points x, $y \in E$, let σ be a unit speed minimizing geodesic from y to $\gamma(x)$ and k be any positive number with

$$\frac{d(y, \gamma(x))}{k} < \nu.$$

Put $z_j := \sigma(jd(y, \gamma(x))/k)$, for $j = 0, \ldots, k$. Then $d(z_{j-1}, z_j) < \nu$, $j = 1, \ldots, k$. Let $\gamma_0 = 1$ and $\gamma_j \in \pi_1(M)$ such that $z_j = \gamma_j(x_j)$, where $x_j \in E$, for $j = 1, \ldots, k - 1$. Hence,

$$d(x_{j-1}, \gamma_{j-1}^{-1}\gamma_j(x_j)) < \nu = \inf_{\gamma \in \pi_1(M) - \Gamma_E} d(E, \gamma(E)),$$

which implies that $\gamma_{j-1}^{-1}\gamma_j \in \Gamma_E$ for $j = 1, \ldots, k - 1$. Since $z_k = \sigma(d(y, \gamma(x))) = \gamma(x)$, then $d(\gamma_{k-1}(x_{k-1}), \gamma(x)) = d(z_{k-1}, z_k) < \nu$, that is $\gamma_{k-1}^{-1}\gamma \in \Gamma_E$. Note

$$\gamma = (\gamma_0^{-1}\gamma_1) \cdots (\gamma_{k-2}^{-1}\gamma_{k-1})(\gamma_{k-1}^{-1}\gamma).$$

Therefore, Γ_E is a generating set of $\pi_1(M)$. Let $\| \cdot \|_{alg}$ denote the algebra norm associated with Γ_E. From the above inequality,

$$\|\gamma\|_{alg} \leq k \leq \left\lceil \frac{d(y, \gamma(x))}{\nu} \right\rceil + 1. \qquad \square$$

Lemma 8.3. *Let $(M, F, d\mu)$ be a compact Finsler manifold of diameter d and $\psi : \widetilde{M} \to M$ be the universal cover. Given any point $\widetilde{p} \in \widetilde{M}$, there exists a positive number $\nu = \nu(\widetilde{p})$ such that*

$$N(r) \geq \frac{\mu(B^+(\widetilde{p}, \nu r - (\nu + (1 + 2\lambda)d)))}{\mu(B^+(\widetilde{p}, d))}, \quad \text{for } r > \frac{2(1 + \lambda)d}{\nu} + 1,$$

where λ denotes the reversibility of (M, F), $N(\cdot)$ denotes the counting function associated with $\Gamma_{\overline{B^+(\widetilde{p},d)}}$, and μ denotes the volume with respect to the pull-back volume form $\psi^*(d\mu)$ on $\widetilde{M}$.

Proof. Let Ω be the fundamental domain constructed as before, which contains $\widetilde{p}$. Then $\mathrm{diam}(\Omega) \leq d$ and $\overline{B^+(\widetilde{p},d)} \supset \Omega$. From the above lemma, $\Gamma_{\overline{B^+(\widetilde{p},d)}}$ is a finite generating set of $\pi_1(M)$. Set $E := \overline{B^+(\widetilde{p},d)}$, and define $\nu = \nu(\widetilde{p})$ as in the above lemma.

For each $r > 0$, define $\Gamma_r := \{\gamma \in \pi_1(M) : \gamma(E) \cap \overline{B^+(\widetilde{p}, d + r)} \neq \emptyset\}$. It is clear that $\Gamma_r \supset \Gamma_E$. Hence, Γ_r is also a finite generating set of $\pi_1(M)$ and $\overline{B^+(\widetilde{p}, d + r)} \subset \cup_{\gamma \in \Gamma_r} \gamma(E)$, which implies $\mu(\overline{B^+(\widetilde{p}, d + r)}) \leq \sharp(\Gamma_r)\mu(E)$.

For each $\gamma \in \Gamma_r$, using the above lemma, we have

$$\|\gamma\|_{alg} \leq \left[\frac{d(y, \gamma(x))}{\nu}\right] + 1$$

for each $y, x \in E$, where $\|\cdot\|_{alg}$ is the algebra norm associated with Γ_E. Hence, $\|\gamma\|_{alg} \leq \frac{r+2(1+\lambda)d}{\nu} + 1$, for each $\gamma \in \Gamma_r$. Let $N(\cdot)$ denote the counting function associated with Γ_E. From above, we have

$$N\left(\frac{r + 2(1 + \lambda)d}{\nu} + 1\right) \geq \sharp(\Gamma_r) \geq \frac{\mu(B^+(\widetilde{p}, d + r))}{\mu(E)}. \qquad \square$$

Definition 8.5. Let $(M, F, d\mu)$ be a forward complete Finsler manifold. We say that M has *exponential volume growth* (associated with μ) if

$$\limsup_{r \to \infty} \frac{\log \mu(B^+(p, r))}{r} > 0$$

for a point $p \in M$. We say that M has *polynomial volume growth* (associated with μ) if

$$\mu(B^+(p, r)) \leq C \cdot r^n$$

for some constant C and a point $p \in M$.

It is easy to check that types of the volume growth of (M, F) are independent of the based point p. And if (M, F) is compact, then the types of the volume growth are independent of the choice of volume forms. In fact, let $d\mu_1$ and $d\mu_2$ be two volume forms. There must be a positive function κ on M such that $d\mu_1 = \kappa \cdot d\mu_2$. Since M is compact, one can find two positive constant number $C_1 := \min \kappa$, $C_2 := \max \kappa$ such that $C_1 d\mu_2 \leq d\mu_1 \leq C_2 d\mu_2$. Hence, if (M, F) is compact and $f : \widetilde{M} \to M$ is a covering space, then the types of volume growth of $(\widetilde{M}, f^*F)$ are independent of choices of volume forms as well.

Proposition 8.7. *Let $(M, F, d\mu)$ be a compact Finsler manifold and $\psi :$ $\widetilde{M} \to M$ be the universal covering. Then for any $\widetilde{p} \in \widetilde{M}$, the limit*

$$\lim_{r \to \infty} \frac{\log \mu(B^+(\widetilde{p}, r))}{r}$$

exists, the value is independent of $\widetilde{p}$, and the convergence is uniform with respect to $\widetilde{p}$.

Proof. If the limit exists, then it is easy to check that the value is independent of $\widetilde{p}$. Let $\Omega \subset \widetilde{M}$ be a fundamental domain constructed as before and d be the diameter of M. Thus, $\mathrm{diam}(\Omega) \leq d$. Given any two points x, $y \in \Omega$, and any positive number $t > d$, one has $B^+(x, t - d) \subset B^+(y, t) \subset B^+(x, t + d)$, which implies that

$$\mu(B^+(\widetilde{p}, t - d)) \leq \mu(B^+(\widetilde{q}, t)) \leq \mu(B^+(\widetilde{p}, t + d)), \quad \text{for any } \widetilde{p}, \widetilde{q} \in \widetilde{M}.$$

Hence if the limits exists, then the convergence is uniform with respect to $\widetilde{p}$.

Below is the proof of the existence of the limit (see [25], Theorem 4.6). Fix $\widetilde{p} \in \widetilde{M}$, for any $r, s > 0$, we have

$$B_{\widetilde{p}}^+(r + s) \subset \bigcup_{\widetilde{q} \in B_{\widetilde{p}}^+(r)} B_{\widetilde{q}}^+(s).$$

Then fix some $b > 0$ and let Q denote the set of points in $B_{\widetilde{p}}^+(r)$ with pairwise distance at least b. Let λ denote the reversibility number of M. Then

$$\bigcup_{\widetilde{q} \in Q} B_{\widetilde{q}}^+\left(\frac{d}{2\lambda}\right) \subset B_{\widetilde{p}}^+\left(r + \frac{b}{2\lambda}\right),$$

this implies

$$\mu\left(B_{\widetilde{p}}^+\left(r + \frac{b}{2\lambda}\right)\right) \geq \sum_{\widetilde{q} \in Q} \mu\left(B_{\widetilde{q}}^+\left(\frac{b}{2\lambda}\right)\right) \geq c_b \cdot \sharp(Q),$$

where $\sharp(Q)$ denotes the number of elements in Q. Then

$$\sharp(Q) \leq c_b^{-1} \mu\left(B_{\widetilde{p}}^+\left(r + \frac{b}{2\lambda}\right)\right).$$

Now take $Q \subset B_{\widetilde{p}}^+(r)$ the largest set satisfying the above conditions. Then every point in $B_{\widetilde{p}}^+(r) \setminus \{\widetilde{p}\}$ is within b-distance of Q. This implies that for every $s > 0$,

$$B_{\widetilde{p}}^+(r + s) \subset \bigcup_{\widetilde{q} \in Q} B_{\widetilde{q}}^+(s + b).$$

Thus

$$\mu(B_{\tilde{p}}^+(r+s)) \leq \sharp(Q) \max_{\tilde{q} \in Q} \mu(B_{\tilde{q}}^+(s+b))$$

$$\leq c_b^{-1} \mu\left(B_{\tilde{p}}^+\left(r+\frac{b}{2\lambda}\right)\right)\mu(B_{\tilde{p}}^+(s+b+d)).$$

It can be rewritten as

$$\mu\left(B_{\tilde{p}}^+\left(r+\frac{b}{2\lambda}+s-\frac{b}{2\lambda}\right)\right)$$

$$\leq c_b^{-1} \mu\left(B_{\tilde{p}}^+\left(r+\frac{b}{2\lambda}\right)\right)\mu\left(B_{\tilde{p}}^+\left(s-\frac{b}{2\lambda}+\frac{b}{2\lambda}+b+d\right)\right).$$

Then for any $r > \frac{b}{2\lambda}$, $s > -\frac{b}{2\lambda}$, $b > 0$, we have

$$\mu(B_{\tilde{p}}^+(r+s)) \leq c_b^{-1}\mu(B_{\tilde{p}}^+(r))\mu(B_{\tilde{p}}^+(s+A)),$$

where $A := \frac{b}{2\lambda} + b + d$. We conclude that for any $r > \frac{b}{2\lambda}$ and $k \in N^*$,

$$\mu(B_{\tilde{p}}^+((k+1)r)) \leq c_b^{-k}\mu(B_{\tilde{p}}^+(r+A))^{k+1}.$$

Hence, for any $l \in (0, r)$,

$$\mu(B_{\tilde{p}}^+(kr+l)) \leq \mu(B_{\tilde{p}}^+((k+1)r)) \leq c_b^{-k}\mu(B_{\tilde{p}}^+(r+A))^{k+1}.$$

Then

$$\frac{\log \mu(B_{\tilde{p}}^+(kr+l))}{kr+l} \leq \frac{k \log c_b^{-1}}{kr+l} + \frac{k+1}{kr+l}\log \mu(B_{\tilde{p}}^+(r+A)).$$

Letting $k \to +\infty$, for and fixed $r > \frac{b}{2\lambda}$, we have

$$\limsup_{s \to +\infty} \frac{\log \mu(B_{\tilde{p}}^+(s))}{s} \leq \frac{\log c_b^{-1}}{r} + \frac{\log \mu(B_{\tilde{p}}^+(r+A))}{r}.$$

This implies

$$\lim_{s \to +\infty} \frac{\log \mu(B_{\tilde{p}}^+(s))}{s} \leq \liminf_{s \to +\infty} \frac{\log \mu(B_{\tilde{p}}^+(s))}{s},$$

that is, the limit exists. $\qquad\square$

We now can show the following

Theorem 8.2 ([130]). *Let (M, F) be a compact Finsler manifold and $\psi : \widetilde{M} \to M$ be the universal cover. Then $\pi_1(M)$ has polynomial (resp., exponential) growth if and only if $\widetilde{M}$ has polynomial (resp. exponential) volume growth.*

Proof. Since types of the growth of groups are independent of the choice of finite generating sets, we choose any finite generating set S of $\pi_1(M)$ (there always exists a finite generating set of $\pi_1(M)$ (cf. Proposition 8.6 below)). Given any $\widetilde{p} \in \widetilde{M}$, let $|\cdot|_{alg}$ denote the algebra norm associated with S and let $N(\cdot)$ denote the counting function associated with S. By Lemma 8.1, it implies that

$$N(r) \le \frac{\mu(B^+(\widetilde{p}, \eta r + \epsilon))}{\mu(B^+(\widetilde{p}, \epsilon))}$$

for all $r > 0$, where ϵ and η are positive numbers as independent of r. Since the types of volume growth are independent of base point, using Proposition 8.7, then we have

(i) If $\pi_1(M)$ has exponential growth (i.e., $\lim \frac{\log N(r)}{r} > 0$), then $\widetilde{M}$ has exponential volume growth.

(ii) If $\widetilde{M}$ has polynomial volume growth, then $\pi_1(M)$ has polynomial growth.

Now taking the generating set of $\pi_1(M)$ as in Lemma 8.3, let $N(\cdot)$ denote the corresponding counting number. By Lemma 8.3, for $r > \frac{2(1+\lambda)d}{\nu} + 1$,

$$N(r) \ge \frac{\mu(B^+(\widetilde{p}, \nu r - (\nu + (1 + 2\lambda)d)))}{\mu(B_{\widetilde{p}}^+(d))},$$

where λ is the reversibility number of (M, F), ν is a positive number depending on $\widetilde{p}$, and d is the diameter of M. By Proposition 8.7 again, we have

(i′) If $\widetilde{M}$ has exponential volume growth, then $\pi_1(M)$ has exponential growth;

(ii′) If $\pi_1(M)$ has polynomial growth, then $\widetilde{M}$ has exponential volume growth.   □

Remark. Let $(M, F, d\mu)$ be a Finsler manifold with $|\mathbf{S}| \le \Lambda$ and $\psi : \widetilde{M} \to M$ be the universal covering. Suppose that one of the following two conditions holds:

(i) the flag curvature of M satisfies $\mathbf{K}(V; W) \le -a^2$ with $a > \Lambda/(n-1)$;

(ii) M has non-positive flag curvature and $Ric_M \le -a^2$ with $a > \Lambda$.

By Lemma 8.1 of [143], $(\widetilde{M}, f^*F)$ has exponential volume growth. It follows from Theorem 8.2 that $\pi_1(M)$ has exponential growth.

8.2 Entropy and finiteness of fundamental group

8.2.1 Entropy of fundamental group

For Riemannian manifolds, there is a close relationship between the growth and the entropy of the fundamental group (cf. [51], Chapter 5). We now extend this result to Finsler manifolds.

Definition 8.6. Let $(M, F, d\mu)$ be a forward complete Finsler manifold and $f : \widetilde{M} \to M$ be the universal covering. Then for any $\widetilde{p} \in \widetilde{M}$, the limit

$$h(M, F) := \liminf_{r \to \infty} \frac{\log \mu(B^+(\widetilde{p}, r))}{r} \tag{8.2.1}$$

is called the *entropy* of (M, F).

If $(M, F, d\mu)$ is compact, then, by Proposition 8.7,

$$h(M, F) = \lim_{r \to \infty} \frac{\log \mu(B^+(\widetilde{p}, r))}{r}. \tag{8.2.1'}$$

The theorem below gives the relationship between the entropy and the fundamental group of a Finsler manifold.

Theorem 8.3 ([130]). *If (M, F) is a compact Finsler manifold with reversibility λ and diameter d, then*

$$h(\pi_1(M, p)) \leq (1 + \lambda) d h(M, F) \tag{8.2.2}.$$

Remark. When (M, F) is a Riemannian manifold, $\lambda = 1$. This is Theorem 5.16 in [51] (Note: there is a typo in this book, $h(V)$ and $h(\pi_1(V))$ should be switched in Theorem 5.16).

Proof. Since M is compact, the injective radius $i_M > 0$. Let ϵ denote $i_M/2$. Thus every closed curve in M of length less than 2ϵ based at p is homotopic to constant loop p. Therefore, each element of $\pi_1(M, p)$ has geometric norm greater than ϵ (except the identity), which implies that the forward balls $\widetilde{B^+}(\alpha\widetilde{p}, \epsilon/(2\lambda))$ centered at points of the orbit $\pi_1(M, p)\widetilde{p}$ are disjoint. Since $\pi_1(M, p)$ acts on $(\widetilde{M}, f^*F)$ by isometries (i.e., by deck transformations), then all these small balls have the same volume, say ν. Let $N_1(R)$ denote the number of the elements of $\pi_1(M, p)\widetilde{p}$ lying within the forward ball $\widetilde{B^+}(\widetilde{p}, R)$, thus $N_1(R) \leq \nu^{-1}\mu(\widetilde{B^+}(\widetilde{p}, R + \epsilon/(2\lambda)))$. Hence,

$$h(M, F) = \liminf_{R \to \infty} \frac{\log \mu(\widetilde{B^+}(\widetilde{p}, R + \frac{\epsilon}{2\lambda}))}{R} \geq \liminf_{R \to \infty} \frac{\log N_1(R)}{R}.$$

By Proposition 8.6 below and the triangle inequality, one can choose a generating set $S := \{\alpha \in \pi_1(M,p) : \|\alpha\|_{geo} \leq (1+\lambda)d\}$ of $\pi_1(M,p)$ such that the algebraic norm $\|\cdot\|_{alg}$ associated with S satisfies the inequality $\|\cdot\|_{geo} \leq (1+\lambda)d\|\cdot\|_{alg}$. Then

$$N(R) = \sharp\{\alpha \in \pi(M,p) : \|\alpha\|_{alg} \leq R\} \leq N_1((1+\lambda)dR).$$

Therefore,

$$h(\pi_1(M,p)) \leq \liminf_{R\to\infty}\frac{\log N(R)}{R} \leq \liminf_{R\to\infty}\frac{\log N_1((1+\lambda)dR)}{R}$$
$$\leq (1+\lambda)dh(M,F). \qquad \square$$

By Theorem 8.3, one can get the following

Corollary 8.1. *Let (M,F) be a compact Finsler n-manifold with reversibility λ and diameter d satisfying $Ric \geq -(n-1)(k_1)^2$, $\mathbf{S} \geq (n-1)k_2$, where $k_1 \geq 0$.*

(1) If the fundamental group is free, then the number of its free generators is at most

$$\frac{1 + \exp((n-1)d(1+\lambda)(k_1-k_2))}{2};$$

(2) The cardinality of any finite generating set (for the fundamental group) with p relations is at most

$$p + \frac{1 + \exp((n-1)d(1+\lambda)(k_1-k_2))}{2}.$$

Proof. Let $d\mu_B$ denote the Busemann-Hausdorff volume form. Using Corollary 7.1 (see §7.1.3), one has

$$\mu(B^+(p,r)) \leq \text{vol}_{\mathbb{R}^n}(\mathbb{S}^{n-1}) \int_0^r \left[\frac{e^{-k_2 t}\sinh(k_1 t)}{k_1}\right]^{n-1} dt$$
$$\leq ce^{(n-1)(k_1-k_2)r},$$

where c is a constant.

On the other hand, it is known that for any free group Γ with k generators, its entropy $h(\Gamma) = \log(2k-1)$. If Γ is a finitely generated group with k generators and p ($p < k$) relations among them, then $h(\Gamma) \geq \log[2(k-p)-1]$ (cf. [51], pp. 281-282, or [99]).

(1) Let s denote the number of the free generators in $\pi_1(M)$. By Theorem 8.3, one has

$$\log(2s-1) = h(\pi_1(M)) \leq (1+\lambda)dh(M,F) \leq (1+\lambda)d(n-1)(k_1-k_2).$$

Thus, $s \leq [1 + \exp((n-1)d(1+\lambda)(k_1 - k_2))]/2$.

(2) Let G be any generating set for the fundamental group with p relations and let s denote $\sharp(G)$. If $s \leq p$, then (2) is proved. Suppose $s > p$. Then there is $s - p$ free generators in G, hence

$$(1+\lambda)d(n-1)(k_1 - k_2) \geq h(\pi_1(M)) \geq \log(2(s-p) - 1),$$

i.e.,

$$s \leq p + \frac{1 + \exp((n-1)d(1+\lambda)(k_1 - k_2))}{2}. \qquad \Box$$

Let (M, F) be a forward complete Finsler manifold and a, c be any two positive number such that $a \geq c$. Let $N(p, a, c, M)$ denote the maximal number of disjoint open forward c-balls inside the forward ball $B^+(p, a) \subset M$ and the packing number

$$N(a, c, M) := \sup_{p \in M} N(p, a, c, M).$$

Lemma 8.4. *Let (M, F) be a forward complete Finsler manifold of finite reversibility λ and a, b, c be any positive numbers such that $a \geq b > (3 + \lambda(2+\lambda))c$. Then*

$$N(a, c, M) \leq N(b, c, M)^k, \quad k = \left[\frac{a-b}{b - (3 + \lambda(2+\lambda))c}\right] + 1.$$

Proof. Given any forward ball $B^+(p, a)$, there exists a maximal family $\mathcal{F} = \{B^+(q, c) : q \in \Lambda\}$ of disjoint open forward balls inside $B^+(p, a)$. For each R satisfying $b \leq R \leq a$, define

$$\Lambda(R) := \{q \in \Lambda : B^+(q, c) \subset B^+(p, R)\}.$$

Given any point $q \in \Lambda(R + b - (3 + \lambda(2+\lambda))c) - \Lambda(R)$, we can find a point p' on any minimal geodesic from p to q such that $d(p', q) = b - (1 + \lambda(1+\lambda))c$, which implies that $d(p, p') < R - (2+\lambda)c$ and $B^+(p', (1+\lambda)c) \subset B^+(p, R-c)$. There must be a point $q' \in \Lambda \cap B^+(p', (1+\lambda)c)$. Otherwise, one would have $B^+(p', c) \cap B^+(q, c) = \emptyset$, for all $q \in \Lambda$ and $B^+(p', c) \subset B^+(p, R)$, which would contradict the maximality of $\mathcal{F}$. Then we have $d(p', q') < (1+\lambda)c$. Using the triangle inequality, we have

$$d(p, q') \leq d(p, p') + d(p', q') < R - c,$$

hence, $B^+(q', c) \subset B^+(p, R)$ and $q' \in \Lambda(R)$. Since $d(q', q) \leq d(q', p') + d(p', q) < b - c$, hence $B^+(q, c) \subset B^+(q', b)$.

Thus, we have proved the following fact: for each $q \in \Lambda(R+b-(3+\lambda(2+\lambda))c) - \Lambda(R)$, there exists a point $q' \in \Lambda(R)$ such that $B^+(q,c) \subset B^+(q',b)$. By the definitions of Λ, $\Lambda(\cdot)$ and $N(b,c,M)$, we have the following

$$\sharp\{\Lambda(R+b-(3+\lambda(2+\lambda))c) - \Lambda(R)\} \leq \sharp(\Lambda(R))(N(b,c,M) - 1),$$

that is $\sharp\{\Lambda(R+b-(3+\lambda(2+\lambda))c)\} \leq \sharp(\Lambda(R))N(b,c,M)$. Put $a = R + b - (3 + \lambda(2 + \lambda))c$. Thus we have $\sharp(\Lambda(a)) \leq N(b,c,M)^k$, where $k = \left[\frac{a-b}{b-(3+\lambda(2+\lambda)c)}\right] + 1$. Since p is arbitrary, we are done by the definition of $N(a,c,M)$. $\square$

Using the above lemma, we can obtain a better estimate on entropies. In the Riemannian case, it is just Theorem 1 in [45].

Theorem 8.4 ([130]). *Let* (M,F) *be a compact Finsler manifold of diameter* d, *injective radius* i_M *and reversibility* λ. *Let* N_0 *denote* $N(i_M, \frac{i_M}{4+\lambda(2+\lambda)}, M)$. *Then we have*

$$h(M,F) \leq \frac{4+\lambda(2+\lambda)}{i_M} \log N_0,$$

$$h(\pi_1(M)) \leq \frac{(1+\lambda)(4+\lambda(2+\lambda))d}{i_M} \log N_0.$$

Proof. By Theorem 8.3, it suffices to show the first inequality. Let $\psi : \widetilde{M} \to M$ be the universal cover. Now let $a \geq i_M$ and set $c = i_M/(4 + \lambda(2 + \lambda))$. For a fixed point $\widetilde{p} \in \widetilde{M}$, we choose a maximal family $\mathcal{F} = \{B^+(q,c) : q \in \Lambda\}$ of disjoint open forward balls inside $B^+(\widetilde{p}, a + c)$. It follows from the maximality of F that $\overline{B^+(\widetilde{p}, a)} \subset \cup_{q \in \Lambda} B^+(q, (1+\lambda)c)$. By the properties of cover spaces, we get $N(i_M, c, \widetilde{M}) = N(i_M, c, M) = N_0$. Using Lemma 8.4 and the above arguments, we obtain

$$\sharp(\Lambda) \leq N(a+c, c, \widetilde{M}) \leq N(i_M, c, \widetilde{M})^k = N_0^k,$$

where $k = \frac{a-(2+\lambda(2+\lambda))c}{i_M - (3+\lambda(2+\lambda))c}$. Therefore,

$$\mu(B^+(\widetilde{p}, a)) \leq N_0^k \mu(B^+(q, (1+\lambda)c)) \leq N_0^k \mu(M),$$

which implies $h(M,F) \leq \frac{4+\lambda(2+\lambda)}{i_M} \log N_0$. $\square$

By the same argument as Corollary 8.1, we may get from Theorem 8.4 the following corollary immediately. The proof will be left for exercise.

Corollary 8.2. *Let* (M, F) *be a compact Finsler manifold of diameter* d, *injective radius* i_M *and reversibility* λ. *Let* N_0 *denote* $N(i_M, \frac{i_M}{4+\lambda(2+\lambda)}, M)$. *Then the cardinality of any finite generating set (for the fundamental group) with* p *relations is at most*

$$p + \frac{1}{2}\left(N_0^{\frac{(1+\lambda)(4+\lambda(2+\lambda))d}{i_M}} + 1\right).$$

8.2.2 The first Betti number

Let (M, F) be a compact Finsler n-manifold of reversibility λ and $\widetilde{M}$ be its universal covering space. By the Hurewicz theorem,

$$H_1(M, \mathbb{Z}) = \pi_1(M)/[\pi_1(M), \pi_1(M)].$$

Then $H_1(M, \mathbb{Z})$ acts by deck transformations on the covering space

$$\overline{M} := \widetilde{M}/[\pi_1(M), \pi_1(M)]$$

with quotient M. $H_1(M, \mathbb{Z})$ is a finitely generated Abelian group, and the rank of $H_1(M, \mathbb{Z})$ is called the *first Betti number* denoted by $b_1(M)$. Since

$$H_1(M, \mathbb{R}) \equiv H_1(M, \mathbb{Z}) \otimes \mathbb{R}, \quad H_1(M, \mathbb{Z}) \equiv \mathbb{Z}_{k_1} \oplus \cdots \oplus \mathbb{Z}_{k_r} \oplus \mathbb{Z} \oplus \cdots \oplus \mathbb{Z},$$

where $k_1, \cdots, k_r$ are some positive integers, one can see that $b_1(M) = \dim H_1(M, \mathbb{R})$.

For simplicity, set $\Gamma := H_1(M, \mathbb{Z})$. Recall any finite-index subgroup of Γ has the same rank as Γ (cf. [51], §5, C).

The following lemma is an extension of Lemma 5.19 in [51] to Finsler manifolds.

Lemma 8.5 ([131]). *Given any fixed point* $x \in \overline{M}$, *there exists a finite-index subgroup* $\Gamma' \subset \Gamma$ *that is generated by elements* $\gamma_1, \cdots, \gamma_{b_1}$ *such that*

$$d(x, \gamma_i(x)) \leq (1+\lambda)\mathrm{diam}(M). \tag{8.2.3}$$

Furthermore, for each $\gamma \in \Gamma' - \{1\}$, *we have*

$$d(x, \gamma(x)) > \mathrm{diam}(M). \tag{8.2.4}$$

Proof. Firstly, we show that there exists a finite-index subgroup of Γ which can be generated by elements satisfying (8.2.3).

For each $\epsilon > 0$, let Γ_ϵ be the subgroup of Γ generated by

$$\{\gamma \in \Gamma : d(x, \gamma(x)) < (1+\lambda)\mathrm{diam}(M) + \epsilon\}.$$

Let $\pi_\epsilon : \overline{M} \to \overline{M}/\Gamma_\epsilon$ denote the covering space. We claim that for each $y \in \overline{M}$, $d(\pi_\epsilon(x), \pi_\epsilon(y)) \leq \text{diam}(M)$. Otherwise, by connectedness, one can find $y \in \overline{M}$ such that

$$\text{diam}(M) < d(x,y) = d(\pi_\epsilon(x), \pi_\epsilon(y)) \leq \text{diam}(M) + \epsilon.$$

There exists $\gamma \in \Gamma$ such that $d(\gamma(x), y) \leq \text{diam}(M)$, since $\overline{M} \to M$ is a covering. Hence, $d(x, \gamma(x)) \leq d(x,y) + d(y, \gamma(x)) \leq (1 + \lambda)\text{diam}(M) + \epsilon$, that is $\gamma \in \Gamma_\epsilon$. Thus, $d(\pi_\epsilon(x), \pi_\epsilon(y)) \leq d(\gamma(x), y) \leq \text{diam}(M)$, which is a contradiction. Hence, $\overline{M}/\Gamma_\epsilon$ is compact, which implies that $\Gamma_\epsilon \subset \Gamma$ has finite index and $\text{rank}(\Gamma_\epsilon) = b_1$.

Since Γ acts properly discontinuously on $\overline{M}$, for each $r > 0$, there are at most finitely many elements in $\{\gamma \in \Gamma : d(x, \gamma(x)) < r\}$. Hence, there exists a sufficiently small $\epsilon > 0$ such that

$$\Gamma_\epsilon = \{\gamma \in \Gamma : d(x, \gamma(x)) \leq (1 + \lambda)\text{diam}(M)\}.$$

Then we have a finite-index subgroup Γ_ϵ of Γ generated by

$$\{\gamma \in \Gamma : d(x, \gamma(x)) \leq (1 + \lambda)\text{diam}(M)\} = \{\gamma_1, \cdots, \gamma_m\}.$$

Note $\text{rank}(\Gamma_\epsilon) = b_1$. Hence, we can assume that $\{\gamma_1, \cdots, \gamma_{b_1}\}$ are linearly independent and generate a subgroup $\Gamma'' \subset \Gamma$ of finite index.

Secondly, we modify this group Γ'' so that it also satisfies the second condition.

There exists only finitely many elements in $\Gamma'' \cap \{\gamma \in \Gamma : d(x, \gamma(x)) \leq (1 + \lambda)\text{diam}(M)\}$. We can therefore choose

$$\{\gamma_1', \ldots, \gamma_{b_1}'\} \subset \{\gamma \in \Gamma : d(x, \gamma(x) \leq (1 + \lambda)\text{diam}(M)\}$$

with the following properties:

(1) $\gamma_k' = l_{k1} \cdot \gamma_1 + \cdots + l_{kk} \cdot \gamma_k$ is chosen such that l_{kk} is maximal in absolute value among all elements in $\Gamma'' \cap \{\gamma \in \Gamma : d(x, \gamma(x)) \leq (1 + \lambda)\text{diam}(M)\}$. That is, if $\gamma \in \Gamma'' \cap \{\gamma \in \Gamma : d(x, \gamma(x)) \leq (1 + \lambda)\text{diam}(M)\}$ and $\gamma = \sum_{i=1}^{b_1} n_i \gamma_i$, then $|n_i| \leq |l_{ii}|$ for each i. Hence $|l_{ii}| \geq 1$.

(2) $\text{span}_{\mathbb{Z}}\{\gamma_1', \ldots, \gamma_k'\} \subset \text{span}_{\mathbb{Z}}\{\gamma_1, \ldots, \gamma_k\}$ has finite index for all $k = 1, \ldots, b_1$.

The group Γ' generated by $\{\gamma_1', \ldots, \gamma_{b_1}'\}$ has finite index in Γ'' and hence also in Γ. Clearly, the generators $\{\gamma_1', \ldots, \gamma_{b_1}'\}$ satisfy the first condition (i.e., $d(x, \gamma_i'(x)) \leq (1+\lambda)\text{diam}(M)$). It only remains to show that the group also satisfies the second condition. To see this, let $\gamma = m_1 \cdot \gamma_1' + \cdots + m_k \cdot \gamma_k'$ with $m_k \neq 0$. If $d(x, \gamma(x)) \leq \text{diam}(M)$, then

$$d(x, \gamma^2(x)) \leq d(x, \gamma(x)) + d(\gamma(x), \gamma^2(x)) \leq (1 + \lambda)\text{diam}(M).$$

Thus $\gamma^2 \in \Gamma'' \cap \{\gamma \in \Gamma : d(x, \gamma(x)) \le (1+\lambda)\mathrm{diam}(M)\}$. But

$$\gamma^2 = \sum_{i=1}^{k} 2m_i \left(\sum_{j=1}^{i} l_{ij}\gamma_j \right) = \sum_{i=1}^{k-1} n_i\gamma_i + 2m_k l_{kk} \cdot \gamma_k.$$

But this violates the maximality of $|l_{kk}|$, since $m_k \ne 0$. □

Lemma 8.6. *For each $r \in \mathbb{N}$, the number $T(r)$ of the solutions of the following equation*

$$\sum_{i=1}^{k} |x_i| \le r, \quad (x_i) \in \mathbb{Z}^k$$

equals to $\sum_{i=0}^{r} \binom{r}{i}\binom{k+r-i}{r}$.

Proof. Define $z := r - \sum_{i=1}^{k} |x_i|$. Thus, the equation $\sum_{i=1}^{k} |x_i| \le r$ is equivalent to the following equation

$$\sum_{i=1}^{k} |x_i| + z = r, \quad \text{where } z \in \mathbb{N} \cup \{0\}.$$

Consider the polynomial $A(t) := (\sum_{i \in \mathbb{Z}} t^{|i|})^k (\sum_{j=0}^{\infty} t^j) = \sum_{k=0}^{\infty} a_i t^i$, for $|t| < 1$. Then $T(r) = a_r$. It is easy to check that

$$a_r = \frac{A^{(r)}(0)}{r!}, \quad A(t) = (1+t)^k (1-t)^{-(k+1)}.$$

For simplicity, define $f(t) := (1+t)^k$ and $g(t) := (1-t)^{-(k+1)}$. From above, we have

$$a_r = \frac{1}{r!} \sum_{i=0}^{r} \binom{r}{i} f^{(i)}(0) g^{(r-i)}(0) = \sum_{i=0}^{r} \frac{(k+r-i)!}{(k-i)!(r-i)!i!}$$

$$= \sum_{i=0}^{r} \binom{r}{i}\binom{k+r-i}{r}. \quad □$$

Theorem 8.5 ([131]). *Let (M, F) be a compact Finsler n-manifold of diameter d and reversibility λ. If $\mathrm{Ric} \ge -(n-1)k^2$ and $\mathbf{S} \ge (n-1)h$, where $k \ge 0$, then there exists a finite constant $C(n, d, \lambda, k, h)$ only dependent on n, d, λ, k and h such that the first Betti number $b_1 \le C(n, d, \lambda, k, h)$. Moreover, if $h \ge 0$ and dk is sufficiently small, then $b_1 \le n$.*

Proof. By Lemma 3.1, we can choose a covering $\overline{M}$ of M with free Abelian group of deck transformations $\Gamma = \langle \gamma_1, \ldots, \gamma_{b_1} \rangle$ such that for some point $x \in \overline{M}$, $d(x, \gamma_i(x)) \leq (1 + \lambda)d$ and $d(x, \gamma(x)) > d$, for $\gamma \in \Gamma - \{1\}$. If $\gamma = \sum_{i=1}^{b_1} k_i \cdot \gamma_i$, where $(k_i) \in \mathbb{Z}^{b_1}$, then

$$d(x, \gamma(x)) \leq \sum_{i=1}^{b_1} |k_i| d(x, \gamma_i(x)) \leq (1 + \lambda)d \sum_{i=1}^{b_1} |k_i|.$$

Now define

$$I_r := \left\{ \gamma \in \Gamma : \gamma = k_1 \cdot \gamma_1 + \cdots + k_{b_1} \cdot \gamma_{b_1}, \sum_{i=1}^{b_1} |k_i| \leq r \right\}.$$

From above, for $\gamma \in I_r$, we have

$$B^+\left(\gamma(x), \frac{d}{2\lambda}\right) \subset B^+\left(x, r(1+\lambda)d + \frac{d}{2\lambda}\right),$$

and all the forward balls $B^+(\gamma_i(x), d/(2\lambda))$, $i \in \{1, \ldots, b_1\}$ are disjoint and have the same volume. Define $T(r) := \sharp I_r = \sum_{i=0}^{r} \binom{r}{i}\binom{b_1+r-i}{r}$. Then

$$b_1 \leq T(r) \leq \frac{\mu\left(B^+\left(x, r(1+\lambda)d + \frac{d}{2\lambda}\right)\right)}{\mu\left(B^+\left(x, \frac{d}{2\lambda}\right)\right)}$$

$$\leq \left(\int_0^{r(1+\lambda)d+d/(2\lambda)} \left[e^{-ht}\sinh(kt)\right]^{n-1} dt\right)$$

$$\times \left(\int_0^{d/(2\lambda)} \left[e^{-ht}\sinh(kt)\right]^{n-1} dt\right)^{-1}$$

$$=: C(n, d, \lambda, k, h) < \infty.$$

Now we show the second result. It suffices to show the case when $k > 0$. Let c denote $1/5$. There exists $\eta > 0$ such that when $0 < t < \eta$, then $c < \sinh(t)/t < 1/c$. Take $dk < \eta/((2+\lambda)r)$. Since $h \geq 0$, by ([25], Lemma 3.1), we have

$$\frac{r^{b_1}}{b_1!} \leq T(r) \leq \left(\int_0^{(2+\lambda)dkr} (t/c)^{n-1} dt\right)\left(\int_0^{dk/(2\lambda)} (ct)^{n-1} dt\right)^{-1}$$

$$\leq \frac{(2\lambda(2+\lambda)r)^n}{c^{2(n-1)}}.$$

Hence, when r is sufficiently large (that is, dk is sufficiently small), we have $b_1 \leq n$. $\square$

Remark. In the Riemannian case, $\mathbf{S}_B = 0$, $\lambda = 1$. The above theorem is Theorem 5.21 in [51].

8.2.3 Finiteness of fundamental group

Definition 8.7. The *first systole* of a Finsler manifold (M, F) is defined to be the least length of a noncontractible loop in M, denoted by $\mathrm{sys}_1(M)$.

Lemma 8.7. *Let* (M, F) *be a forward complete Finsler manifold of reversibility* $\leq \delta$ *and* $\gamma_\alpha : [0, 1] \to M$, $\alpha = 1, 2$, *be two continuous curves such that* $\gamma_1(0) = \gamma_2(0)$, $\gamma_1(1) = \gamma_2(1)$. *If* $\mathrm{sys}_1(M) \geq (1 + \delta)\sigma$ *and* $d(\gamma_1(t), \gamma_2(t)) < \sigma$ *for all* $t \in [0, 1]$, *then* $\gamma_1 \simeq \gamma_2$ rel$\{0, 1\}$, *i.e., the homotopy with fixed ends.*

Proof. Choose $\epsilon > 0$ such that $d(\gamma_1(t), \gamma_2(t)) + \epsilon < \sigma$. There exists a partition $0 = t_0 < t_1 < \cdots < t_N = 1$ such that $L(\gamma_\alpha|_{[t_{i-1}, t_i]}) < \epsilon$, $\alpha = 1, 2$. Let ζ_i denote a minimizing geodesic from $\gamma_1(t_i)$ to $\gamma_2(t_i)$. For any continuous curve $\gamma : [0, 1] \to M$, let $\gamma^{-1}(t)$ denote $\gamma(1 - t)$. Thus, the length of the loop $\gamma_1([t_{i-1}, t_i]) * \zeta_i * \gamma_2^{-1}([1 - t_i, 1 - t_{i-1}]) * \zeta_{i-1}^{-1}$ is strictly less than $(1 + \delta)\sigma$. Hence $\gamma_1 \simeq \gamma_2$ rel$\{0, 1\}$. $\square$

Theorem 8.6 ([131]). *Let* (M_i, F_i), $i = 1, 2$, *be two connected forward complete Finsler manifolds of reversibility* $\leq \delta$ *such that*

$$\mathrm{sys}_1(M_i) \geq (1 + \delta)\sigma, \quad \text{for } i = 1, 2,$$

where σ *is some positive number. If* $d_{GH}^\delta(M_1, M_2) < \frac{\sigma}{\delta(4+3\delta)}$, *then* $\pi_1(M_1)$ *and* $\pi_1(M_2)$ *are isomorphic.*

Proof. Since $d_{GH}^\delta(M_1, M_2) < \frac{\sigma}{\delta(4+3\delta)}$, there exist a positive number ϵ and a δ-admissible metric d on $M_1 \sqcup M_2$ such that

$$d_H(M_1, M_2) < \frac{\epsilon}{\delta} < \frac{\sigma}{\delta(4 + 3\delta)}.$$

Hence, we can choose $x_i \in M_i$, $i = 1, 2$, such that $d(x_1, x_2) < \epsilon$ and $d(x_2, x_1) < \epsilon$. Let η be a positive number such that $(4+3\delta)\epsilon + 2(1+\delta)\eta < \sigma$.

Given any loop $\gamma_i : [0, 1] \to M_i$ based at $x_i \in M_i$, $i = 1, 2$, let $[\gamma_i]$ denote the homotopy class of γ_i in $\pi_1(M_i, x_i)$. Now we construct a map $\alpha : \pi_1(M_1, x_1) \to \pi_2(M_2, x_2)$ as follows.

For each loop γ based at x_1 in M_1, we construct a loop γ_2 based at x_2 in M_2. Choose a partition $P = \{0 = t_0 < t_1 < \cdots < t_N = 1\}$ of $[0, 1]$ such that $L(\gamma|_{[t_i, t_{i+1}]}) < \eta$, for $i \in \{0, 1, \ldots, N-1\}$. For each $i \in \{1, \ldots, N-1\}$, there exists a point $y_i \in M_2$ such that $d(y_i, \gamma(t_i)) < \epsilon$. Note $y_N = y_0 = x_2$. Let $\gamma_2 : [0, 1] \to M_2$ be the loop based at x_2 obtained by joining y_i to y_{i+1} by a minimizing geodesic (from y_i to y_{i+1}) with $\gamma_2(t_i) = y_i$. Thus, for each $t \in [t_i, t_{i+1}]$, $L(\gamma_2|_{[t, t_{i+1}]}) = d(\gamma_2(t), \gamma_2(t_{i+1})) \leq d(\gamma_2(t_i), \gamma_2(t_{i+1}))$.

Now we define $\alpha : \pi_1(M_1, x_1) \to \pi_1(M_2, x_2)$ by $\alpha([\gamma]) = [\gamma_2]$. We show that α is well-defined.

Let γ_2' be a loop obtained from another partition $P' = \{0 = t_0' < t_1' < \cdots < t_K' = 1\}$ satisfying $L(\gamma|_{[t_j', t_{j+1}']}) < \eta$ for $j \in \{0, \ldots, K-1\}$. For each $t \in [0, 1]$, there exist i and j such that $t \in [t_i, t_{i+1}] \cap [t_j', t_{j+1}']$. Without loss of generality, let us assume that $t_i \leq t_j' \leq t_{i+1}$. Then $d(\gamma(t_j'), \gamma(t_{i+1})) \leq \eta$ and $d(\gamma(t_{i+1}), \gamma(t_j')) \leq \delta\eta$. Using the triangle inequality, we have

$$d(\gamma_2(t), \gamma_2(t_{i+1})) \leq d(\gamma_2(t_i), \gamma_2(t_{i+1}))$$
$$\leq d(\gamma_2(t_i), \gamma(t_i)) + d(\gamma(t_i), \gamma(t_{i+1})) + d(\gamma(t_{i+1}), \gamma_2(t_{i+1}))$$
$$\leq (1 + \delta)\epsilon + \eta.$$

Likewise, one can get $d(\gamma_2'(t_j), \gamma_2'(t)) \leq (1+\delta)\epsilon + \eta$. From above, we obtain

$$d(\gamma_2(t), \gamma_2'(t)) \leq d(\gamma_2(t), \gamma_2(t_{i+1})) + d(\gamma_2(t_{i+1}), \gamma(t_{i+1})) + d(\gamma(t_{i+1}), \gamma(t_j'))$$
$$+ d(\gamma(t_j'), \gamma_2'(t_j')) + d(\gamma_2'(t_j'), \gamma_2'(t))$$
$$\leq (1+\delta)\epsilon + \eta + \epsilon + \delta\eta + \delta\epsilon + (1+\delta)\epsilon + \eta$$
$$= 3(1+\delta)\epsilon + (2+\delta)\eta < \sigma.$$

By Lemma 8.2, we obtain $[\gamma_2] = [\gamma_2'] \in \pi_1(M_2, x_2)$.

Let γ be as above and let ρ be a loop such that $[\rho] = [\gamma]$. Hence there exists a homotopy $H : [0, 1] \times [0, 1] \to M_1$ such that $H(0, t) = \gamma(t)$, $H(1, t) = \rho(t)$ and $H(s, 0) = H(s, 1) = x_1$, for $0 \leq t, s \leq 1$. One can choose partitions $0 = s_0 < s_1 < \cdots < s_N = 1$ and $0 = t_0 < t_1 < \cdots < t_N = 1$ such that $L(H([s_j, s_{j+1}], t_i)) < \eta$ and $L(H(s_j, [t_i, t_{i+1}])) < \eta$.

We construct a homotopy $G : [0, 1] \times [0, 1] \to M_2$ by H. Let $G(s, 0) = G(s, 1) = x_2$. For each $H(s_i, t_j)$, there exists $y_{ij} \in M_2$ such that $d(y_{ij}, H(s_i, t_j)) < \epsilon$. Define $G(s_i, y_j) := y_{ij}$. Define $G(s_i, t)$ be the loop obtain by joining $G(s_i, t_j)$ to $G(s_i, t_{j+1})$ by a minimizing geodesic, and define $G(s, t_j)$ likewise. Each loop

$$G(s_i, [t_j, t_{j+1}]) * G([s_i, s_{i+1}], t_{j+1})$$
$$* G_t^{-1}(s_{i+1}, [1 - t_j, 1 - t_{j+1}]) * G_s^{-1}([1 - s_{i+1}, 1 - s_i], t_j)$$

has length less than $2(1 + \delta)[(1 + \delta)\epsilon + \eta] < (1 + \delta)\sigma$, where $G_t^{-1}(s, t) := G(s, 1 - t)$ and $G_s^{-1}(s, t) := G(1 - s, t)$. Since they are all homotopically trivial, they can be filled in, yielding the homotopy G, that is $\alpha[\rho] = \alpha[\gamma]$. This implies that the map $\alpha : \pi_1(M_1, x_1) \to \pi_1(M_2, x_2)$ is well-defined. Similarly, we can define a map $\beta : \pi_1(M_2, x_2) \to \pi_1(M_1, x_1)$.

Now we show $\beta\alpha = $ identity. Let γ, the partition P and γ_2 be as above. Let γ_1 be a loop based at x_1 obtained from β and γ_2, i.e., $\gamma_1 \in \beta\alpha[\gamma] = \beta[\gamma_2]$.

For each $t \in [0,1]$, there exists i such that $t \in [t_i, t_{i+1}]$. Since

$$d(\gamma_2(t_i), \gamma_2(t_{i+1})) \le d(\gamma_2(t_i), \gamma(t_i)) + d(\gamma(t_i), \gamma(t_{i+1})) + d(\gamma(t_{i+1}), \gamma_2(t_{i+1}))$$
$$\le \epsilon + \eta + \delta\epsilon,$$

$$d(\gamma(t_{i+1}), \gamma(t)) \le \delta d(\gamma(t), \gamma(t_{i+1})) \le \delta d(\gamma(t_i), \gamma(t_{i+1})) < \delta\eta,$$

hence,

$$d(\gamma_2(t), \gamma(t)) \le d(\gamma_2(t), \gamma_2(t_{i+1})) + d(\gamma_2(t_{i+1}), \gamma(t_{i+1})) + d(\gamma(t_{i+1}), \gamma(t))$$
$$\le (1+\delta)\epsilon + \eta + \epsilon + \delta\eta = (2+\delta)\epsilon + (1+\delta)\eta.$$

Likewise, we have $d(\gamma_1(t), \gamma_2(t)) \le (2+\delta)\epsilon + (1+\delta)\eta$. Therefore, we have $d(\gamma_1(t), \gamma(t)) \le 2[(2+\delta)\epsilon + (1+\delta)\eta] < \sigma$. By Lemma 7.15 again, we have $[\gamma_1] = [\gamma]$, that is $\beta\alpha = $ identity. One can show $\alpha\beta = $ identity similarly. $\square$

Let $\mathfrak{N}(n, \delta)$ be a pre-compact family of forward complete Finsler n-manifolds of reversibility $\le \delta$ with respect to δ-Gromov-Hausdorff distance. This means for every $\epsilon > 0$, there exist finitely many elements $M_1, \cdots, M_{N(\epsilon)}$ in $\mathfrak{N}(n, \delta)$ such that for each $M \in \mathfrak{N}(n, \delta)$, there exists $i \in \{1, \dots, N(\epsilon)\}$ satisfying $d_{GH}^\delta(M, M_i) < \epsilon$. Let $\mathfrak{N}(n, \delta, \sigma) = \{(M, F) \in \mathfrak{N}(n, \delta) | \mathrm{sys}_1(M) \ge \sigma\}$.

Theorem 8.7 ([131]). *There are only finitely many isomorphism classes of fundamental groups in $\mathfrak{N}(n, \delta, \sigma)$.*

Proof. Given $\sigma > 0$, let $\epsilon = \frac{\sigma}{\delta(1+\delta)(4+3\delta)}$. Thus, there exist finitely many elements $M_1, \dots, M_{N(\epsilon/2)}$ in $\mathfrak{N}(n, \delta)$ such that

$$\mathfrak{N}(n, \delta, \sigma) \subset \bigcup_{i=1}^{N(\epsilon/2)} B^\delta(M_i, \epsilon/2), \quad B^\delta(M_i, \epsilon/2) \cap \mathfrak{N}(n, \delta, \sigma) \ne \emptyset,$$

where $B^\delta(M_i, \epsilon/2) := \{Y \in \mathfrak{N}(n, \delta) | d_{GH}^\delta(M_i, Y) < \epsilon/2\}$. For each $1 \le i \le N(\epsilon/2)$, we choose an element $M_i' \in B^\delta(M_i, \epsilon/2) \cap \mathfrak{N}(n, \delta, \sigma)$. Since δ-Gromov-Hausdorff distance is reversible, we have

$$\mathfrak{N}(n, \delta, \sigma) \subset N(\epsilon/2)_{i=1} \cup B^\delta(M_i', \epsilon).$$

It follows from Theorem 4.2 that for each i, all the fundamental groups of the manifolds in $B^\delta(M_i', \epsilon) \cap \mathfrak{N}(n, \delta, \sigma)$ are isomorphic. This completes the proof. $\square$

Let $\mathfrak{N}(n,k,h,\delta,\sigma,D)$ denote the class of compact Finsler n-manifolds $\{(M,F)\}$ with

$$Ric \geq (n-1)k, \quad \mathbf{S} \geq (n-1)h, \quad \lambda_F \leq \delta, \quad \mathrm{sys}_1 \geq \sigma, \quad \mathrm{diam} \leq D.$$

By Theorem 8.13 in the next section, the class $\mathfrak{N}(n,k,h,\delta,\sigma,D)$ is precompact with respect to δ-Gromov-Hausdorff distance. From Theorem 8.7 we then obtain the following

Corollary 8.3. *Given $n \in N$, k, $h \in R$, $\delta \in [1,\infty)$, and $\sigma, D \in (0,\infty)$, there are only finitely many isomorphism classes of fundamental groups among $\mathfrak{N}(n,k,h,\delta,\sigma,D)$.*

The following lemma should be viewed as a generalized version of the result of M. Gomov ([51], Proposition 5.28).

Lemma 8.8 ([131]). *Let (M,F) be a compact Finsler n-manifold of reversibility λ and $\widetilde{M}$ be its universal covering. For each $p \in M$, there always exists a generating set $\{\gamma_1,\ldots,\gamma_m\}$ of the fundamental group $\Gamma = \pi_1(M,p)$ such that $d(\widetilde{p},\gamma_i\widetilde{p}) \leq (1+\lambda)\,\mathrm{diam}\,(M)$, where $\widetilde{p} \in \widetilde{M}$ is a point in the fiber over $p \in M$ and all relations among these generators are of form $\gamma_i\gamma_j\gamma_k^{-1} = 1$.*

Proof. For any $\epsilon \in (0, \mathrm{i}_M/(2\lambda))$, choose a triangularization K of M such that p is a vertex and adjacent vertices in this triangularization are joined by a cue of length less than ϵ. Let $\{p, x_1, \cdots, x_k\}$ denote the set of vertices and $\{e_{ij}\}$ denote the edges joining adjacent vertices x_i, x_j (e_{ij} is not necessarily defined of all i, j). Join p and x_i by a minimizing geodesic σ_i from p to x_i, of all $i = 1,\ldots,k$ and construct the loops $\sigma_{ij} = \sigma_i e_{ij}\sigma_j^{-1}$. Let γ denote the homotopy class of σ_{ij} in $\pi_1(M,p)$. It is easy to check that $d(\widetilde{p},\gamma\widetilde{p}) \leq (1+\lambda)\mathrm{diam}(M) + \epsilon$. The remaining proof is same as ([94], Lemma 2.3, p.254), and we omit it here. $\qquad\square$

Given $n \in \mathbb{N}$, $k, h \in \mathbb{R}$, $\delta \in [1,\infty)$, and $v, D \in (0,\infty)$, let $\mathfrak{M}(n,k,h,\delta,v,D)$ denote the class of compact Finsler n-manifolds with

$$\mathbf{ic} \geq (n-1)k, \quad \mathbf{S} \geq (n-1)h, \quad \lambda_F \leq \delta, \quad \mu_F \geq v, \quad \mathrm{diam} \leq D,$$

and let $\mathfrak{M}(n,k,h,v,D)$ denote the class of compact Finsler n-manifolds with

$$\mathbf{ic} \geq (n-1)k, \quad \mathbf{S} \geq (n-1)h, \quad \mu_F \geq v, \quad \mathrm{diam} \leq D,$$

where μ_F is the Busemann-Hausdorff volume of M. Then we have the following theorem, which are the extensions of the results due to M. Andeson ([2], Theorem 2.1).

Theorem 8.8 ([131]). *There are only finitely many isomorphism classes of fundamental groups in* $\mathfrak{M}(n, k, h, \delta, v, D)$ *for fixed* n, k, h, δ, v, D.

Proof. Choose the generating set $\{\gamma_1, \ldots, \gamma_m\}$ of $\pi_1(M, p)$ as in the above lemma. Since the number of possible relations is bounded by 2^{m^3}, it suffices to show m is bounded. Let $\Omega_p \subset \widetilde{M}$ be a fundamental domain constructed as before. The sets $\gamma_i(\Omega_p)$, $1 \le i \le m$ are disjoint, and have the same volume. Since $d(\widetilde{p}, \gamma_i\widetilde{p}) \le (1 + \delta)D$, $\gamma_i(\Omega_p) \subset B^+(\widetilde{p}, 2(1 + \delta)D)$, for each $1 \le i \le m$. Hence,

$$m \le \frac{\mu_F(B^+(\widetilde{p}, 2(1 + \delta)D))}{\mu_F(\Omega_p)} \le \frac{V_{k,h,n}(2(1 + \delta)D)}{v} < \infty. \qquad \square$$

As an application of Theorem 8.8, we have the following corollary, which is a Finslerian version of [141], Theorem 1.

Corollary 8.4 ([131]). *Given any constant* $\delta \ge 1$ *and* $v > 0$, *there exists* $\epsilon = \epsilon(n, \delta, v) > 0$ *such that if a compact manifold* M^n *admits a Finsler metric* F *satisfying the conditions* **ic** $\ge -\epsilon$, **S** ≥ 0, $\mathrm{diam}(M) = 1$, $\lambda_F \le \delta$ *and* $\mathrm{vol}_F(M) \ge v$, *then the fundamental group of* M *is of polynomial growth with degree* $\le n$.

Proof. Take a point $p \in M$. Let $f : \widetilde{M} \to M$ be the universal covering and $\widetilde{p}$ be any point in the fiber $f^{-1}(p)$. Ω_p denotes a fundamental domain constructed as above. Let $S := \{\gamma_1, \ldots, \gamma_k\}$ be a generating set of $\pi_1(M)$ and $\| \cdot \|_{alg}$ denote the algebraic norm associated with S. Define $\Gamma(s) := \{\gamma \in \pi_1(M) : \|\gamma\|_{alg} \le s\}$ and $\ell := \max_{\{1 \le i \le k\}} d(\widetilde{p}, \gamma_i(\widetilde{p}))$. Since $\gamma(\Omega_p) \subset B_{\widetilde{p}}^+(s\ell + \mathrm{diam}(M))$ for each $\gamma \in \Gamma(s)$, where $\mathrm{diam}(M) = 1$, we have

$$\sharp(\Gamma(s)) \le \frac{\mu_F(B_{\widetilde{p}}^+(s\ell + 1))}{v}. \qquad (8.2.5)$$

Suppose that for any $1 > \epsilon > 0$, there exists a Finsler metric F satisfying **ic** $\ge -\epsilon$, **S** ≥ 0, $\mathrm{diam}(M) = 1$, $\lambda_F \le \delta$ and $\mu_F(M) \ge v$ such that $\pi_1(M)$ is not of polynomial growth with degree $\le n$. Clearly, $(M, F) \in \mathfrak{M}(n, -1, 0, \delta, v, 1)$. By Lemma 4.6 and Theorem 1.3, one can choose a finite generating set $\{\gamma_1, \cdots, \gamma_m\}$ of $\pi_1(M)$ such that
  (i) $m \le N(n, \delta, v)$,
  (ii) $d(\widetilde{p}, \gamma_i(\widetilde{p})) \le (1 + \delta)$, for each $i = 1, \ldots, m$,
  (iii) every relation is of the form $\gamma_i\gamma_j\gamma_k^{-1} = 1$.
  Since $\pi_1(M)$ is not of polynomial growth with degree, for each $j \in \mathbb{N}$, thee exists $s_j \in \mathbb{N}$ such that

$$(\Gamma(s_j)) > j \cdot (s_j)^n. \qquad (8.2.6)$$

It follows from (i) and (iii) that the relationship (8.2.6) is independent of ϵ. Now, by (8.2.5), we have

$$(\Gamma(s)) \le \frac{\omega(n)}{v} \int_0^{(1+\delta)s+1} \left(\frac{\sinh \sqrt{\epsilon}t}{\sqrt{\epsilon}} \right)^{n-1} dt,$$

where $\omega(n) = \mathrm{Vol}_{\mathbb{R}^{n-1}}(\mathbb{S}^{n-1})$. Given a fixed, sufficiently large number c, there exists a positive number $\eta < 1$ such that when $0 < t < \eta$, $\sinh t < ct$. Hence, if $\sqrt{\epsilon}[(1+\delta)s + 1] < \eta$, then

$$(\Gamma(s)) \le \frac{\omega(n)}{v} \int_0^{(1+\delta)s+1} (ct)^{n-1} dt \le \frac{\omega(n)c^{n-1}(2(1+\delta))^n}{v} s^n.$$

Hence, for any fixed, sufficiently large s_0, there is $\epsilon_0 = \epsilon(s_0) < 1$ such that $\sqrt{\epsilon_0}[(1+\delta)s_0 + 1] < \eta$. Thus, for each $s \le s_0$ and each $\epsilon \le \epsilon_0$,

$$(\Gamma(s)) \le C(n,\delta,v)s^n, \tag{8.2.7}$$

where $C(n,\delta,v) = \frac{\omega(n)(2c^{n-1}(1+\delta))^n}{v}$.

Now let $j_0 > C(n,\delta,v)$, by (8.2.6), thee exists s_{j_0} such that

$$(\Gamma(s_{j_0})) > C(n,\delta,v) \cdot (s_{j_0})^n.$$

But we get a contradiction by taking $\epsilon \le \epsilon(s_{j_0})$ and (8.2.7). $\qquad\square$

8.3 Gromov pre-compactness theorems

8.3.1 General metric spaces

As it is well known, the distance function d of a normal metric space X (e.g., Riemannian spaces) is symmetric (or reversible), i.e., $d(x,y) = d(y,x)$ for any $x,y \in X$. However, Finsler manifolds are non-reversible in general (see §2.4.3). Hence we would like to introduce general metric spaces without reversible restriction. Refer to [7, 51] for the properties of normal metric spaces.

Definition 8.8. A *general metric space* is a pair (X,d), where X is a set and $d : X \times X \to \mathbb{R}^+ \cup \{\infty\}$, called a *metric*, is a function with the following properties: for all $x,y,z \in X$,
  (i) $d(x,y) \ge 0$ with the equality if and only if $x = y$;
  (ii) $d(x,y) + d(y,z) \ge d(x,z)$.

All of the spaces under our consideration here are general metric spaces, and we still call them metric spaces for simplicity. Unless otherwise metrics on the same set X are considered, we shall simply write "a metric space X" instead of "a metric space (X, d)".

In a metric space X we define the *forward* (resp. *backward*) ε-*ball* for $\varepsilon > 0$, centered at $x \in X$ by

$$B_x^+(\varepsilon) := \{y \in X \,|\, d(x, y) < \varepsilon\} \quad (\text{resp. } B_x^-(\varepsilon) := \{y \in X \,|\, d(y, x) < \varepsilon\}).$$

A subset $U \subset X$ is said to be *open* if, for each point $x \in U$, there is a forward ε-ball about x contained in U. Then we get the topology on X. And all metric spaces are first countable and T_1-spaces. In general, we assume that the metric d of any metric space (X, d) is continuous with respect to the product topology on $X \times X$. Thus, every backward ε-ball is open and the metric space is a Hausdorff (T_2-) space. Hence the compact sets in such a space are closed.

From the above discussions we have the following proposition immediately.

Proposition 8.8. *In a metric space (X, d) the following are equivalent:*
(1) A sequence $\{x_n\}$ in (X, d) converges to $x \in X$ in the sense of topology.
(2) $\lim_{n \to \infty} d(x, x_n) = 0$.

By using Proposition 8.8, we have following

Proposition 8.9. *If X is a metric space and $A \subset X$, then the closure $\overline{A}$ of A coincides with the set of limits in X of sequences of points in A.*

Proof. Suppose that x is a limit of some a sequence in A. Then Proposition 8.8 implies that any open set of x contains a point of A, and therefore $x \overline{\in} \text{int}(X - A)$. Since $X - \text{int}(X - A) = \overline{A}$, $x \in \overline{A}$. On the other hand, if $x \in \overline{A}$, then $B_x^+(1/n)$ must contain a point of A for any $n \in \mathbb{N}$. Otherwise, $x \in \text{int}(X - A)$. Denote by x_n the point in $B_x^+(1/n) \cap A$. Then Proposition 8.8 implies that $\{x_n\}$ converges to x in the sense of topology. $\square$

Definition 8.9. (i) A *forward* (resp. *backward*) *Cauchy sequence* in a metric space (X, d) is a sequence $\{x_n\}$ such that for each $\epsilon > 0$, there exists $N > 0$ such that $d(x_i, x_j) < \epsilon$ (resp. $d(x_j, x_i) < \epsilon$) when $j \geq i > N$. A metric space X is called *forward* (resp. *backward*) *complete* if every forward (resp. backward) Cauchy sequence in X converges in X. A metric space X is said to be *complete* if it is both forward complete and backward complete.

(ii) A metric space X is *forward* (resp. *backward*) *totally bounded* if, for each $\epsilon > 0$, X can be covered by a finite number of forward (resp.

backward) ϵ-balls. A metric space X is *totally bounded* if it is both forward and backward totally bounded.

(iii) Let (X, d) be a metric space and $A \subset X$. A is called a *forward* (resp. *backward*) ϵ-net of X if, for each $x \in X$, there exists $y \in A$ such that $d(y, x) \leq \epsilon$ (resp. $d(x, y) \leq \epsilon$).

Clearly, (X, d) is forward (resp. backward) totally bounded if and only if it has a finite forward (resp. backward) ϵ-net for each $\epsilon > 0$.

Definition 8.10. Let (X, d) be a metric space. The *reversibility* λ of (X, d) is defined by

$$\lambda_d := \sup_{\substack{x, y \in X, \\ x \neq y}} \frac{d(x, y)}{d(y, x)}.$$

It is easy to see that the reversibility of a metric space satisfies $\lambda_d \geq 1$ where the equality holds if and only if the metric d is reversible. Metric spaces with $\lambda_d = 1$ are also called *reversible (metric) spaces*. If it is clear from the context that the metric d gives rise to the reversibility λ_d, we usually drop d in the notation λ_d.

Proposition 8.10. *Let (X, d) be a metric space with finite reversibility. Then any convergent sequence is both a forward and backward convergent Cauchy sequence. Hence, the following are equivalent for (X, d):*

(i) X is forward complete.
(ii) X is backward complete.
(iii) X is complete.

Proof. Let $\{x_n\}$ be any convergent sequence in X and let $x \in X$ denote the limit of $\{x_n\}$. For each $\epsilon > 0$, there exists $N > 0$ such that when $m \geq n > N$, then $d(x, x_n) < \frac{\epsilon}{2\lambda}$, $d(x, x_m) < \frac{\epsilon}{2\lambda}$, where λ denotes the reversibility of X. By the triangle inequality, $d(x_n, x_m) < \epsilon$, $d(x_m, x_n) < \epsilon$. Hence $\{x_n\}$ is a convergent both forward and backward Cauchy sequence. □

Let (X, d) be a metric space with finite reversibility. Thus, $B_x^+(r) \subset B_x^-(\lambda r)$ and $B_x^-(r) \subset B_x^+(\lambda r)$ for all $x \in X$ and all $r > 0$, where λ denotes the reversibility of X. Therefore we have

Proposition 8.11. *In a metric space (X, d) with finite reversibility, the following are equivalent:*

(i) X is forward totally bounded.
(ii) X is backward totally bounded.

(iii) X *is totally bounded.*

We now have the following

Theorem 8.9 ([129]). *In a metric space* (X, d) *with finite reversibility, the following are equivalent:*
(i) X *is compact.*
(ii) X *is sequentially compact.*
(iii) X *is complete and totally bounded.*

Proof. (i)$\Rightarrow$(ii): Suppose that X is not sequentially compact. Then there is an infinite sequence $\{x_n\}$ with no convergent subsequences. For an arbitrary point $x \in X$, since x is not the limit of any subsequence of $\{x_n\}$, there exists a neighborhood U_x of x such that U_x contains only a finite number of points of $\{x_n\}$. It follows from (i) that X can be covered by a finite number of such U_x. Hence, $\{x_n\}$ is a finite points sequence, which is a contradiction.

(ii)$\Rightarrow$(iii): Let $\{x_n\}$ be a (forward or backward) Cauchy sequence. (ii) then yields that there exists a subsequence $\{x_{n_j}\}$ such that $x_{n_j} \to x \in X$. By the triangle inequality and the finite reversibility, one has $x_n \to x$, i.e., X is complete. Suppose that X cannot be covered by a finite number of forward ϵ-balls. Then one can find $x_1, x_2, \cdots$ such that $d(x_i, x_j) > \epsilon$ if $j > i$. Thus, any subsequence of $\{x_n\}$ is divergent, that contradicts (ii). Hence, X is forward complete. Then Proposition 8.11 implies that X is totally bounded.

(iii)$\Rightarrow$(ii): Let $\{x_i\}$ be an arbitrary sequence in X. Since X is totally bounded, it can be covered by a finite number of forward 1-balls. Thus, one of these balls, say B_1, must contain infinitely many x_i's. Next, X and hence B_1 can be covered by a finite number of forward 2-balls and so one of these balls, say B_2, must be such that $B_1 \cap B_2$ contains x_i for infinitely many i's. Continuing in this way, we can find a sequence of forward balls $\{B_n\}$ such that B_n is a forward $1/n$-ball and $B_1 \cap \cdots \cap B_n$ contains infinitely many x_i's. Thus, we can choose a subsequence $\{x_{i_n}\} \subset \{x_i\}$ such that $x_{i_n} \in B_1 \cap \cdots \cap B_n$. If $n < m$, then x_{i_n} and x_{i_m} are both in B_n. Hence, $d(x_{i_n}, x_{i_m}) < (1 + \lambda)\frac{1}{n}$. That is, $\{x_{i_n}\}$ is a (both forward and backward) Cauchy sequence and it must be convergent by (iii).

(ii)$\Rightarrow$(i): Suppose $\{U_\alpha \mid \alpha \in \Lambda\}$ is an open covering of X. Since X is totally bounded (by (ii)$\Rightarrow$(iii)), then given an arbitrary integer $n > 0$, we can find a finite number of forward $\frac{1}{n}$-balls $\{B^+_{x_{n,i}}(\frac{1}{n}), i = 1, \ldots, k(n)\}$ such that X can be covered by them. Set

$$S_n := \bigcup_{i=1}^{k(n)} x_{n,i}, \quad S := \bigcup_{n=1}^{\infty} S_n.$$

Thus, S_n is a finite forward $(1/n)$-net, and S is countable and dense set as in X. Let us rename this countable dense set $S = \{x_1, x_2, \dots\}$. For each $x_i \in S$, there is a positive integer n such that $B_{x_i}^+(\frac{1}{n\lambda}) \subset U_\alpha$ for some α, where λ is the reversibility of X. Denote one of such U_α by $V_{n,i}$. Now given $x \in X$, there is an $\tilde{n}$ such that $B_x^+(\frac{2}{\tilde{n}}) \subset U_\beta$ for some $\beta \in \Lambda$. The density then yields that there is $x_j \in S$ such that $d(x_j, x) < \frac{1}{\tilde{n}\lambda}$. Let $z \in B_{x_j}^+(\frac{1}{\tilde{n}\lambda})$, we have

$$d(x, z) \leq d(x, x_j) + (x_j, z)$$
$$\leq \lambda d(x_j, x) + d(x_j, z)$$
$$< \frac{1}{\tilde{n}} + \frac{1}{\tilde{n}\lambda} = (1 + \lambda^{-1})\frac{1}{\tilde{n}} \leq \frac{2}{\tilde{n}}.$$

Hence, $B_{x_j}^+(\frac{1}{\tilde{n}\lambda}) \subset B_x^+(\frac{2}{\tilde{n}}) \subset U_\beta$, and $V_{\tilde{n},j}$ is defined. Thus, $x \in B_{x_j}^+(\frac{1}{\tilde{n}\lambda}) \subset V_{\tilde{n},j}$. Therefore, the set $\{V_{n,i}\}$ covers X and this is a countable subcovering of the original covering. Let us rename this countable subcovering as $\{V_1, V_2, \cdots\}$. If it has a finite subcovering, then we are done. If not, the closed sets

$$C_1 = X - V_1,$$
$$C_2 = X - (V_1 \cup V_2),$$
$$C_3 = X - (V_1 \cup V_2 \cup V_3),$$
$$\cdots$$

are all non-empty and $C_1 \supset C_2 \supset C_3 \supset \cdots$. Choose $x_i \in C_i$ for each i. Then (ii) implies that there is a convergent subsequence, say, $x_{n_i} \to x$. Since $x_{n_i} \in C_n$ for all $n_i > n$, and C_n is closed, Proposition 8.9 then implies that x must be in C_n, for all n. Thus

$$x \in \bigcap_n C_n = X - \bigcup_n V_n = \emptyset.$$

It is a contradiction. This completes the proof. $\qquad \square$

From the above theorem, we have immediately the following

Corollary 8.5. *Let X be a compact metric space with finite reversibility. Then X is separable.*

Now we consider the convergence of maps in general metric spaces.

Definition 8.11. Let $\{f_i : X \to Y\}$ be a sequence of maps from a topological space X to a metric space Y. $\{f_i\}$ is said to *converge uniformly to a map* $f : X \to Y$ if, for each $\epsilon > 0$, there is a number N such that if $i > N$ then $d(f(x), f_i(x)) + d(f_i(x), f(x)) < \epsilon$ for all $x \in X$.

Similar to the case for normal metric spaces, from the above definition we obtain directly the following proposition, of which the proof is remained as an exercise.

Proposition 8.12. *(1) A map $f : X \to Y$ between two metric spaces is continuous at a point $x \in X$ if and only if given an arbitrary sequence $\{x_n\}$ in X convergent to x, $\lim_{n \to \infty} d(f(x), f(x_n)) = 0$, i.e., $f(x_n) \to f(x)$ $(n \to \infty)$.*

(2) If a sequence $\{f_1, f_2, \ldots\}$ of continuous maps from a topological space X to a metric space Y converges uniformly to a map $f : X \to Y$, then f is continuous.

Theorem 8.10 ([129]). *Let $\{f_1, f_2, \ldots\}$ be a sequence of maps from a topological space X to a forward complete metric space Y. If the reversibility of Y is finite, then the sequence $\{f_1, f_2, \ldots\}$ converges uniformly to a map f if and only if $\forall \epsilon > 0$, $\exists N > 0$ such that for if $n \geq m > N$, then $d(f_m(x), f_n(x)) < \epsilon$ for all $x \in X$.*

Proof. Denote by λ the reversibility of Y. The necessity follows from Definition 8.11 and the assumption $\lambda < \infty$. In what follows, we shall prove the sufficiency.

By assumption, $\{f_n(x)\}$ is a forward Cauchy sequence in Y, for each point $x \in X$. The completeness of Y implies that there is $y \in Y$ such that $f_n(x) \to y$ $(n \to \infty)$. Thus, we can define a map $f(x) := \lim_{n \to \infty} f_n(x)$, for all $x \in X$. We assert that for each $\epsilon > 0$, if there exists $N > 0$ such that $d(f(x), f_n(x)) < \epsilon$ for all $x \in X$ when $n > N$.

We now use reductio ad absurdum. Assume that there exists $\epsilon_0 > 0$ such that for each $N > 0$, there are a number $n' > N$ and a point $x' \in X$ with

$$d(f(x'), f_{n'}(x')) \geq \epsilon_0. \tag{8.3.1}$$

The assumption implies that there exists $N_1 > 0$ such that if $m \geq n > N_1$, then

$$d(f_n(x), f_m(x)) < \frac{\epsilon_0}{2\lambda}, \quad \forall x \in X. \tag{8.3.2}$$

From (8.3.1) it follows that there exist $n_0 > N_1 + 1$ and $x_0 \in X$ with $d(f(x_0), f_{n_0}(x_0)) \geq \epsilon_0$. The definition of f implies that there is N_2 ($N_2 > n_0$) such that if $m > N_2$ then $d(f(x_0), f_m(x_0)) < \frac{\epsilon_0}{2}$. Moreover, by (8.3.2) we see that for $m > N_2$,

$$d(f_m(x_0), f_{n_0}(x_0)) \leq \lambda d(f_{n_0}(x_0), f_m(x_0)) < \frac{\epsilon_0}{2}.$$

Therefore, we have

$$\epsilon_0 \leq d(f(x_0), f_{n_0}(x_0)) \leq d(f(x_0), f_{N_2+1}(x_0)) + d(f_{N_2+1}(x_0), f_{n_0}(x_0))$$
$$< \frac{\epsilon_0}{2} + \frac{\epsilon_0}{2} = \epsilon_0.$$

This is a contradiction. Then the sufficiency is proved. $\qquad\square$

8.3.2 δ-Gromov-Hausdorff convergence

Definition 8.12. Let (X, d) be a metric space. The *diameter* of (X, d) is defined by

$$\text{diam}(X) := \sup_{x,y \in X} d(x, y).$$

Let A, B be two subsets of X. The *distance* from A to B is defined by

$$d(A, B) := \inf\{d(a, b) \mid a \in A, b \in B\}.$$

Set $\mathcal{B}^+(A, \varepsilon) := \{x \in X \mid d(A, x) < \varepsilon\}$. The *Hausdorff distance* between A and B is defined by

$$d_H(A, B) := \inf\{\varepsilon \mid A \subset \mathcal{B}^+(B, \varepsilon), B \subset \mathcal{B}^+(A, \varepsilon)\}.$$

Obviously, the Hausdorff distance d_H is always symmetric (reversible), i.e., $d_H(A, B) = d_H(B, A)$.

Let (X_i, d_i), $i = 1, 2$, be two metric spaces. An *admissible metric* on the disjoint union $X \sqcup Y$ is a metric which extends the given metrics on X_1 and X_2. A *δ-admissible metric* on $X_1 \sqcup X_2$ is an admissible metric whose reversibility is not larger than $\delta < \infty$.

Example 8.1. Let $\rho_i := \text{diam}(X_i)$. We can define an admissible metric on $X_1 \sqcup X_2$ as follows:

$$d(x, y) := d_i(x, y), \quad \text{for all } x, y \in X_i, \ i = 1, 2,$$
$$d(x_1, x_2) := \rho_1 + \rho_2 + \varepsilon =: d(x_2, x_1), \quad \text{for all } x_1 \in X_1, x_2 \in X_2$$

where ε is an arbitrary positive constant. If the reversibilities of (X_i, d_i), $i = 1, 2$ are not larger than δ, then the admissible metric defined above is a δ-admissible metric.

Definition 8.13. Let (X_i, d_i), $i = 1, 2$, be two metric spaces whose reversibilities are not larger than $\delta < \infty$. The δ-*Gromov-Hausdorff distance* between X_1 and X_2 is defined by

$$d_{GH}^\delta(X_1, X_2) := \inf\{d_H(X_1, X_2) | \ \delta\text{-admissible metrics on } X_1 \sqcup X_2\}.$$

Clearly, the δ-Gromov-Hausdorff distance is always symmetric (reversible), since the Hausdorff distance is symmetric (reversible).

Remark. There is another equivalent definition of δ-Gromov-Hausdorff distance. Let X_i, $i = 1, 2$ be the metric spaces as above. The δ-Gromov-Hausdorff distance between them is defined by the following relation. For an $r > 0$, $d_{GH}^\delta(X_1, X_2) < r$ if and only if there exist a metric space Z, whose reversibility are not larger than δ, and subspaces X_1' and X_2' of Z, which are isometric to X_1 and X_2 respectively, satisfy $d_H(X_1', X_2') < r$. In other words, $d_{GH}^\delta(X_1, X_2)$ is the infimum of positive r for which the above Z, X_1' and X_2' exist (cf. [129]).

Proposition 8.13. *Let X, Y and Z be metric spaces whose reversibilities are not larger than $\delta < \infty$. Then*

$$d_{GH}^\delta(X, Z) \leq d_{GH}^\delta(X, Y) + d_{GH}^\delta(Y, Z).$$

Proof. For each $\epsilon > 0$, there is a δ-admissible metric d_1 on $X \sqcup Y$, whose Hausdorff distance d_{H1} satisfies

$$d_{GH}^\delta(X, Y) + \frac{\epsilon}{3} \geq d_{H1}(X, Y).$$

Similarly, there is a δ-admissible metric d_2 on $Y \sqcup Z$ such that its Hausdorff distance d_{H2} satisfies

$$d_{GH}^\delta(Y, Z) + \frac{\epsilon}{3} \geq d_{H2}(Y, Z).$$

Define

$$d_3(x, z) := \inf_{y \in Y}\{d_1(x, y) + d_2(y, z)\},$$

$$d_3(z, x) := \inf_{y \in Y}\{d_2(z, y) + d_1(y, x)\},$$

$$d_3(x_1, x_2) := d_1(x_1, x_2),$$

$$d_3(z_1, z_2) := d_2(z_1, z_2),$$

for all x, x_1, $x_2 \in X$, $y \in Y$ and z, z_1, $z_2 \in Z$. One can verify that d_3 is a δ-admissible metric on $X \sqcup Z$. Let d_{H3} denote Hausdorff distance on $X \sqcup Z$ induced by d_3. The definition of d_3 yields

$$d_{H3}(X, Z) \leq d_{H1}(X, Y) + d_{H2}(Y, Z) + \frac{\epsilon}{3}.$$

Hence,

$$d_{GH}^{\delta}(X,Z) \le d_{H3}(X,Z) \le d_{H1}(X,Y) + d_{H2}(Y,Z) + \frac{\epsilon}{3}$$
$$\le d_{GH}^{\delta}(X,Y) + d_{GH}^{\delta}(Y,Z) + \epsilon.$$

We are done by letting $\epsilon \to 0$. □

In the following, we denote by $\mathcal{M}^{\delta}$ the collection of compact metric spaces whose reversibilities are not larger than $\delta < \infty$.

Proposition 8.14 ([129]). *If $X, Y \in \mathcal{M}^{\delta}$ satisfy $d_{GH}^{\delta}(X,Y) = 0$, then X and Y are isometric.*

Proof. Choose a sequence of δ-admissible metrics d_i on $X \sqcup Y$ such that the Hausdorff distance between X and Y in this metric is less than i^{-1}. Then one can find (possibly discontinuous) maps

$$I_i : X \to Y, \text{ where } d_i(I_i(x), x) \le i^{-1},$$
$$J_i : Y \to X, \text{ where } d_i(J_i(y), y) \le i^{-1}.$$

Using the fact that d_i restricted to either X or Y is the given metric d on these spaces, we have

$$d(I_i(x_1), I_i(x_2)) \le d_i(I_i(x_1), x_2) + d_i(x_2, I_i(x_2))$$
$$\le d_i(I_i(x_1), x_1) + d(x_1, x_2) + d_i(x_2, I_i(x_2))$$
$$\le (1+\delta)i^{-1} + d(x_1, x_2),$$

and

$$d(J_i \circ I_i(x), x) \le d_i(J_i \circ I_i(x), I_i(x)) + d_i(I_i(x), x)$$
$$\le 2i^{-1}.$$

Likewise,

$$d(J_i(y_1), J_i(y_2)) \le (1+\delta)i^{-1} + d(y_1, y_2),$$
$$d(I_i \circ J_i(y), y) \le 2i^{-1}.$$

Since X is compact and its reversibility is $\le \delta < \infty$, by Corollary 8.5, we can find a countable dense subset $S = \{x_1, x_2, \ldots\}$ of X. By Theorem 8.9, using the Cantor diagonal procedure, we can choose a subsequence $\{I_{i,i}\}$ of $\{I_i\}$ such that $\{I_{i,i}\}$ converges at each point of S.

Set $g_i := I_{i,i}$. For each $\epsilon > 0$, let $N_0 = \left[\frac{6\delta+1}{\epsilon}\right]^{-1}$. Thus, there exists a finite forward N_0-net $S_{N_0} \subset S$ (compare with the proof of Theorem 8.9). Since $\{g_i\}$ converges at each point of S_{N_0}, there exists $N_1 > 0$, such that

$$\text{if } n \ge m > N_1, \text{ then } d(g_m(x), g_n(x)) < \frac{\epsilon}{3}, \text{ for all } x \in S_{N_0}. \quad (8.3.3)$$

Set $N_2 = \left[\frac{6(1+\delta)\delta}{\epsilon}\right]$. For each $n > N_2$ and $x, x' \in X$, we have

$$d(g_n(x), g_n(x')) \leq (1+\delta)n^{-1} + d(x, x')$$
$$< \frac{\epsilon}{6\delta} + d(x, x').$$

For each $x \in X$, there exists $x' \in S_{N_0}$ with $d(x', x) < \frac{\epsilon}{6\delta}$. Let $N = \max\{N_1, N_2\}$. For $n \geq m > N$, by (8.3.3) and the inequality above, we have

$$d(g_m(x), g_n(x)) \leq d(g_m(x), g_m(x')) + d(g_m(x'), g_n(x')) + d(g_n(x'), g_n(x))$$
$$< \frac{\epsilon}{6\delta} + d(x, x') + \frac{\epsilon}{3} + \frac{\epsilon}{6\delta} + d(x', x) < \epsilon.$$

Theorem 8.10 implies that there exists a map $I : X \to Y$ such that $\{g_i\}$ converges uniformly to I. Similarly, we also get a map $J : Y \to X$.

The inequalities $d(J_i \circ I_i(x), x) \leq 2^{-i}$ and $d(I_i \circ J_i(y), y) \leq 2^{-i}$ imply that I and J inverse to each other. Then

$$d(x_1, x_2) = d(J \circ I(x_1), J \circ I(x_2)) \leq d(I(x_1), I(x_2)) \leq d(x_1, x_2),$$

which implies I is an isometry. So is J. □

From the above, one can see that the quotient space $\left(\mathcal{M}^\delta / \sim, d_{GH}^\delta\right)$, which consists of all equivalence classes of isometric spaces, is a reversible metric space.

Definition 8.14. A sequence $\{X_n\}_{n=1}^\infty$ of compact metric spaces in $(M^\delta, d_{GH}^\delta)$ is said to be convergent to a compact metric space $X \in M^\delta$ if $\lim_{n \to \infty} d_{GH}^\delta(X_n, X) = 0$. In this case, we will write $X_n \stackrel{\delta - GH}{\longrightarrow} X$ and call X *the δ-Gromov-Hausdorff limit* of $\{X_n\}$. By Proposition 8.14, the limit is unique up to an isometry.

Lemma 8.9. *Suppose* X, $Y \in \mathcal{M}^\delta$ *and* $A = \{x_1, \ldots, x_s\} \subset X$, $B = \{y_1, \ldots, y_s\} \subset Y$. *If*

$$|d(x_i, x_j) - d(y_i, y_j)| \leq \epsilon, \quad 1 \leq i, j \leq s,$$

then $d_{GH}^\delta(A, B) \leq \epsilon$. *Moreover, the inequality still holds, even if some points of A or B coincide.*

Proof. We will construct a δ-admissible metric on $X \sqcup Y$ such that its Hausdorff distance satisfies $d_H(A, B) \leq \epsilon$. In fact, we define a metric d on $X \sqcup Y$ as follows:

$$d(x_i, y_j) := \min_{1 \leq k \leq s} \{d(x_i, x_k) + \epsilon + d(y_k, y_j)\},$$
$$d(y_j, x_i) := \min_{1 \leq k \leq s} \{d(y_j, y_k) + \epsilon + d(x_k, x_i)\}.$$

Clearly, the reversibility of d is not larger than δ. And the triangle inequality follows from a direct calculation. $\quad\square$

Proposition 8.15 ([129]). *For compact metric spaces $\{X_n\}_{n=1}^{\infty}$ and X in $(M^\delta, d_{GH}^\delta)$, $X_n \overset{\delta-GH}{\longrightarrow} X$ if and only if, for every $\epsilon > 0$ there exist a finite forward ϵ-net S in X and a forward ϵ-net S_n in each X_n such that $S_n \overset{\delta-GH}{\longrightarrow} S$.*

Moreover, these forward ϵ-nets can be chosen so that, for all sufficiently large n, S_n have the same cardinality as S.

Proof. For each $\epsilon > 0$, it is clear that $d_{GH}^\delta(X, S) \leq \epsilon$ and $d_{GH}^\delta(X_n, S_n) \leq \epsilon$ for each n (cf. Remark of Definition 8.13). If such forward ϵ-nets exist, then for all sufficiently large n, we have $d_{GH}^\delta(S_n, S) \leq \epsilon$. $X_n \overset{\delta-GH}{\longrightarrow} X$ follows from the triangle inequality of d_{GH}^δ.

Conversely, take a finite forward $(\epsilon/2)$-net $S := \{x_1, \ldots, x_k\}$ in X. Note that S is also a finite forward ϵ-net of X. We will construct corresponding forward ϵ-nets S_n in X_n. For each $\eta > 0$ (and $\eta < \frac{\epsilon}{4}$), there exists a natural number $N > 0$ such that if $n > N$, then $d_{GH}^\delta(X_n, X) < \eta$. Hence, for such an n, there exists a δ-admissible metric d on $X_n \sqcup X$ such that its Hausdorff distance d_H satisfies $d_H(X_n, X) < \eta$. Therefore, for every $n > N$, we can obtain a finite set $S_n := \{x_1^n, \ldots, x_k^n\}$ in X_n with $d(x_i^n, x_i) < \eta$, for all $1 \leq i \leq k$. The construction yields that for each $y \in X_n$ $(n > N)$, there exist $x \in X$, $x_j \in S$ and $x_j^n \in S_n$ with

$$d(x, y) < \eta, \quad d(x_j, x) \leq \epsilon/2, \quad d(x_j^n, x_j) < \eta.$$

Hence, $d(x_j^n, y) < \epsilon/2 + 2\eta < \epsilon$, i.e., S_n is a forward ϵ-net of X_n for every $n > N$.

By the triangle inequality of d, we have

$$d(x_i^n, x_j^n) \leq d(x_i^n, x_i) + d(x_i, x_j) + d(x_j, x_j^n) < d(x_i, x_j) + (1 + \delta)\eta.$$

Likewise, one can show

$$|d(x_i^n, x_j^n) - d(x_i, x_j)| < (1 + \delta)\eta,$$

for all $n > N$. Proposition 8.9 then implies that $d_{GH}^\delta(S_n, S) < (1 + \delta)\eta$ for $n > N$, i.e., $S_n \overset{\delta-GH}{\longrightarrow} S$. $\quad\square$

Definition 8.15. For a compact metric space X, define the *capacity* Cap_X and *covering* Cov_X as follows:

$$\mathrm{Cap}_X(\epsilon) := \text{maximum number of disjoint forward } \frac{\epsilon}{2}\text{-balls in } X,$$

$$\mathrm{Cov}_X(\epsilon) := \text{minimum number of forward } \epsilon\text{-balls it takes to cover } X.$$

Let (X, d) be a compact metric space with finite reversibility λ. The definition above implies that for all $\epsilon > 0$,

$$\operatorname{Cap}_X \left(\frac{\epsilon}{\lambda} \right) \geq \operatorname{Cov}_X(\epsilon). \tag{8.3.4}$$

In fact, if one select disjoint forward balls $\{B^+_{x_i}(\frac{\epsilon}{2\lambda})\}$ $(i = 1, \cdots, \operatorname{Cap}_X(\frac{\epsilon}{\lambda}))$ in X, then they must cover X and (8.3.4) follows. Otherwise, there would be $x' \in X \backslash \cup_i B^+_{x_i}(\epsilon)$, that is $d(x_i, x') \geq \epsilon$, for all i. This would imply $B^+_{x_i}(\frac{\epsilon}{2\lambda}) \cap B^+_{x'}(\frac{\epsilon}{2\lambda}) = \emptyset$, for all i. Hence, the former forward balls do not form a maximal disjoint family, which contradicts the definition of $\operatorname{Cap}_X(\frac{\epsilon}{\lambda})$.

Theorem 8.11 ([129]). *Let* $\mathfrak{C} \subset (\mathcal{M}^\delta, d^\delta_{GH})$ *be a family of compact metric spaces satisfying the following conditions:*
(i) There is a constant D such that $\operatorname{diam}(X) \leq D$ *for all $X \in \mathfrak{C}$.*
(ii) For every $\epsilon > 0$, there exists a natural number $N = N(\epsilon)$ such that $\operatorname{Cov}_X(\epsilon) \leq N(\epsilon)$ *for all $X \in \mathfrak{C}$.*

Then $\mathfrak{C}$ is pre-compact in the δ-Gromov-Hausdorff topology, that is, any sequence of elements of $\mathfrak{C}$ contains a converging subsequence (but the limit might not be in $\mathfrak{C}$).

Proof. The condition (ii) implies that for each $\epsilon > 0$ and every $X \in \mathfrak{C}$, there exists a finite forward ϵ-net whose cardinality is not greater than $N(\epsilon)$. Defined $N_1 := N(1)$ and $N_k = N_{k-1} + N(1/k)$ for all $k \geq 2$. Let $\{X_n\}_{n=1}^\infty$ be a sequence in $\mathfrak{C}$. In each X_n, we can construct a countable dense collection $S_n = \{x^i_n\}_{i=1}^\infty \subset X_n$ such that for every k, the first N_k points of S_n form a $1/k$-net in X_n (compare with the proof of Theorem 8.9).

The condition (i) implies that for each n, the distances $d(x^i_n, x^j_n)$ are not larger than D, i.e., belong to a compact interval. Hence, using the Cantor diagonal procedure, we can obtain a subsequence $\{X_{n_\alpha}\}$ of $\{X_n\}$ such that $\{d(x^i_{n_\alpha}, x^j_{n_\alpha})\}_{\alpha=1}^\infty$ converge for all i, j. To simplify the notation, assume that they converge without passing to a subsequence.

Now we construct the limit space for $\{X_n\}$. Set $x^i := \{x^i_n\}_{n=1}^\infty$ for all i, and $X := \{x^i\}_{i=1}^\infty$. Define a semi-metric d' on X by $d'(x^i, x^j) := \lim_{n \to \infty} d(x^i_n, x^j_n)$. One can verify that $d'(x^i, y^i)$ satisfies the triangle inequality and $d'(x^i, y^i) \leq \delta d'(y^i, x^i)$, for any $x^i, y^i \in X$. Define an equivalence relation $\sim$ on X: $x^i \sim y^i \Leftrightarrow d'(x^i, y^i) = 0$. Then we have a δ-admissible metric on the quotient space $X/\sim$.

Let $\bar{x}_i$ denote the point of $X/\sim$ obtained from x_i and let $\overline{X}$ be the completion of $X/\sim$. For a natural number $k > 0$, we show $S^k := \{\bar{x}^i : 1 \leq i \leq N_k\} \subset \overline{X}$ is a finite forward $(1/k)$-net in $\overline{X}$. It suffices to show that for every $\overline{x}^i \in \overline{X}$, there exists a point $\overline{x}^j \in S^k$ such that $d(\overline{x}^j, \overline{x}^i) \leq 1/k$. Each $S_n^k := \{x_n^i : 1 \leq i \leq N_k\}$ is a $(1/k)$-net in X_n. For every $x_n^i \in S_n$, there is a $j \leq N_k$ such that $d(x_n^j, x_n^i) \leq 1/k$. Since N_k is independent of n and $N_k < \infty$, for every fixed $i \in \mathbb{N}$, there must be a $j \leq N_k$ such that $d(x_n^j, x_n^i) \leq 1/k$ for infinitely many n. Passing to the limit we obtain that $d(\overline{x}^j, \overline{x}^i) \leq 1/k$. Thus, S^k is a finite forward $(1/k)$-net in $X/\sim$ and hence, in $\overline{X}$. Since $\overline{X}$ is complete, it is compact.

Now we show $X_n \overset{\delta-GH}{\longrightarrow} \overline{X}$. Given $k \in \mathbb{N}$, for every $\epsilon > 0$, the construction above and $N_k < \infty$ implies that there exists a natural number $m > 0$ such that if $n > m$, then $|d(x_n^i, x_n^j) - d(\overline{x}^i, \overline{x}^j)| < \epsilon$ for all $1 \leq i, j \leq N_k$. Lemma 8.9 then yields $d_{GH}^\delta(S_n^k, S^k) \leq \epsilon$ for $n > m$, i.e., $S_n^k \overset{\delta-GH}{\longrightarrow} S^k$. It follows from Proposition 8.15 that $X_n \overset{\delta-GH}{\longrightarrow} \overline{X}$. $\qquad\square$

From (8.3.4) together with Theorem 8.11, we have the following

Corollary 8.6 ([129]). *Let $\mathfrak{C} \subset \left(\mathcal{M}^\delta, d_{GH}^\delta\right)$ be a class satisfying the following conditions:*
(i) There is a constant D such that $\mathrm{diam}(X) \leq D$ *for all $X \in \mathfrak{C}$.*
(ii) For every $\epsilon > 0$, there exists a natural number $N = N(\epsilon)$ such that $\mathrm{Cap}_X(\epsilon) \leq N(\epsilon)$ *for all $X \in \mathfrak{C}$.*
Then $\mathfrak{C}$ is pre-compact in the δ-Gromov-Hausdorff topology. That is, any sequence of elements of $\mathfrak{C}$ contains a converging subsequence.

Remark. In the case of $\delta = 1$, the above result is Gromov's pre-compactness theorem for reversible metric spaces ([51, 94]).

Now we deal with non-compact spaces. A *pointed space* is a topological space X with a distinguished base point x_0 in X. Maps of pointed spaces are continuous maps preserving base points, i.e., a continuous map $f : (X, x_0) \to (Y, y_0)$ such that $f(x_0) = y_0$.

A metric space (X, d) is said to be *proper* if every bounded closed subset in (X, d) is compact. Set

$$\mathcal{M}_*^\delta := \{(X, d)| \text{ pointed proper metric spaces with reversibilities } \delta < \infty\}. \tag{8.3.5}$$

Definition 8.16. Let (X, x), (Y, y) be pointed metric spaces in $\mathcal{M}_*^\delta$. The *pointed δ-Gromov-Hausdorff distance* between (X, x) and (Y, y) is defined by

$$d_{GH}^{\delta}((X,x),(Y,y))$$

$$:= \inf\left\{ d_H(X,Y) + \frac{d(x,y)+d(y,x)}{2} \,\middle|\, \delta\text{-admissible metrics } d \text{ on } X \sqcup Y \right\}.$$

It is clear that this metric is still symmetric (reversible). As similar to the case of compact metric spaces, we have the following results, whose proofs are omitted (see [129] for details).

Theorem 8.12 ([129]). *A family* $\mathfrak{C} \subset \left(\mathcal{M}_*^{\delta}, d_{GH}^{\delta}\right)$ *is pre-compact if, for each* $r > 0$ *and* $\epsilon > 0$, *there exists an* $N = N(r,\epsilon) < \infty$ *such that for every* $\overline{B_x^+(r)} \subset (X,x) \in \mathfrak{C}$. *The covering of such forward balls satisfies* $\mathrm{Cov}_{\overline{B_x^+(r)}}(\epsilon) \leq N(r,\epsilon)$.

Corollary 8.7. *A family* $\mathfrak{C} \subset \left(\mathcal{M}_*^{\delta}, d_{GH}^{\delta}\right)$ *is pre-compact if, for each* $r > 0$ *and* $\epsilon > 0$, *there exists an* $N = N(r,\epsilon) < \infty$ *such that for every* $\overline{B_x^+(r)} \subset (X,x) \in \mathfrak{C}$. *The capacity of such forward balls satisfies* $\mathrm{Cap}_{\overline{B_x^+(r)}}(\epsilon) \leq N(r,\epsilon)$.

Remark. In the Riemannian case, the above corollary is Proposition 5.2 in [51].

8.3.3 Pre-compactness of Finsler manifolds

By the definition of the reversibility for a Finsler manifold (M,F) (§2.4.3, Definition 2.5), one can easily see that if $\lambda_F < \infty$, then $d_F(x_1,x_2) \leq \lambda_F d_F(x_2,x_1)$ for any two points $x_1, x_2 \in M$. Hence, we have the following

Lemma 8.10. *Let* F *be a Finsler metric on a manifold* M *and* d_F *the induced distance function. Let* $\lambda_F < \infty$ *be the reversibility of the Finsler manifold* (M,F) *and let* λ_d *be the reversibility of* (M,d_F). *Then we have*

$$\lambda_d \leq \lambda_F < \infty. \tag{8.3.6}$$

Theorem 8.13 ([129]). *Given an integer* $n \geq 2$ *and real numbers* k, h, D (≥ 0), *we have*

(i) The family $\{(M_i, F_i, d\mu_i)\}$ *of compact Finsler* n-*manifolds satisfying the following conditions is pre-compact in the* δ-*Gromov-Hausdorff topology:*

$$Ric_{M_i} \geq (n-1)k, \quad \mathbf{S}_{M_i} \geq (n-1)h, \quad \mathrm{diam}(M_i) \leq D, \quad \lambda_{F_i} \leq \delta < \infty;$$

(ii) The family $\{(M_i, F_i, d\mu_i)\}$ *of compact Finsler* n-*manifolds satisfying the following conditions is pre-compact in the pointed* δ-*Gromov-Hausdorff*

topology:

$$Ric_{M_i} \geq (n-1)k, \quad \mathbf{S}_{M_i} \geq (n-1)h, \quad \lambda_{F_i} \leq \delta < \infty,$$

where Ric_{M_i} denotes the Ricci curvature of F_i, $\mathbf{S}_{M_i}$ denotes the $\mathbf{S}$-curvature of $d\mu_i$, λ_{F_i} and $\mathrm{diam}(M_i)$ denote respectively the reversibility and the diameter of (M_i, F_i).

Proof. (i) According to Lemma 8.10, $\{(M_i, F_i, d\mu_i)\} \subset (M^\delta, d_{GH}^\delta)$. For each $(M_i, F_i, d\mu_i)$, there exists a point $x_i^0 \in M_i$ such that $\overline{B_{x_i^0}^+(D)} = M_i$. Since M_i is compact, there are finitely many disjoint forward ϵ-balls inside M_i. Denote them by $B_{x_1}^+(\epsilon), \ldots, B_{x_\beta}^+(\epsilon) (\subset M_i = \overline{B_{x_i^0}^+(D)})$.

Let $B_{x_\alpha}^+(\epsilon)$ be the forward ball with the smallest volume. Given $x \in B_{x_i^0}^+(D)$, by the triangle inequality, we have

$$d(x_\alpha, x) \leq d(x_\alpha, x_i^0) + d(x_i^0, x) \leq \delta d(x_i^0, x_\alpha) + d(x_i^0, x) < (1+\delta)D,$$

which implies $B_{x_\alpha}^+((1+\delta)D) \supset B_{x_i^0}^+(D)$. Thus, the volume comparison theorem 7.2 yields

$$\beta \leq \frac{\mathrm{Vol}_{\mu_i}[B_{x_i^0}^+(D)]}{\mathrm{Vol}_{\mu_i}[B_{x_\alpha}^+(\epsilon)]} \leq \frac{\mathrm{Vol}_{\mu_i}[B_{x_\alpha}^+((1+\delta)D)]}{\mathrm{Vol}_{\mu_i}[B_{x_\alpha}^+(\epsilon)]} \leq \frac{V_{k,h,n}((1+\delta)D)}{V_{k,h,n}(\epsilon)}.$$

(i) then follows from Corollary 8.6.

(ii) By Corollary 8.7, the proof of (ii) is similar to that of (i). $\quad\square$

Remark. If $\delta = 1$, then (i) in the above theorem is Gromov's precompactness theorem for reversible Finsler manifolds in [103].

The further argument yields that the δ-Gromov-Hausdorff limit of a convergent sequence in Theorem 8.13 is a length space, on which the metric is strictly intrinsic. Here, we give the result without proof. See [129] for details.

Theorem 8.14 ([129]). *Given an integer $n \geq 2$ and real numbers k, h, D (≥ 0), we have*

(i) Let $\{(M_i, F_i, d\mu_i)\}$ be a family of compact Finsler n-manifolds satisfying the following conditions

$$Ric_{M_i} \geq (n-1)k, \quad \mathbf{S}_{M_i} \geq (n-1)h, \quad \mathrm{diam}(M_i) \leq D, \quad \lambda_{F_i} \leq \delta < \infty.$$

Given any sequence in $\{(M_i, F_i, d\mu_i)\}$, there exists a convergent subsequence whose δ-Gromov-Hausdorff limit, say (X, d), is a length space and d is strictly intrinsic.

(ii) Let $\{(M_i, x_i, F_i, d\mu_i)\}$ be a family of pointed forward complete Finsler n-manifolds satisfying the following conditions

$$Ric_{M_i} \geq (n-1)k, \quad \mathbf{S}_{M_i} \geq (n-1)h, \quad \lambda_{F_i} \leq \delta < \infty.$$

Given any sequence in $\{(M_i, F_i, d\mu_i)\}$, there exists a convergent subsequence whose δ-Gromov-Hausdorff limit, say (X, x, d), is a length space and d is strictly intrinsic.

Now we give some examples. Let (M, p, F) be an n-dimensional Finsler manifold with the point $p \in M$ satisfying

$$Ric \geq (n-1)k, \quad \mathbf{S} \geq (n-1)h, \quad \lambda_F \leq \delta < \infty.$$

For each $r > 0$, define $F_r^- := r^{-1}F$. Thus, $Ric_r^- = r^2 Ric$, $\mathbf{S}_r^- = \mathbf{S}$ and $\lambda_r^- \leq \delta$, where Ric_r^-, $\mathbf{S}_r^-$ and λ_r^- denote the Ricci curvature, the $\mathbf{S}$-curvature and the reversibility of (M, p, F_r^-) respectively. If $k \geq 0$, then the pre-compactness theorem as above implies that any sequence $\{r_i \to \infty\}$ has a subsequence $\{r_j \to \infty\}$ such that the rescaled manifolds $(M, p, F_{r_j}^-)$ converge in the pointed δ-Gromov-Hausdorff topology to a length space, M_∞. And if $k > 0$, then Theorem 1.3 implies that M_∞ must be a simple point space.

Now let us consider another case. For each $\kappa > 0$, define $F_\kappa^+ := \kappa F$. Thus, $Ric_\kappa^+ = \kappa^{-2} Ric$, $\mathbf{S}_\kappa^+ = \mathbf{S}$ and $\lambda_\kappa^+ \leq \delta$, where Ric_κ^+, $\mathbf{S}_\kappa^+$ and λ_κ^+ denote the Ricci curvature, the $\mathbf{S}$-curvature and the reversibility of (M, p, F_κ^+) respectively. If $k \leq 0$, the above pre-compactness theorem implies that any sequence $\{\kappa_i \to \infty\}$ has a subsequence $\{\kappa_j \to \infty\}$ such that the rescaled manifolds $(M, p, F_{\kappa_j}^+)$ converge in the pointed δ-Gromov-Hausdorff topology to a length space M_∞.

8.3.4 On the Gauss-Bonnet-Chern theorem

We now cite the Gauss-Bonnet-Chern theorem in Finsler geometry to end this chapter.

Recall that the Gauss-Bonnet-Chern (GBC for simplicity) formula for an oriented closed n-dimensional Riemannian manifold (M, g) is

$$\int_M \mathbf{\Omega} = \chi(M), \tag{8.3.7}$$

where

$$\mathbf{\Omega} = \begin{cases} \dfrac{(-1)^p}{2^{2p}\pi^p p!}\epsilon_{i_1 \ldots i_{2p}}\Omega_{i_1}^{i_2} \wedge \cdots \wedge \Omega_{i_{2p-1}}^{i_{2p}}, & n = 2p, \\ 0, & n = 2p + 1, \end{cases}$$

where $\epsilon_{i_1 \ldots i_{2p}}$ is the multi-Kronecker delta and (Ω_i^j) is the local curvature 2-forms on (M, g). S. S. Chern ([24]) gave an intrinsic proof of this formula.

Let (M, F) be an n-dimensional Finsler manifold. Denote by $\pi : SM \to M$ the projective sphere bundle and $\pi^* TM$ the pull-back bundle. F induces a natural Riemannian metric on $\pi^* TM$. There are many important linear connections on $\pi^* TM$, but none of them is both "torsion-free" and "metric-compatible". For example, the Cartan connection is metric-compatible while the Chern connection is torsion-free. (See §3.1-§3.2, in Chapter 3.)

In 1949, Lichnerowicz ([70]) obtained a GBC formula for Cartan-Berwald spaces by the Cartan connection. Fifty years later, Bao and Chern ([9]) reconsidered this problem and established a GBC formula for Finsler manifolds with $\widetilde{V}(x) = $ constant for $x \in M$ by using the Chern connection, where $\widetilde{V}(x)$ denotes the Riemannian volume of $S_x M$ (§2.2.1) induced by F. In the same year, Shen ([115]) obtained several formulas of GBC type by the Cartan connection for a certain class of Finsler manifolds.

In 2002, Lackey ([66]) used a nice trick to deal with $\widetilde{V}(x)$ and generalized the result of [9] to any Finsler manifolds. In fact, Lackey established a GBC formula for any torsion-free connection. The same technique also appeared in an unpublished work of Shen ([116]) and the GBC formula for any metric-compatible connection was established.

Given a linear connection D on $\pi^* TM$, we define

$$\Omega^D = \begin{cases} \dfrac{(-1)^p}{2^{2p} \pi^p p!} \epsilon_{i_1 \ldots i_{2p}} \Omega_{i_1}^{i_2} \wedge \cdots \wedge \Omega_{i_{2p-1}}^{i_{2p}}, & n = 2p, \\ 0, & n = 2p + 1, \end{cases} \tag{8.3.8}$$

where $\epsilon_{i_1 \ldots i_{2p}}$ is the multi-Kronecker delta, (Ω_j^i) is the local curvature 2-forms of D. We have the following

Theorem 8.15 ([66]). *Let (M, F) be an n-dimensional compact oriented Finsler manifold without boundary, and $X : TM \to M$ be a vector field possibly with isolated zeros $\{x_i\} \subset M$. Let ∇ be any torsion-free Finsler connection with curvature form Ω^∇ defined similarly by (8.3.8). Then we have*

$$\int_M [X]^* \left(\frac{\Omega^\nabla + \mathfrak{D}}{\widetilde{V}(x)} \right) = \frac{\chi(M)}{\mathrm{Vol}(\mathbb{S}^{n-1})},$$

where $\chi(M)$ is the Euler characteristic of M, $[X] : M \backslash \cup \{x_i\} \to SM$ is the section induced by X, $\widetilde{V}(x)$ is the Riemannian volume of $S_x M$, and $\mathfrak{D}$ is an n-form on SM.

Note that the GBC formula (8.3.7) is the simplest case of the Atiyah-Singer Index Theorem ([12,81]). Recently, Zhao ([162]) gave a simple proof of the GBC formula for any metric-compatible connection from the point of view of index theory.

Theorem 8.16 ([162]). *Let (M, F) be an n-dimensional compact oriented Finsler manifold without boundary, and $X : TM \to M$ be a vector field possibly with isolated zeros $\{x_i\} \subset M$. Let $\widetilde{\nabla}$ be any metric-compatible Finsler connection with curvature form $\mathbf{\Omega}^{\widetilde{\nabla}}$ defined similarly by (8.3.8). Then we have*

$$\int_M [X]^* \left(\frac{\mathbf{\Omega}^{\widetilde{\nabla}} + \mathfrak{E}}{\widetilde{V}(x)} \right) = \frac{\chi(M)}{\mathrm{Vol}(\mathbb{S}^{n-1})},$$

where $\chi(M)$ is the Euler characteristic of M, $[X] : M \backslash \cup \{x_i\} \to SM$ is the section induced by X, $\widetilde{V}(x)$ is the Riemannian volume of $S_x M$, and $\mathfrak{E}$ is an n-form on SM.

Corollary 8.8 ([162]). *Under the same hypothesis as in Theorem 8.16, let $^c\widetilde{\nabla}$ be the Cartan connection with curvature form $\mathbf{\Omega}^{c\widetilde{\nabla}}$ defined similarly by (8.3.8). Then we have*

$$\int_M [X]^* \left(\frac{\mathbf{\Omega}^{c\widetilde{\nabla}} + \mathfrak{F} + \mathfrak{E}}{\widetilde{V}(x)} \right) = \frac{\chi(M)}{\mathrm{Vol}(\mathbb{S}^{n-1})},$$

where $\mathfrak{F}$ is an exact n-form on SM.

In Riemannian case, $\mathbf{\Omega}^{\widetilde{\nabla}} = \pi^* \mathbf{\Omega}$, $\widetilde{V}(x) = \mathrm{Vol}(\mathbb{S}^{n-1})$, $\int_M [X]^* \mathfrak{E} = 0$ and $\mathfrak{F}$ is an exact n-form pulled back from M. Since $[X]^* \pi^* = id$, Theorem 8.16 implies the GBC formula for Riemannian manifolds.

Proofs of Theorem 8.15 and 8.16 may be found in [66] and [162] respectively, and they are omitted here.

Exercises

8.1 Prove Corollary 8.2 in details.

8.2 Prove that types of the volume growth of a Finsler manifold (M, F) are independent of the choice of the based point.

8.3 Prove that types of the growth of groups are independent of the choice of finite generating sets.

8.4 Let $(M, F, d\mu)$ be a Finsler manifold satisfying $|\mathbf{S}| \leq \Lambda$, $\psi : \widetilde{M} \to M$ its universal covering. Prove that if one of the following conditions is satisfied:

   (i)   the flag curvature of (M, F) satisfies $\mathbf{K}(V; W) \leq -a^2$, where $a > \Lambda/(n-1)$,

  (ii) M has non-positive flag curvature and $Ric_M \leq -a^2$, where $a > \Lambda$,

then $(\widetilde{M}, \psi^* F)$ has the exponential volume growth ([143]).

8.5   Verify the following formula

$$a_r = \frac{A^{(r)}(0)}{r!}, \quad A(t) = (1+t)^k (1-t)^{-(k+1)}$$

in the proof of Lemma 8.6.

8.6   Prove Theorem 8.14 in details ([129]).

Chapter 9

Minimal Immersions and Harmonic Maps

9.1 Isometric immersions

9.1.1 Finsler submanifolds

Let (M, F) and $(\widetilde{M}, \widetilde{F})$ be Finsler manifolds, $f : M \to \widetilde{M}$ be a smooth map and its induced tangent map $df := f_* : TM \to T\widetilde{M}$.

Definition 9.1. If the rank of df equals the dimension of M, and $F = f^*\widetilde{F}$, then f is called the *isometric immersion* from (M, F) to $(\widetilde{M}, \widetilde{F})$. If in addition, $f(M) \subset \widetilde{M}$ does not have self-intersection points, then f is called the *isometric embedding*. For simplicity, we call (M, F) the *immersed* or *embedded submanifold* of $(\widetilde{M}, \widetilde{F})$.

In local coordinates, let (x, y) and $(\widetilde{x}, \widetilde{y})$ be the local coordinates in M and $\widetilde{M}$, respectively. Under the map $f : M \to \widetilde{M}$, denote by $\widetilde{x} = f(x)$, $\widetilde{y} = df(y)$. We shall use the following indices:

$$1 \leq i, j, k, \cdots \leq n; \quad 1 \leq \alpha, \beta, \gamma, \cdots < m = n + p.$$

Then we have

$$y^i f_i^\alpha = \widetilde{y}^\alpha, \quad [F]_{y^i} = [\widetilde{F}]_{\widetilde{y}^\alpha} f_i^\alpha, \quad f_i^\alpha = \frac{\partial f^\alpha}{\partial x^i}, \tag{9.1.1}$$

where the variable y^i at the lower right corner of the brackets means that the partial derivative with respect to y^i. Thus, their fundamental tensors are related by

$$g_{ij}(x, y) = \widetilde{g}_{\alpha\beta} f_i^\alpha f_j^\beta, \tag{9.1.2}$$

where g and $\widetilde{g}$ denote the fundamental tensors of (M, F) and $(\widetilde{M}, \widetilde{F})$, respectively. In the future, we shall denote all geometric quantities on $(\widetilde{M}, \widetilde{F})$ corresponding to that of (M, F) with $\sim$ on the top.

Let G^i and $\widetilde{G}^i$ denote the geodesic coefficients of (M, F) and $(\widetilde{M}, \widetilde{F})$ respectively (see Section 2.4.2). Using (2.4.3) and

$$[F]_{x^i} = [\widetilde{F}]_{\widetilde{x}^\alpha} f_i^\alpha + [\widetilde{F}]_{\widetilde{y}^\alpha} f_{ik}^\alpha y^k, \quad f_{ik}^\alpha = \frac{\partial^2 f^\alpha}{\partial x^i \partial x^k}, \tag{9.1.3}$$

we obtain by a direct computation that

$$G^k - g^{kl} f_l^\beta \widetilde{g}_{\alpha\beta} \left(f_{ij}^\alpha y^i y^j + \widetilde{G}^\alpha \right). \tag{9.1.4}$$

Clearly, when $\widetilde{F}$ is Riemannian, so is $F = f^*\widetilde{F}$. This is the Riemannian case. As we know, according to the famous Nash Theorem, any Riemannian manifold can be isometrically embedded into a higher dimensional Euclidean space. A natural question arises: whether or not can a Finsler manifold be isometrically immersed (resp. embedded) into a sufficiently higher dimensional Minkowski space? A negative answer of the problem is given by the following theorem and corollary.

Let $\mathbf{C} = C_{ijk}(x, y) dx^i \otimes dx^j \otimes dx^k$ be the Cartan tensor of (M, F) (see §2.2.1), whose *norm* $||\mathbf{C}||_x$ at the point $x \in M$ is defined by

$$||\mathbf{C}||_x := \sup_{y, v \in S_x M} \frac{|\mathbf{C}_{(x,y)}(v, v, v)|}{|g_{(x,y)}(v, v)|^{3/2}},$$

where $S_x M$ is the indicatrix of (M, F) at x (see §2.2.1).

Theorem 9.1. *Let $f : (M, F) \to (\widetilde{M}, \widetilde{F})$ be an isometric immersion, $\mathbf{C}$ and $\widetilde{\mathbf{C}}$ the Cartan tensors of F and $\widetilde{F}$, respectively. We then have*

$$||\mathbf{C}||_x \le ||\widetilde{\mathbf{C}}||_{f(x)}, \quad \forall x \in M. \tag{9.1.5}$$

Proof. By (9.1.1) and (9.1.2), one can easily see

$$F(y) = \widetilde{F}(f_*y), \quad g_y(u, v) = \widetilde{g}_{f_*y}(f_*u, f_*v),$$
$$\mathbf{C}_y(u, v, w) = \widetilde{\mathbf{C}}_{f_*y}(f_*u, f_*v, f_*w), \quad \forall y, u, v, w \in TM.$$

Thus, we have

$$||\mathbf{C}||_x = \sup_{y, v \in T_x M} \frac{|\mathbf{C}_{(x,y)}(v, v, v)|}{|g_{(x,y)}(v, v)|^{3/2}}$$
$$= \sup_{y, v \in T_x M} \frac{|\widetilde{\mathbf{C}}_{(f(x), f_*y)}(f_*v, f_*v, f_*v)|}{\widetilde{g}_{(f(x), f_*y)}(f_*v, f_*v)|^{3/2}}$$
$$\le \sup_{\widetilde{y}, \widetilde{v} \in T_{f(x)} \widetilde{M}} \frac{|\widetilde{\mathbf{C}}_{(f(x), \widetilde{y})}(\widetilde{v}, \widetilde{v}, \widetilde{v})|}{\widetilde{g}_{(f(x), \widetilde{y})}(\widetilde{v}, \widetilde{v})|^{3/2}} = ||\widetilde{\mathbf{C}}||_{f(x)}. \qquad \square$$

Corollary 9.1. *Let $(\widetilde{M}, \widetilde{F})$ be a finite dimensional Minkowski space. If $f :$ $(M, F) \to (\widetilde{M}, \widetilde{F})$ is an isometric immersion, then the norm of the Cartan tensor of (M, F) must be bounded.*

Proof. Since $(\widetilde{M}, \widetilde{F})$ is a finite dimensional Minkowski space, $\widetilde{F}(\widetilde{x}, \widetilde{y}) = \widetilde{F}(\widetilde{x}_0, \widetilde{y})$, where $\widetilde{x}_0 \in \widetilde{M}$ is an arbitrary point. Hence,

$$||\widetilde{\mathbf{C}}||_{f(x)} = ||\widetilde{\mathbf{C}}||_{\widetilde{x}_0} = \text{const.} < +\infty. \qquad \square$$

It follows from Corollary 9.1 that a Finsler manifold with the Cartan tensor whose norm is unbounded cannot be isometrically immersed (or embedded) in any Minkowski space. This shows the difference between Riemannian submanifolds and Finsler submanifolds.

Example 9.1. Consider the following Finsler metric defined in the open unit Euclidean ball $B^n(1) \subset \mathbb{R}^n$ (see §5.2.2, Example 5.1)

$$F(x, y) = \frac{\left(\sqrt{|y|^2 - (|x|^2|y|^2 - \langle x, y \rangle^2)} + \langle x, y \rangle\right)^2}{(1 - |x|^2)^2 \sqrt{|y|^2 - (|x|^2|y|^2 - \langle x, y \rangle^2)}},$$

where $y \in T_x B^n(1) \equiv \mathbb{R}^n$. It is a forward complete non-Berwaldian Finsler metric with vanishing flag curvature. By [5], a forward complete Finsler metric F with vanishing flag curvature is locally Minkowskian if the norm of the Cartan tensor of F is bounded. So, the norm of the Cartan tensor of (5.2.13) is unbounded. Hence, the metric (5.2.13) can not be isometrically immersed (or embedded) in any Minkowski space.

Let $(\widetilde{V}^n, \widetilde{F})$ be an n-dimensional Minkowski space, $V^{n-1} \subset \widetilde{V}^n$ its hyperplane. Then there is a covector ξ such that $V^{n-1} = \ker \xi$, where ξ is determined up to a sign. By means of the Legendre transformation (§3.4), there is a unique unit vector $\nu \in \widetilde{V}^{n+1}$ such that

$$\xi(\nu) = 1, \quad \xi(\widetilde{X}) = \widetilde{g}_\nu(\nu, \widetilde{X}), \quad \forall \widetilde{X} \in \widetilde{V}^n.$$

ν is called the *normal vector* to $V^{n-1} \subset \widetilde{V}^n$.

Now let $\mathfrak{D} \subset M$ be a compact domain with smooth boundary $\partial\mathfrak{D}$ in an n-dimensional Finsler manifold (M, F). Let $\mathcal{I} : \partial\mathfrak{D} \to M$ be the natural embedding. Thus, for each point $x \in \mathfrak{D}$, there are exactly two unit vectors along $\mathcal{I}$, which are orthogonal to $T_x(\partial\mathfrak{D})$ and are not parallel unless F is reversible. Let $\xi \in T_x^* M$ be a unit covector such that $T_x(\partial\mathfrak{D}) = \ker \xi$. Then there is a unique normal vector $\nu \in T_x M$ satisfying

$$\xi(\nu) = 1, \quad \xi(X) = g_\nu(\nu, X), \quad \forall X \in T_x M. \qquad (9.1.6)$$

We call ν the *normal vector field* to $\partial\mathfrak{D}$.

We choose a local coordinate system $\{x^i\}$ in M such that (cf. Chapter 1, Exercise 1.2)

$$\nu = \frac{\partial}{\partial x^1} \Big/ \left\| \frac{\partial}{\partial x^1} \right\|_{g_\nu}$$

along $\partial\mathfrak{D}$. Suppose that the volume form of (M, F) is (cf. §4.1)

$$dV_F = \sigma_F(x) dx^1 \wedge \cdots \wedge dx^n$$

in such a coordinate system. Thus, the induced volume form of $\partial\mathfrak{D}$ by dV_F is

$$dA_F = (\sigma_F)|_{\partial\mathfrak{D}} \mathcal{I}^* (dx^2 \wedge \cdots \wedge dx^n)$$

along $\mathcal{I}$.

As it is well known, for a vector field X on M, its divergence (with respect to dV_F) is

$$(\operatorname{div}_F X) dV_F := d(X \lrcorner dV_F), \tag{9.1.7}$$

where

$$(X \lrcorner dV_F)(X_1, \cdots, X_{n-1}) := dV_F(X, X_1, \cdots, X_{n-1}),$$
$$\forall X_1, \cdots, X_{n-1} \in TM.$$

It is easy to verify that

$$\mathcal{I}^*(X \lrcorner dV_F) = \xi(X) dA_F = g_\nu(\nu, X) dA_F,$$
$$\operatorname{div}_F(X) = \frac{1}{\sigma_F(x)} \frac{\partial}{\partial x^i} \left[\sigma_F(x) X^i \right]. \tag{9.1.8}$$

As the above, by using Stokes' formula, we obtain the following divergence lemma ([106]).

Lemma 9.1. *Let (M, F, dV_f) be an n-dimensional oriented measurable Finsler manifold, $\mathfrak{D} \subset M$ be a compact domain with smooth boundary $\partial\mathfrak{D}$ in (M, F). Then for any vector field X on M, the following formula holds*

$$\int_{\mathfrak{D}} \operatorname{div}_F(X) dV_F = \int_{\partial\mathfrak{D}} \xi(X) dA_F = \int_{\partial\mathfrak{D}} g_\nu(\nu, X) dA_F,$$

where ν is the outward pointing normal vector to $\partial\mathfrak{D}$, ξ is the Legendre dual covector of ν.

9.1.2 The variation of the volume

Let $(\widetilde{V}^m, \widetilde{F})$ be an m-dimensional Minkowski space, $V^n \subset \widetilde{V}^m$ $(n < m)$ be its submanifold. Let $\mathbf{E} := \{e_i\}_{i=1}^n$ be an oriented base in V^n, whose dual base is $\theta := \{\theta^i\}_{i=1}^n$. If there are a base $\widetilde{\mathbf{E}} := \{\widetilde{e}_\alpha\}_{\alpha=1}^m$ in $\widetilde{V}^m$ and a matrix $z = (z_i^\alpha) \in GL(n, m)$ such that $F(e_i) = \widetilde{F}(z_i^\alpha \widetilde{e}_\alpha)$ is a Minkowski metric in V^n, then $F(e_i)$ is said to be *induced* by $\widetilde{F}$. Let $\mathfrak{E}$ and $\mathfrak{F}$ be the sets of all oriented basis and induced metrics in V^n, respectively. Then the measure function $\sigma_F : \mathfrak{F} \times \mathfrak{E} \to \mathbb{R}$ of an admissible volume form

$$dV_F := \sigma_F(F, \mathbf{E})\theta^1 \wedge \cdots \wedge \theta^n$$

in V^n should satisfy the following conditions: (i) $\sigma_F(F, \mathbf{e}) > 0$ for any $F \in \mathfrak{F}$ and $\mathbf{E} \in \mathfrak{E}$; (ii) $\sigma_F(F, Q\mathbf{E}) = \det(Q)\sigma_F(F, \mathbf{E})$ for any $Q \in GL(n, m)$; (iii) if $F(y) = \sqrt{\langle y, y \rangle}$, $\forall y \in V^n$, then $\sigma_F(F, \mathbf{E}) = \sqrt{\det(\langle e_i, e_j \rangle)}$. Moreover, for the application of the calculus, it is required that σ_F is differentiable with respect to $z = (z_i^\alpha)$.

We now discuss the measure function σ_F from another point of view. Define the function $\mathcal{F}_{\widetilde{e}}^\sigma : GL(n, m) \to \mathbb{R}$ by

$$\mathcal{F}_{\widetilde{e}}^\sigma := \sigma_F(F, \mathbf{E}).$$

According to the requirement of σ_F, it is obvious that

$$\begin{aligned} \mathcal{F}_{T\widetilde{e}}^\sigma(z) &= \mathcal{F}_{\widetilde{e}}^\sigma(zT), \quad \forall T \in GL(m, m), \\ \mathcal{F}_{\widetilde{e}}^\sigma(Qz) &= \det(Q)\mathcal{F}_{\widetilde{e}}^\sigma(z), \quad \forall Q \in GL(n, n). \end{aligned} \tag{9.1.9}$$

Let $P = (p_i^j) \in GL(n, n)$ be the inverse matrix of Q. Then it follows that

$$\frac{\partial(\det Q)}{\partial q_i^j} = (\det Q)p_j^i.$$

Differentiating the second equation of (9.1.9) and using the above formula, we obtain

$$\frac{\partial \mathcal{F}_{\widetilde{e}}^\sigma}{\partial z_i^\alpha}(Qz)z_j^\alpha = \mathcal{F}_{\widetilde{e}}^\sigma(z)(\det Q)p_j^i,$$

in which we put $Q = (\delta_i^j)$ and get

$$\frac{\partial \mathcal{F}_{\widetilde{e}}^\sigma}{\partial z_i^\alpha}(z)z_j^\alpha = \mathcal{F}_{\widetilde{e}}^\sigma(z)\delta_j^i, \quad \frac{\partial \mathcal{F}_{\widetilde{e}}^\sigma}{\partial z_i^\alpha}(z)z_i^\alpha = n\mathcal{F}_{\widetilde{e}}^\sigma(z). \tag{9.1.10}$$

Given a linear imbedding $Z : V^n \to (\widetilde{V}^m, \widetilde{F})$, $Z(e_i) = z_i^\alpha \widetilde{e}_\alpha$, we define a linear mapping $P_Z^\sigma : \widetilde{V}^m \to V^n$ by

$$P_Z^\sigma(\widetilde{X}) := \frac{1}{\mathcal{F}_{\widetilde{e}}^\sigma(z)}\frac{\partial \mathcal{F}_{\widetilde{e}}^\sigma}{\partial z_i^\alpha}(z)z_i^\alpha \widetilde{X}^\alpha e_i, \quad \forall \widetilde{X} = \widetilde{X}^\alpha \widetilde{e}_\alpha \in \widetilde{V}^m, \tag{9.1.11}$$

where $\{e_i\}$ and $\{\widetilde{e}_\alpha\}$ are the bases in V^n and $\widetilde{V}^m$, respectively.

Lemma 9.2. *The mapping P_Z^σ is independent of the choice of bases in V^n and $\widetilde{V}^m$. Moreover,*

$$P_Z^\sigma(Z(X)) = X, \quad \forall X \in V^n.$$

Proof. Let $e'_i = q_i^j e_j$ be another base in V^n. Write $Z(e'_i) = z'^\alpha_i \widetilde{e}_\alpha$, $Q = (q_j^i)$. It is easy to see that $z' = Qz$. From the second formula of (9.1.9) we have

$$\frac{\partial \mathcal{F}_{\widetilde{e}}^\sigma}{\partial z_j^\alpha}(Qz)q_j^i = \frac{\partial \mathcal{F}_{\widetilde{e}}^\sigma}{\partial z_i^\alpha}(z)(\det Q).$$

It follows that

$$\frac{1}{\mathcal{F}_{\widetilde{e}}^\sigma(z)}\frac{\partial \mathcal{F}_{\widetilde{e}}^\sigma}{\partial z_i^\alpha}(Qz)e'_i = \frac{1}{\mathcal{F}_{\widetilde{e}}^\sigma(z)}\frac{\partial \mathcal{F}_{\widetilde{e}}^\sigma}{\partial z_i^\alpha}(z)e_i,$$

i.e., P_Z^σ is independent of the choice of the base in V^n. Furthermore, from the first formula of (9.1.9) one can see that P_Z^σ is independent of the choice of the base in $\widetilde{V}^m$.

By (9.1.10), for $X = X^i e_i$ we have

$$P_Z^\sigma(Z(X)) = \frac{1}{\mathcal{F}_{\widetilde{e}}^\sigma(z)}\frac{\partial \mathcal{F}_{\widetilde{e}}^\sigma}{\partial z_i^\alpha}(z)z_j^\alpha X^j e_i = \delta_j^i X^j e_i = X. \qquad \square$$

Let $f : (M, F) \to (\widetilde{M}, \widetilde{F})$ be an isometric immersion, $\mathfrak{D} \subset M$ be a compact domain with smooth boundary $\partial\mathfrak{D}$. Consider a family of isometric immersions $f_t : M \to (\widetilde{M}, \widetilde{F})$ such that $f_0 = f$ and $f_t = f_0$ on $\partial\mathfrak{D} \cup (M \setminus \{\mathfrak{D}\})$. f_t is called a *variation* of f preserving the boundary invariant. Thus, f_t induces a family of Finsler metrics $F_t = f_t^* \widetilde{F}$ on M. Moreover, it induces the following *variation vector field* along f:

$$\widetilde{X} := \frac{\partial f_t}{\partial t}\bigg|_{t=0} := \widetilde{X}^\alpha \frac{\partial}{\partial \widetilde{x}^\alpha}, \quad \widetilde{X}\bigg|_{\partial\mathfrak{D}} = 0. \qquad (9.1.12)$$

Suppose that $f_t(\mathfrak{D}) \subset M$ for small t enough. At each point $x \in \mathfrak{D}$, the differential of f_t gives a linear imbedding $df_t : T_x M \to T_{f(x)}\widetilde{M}$ and its linear projection $P_{f_*} : T_{f(x)}\widetilde{M} \to T_x M$, so that $P_{f_*}(\widetilde{X})$ is a smooth vector field on M.

Let $\{e_i\}$ be a base in $T_x M$, $\{\theta^i\}$ its dual base. By the definition of $\mathcal{F}_{\widetilde{e}}^\sigma$, the volume element of (M, F_t) is

$$dV_{F_t} = \sigma_t(x)\theta^1 \wedge \cdots \wedge \theta^n = \mathcal{F}_{\widetilde{e}}^\sigma(f_t(x), z(x, t))\theta^1 \wedge \cdots \wedge \theta^n,$$

where $z(x, t) := df_t(x) = ((f_t)_i^\alpha(x))$ is determined by $(f_t)_i^\alpha \widetilde{e}_\alpha = e_i$. From the first equation of (9.1.9) one can see that $\sigma_t(x) := \mathcal{F}_{\widetilde{e}}^\sigma(f_t(x), z(x, t))$ is independent of the choice of the base $\widetilde{\mathbf{E}}$ in $T_{f_t(x)}\widetilde{M}$. We then have the following volume functional

$$V(t) := \mathrm{Vol}_{F_t}^{\sigma}(\mathfrak{D}) = \int_{\mathfrak{D}} dV_{F_t} = \int_{\mathfrak{D}} \sigma_t(x)\theta^1 \wedge \cdots \wedge \theta^n.$$

Thus, we have

$$\begin{aligned} V'(0) &= \frac{dV(t)}{dt}\bigg|_{t=0} = \int_{\mathfrak{D}} \frac{\partial \sigma_t}{\partial t}\bigg|_{t=0} \theta^1 \wedge \cdots \wedge \theta^n \\ &= \int_{\mathfrak{D}} \frac{d}{dt}[\log \sigma_t]\bigg|_{t=0} dV_F := \int_{\mathfrak{D}} B_x^{\sigma}(\widetilde{X}) dV_F, \end{aligned} \tag{9.1.13}$$

where

$$B_x^{\sigma}(\widetilde{X}) := \frac{d}{dt}[\log \sigma_t(x)]\bigg|_{t=0} = \frac{d}{dt}[\log \mathcal{F}_{\tilde{e}}^{\sigma}(f_t(x), z(x,t))]\bigg|_{t=0}. \tag{9.1.14}$$

Lemma 9.3. $B_x^{\sigma}(\widetilde{X})$ *expressed by (9.1.14) is well defined, i.e., it is independent of the choice of the bases* $\mathbf{E}$ *and* $\widetilde{\mathbf{E}}$.

Proof. As the above statement, $\sigma_t(x)$ is independent of the choice of the base $\widetilde{\mathbf{E}}$. In the following, it is sufficient to prove that $\sigma_t(x)$ is independent of the choice of the base $\mathbf{E}$.

Let $e'_i = q_i^j e_j$ be another base in $T_x M$, θ'^i its dual base. Writing

$$dV_F = \sigma_t(x)\theta^1 \wedge \cdots \wedge \theta^n = \sigma'_t(x)\theta'^1 \wedge \cdots \wedge \theta'^n,$$

we have

$$\sigma'_t(x) = (\det Q)\sigma_t(x), \quad Q := (q_i^j).$$

Hence, $\frac{d}{dt}[\log \sigma_t(x)]|_{t=0} = B_x^{\sigma}(\widetilde{X})$ is independent of the choice of the base $\mathbf{E}$. $\square$

By using Lemma 9.2, Lemma 9.3 and (9.1.12), we can give the following

Definition 9.2. Let $f : (M, F) \to (\widetilde{M}, \widetilde{F})$ be an isometric immersion. For any variation vector field $\widetilde{X} \in T\widetilde{M}$ along f, we define

$$\mathcal{H}_f^{\sigma}(\widetilde{X})\bigg|_x := B_x^{\sigma}(\widetilde{X}) - \mathrm{div}_F\left(P_{f_*}^{\sigma}(\widetilde{X})\right)\bigg|_x, \tag{9.1.15}$$

which is called the *mean curvature* of the isometric immersion f with respect to σ_F, or the σ_F-*mean curvature*.

According to Lemma 9.1, the formula (9.1.13) can be written as

$$V'(0) = \int_{\mathfrak{D}} \mathcal{H}_f^{\sigma}(\widetilde{X}) dV_F, \tag{9.1.16}$$

where $\widetilde{X}$ is the variation field (9.1.12) along f.

Definition 9.3. If $V'(0) = 0$ for any compact domain $\mathfrak{D} \subseteq M$ and any variation field $\widetilde{X}$, then (M, F) is called a *minimal submanifold* in $(\widetilde{M}, \widetilde{F})$ with respect to the volume measure σ_F, or a σ_F-*minimal submanifold*.

In particular, with respect to the Busemann-Hausdorff volume measure σ_B and the Holmes-Thompson volume measure σ_H (cf. §4.1), (M, F) is called a BH-minimal submanifold and a HT-minimal submanifold, respectively. Similarly, for Definition 9.1, $\mathcal{H}_f^\sigma(\widetilde{X})$ is called the BH-*mean curvature* and the HT-*mean curvature*, respectively.

From (9.1.16) and the following proposition we can see that (M, F) is a σ_F-minimal submanifold in $(\widetilde{M}, \widetilde{F})$ if and only if its mean curvature vanishes identically, i.e.,

$$\mathcal{H}_f^\sigma \equiv 0.$$

Proposition 9.1. *The mean curvature $\mathcal{H}_f^\sigma$ of an isometric immersion f with respect to any volume measure σ_F depends linearly on the variation field $\widetilde{X}$, and $\mathcal{H}_f^\sigma$ vanishes identically on $f_*(TM)$, i.e.,*

$$\mathcal{H}_f^\sigma(f_*(X)) = 0, \quad \forall X \in TM.$$

Proof. We will give the expression of the mean curvature in a local coordinate system. Let $\{x^i\}$ and $\{\widetilde{x}^\alpha\}$ be local coordinate systems of M and $\widetilde{M}$, respectively. An isometric immersion f can be expressed by

$$\widetilde{x}^\alpha = f^\alpha(x^i, \cdots, x^n).$$

We choose the following local bases:

$$e_i = \frac{\partial}{\partial x^i}, \quad \widetilde{e}_\alpha = \frac{\partial}{\partial \widetilde{x}^\alpha}, \quad \frac{\partial}{\partial x^i} = \frac{\partial f^\alpha}{\partial x^i} \frac{\partial}{\partial \widetilde{x}^\alpha}.$$

Consider a variation f_t with $f_0 = f$. Set $dV_{F_t} = \sigma_t(x) dx^1 \wedge \cdots \wedge dx^n$, where

$$\sigma_t := \mathcal{F}^\sigma(f_t(x), z(x, t)), \quad z(x, t) = df_t(x) = \left(\frac{\partial f_t^\alpha}{\partial x^i}(x)\right).$$

By (9.1.14), it is easy to see that

$$B^\sigma(\widetilde{X}) = \frac{1}{\mathcal{F}^\sigma}\left(\frac{\partial \mathcal{F}^\sigma}{\partial \widetilde{x}^\alpha}\widetilde{X}^\alpha + \frac{\partial \mathcal{F}^\sigma}{\partial z_i^\alpha}\frac{\partial \widetilde{X}^\alpha}{\partial x^i}\right). \tag{9.1.17}$$

From (9.1.11) it follows that

$$P_{f_*}^\sigma(\widetilde{X}) = \frac{1}{\mathcal{F}^\sigma}\frac{\partial \mathcal{F}^\sigma}{\partial z_i^\alpha}\widetilde{X}^\alpha \frac{\partial}{\partial x^i}. \tag{9.1.18}$$

By virtue of (9.1.8), (9.1.15), (9.1.17) and (9.1.18), we can obtain

$$\mathcal{H}_f^\sigma(\widetilde{X}) = \frac{1}{\mathcal{F}^\sigma}\left[\frac{\partial \mathcal{F}^\sigma}{\partial \widetilde{x}^\alpha} - \frac{\partial^2 \mathcal{F}^\sigma}{\partial z_i^\alpha \partial z_j^\beta}\frac{\partial^2 f^\beta}{\partial x^i \partial x^j} - \frac{\partial^2 \mathcal{F}^\sigma}{\partial z_i^\alpha \partial \widetilde{x}^\beta}\frac{\partial f^\beta}{\partial x^i}\right]\widetilde{X}^\alpha. \qquad (9.1.19)$$

This proves the first conclusion of Proposition 9.1.

We now prove the second conclusion of Proposition 9.1. Let $X \in TM$ be an arbitrary vector field, φ be a smooth function with compact support $\operatorname{supp}\varphi \subset \mathfrak{D}$ in M. Let Φ_t be the one-parameter group of transformations generated by φX. Thus, $\Phi_t(x) = x$, $\forall x \in M \setminus \mathfrak{D}$. Consider a variation $f_t := f \circ \Phi_t : M \to (\widetilde{M}, \widetilde{F})$, whose variation field is

$$(\varphi f)_*(X) = \left.\frac{\partial f_t}{\partial t}\right|_{t=0}.$$

$\Phi_t : \mathfrak{D} \to \mathfrak{D}$ is a diffeomorphism for small t enough. Hence, $V(t) := \operatorname{Vol}_{\Phi_t^* F}^\sigma(\mathfrak{D})$ is constant. Thus,

$$0 = V'(0) = \int_M \mathcal{H}_f^\sigma(f_*(X))\varphi dV_F^\sigma.$$

Because of the arbitrariness of φ, the second conclusion of Proposition 9.1 is obtained. $\qquad\square$

Remark. By the first conclusion of the proposition, one can see that $\mathcal{H}_f^\sigma$ is a 1-form in $\widetilde{M}$ along f, which is called the *mean curvature form*.

9.1.3 Non-existence of compact minimal submanifolds

As is known that there is no any compact minimal submanifold in the Euclidean space. The similar result holds too in Finsler geometry.

Theorem 9.2. *Let $(\widetilde{M}, \widetilde{F})$ be a Minkowski space with finite dimension. Then there is no any compact oriented minimal submanifold in $(\widetilde{M}, \widetilde{F})$.*

Proof. Let $f:(M, F) \to (\widetilde{M}, \widetilde{F})$ be an isometric immersion. Since $(\widetilde{M}, \widetilde{F})$ is a Minkowski space, in local coordinate, the volume form of (M, F) is

$$dV_F^\sigma = \mathcal{F}_f^\sigma(z)dx^1 \wedge \cdots \wedge dx^n, \quad z = (z_i^\alpha) = \left(\frac{\partial f^\alpha}{\partial x^i}\right).$$

Note that $\mathcal{F}_f^\sigma(z)$ is independent of $\widetilde{x}^\alpha$. By (9.1.10) and (9.1.17),

$$B^\sigma(f) = n.$$

Thus from (9.1.15) we can get

$$\mathcal{H}_f^\sigma(f) = n - \operatorname{div}_F(P_{f*}^\sigma)(f).$$

Integrating on both sides of the above equation, we have

$$\int_M \mathcal{H}_f^\sigma(f)dV_F^\sigma = n\mathrm{Vol}_F^\sigma(M),$$

which proves Theorem 9.2 according to Definition 9.2.   □

Remark. For Busemann-Hausdorff volume measure and Holmes-Thompson volume measure, Theorem 9.2 appears respectively in [106] and [56]. For the general volume measure Theorem 9.2 is given in [142].

9.2   Rigidity of minimal submanifolds

In global differential geometry, the well-known Bernstein theorem for minimal surfaces gives that any complete minimal graph (non-parameterized minimal surface) in the Euclidean 3-space must be a plane. Various generalizations of this are collectively called Bernstein type theorem. In this section we discuss similar problems in Finsler geometry.

9.2.1   Minimal surfaces in Minkowski spaces

Let $(\widetilde{M}, \widetilde{F}) = (\widetilde{V}^m, \widetilde{F})$ be an m-dimensional Minkowski space, $f : (M^n, F) \to (\widetilde{V}^m, \widetilde{F})$ be an isometric immersion. We take Holmes-Thompson volume measure (i.e. volume measure induced from sphere bundle, see Section 4.1.2)

$$dV_F = \sigma_H(x)dx, \quad \sigma_H(x) = \frac{1}{c_{n-1}}\int_{S_xM}\sqrt{\det(g)}d\nu,$$

$$d\nu = \frac{\sqrt{\det(g)}}{F^n}d\eta, \quad d\eta := \sum_i(-1)^{i-1}y^i dy^1 \wedge \cdots \wedge \widehat{dy^i} \wedge \cdots \wedge dy^n. \tag{9.2.1}$$

By using a direct computation, it is not hard to obtain the HT-mean curvature (also see [56])

$$\mathcal{H}_H = \frac{1}{c_{n-1}}\left(\int_{S_xM}\frac{\widetilde{g}_{\alpha\beta}h^\beta}{F^2}\sqrt{\det(g)}d\nu\right)d\widetilde{x}^\alpha,$$

$$h^\alpha := f_{ij}^\alpha y^i y^j - f_k^\alpha G^k, \quad f_i^\alpha := \frac{\partial f^\alpha}{\partial x^i}, \quad f_{ij}^\alpha := \frac{\partial^2 f^\alpha}{\partial x^i \partial x^j}, \tag{9.2.2}$$

where G^k is the spray coefficients of (M^n, F). Since $\widetilde{G}^\alpha \equiv 0$ in the Minkowski space, according to (9.1.4), we have

$$G^k = g^{kl}f_l^\beta \widetilde{g}_{\alpha\beta}(f_{ij}^\alpha y^i y_j).$$

Then, the combination of the above equation and (9.2.2) gives

$$h_\alpha := \widetilde{g}_{\alpha\beta} h^\beta = T_{\alpha\beta} f_{ij}^\beta y^i y^j, \quad T_{\alpha\beta} := \widetilde{g}_{\alpha\beta} - \widetilde{g}_{\alpha\gamma} \widetilde{g}_{\beta\delta} f_i^\gamma f_j^\delta g^{ij}. \tag{9.2.3}$$

By (9.2.2) and (9.2.3), the equivalent condition for f to be HT-minimal immersion is

$$\int_{S_x M} \frac{1}{F^2} T_{\alpha\beta} f_{ij}^\beta y^i y^j \sqrt{\det(g)} d\nu = 0, \quad \forall \, \alpha. \tag{9.2.4}$$

For any $y \in T_x M$ and $\widetilde{y} = df(y) \in T\widetilde{V}^m$, let $p_y^\perp : f^{-1} T\widetilde{V}^m \to (TM)^\perp$ denote the orthogonal projection with respect to $\widetilde{g}(\widetilde{y}) := \langle,\rangle_{\widetilde{g}}$, and set $T = T_{\alpha\beta} d\widetilde{x}^\alpha \bigotimes d\widetilde{x}^\beta$. By the second equation of (9.2.3),

$$T(\widetilde{X}, \widetilde{Y}) = \langle p_y^\perp \widetilde{X}, \widetilde{Y} \rangle_{\widetilde{g}} = \langle \widetilde{X}, p_y^\perp \widetilde{Y} \rangle_{\widetilde{g}}, \quad \forall \widetilde{X}, \widetilde{Y} \in f^{-1} T\widetilde{V}^m.$$

So, (9.2.4) can be rewritten as

$$f_{ij}^\alpha(x) \int_{S_x M} \frac{1}{F^2} \left\langle p_y^\perp \widetilde{X}, \frac{\partial}{\partial \widetilde{x}^\alpha} \right\rangle_{\widetilde{g}} y^i y^j \sqrt{\det(g)} d\nu = 0,$$
$$\forall \widetilde{X} \in f^{-1} T\widetilde{V}^m. \tag{9.2.5}$$

Now assume that $m = n + 1$, i.e., (M^n, F) is a hypersurface of $\widetilde{V}^{n+1}$. Let $\widetilde{e}_\alpha$ be a given orthonormal basis of $\widetilde{V}^{n+1}$ with respect to the Euclidean metric $\langle,\rangle$, i.e., $\langle \widetilde{e}_\alpha, \widetilde{e}_\beta \rangle = \delta_{\alpha\beta}$. Let $\mathbf{n} = n^\alpha \widetilde{e}_\alpha$ be the unit normal vector field of the hypersurface $f(M)$ in $\widetilde{V}^{n+1}$ with respect to Euclidean metric $\langle,\rangle$, i.e.,

$$\sum_\alpha (n^\alpha)^2 = 1, \quad \sum_\alpha n^\alpha f_i^\alpha = 0. \tag{9.2.6}$$

On the other hand, for any point $\widetilde{x} = f(x), x \in M$, we have the fundamental metric $\widetilde{g} = \widetilde{g}_{\alpha\beta} d\widetilde{y}^\alpha d\widetilde{y}^\beta$ induced by Minkowski metric $\widetilde{F}$. Let $\widetilde{\mathbf{n}} = \widetilde{n}^\alpha \widetilde{e}_\alpha$ be the unit normal vector field of $f(M)$ with respect to $\widetilde{g}$, i.e.,

$$\widetilde{g}_{\alpha\beta} \widetilde{n}^\alpha \widetilde{n}^\beta = 1, \quad \widetilde{g}_{\alpha\beta} = \widetilde{g}(\widetilde{e}_\alpha, \widetilde{e}^\beta), \quad \widetilde{g}_{\alpha\beta} \widetilde{n}^\alpha f_i^\beta = 0. \tag{9.2.7}$$

Noting that $\text{rank}(f_i^\alpha) = n$ and using (9.2.6) and (9.2.7), one can see

$$\lambda n^\alpha = \widetilde{g}_{\alpha\beta} \widetilde{n}^\beta, \quad \lambda = \widetilde{g}(n, \widetilde{n}) = \langle n, \widetilde{n} \rangle^{-1}. \tag{9.2.8}$$

Since $\mathbf{n} = n^\alpha \widetilde{e}_\alpha$ is linearly independent of $\{\frac{\partial}{\partial x^i}\}$, from (9.2.5), f is HT-minimal immersion if and only if

$$f_{ij}^\alpha(x) \int_{S_x M} \frac{1}{F^2} \langle \mathbf{n}^\perp, \widetilde{e}^\alpha \rangle_{\widetilde{g}} y^i y^j \sqrt{\det(g)} d\nu = 0, \quad \mathbf{n}^\perp := p_y^\perp \mathbf{n}. \tag{9.2.9}$$

It follows from (9.2.6), (9.2.7) and (9.2.8) that

$$\widetilde{g}(\mathbf{n}^\perp, \widetilde{e}_\alpha) = \widetilde{g}(\mathbf{n}, \widetilde{\mathbf{n}}) \widetilde{g}(\widetilde{\mathbf{n}}, \widetilde{e}_\alpha) = \lambda \widetilde{g}_{\alpha\beta} \widetilde{n}^\beta = \lambda^2 n^\alpha. \tag{9.2.10}$$

Set

$$a_{ij}(x) := \sum_{\alpha} f_i^{\alpha} f_j^{\beta}, \quad a := \det(a_{ij}), \quad \partial_i := f_i^{\alpha} e^{\alpha}.$$

Since

$$\begin{pmatrix} \tilde{\mathbf{n}} \\ \partial_i \end{pmatrix} (\tilde{g}_{\alpha\beta}) \begin{pmatrix} \tilde{\mathbf{n}} \\ \partial_j \end{pmatrix}^T = \begin{pmatrix} 1 & 0 \\ 0 & g_{ij} \end{pmatrix},$$

$$\begin{pmatrix} \mathbf{n} \\ \partial_i \end{pmatrix} (\tilde{g}_{\alpha\beta}) \begin{pmatrix} \mathbf{n} \\ \partial_j \end{pmatrix}^T = \begin{pmatrix} \lambda & * \\ 0 & g_{ij} \end{pmatrix}, \quad \begin{pmatrix} \mathbf{n} \\ \partial_i \end{pmatrix} \begin{pmatrix} \mathbf{n} \\ \partial_j \end{pmatrix}^T = \begin{pmatrix} 1 & 0 \\ 0 & a_{ij} \end{pmatrix},$$

we have

$$\det(g_{ij}) = \frac{a}{\lambda^2} \det(\tilde{g}_{\alpha\beta}). \tag{9.2.11}$$

By (9.2.9), (9.2.10) and (9.2.11), f is HT-minimal if and only if

$$\sum_{\alpha,i,j} f_{ij}^{\alpha} n^{\alpha} \int_{S_x} \frac{\det(\tilde{g}_{\alpha\beta})}{F^{n+2}} y^i y^j \sqrt{a} d\eta = 0, \quad S_x := \{y \in R^n | a_{ij} y^i y^j = 1\}.$$

Putting

$$B^{ij} := \int_{S_x} \Phi y^i y^j \sqrt{a} d\eta = \int_{S_x} \Phi y^i y^j dV_{S_x}, \quad \Phi := \frac{\det(\tilde{g}_{\alpha\beta})}{F^{n+2}}, \tag{9.2.12}$$

we see that f is HT-minimal if and only if

$$\sum_{\alpha} B^{ij} f_{ij}^{\alpha} n^{\alpha} = 0.$$

Now assume that M is a graph in $\tilde{V}^{n+1}$ defined by

$$f(x^1, \cdots, x^n) = (x^1, \cdots, x^n, u(x^1, \cdots, x^n)), \tag{9.2.13}$$

where $x = (x^1, \cdots, x^n) \in \mathcal{U} \subseteq \mathbb{R}^n$, u is a differentiable function on $\mathcal{U}$. Thus we have

$$a = 1 + |\bigtriangledown u|^2, \quad \mathbf{n} = a^{-1/2}(-u_1, \cdots, -u_n, 1),$$

where $\bigtriangledown u = (u_1, \cdots, u_n)$, $u_i = \frac{\partial}{\partial x^i}$. Thus, the graph (9.2.13) is HT-minimal if and only if

$$B^{ij}(x, u, \bigtriangledown u) u_{ij} = 0, \quad u_{ij} := \frac{\partial^2 u}{\partial x^i \partial x^j}. \tag{9.2.14}$$

Since $\Phi = \frac{\det(\tilde{g}_{\alpha\beta})}{F^{n+2}} > 0$,

$$B^{ij} \xi_i \xi_j = \int_{S_x} \Phi y^i y^j \xi_i \xi_j dV_{S_x} = \int_{S_x} \Phi (y^i \xi_i)^2 dV_{S_x} \geq 0, \quad \forall \xi \in \mathbb{R}^n,$$

where the equality holds if and only if $y^i\xi_i = 0$, i.e., $\xi = 0$. This implies that the equation (9.2.14) is elliptic.

On the other hand, for $y \in S_x$ we see that $\widetilde{y} = df(y) \in \mathbb{S}^n \subseteq \widetilde{V}^{n+1}$. So,
$$\min\{\Phi(x,y) : y \in S_x\} \geq \min\{\Phi : \widetilde{y} \in \mathbb{S}^n\} = \kappa_1 > 0,$$
$$\max\{\Phi(x,y) : y \in S_x\} \leq \max\{\Phi : \widetilde{y} \in \mathbb{S}^n\} = \kappa_2 > 0,$$
where κ_1 and κ_2 are constants. Thus we have
$$\kappa_1 a^{ij}\xi_i\xi_j \leq B^{ij}\xi_i\xi_j \leq \kappa_2 a^{ij}\xi_i\xi_j, \quad \forall \xi \in \mathbb{R}^n,$$
which implies that the equation (9.2.14) is of mean curvature type ([134]).

When $n = 2$, according to [134], the elliptic equation of mean curvature type defined on the whole $\mathbb{R}^2$ has only trivial solution, i.e., $u(x^1, x^2)$ is a linear function. Hence, we have the following Bernstein type theorem.

Theorem 9.3 ([57]). *Any complete HT-minimal graph in a 3-dimensional Minkowski space $(\widetilde{V}^3, \widetilde{F})$ is a plane.*

The Euclidean space is the special Minkowski space. The above theorem generalized the classical Bernstein theorem. It should be marked that in Theorem 9.1 we use the Holmes-Thompson volume measure, i.e., the volume measure induced from the projective sphere bundle. For the Busemann-Hausdorff volume measure, the above theorem does not necessarily holds. In fact, J. C. Álvarez-Pavia and G. Berck ([1]) constructed a family of 3-dimensional Finsler spaces, where geodesics are straight lines, but planes are not necessarily minimal. They created a family of metrics in $\mathbb{R}^3$
$$F_\lambda(x,y) = \frac{(1 + \lambda^2\|x\|^2)\|y\|^2 + \lambda^2\langle x,y\rangle^2}{\|y\|}$$
where λ is a real parametric, "$\langle,\rangle$" is the Euclidean inner product. All geodesics of $F_\lambda(x,y)$ are straight lines in $\mathbb{R}^3$. However, for the Busemann-Hausdorff volume measure, if all the planes are minimal, then $\lambda = 0$ (see [1]). Therefore, in studying Finslerian minimal immersion, the Holmes-Thompson volume measure has more advantages.

9.2.2 Minimal surfaces in (α, β)-spaces

Let $F = \alpha\phi(s), s := \beta/\alpha$, be an (α,β)-metric, where α is a Riemannian metric, β is a 1-form, and $b := \|\beta\|_\alpha$. Define the following functions with $t > 0$
$$\sigma_B(t) := \frac{\sqrt{\pi}\Gamma(\frac{n-1}{2})}{\Gamma(\frac{n}{2})} \left[\int_0^\pi \frac{\sin^{n-2}\theta}{\phi^n(t\cos\theta)}d\theta\right]^{-1},$$
$$\sigma_H(t) := \frac{\Gamma(\frac{n}{2})}{\sqrt{\pi}\Gamma(\frac{n-1}{2})} \int_0^\pi T(t\cos\theta)\sin^{n-2}\theta d\theta,$$
$$(9.2.15)$$

where
$$T(s) := \phi(\phi - s\phi')^{n-2}[\phi - s\phi' + (b^2 - s^2)\phi''],$$
$$\Gamma(t) = \int_0^{+\infty} x^{t-1}e^{-x}dx \quad (\Gamma \text{ function}). \tag{9.2.16}$$

Proposition 9.2 ([29, 40]). *For an* (α, β)*-metric* $F = \alpha\phi(s)$*, its BH-volume form and HT-volume form are respectively*
$$dV_F^{BH} = \sigma_B(b)dV_\alpha \quad and \quad dV_F^{HT} = \sigma_H(b)dV_\alpha,$$
where $\sigma_B(t)$ *and* $\sigma_H(t)$ *are given by (9.2.15),* dV_α *denotes the standard Riemannian volume form about Riemannian metric* α.

Proof. For any point $x \in M$, we take an orthonormal frame $\{e_i\}$ with respect to α_x in T_xM such that the dual vector $\beta^\sharp$ of β with respect to α is in direction of e_1, and denote by $\{y^i\}$ the corresponding coordinate system. Now we have $\beta_x(y) = \|\beta_x\|_\alpha y^1$, $\alpha_x(y) = \sqrt{\sum_{i=1}^n (y^i)^2}$.

Firstly, we compute the BH-volume form. Let $\mathbf{B}_x^n := \{(y^i) \in \mathbb{R}^n | F(x, y^i \frac{\partial}{\partial x^i}|_x) < 1\}$, so
$$\mathbf{B}_x^n := \left\{ (y^i) \in \mathbb{R}^n | \sqrt{\sum_i (y^i)^2} \phi\left(\frac{\|\beta_x\|_\alpha y^1}{\sum_{i=1}^n (y^i)^2} \right) < 1 \right\}.$$

Consider the following coordinate transformation
$$\begin{cases} y^1 = r\cos\theta^1, \\ y^2 = r\sin\theta^1\cos\theta^2, \\ \cdots\cdots\cdots \\ y^{n-1} = r\sin\theta^1\sin\theta^2\cdots\sin\theta^{n-2}\cos\theta^{n-1}, \\ y^n = r\sin\theta^1\sin\theta^2\cdots\sin\theta^{n-2}\sin\theta^{n-1}, \end{cases}$$
where $r \geq 0, 0 \leq \theta^i \leq \pi, 0 \leq \theta^{n-1} < 2\pi, 1 \leq i \leq n-2$. The Jacobi of the above transformation is $Jac := r^{n-1}\sin^{n-2}\theta^1\cdots\sin\theta^{n-2}$. Thus
$$\mathbf{B}_x^n := \{(r, \theta^1, \cdots, \theta^{n-1}) | 0 \leq r \leq \phi^{-1}(\|\beta_x\|_\alpha \cos\theta^1),$$
$$0 \leq \theta^i \leq \pi, 0 \leq \theta^{n-1} < 2\pi, 1 \leq i \leq n-2\}.$$

Thus,
$$\text{Vol}(\mathbf{B}_x^n) = \int_{\mathbf{B}_x^n} dy^1 \cdots dy^n$$
$$= \int_{\mathbf{B}_x^n} r^{n-1}\sin^{n-2}\theta^1\cdots\sin\theta^{n-2}drd\theta^1\cdots d\theta^{n-1}$$
$$= 2\pi \left(\int_0^\pi \sin^{n-2}\theta^1 d\theta^1 \right) \cdots \left(\int_0^\pi \sin\theta^{n-2}d\theta^{n-2} \right)$$
$$\cdot \left(\int_0^{\phi^{-1}(\|\beta_x\|_\alpha \cos\theta^1)} r^{n-1}dr \right)$$

$$= \frac{2\pi\Gamma(\frac{n-2}{2})\Gamma(\frac{1}{2})}{n\Gamma(\frac{n-1}{2})} \cdots \frac{\Gamma(1)\Gamma(\frac{1}{2})}{\Gamma(\frac{3}{2})} \left(\int_0^\pi \frac{\sin^{n-2}\theta^1}{\phi^n(\|\beta_x\|_\alpha \cos\theta^1)} d\theta^1 \right)$$

$$= \frac{\Gamma(\frac{n}{2})\mathrm{Vol}(B^n)}{\sqrt{\pi}\Gamma(\frac{n-1}{2})} \left(\int_0^\pi \frac{\sin^{n-2}\theta^1}{\phi^n(\|\beta_x\|_\alpha \cos\theta^1)} d\theta^1 \right).$$

By (4.1.1), the BH volume form then is $dV_F^{BH} = \sigma_B(\|\beta\|_\alpha)dV_\alpha$.

Next, we consider HT-volume form. It can be proved that ([112])

$$\det(g_{ij}) = \phi(s)^n T(s)\det(a_{ij}),$$

where $T(s)$ is given by (9.2.16). At a point $x \in M$, it follows from (4.1.6) that

$$\sigma_H(x) = \frac{1}{\mathrm{Vol}(\mathbb{S}^{n-1})} \int_{S_x M} \frac{\det(g_{ij})}{F^n} d\nu$$

$$= \frac{1}{\mathrm{Vol}(\mathbb{S}^{n-1})} \int_{S_x M} \frac{T(s)\det(a_{ij})}{\alpha^n} d\nu$$

$$= \frac{\sqrt{\det(a_{ij})}}{\mathrm{Vol}(\mathbb{S}^{n-1})} \int_{\{y\in\mathbb{R}^n|\alpha_x(y)=1\}} T(s)\sqrt{\det(a_{ij})}d\nu.$$

Then

$$\sigma_H(x) = \frac{\sqrt{\det(a_{ij})}}{\mathrm{Vol}(\mathbb{S}^{n-1})} \int_{\mathbb{S}^{n-1}} T(\|\beta_x\|_\alpha y^1)dV_{\mathbb{S}^{n-1}}$$

$$= \frac{\mathrm{Vol}(\mathbb{S}^{n-2})}{\mathrm{Vol}(\mathbb{S}^{n-1})} \int_{-1}^1 T(\|\beta_x\|_\alpha y^1)(1-(y^1)^2)^{\frac{n-3}{2}} dy^1 \sqrt{\det(a_{ij})}.$$

$$(9.2.17)$$

Note that

$$\frac{\mathrm{Vol}(\mathbb{S}^{n-2})}{\mathrm{Vol}(\mathbb{S}^{n-1})} = \frac{\Gamma(\frac{n}{2})}{\sqrt{\pi}\Gamma(\frac{n-1}{2})}.$$

Set $y^1 = \cos\theta$. The equation (9.2.17) becomes

$$\sigma_H(x) = \sigma_H(\|\beta_x\|_\alpha)\sqrt{\det(a_{ij})},$$

from which it follows that $dV_F^{HT} = \sigma_H(\|\beta_x\|_\alpha)dV_\alpha$.

Now consider the system of ordinary differential equations

$$\begin{cases} \phi(\phi - s\phi')^{n-1} = 1 + p(s) + s^2 q(s), \\ \phi(\phi - s\phi')^{n-2}\phi'' = q(s), \end{cases} \qquad (9.2.18)$$

where $p(s)$ and $q(s)$ are arbitrary smooth odd functions. $\qquad\square$

Proposition 9.3. *Let $F = \alpha\phi(s)$ be an (α,β)-metric, $s = \frac{\beta}{\alpha}$. If $\phi(s) = (1+h(s))^{-\frac{1}{n}}$ where $h(s)$ is arbitrary smooth odd function, then $dV_F^{BH} = dV_\alpha$. If ϕ satisfies (9.2.18), then $dV_F^{HT} = dV_\alpha$.*

Proof. For any odd function $h(s)$, $\int_0^\pi h(t\cos\theta)\sin^{n-2}\theta d\theta = 0$. Note that

$$\int_0^\pi \sin^{n-2}\theta d\theta = \frac{\sqrt{\pi}\,\Gamma(\frac{n-1}{2})}{\Gamma(\frac{n}{2})}.$$

Substituting $\phi(s) = (1+h(s))^{-\frac{1}{n}}$ into $(9.2.15)_1$, we get $\sigma_B(t) = 1$. Similarly, if ϕ satisfies (9.2.18), then $\sigma_H(t) = 1$. □

Now consider an isometric immersion hypersurface $f : (M^n, F) \to (\widetilde{M}^{n+1}, \widetilde{F})$, where $\widetilde{F} = \widetilde{\alpha}\phi(\widetilde{s})$, $\widetilde{s} = \frac{\widetilde{\beta}}{\widetilde{\alpha}}$, $\widetilde{\alpha} = \sqrt{\widetilde{\alpha}_{\alpha\beta}y^\alpha y^\beta}$ is a Riemannian metric, and $\widetilde{\beta} = \widetilde{b}_\alpha d\widetilde{x}^\alpha$ is a 1-form. It is easy to see that the induced metric $F = f^*\widetilde{F}$ is still (α, β)-metric of same type, i.e., $F = \alpha\phi(s)$ with the Riemannian metric $\alpha = \sqrt{\alpha_{ij}y^i y^j}$ and 1-form $\beta = b_i(x)y^i$, where

$$a_{ij}(x) = f_i^\alpha f_j^\beta \widetilde{a}_{\alpha\beta}, \quad b_i(x) = \widetilde{b}_\alpha f_i^\alpha, \quad f_i^\alpha = \frac{\partial f^\alpha}{\partial x^i}. \tag{9.2.19}$$

For ϕ in the Proposition 9.3, the BH-volume form and HT-volume form of (M, F) are same as the volume form of Riemannian submanifold (M, α). Assume that $\widetilde{M}^{n+1}$ is a real vector space V^{n+1} and $\widetilde{\alpha}$ is Euclidean metric. According to Bernstein type theorems on minimal hypersurfaces in the Euclidean space, the following theorems are obtained immediately.

Theorem 9.4 ([40]). *Let $\widetilde{F} = \widetilde{\alpha}\phi(\frac{\widetilde{\beta}}{\widetilde{\alpha}})$ be an (α, β)-metric, where $\widetilde{\alpha}$ is a Euclidean metric, $\phi(s) = (1+h(s))^{-\frac{1}{n}}$, $h(s)$ is an arbitrary smooth odd function (or ϕ satisfies (9.2.18)). Then any complete BH-minimal (or HT-minimal) graph must be a hyperplane in an $(n+1)$-dimensional space $(V^{n+1}, \widetilde{F})$ for $n \leq 7$.*

Theorem 9.5 ([40]). *Let $\widetilde{F} = \widetilde{\alpha}\phi(\frac{\widetilde{\beta}}{\widetilde{\alpha}})$ be an (α, β)-metric, where $\widetilde{\alpha}$ is a Euclidean metric, $\phi(s) = (1+h(s))^{-\frac{1}{n}}$, $h(s)$ is an arbitrary smooth odd function (or ϕ satisfies (9.2.18) for $n = 2$). Then any complete stable BH-minimal (or HT-minimal) graph must be a plane in a 3-dimensional space $(V^{n+1}, \widetilde{F})$.*

Remark. When $\phi(s) = 1+s$, i.e., $\widetilde{F}$ is a Randers metric, the corresponding conclusion has been given in [57]. Other solution to the equation (9.2.18) still is open.

9.2.3 Minimal surfaces in special Minkowskian (α, β)-spaces

Let $(\mathbb{V}, \widetilde{F})$ be a Minkowski space, and $\widetilde{F} = \widetilde{\alpha}\phi(\widetilde{s})$, $\widetilde{s} = \widetilde{\beta}/\widetilde{\alpha}$, be an (α, β)-metric, where α is a Euclidean metric, β is a 1-form satisfying $\widetilde{b} := \|\widetilde{\beta}\|_{\widetilde{\alpha}} = $ constant and $\widetilde{b} \in [0, \widetilde{b}_0)$ such that $\widetilde{F}$ is a positive definite Finsler metric. Such Minkowski spaces $(\mathbb{V}^{n+1}, \widetilde{F})$ are called special Minkowskian (α, β)-spaces, which, Obviously, are a generalization of the Euclidean space.

Given a plane $\mathcal{P}$ passing through the origin in $(\mathbb{V}^{n+1}, \widetilde{F})$, choose an orthonormal base $\{e_1, e_2, \cdots, e_{n+1}\}$ with respect to $\widetilde{\alpha}$ such that $\mathcal{P} = \mathrm{span}\{e_1, e_2, \cdots, e_n\}$. This base gives a coordinate system $\{\widetilde{x}^1, \widetilde{x}^2, \cdots, \widetilde{x}^{n+1}\}$ in $(\mathbb{V}^{n+1}, \widetilde{F})$. Let $\theta_\alpha := \angle_{\widetilde{\alpha}}(\widetilde{\beta}^\sharp, e_\alpha)$ be the angle between the dual vector $\widetilde{\beta}^\sharp$ to β and e_α with respect to $\widetilde{\alpha}$, and set $\lambda_\alpha := \cos\theta_\alpha$. For $\widetilde{y} = \widetilde{y}^\alpha \frac{\partial}{\partial \widetilde{x}^\alpha}$, we have

$$\widetilde{\alpha} = \sqrt{\sum_{\alpha=1}^{n+1}(\widetilde{y}^\alpha)^2}, \quad \widetilde{F}(\widetilde{y}) = \widetilde{\alpha}\phi(s), \quad s = \frac{\widetilde{b}\lambda_\alpha\widetilde{y}^\alpha}{\widetilde{\alpha}}.$$

An isometric immersion $f : (M, F) \to (\mathbb{V}^{n+1}, \widetilde{F})$ can be locally expressed as $\widetilde{x}^\alpha = f^\alpha(x^1, \cdots, x^n)$. On M the metric $\widetilde{F}$ induce a metric $F = f^*\widetilde{F} = \alpha\phi(\beta/\alpha)$, where $\alpha = \sqrt{a_{ij}y^iy^j}$, $\beta = b_iy^i$, and a_{ij} and b_i are given by (9.2.19).

Since $(\mathbb{V}^{n+1}, \widetilde{F})$ is a Minkowski space, $\mathcal{F}_f^\sigma(z)$ in the volume form $dV_F^\sigma = \mathcal{F}_f^\sigma(z)dx^1 \wedge \cdots \wedge dx^n$ of (M, F) (see the proof of Theorem 9.2) is independent of $\widetilde{x}^\alpha$. By Proposition 9.2, $\mathcal{F}_f^\sigma(z)$ becomes

$$\mathcal{F}_f^\sigma(z) = \sigma(b)\sqrt{\det(a_{ij})}, \quad b := \|\beta\|_\alpha,$$

where $\sigma(t)$ is $\sigma_B(t)$ or $\sigma_H(t)$ expressed by (9.2.15), $b = \sqrt{\widetilde{b}^2 a^{ij}\lambda_\alpha\lambda_\beta f_i^\alpha f_j^\beta}$ denotes the length of β with respect to α.

By computing the mean curvature of the isometric immersion f (cf. §9.1), it is not difficult to see that f is either BH-minimal or HT-minimal if and only if ([40])

$$\{a^{ij}[2\widetilde{b}^2\lambda_\alpha\lambda_\beta\sigma'(b)(\delta^{\alpha\eta} - B^{\alpha\eta})(\delta^{\beta\gamma} - B^{\beta\gamma}) + \sigma(b)(\delta^{\gamma\eta} - B^{\gamma\eta})]$$
$$+ 2\widetilde{b}^2\lambda_\delta\lambda_\gamma A^{i\delta}A^{j\gamma}[2\widetilde{b}^2\lambda_\alpha\lambda_\beta\sigma''(b)(\delta^{\alpha\eta} - B^{\alpha\eta})(\delta^{\beta\gamma} - B^{\beta\gamma}) \qquad (9.2.20)$$
$$- \sigma'(b)(\delta^{\gamma\eta} - B^{\gamma\eta})]\}\frac{\partial^2 f^n}{\partial x^i \partial x^j} = 0,$$

where

$$A^{i\alpha} := a^{ij}f_j^\alpha, \quad B^{\alpha\beta} := a^{ij}f_i^\alpha f_j^\beta, \quad \lambda_\alpha = \cos\angle_{\widetilde{\alpha}}(\widetilde{\beta}^\sharp, e_\alpha),$$

and $\sigma(t)$ is defined by (9.2.15).

Now assume that $\mathcal{D}$ is a connected domain on the plane $\mathcal{P}$ and $f :=\mathcal{D} \to (\mathbb{V}^{n+1}, \widetilde{F})$ is a graph defined on $\mathcal{D}$, which can be locally expressed by (9.2.13). Then we have $f_i^k = \delta_i^k$, $f_i^{n+1} = \partial u/\partial x^i = u_i$. A direct computation gives that

$$a_{ij} = \delta_{ij} + u_i u_j, \quad a^{ij} = \delta^{ij} - \frac{u_i u_j}{W^2}, \quad A^{i\alpha} = B^{i\alpha}, \quad B^{ij} = a^{ij},$$

$$B^{i,n+1} = \frac{u_i}{W^2}, \quad B^{n+1,n+1} = 1 - \frac{1}{W^2}, \quad W^2 := 1 + \sum_i u_i^2. \tag{9.2.21}$$

Put $q := \lambda_{n+1} - \sum_k \lambda_k u_k$. By means of a straightforward computation, we obtain

$$\lambda_\alpha(\delta^{\alpha,n+1} - B^{\alpha,n+1}) = \frac{q}{W^2},$$

$$\lambda_\beta(\delta^{k\beta} - B^{k\beta}) = -q\frac{u_k}{W^2}, \tag{9.2.22}$$

$$\lambda_\delta A^{i\delta} = \lambda_i + q\frac{u_i}{W^2}.$$

Substituting (9.2.21) and (9.2.22) into (9.2.20), we have

$$\sum_{i,j}\left\{\Phi(b^2)\left(\delta_{ij} - \frac{u_i u_j}{W^2}\right) + 2\widetilde{b}^2\Phi'(b^2)\left(\lambda_i + q\frac{u_i}{W^2}\right)\left(\lambda_j + q\frac{u_j}{W^2}\right)\right\}u_{ij} = 0,$$

$$\tag{9.2.23}$$

where

$$\Phi(t) := 2(\sigma(\sqrt{t}))'(\widetilde{b}^2 - t) + \sigma(\sqrt{t}), \quad 0 \le t \le \widetilde{b}^2, \quad u_{ij} := \frac{\partial^2 u}{\partial x^i \partial x^j}, \tag{9.2.24}$$

$\sigma(t)$ is $\sigma_B(t)$ or $\sigma_H(t)$ and " $'$ " denotes the derivative with respect to t.

If the hyperplane $\mathcal{P}$ is orthogonal to $\widetilde{\beta}^\sharp$, then it follows from the choose of the coordinate system in $\mathbb{V}^{n+1}$ that the direction of $\widetilde{\beta}^\sharp$ coincides with that of the $\widetilde{x}^{n+1}$-axis. Thus, $\lambda_1 = \lambda_2 = \cdots = \lambda_n = 0$, $\lambda_{n+1} = 1$, so that the equation (9.2.23) is reduced to

$$\sum_{i,j}\left\{\Phi(b^2)\left(\delta_{ij} - \frac{u_i u_j}{W^2}\right) + 2\widetilde{b}^2\Phi'(b^2)\frac{u_i u_j}{W^4}\right\}u_{ij} = 0, \tag{9.2.25}$$

where Φ is defined by (9.2.24).

From the above, we have already proved the following

Theorem 9.6 ([40]). *Let* $(\mathbb{V}^{n+1}, \widetilde{F})$ *be a special Minkowskian* (α, β)-*space,* $f : \mathcal{D} \to (\mathbb{V}^{n+1}, \widetilde{F})$ *be a graph defined on a connected domain* $\mathcal{D}$ *in hyperplane* $\mathcal{P}$. *Then* f *is BH-minimal or HT-minimal if and only if (9.2.23) holds. Particularly, when* $\mathcal{P}$ *is perpendicular to* $\widetilde{\beta}^\sharp$, *then* f *is BH-minimal or HT-minimal if and only if (9.2.25) holds.*

Remark. The equation of a BH-minimal graph in a 3-dimensional special Minkowski-Randers space was given in [136]. The reference [142] gave equations of the BH-minimal graph and the HT-minimal graph in an n-dimensional special Minkowski-Randers space. The equations (9.2.23) and (9.2.25) are a generalization of these results. In the Euclidean space, these equations are reduced to classical forms.

Now consider the case of $n = 2$. An interesting problem is to discuss surfaces that are both BH-minimal and HT-minimal in a 3-dimensional Minkowski space. Obviously, planes and helicoids generated by a line screwing about the x^3-axis are both BH-minimal and HT-minimal. Note that a surface can be locally considered as a graph defined on a connected domain $\mathcal{D}$ in a coordinate plane $\mathcal{P}$. Without loss of generality, we only need to consider the cases of $\mathcal{P} = \{x^3 = 0\}$ and $\mathcal{P} = \{x^1 = 0\}$.

Suppose that $\Phi'(t)/\Phi(t)$ with respect to the two volume forms is different. For $\mathcal{P} = \{x^3 = 0\}$, by (9.2.25), we have the following system of partial differential equations

$$\begin{cases} u_{11} + u_{22} = 0, \\ u_1^2 u_{11} + u_2^2 u_{22} + 2u_1 u_2 u_{12} = 0. \end{cases} \tag{9.2.26}$$

For $\mathcal{P} = \{x^1 = 0\}$, the problem is equivalent to the case of $\lambda_1 = 1$ and $\lambda_2 = \lambda_3 = 0$ in Theorem 9.5. Thus, by (9.2.23), we obtain the another system of partial differential equations

$$\begin{cases} \sum_{i,j} \left(\delta_{ij} - \dfrac{u_i u_j}{W^2} \right) u_{ij} = 0, \\ u_{11} + \dfrac{u_1^2}{W^4} \sum_{i,j} u_i u_j - \dfrac{2}{W^2} \sum_j u_1 u_j u_{1j} = 0, \end{cases} \tag{9.2.27}$$

where $1 \le i, j \le 2$. Hence, we have the following locally rigidity theorem.

Theorem 9.7 ([142]). *Let* $(\mathbb{V}^3, \widetilde{F} = \widetilde{\alpha}\phi(\widetilde{\beta}/\widetilde{\alpha}))$ *be a special Minkowskian* (α, β)*-space with a coordinate system such that the direction of* $\widetilde{\beta}^\sharp$ *coincides with that of the* x^3*-axis. If* $\Phi'(t)/\Phi(t)$ *is different with respect to* $\sigma_B(t)$ *and* $\sigma_H(t)$*, then in* $(\mathbb{V}^3, \widetilde{F})$ *a connected surface* M *which is both* BH*-minimal and* HT*-minimal must locally be a piece of plane, or up to a translation, a piece of helicoid which is generated by a line screwing about the* x^3*-axis.*

Proof. We firstly consider the system (9.2.26) and introduce the complex coordinate $z = x^1 + ix^2$ with $i := \sqrt{-1}$ in the plane $\mathcal{P} = \{x^3 = 0\}$. Set

$$\frac{\partial}{\partial z} := \frac{1}{2}\left(\frac{\partial}{\partial x^1} - i\frac{\partial}{\partial x^2} \right), \quad \frac{\partial}{\partial \overline{z}} := \frac{1}{2}\left(\frac{\partial}{\partial x^1} + i\frac{\partial}{\partial x^2} \right).$$

Thus, (9.2.26) can be rewritten as

$$u_{z\bar{z}} = 0, \quad u_{zz}u_{\bar{z}}^2 + 2u_{z\bar{z}}u_z u_{\bar{z}} + u_{\bar{z}\bar{z}}u_z^2 = 0.$$

It follows that $\frac{1}{u_z}$ is holomorphic and

$$\left(\frac{1}{u_z}\right)_z = -\left(\frac{1}{u_{\bar{z}}}\right)_{\bar{z}}.$$

Consequently, we have

$$\left(\frac{1}{u_z}\right)_{zz} = \left(\frac{1}{u_z}\right)_{z\bar{z}} = 0,$$

and

$$\left(\frac{1}{u_z}\right)_z = c_1, \quad \bar{c}_1 = -c_1 = \text{complex constant.}$$

If $c_1 = 0$, then u is linear, i.e. M is a plane. If $c_1 \neq 0$, then $u_z = 1/c_1(z+c_2)$ with c_2 be a complex constant. Since u is a real function, there exists constant c_3 such that

$$u = \frac{1}{c_1}\log\frac{z+c_2}{z+c_2} + c_3 \quad \text{or} \quad u = a_1\tan^{-1}\frac{x^2+a_2}{x^1+a_3} + a_4, \qquad (9.2.28)$$

where a_i $(1 \leq i \leq 4)$ are all real constants and $a_1 \neq 0$. This shows that M is a piece of helicoid generated by a line screwing about the x^3-axis.

We now consider (9.2.27) and similarly introduce the complex coordinate $z = x^1 + ix^2$. Thus, (9.2.27) becomes

$$\left(\frac{\partial}{\partial z} - \frac{\partial}{\partial\bar{z}}\right)^2 u = 0,$$

which implies $u_{22} = 0$, that is, there exists smooth functions $c(x^1)$ and $d(x^1)$, such that

$$u = c(x^1)x^2 + d(x^1).$$

Substituting it into the first equation of (9.2.27), we get

$$(1+c^2)c'' = 2c(c')^2, \quad (1+c^2)d'' = 2cc'd',$$

where "$'$" means the differential with respect to x^1. Solving the above equations and substituting the solution into the former one, we can easily see that u is either a linear function or an expression as (9.2.28). Theorem 9.7 is proved. □

Now we consider the BH-minimal graph in a 3-dimensional special Minkowskian (α, β)-space. By (9.2.23), its equation can be reduced to

$$\sum_{i,j} B_{ij}(x, u, \triangledown u) u_{ij} = 0, \tag{9.2.29}$$

where

$$B_{ij}(x, u, \triangledown u) := \left(\delta_{ij} - \frac{u_i u_j}{W^2}\right) + 2\tilde{b}^2 \frac{\tilde{\Phi}'}{\Phi}(b^2)\left(\lambda_i + q\frac{u_i}{W^2}\right)\left(\lambda_j + q\frac{u_j}{W^2}\right),$$

$\sigma(b) = \sigma_B(b)$, $\Phi(t)$ is defined by (9.2.24).

(9.2.29) is a quasi-linear partial differential equation. Put

$$\epsilon := \sup\left\{\epsilon' \in [0, \tilde{b}_0) | \Phi(t) \neq 0, \frac{\Phi'(t)}{\Phi(t)} \geq 0, \forall t \in [0, \epsilon'^2]\right\}. \tag{9.2.30}$$

Lemma 9.4. *For $\tilde{b} \in [0, \epsilon)$, the equation (9.2.29) is an elliptic equation of mean curvature type.*

Proof. Firstly, we claim that $\Phi(t)$ defined by (9.2.24) is smooth at $t \in [0, \tilde{b}^2]$. In fact, since $\phi(s)$ is a smooth function defined in the interval $(-\tilde{b}_0, \tilde{b}_0)$, we need only to prove that $\sigma_B(t)$ is smooth at $t = 0$. Write $\tilde{\phi}(s) := \phi^{-n}(s)$. We take Taylor expansion of $\tilde{\phi}(s)$ on $\tilde{\phi}(s)$ up to arbitrary degree k

$$\tilde{\phi}(s) = a_0 + a_1 s + a_2 s^2 + \cdots + a_k s^k + o(s^k).$$

Substituting the above into the first equation of (9.2.15), we get

$$\sigma_B(t) = \frac{\sqrt{\pi}\Gamma\left(\frac{n-1}{2}\right)}{\Gamma\left(\frac{n}{2}\right)}\left[\tilde{a}_0 + \tilde{a}_2 t + \cdots + \tilde{a}_{2k} t^k + o(t^k)\right]^{-1}.$$

Since $a_0 = \phi^{-n}(0) \neq 0$, $\tilde{a}_0 \neq 0$. Hence, we see that $\sigma_B(t)$ is smooth at $t = 0$.

Next, we claim that (9.2.29) is an equation of mean curvature type. It is enough to prove that (cf. [134]) the following inequality

$$\left(\delta_{ij} - \frac{p_i p_j}{W^2}\right)\xi_i \xi_j \leq B_{ij}(x, z, p)\xi^i \xi^j \leq (1 + C)\left(\delta_{ij} - \frac{p_i p_j}{W^2}\right)\xi^i \xi^j \tag{9.2.31}$$

for any $p \in \mathbb{R}^n, \xi \in \mathbb{R}^n$ and a positive constant $C > 0$, where $W^2 = 1 + |p|^2$.

By (9.2.30), $\Phi'(t)/\Phi(t) \geq 0$ for any $t \in [0, \tilde{b}^2]$ when $\tilde{b} \in [0, \epsilon)$. Thus, the first inequality in (9.2.31) holds. To prove the second inequality, we need only to prove the following

$$\frac{\Phi'}{\Phi}(b^2)\left(\langle \lambda, \xi \rangle + q\frac{\langle p, \xi \rangle}{W^2}\right)^2 \leq C\left(|\xi|^2 - \frac{\langle p, \xi \rangle^2}{W^2}\right)$$

for any $p \in \mathbb{R}^n$, $\xi \in \mathbb{R}^n$ and a positive constant $C > 0$, where $\lambda := (\lambda_1, \cdots, \lambda_n) \in \mathbb{R}^n$, and $q = \lambda_{n+1} - \langle \lambda, p \rangle$.

Notice that $b^2 = \|\beta\|^2 = \widetilde{b}^2(1 - \frac{q^2}{W^2}) \in [0, \widetilde{b}^2]$. Since $\Phi(t)$ is smooth at $t \in [0, \widetilde{b}^2]$, we see that $\frac{\Phi'}{\Phi}(b^2)$ is bounded. So, we need only to prove

$$\left(\langle \lambda, \xi \rangle + q \frac{\langle p, \xi \rangle}{W^2} \right)^2 \le C \left(|\xi|^2 - \frac{\langle p, \xi \rangle^2}{W^2} \right).$$

If $\xi = 0$, the above inequality holds obviously. If $\xi \neq 0$, then, putting $\gamma := \angle_{\widetilde{\alpha}}(\lambda, \xi)$ and $\vartheta := \angle_{\widetilde{\alpha}}(p, \xi)$, we have

$$\frac{\left(\langle \lambda, \xi \rangle + q \frac{\langle p, \xi \rangle}{W^2} \right)^2}{|\xi|^2 - \frac{\langle p, \xi \rangle^2}{W^2}} = \frac{\left(W^2 |\lambda| \cos \gamma + q |p| \cos \vartheta \right)^2}{W^2 (1 + |p|^2 \sin^2 \vartheta)}. \tag{9.2.32}$$

We consider two cases separately.

Case (i). If $\sin \vartheta \neq 0$, then the numerator of the right hand side of (9.2.32) can be controlled by the polynomial of $|p|$ where the degree of $|p|$ is not larger than 4. Whereas the degree of $|p|$ in the denominator equals 4. Thus, (9.2.32) is bounded for $|p| \to \infty$.

Case (ii). If $\sin \vartheta = 0$, then the vector p is parallel to the vector ξ. There are two possibilities. If the vector p has the same direction with the vector ξ, then $\cos \vartheta = 1$ and $q = \lambda_{n+1} - |\lambda| \cdot |p| \cos \gamma$. If p has the opposite direction of ξ, then $\cos \vartheta = -1$ and $q = \lambda_{n+1} + |\lambda| \cdot |p| \cos \gamma$. By a direct computation, the right hand side of (9.2.32) becomes

$$\frac{(W^2 |\lambda| \cos \gamma + q |p| \cos \vartheta)^2}{W^2 (1 + |p|^2 \sin^2 \vartheta)} = \frac{(|\lambda| \cos \gamma + \lambda_{n+1} |p| \cos \vartheta)^2}{1 + |p|^2}.$$

Noting that the degrees of $|p|$ in the denominator and the numerator, the right hand side of the above equation is bounded for $|p| \to \infty$. This completes the proof of the inequality (9.2.31).

By the first inequality of (9.2.31), for any $\xi \neq 0$, we have

$$B_{ij}(x, z, p) \xi^i \xi^j \ge |\xi|^2 - \frac{\langle p, \xi \rangle^2}{W^2} = \frac{|\xi|^2}{W^2}(1 + |p|^2 \sin^2 \vartheta) > 0.$$

Hence, the equation (9.2.29) is elliptic. $\square$

Since the elliptic equation of mean curvature type defined on the whole $\mathbb{R}^2$ has only the trivial solution, i.e., $u(x_1, x_2)$ must be a linear function ([134]). Thus, we have the following Bernstein type theorem.

Theorem 9.8 ([40]). *Let $\widetilde{F} = \widetilde{\alpha}\phi(\widetilde{\beta}/\widetilde{\alpha})$ be a special Minkowskian (α, β)-metric, and $\widetilde{b} := \|\widetilde{\beta}\|_{\widetilde{\alpha}} \in [0, \widetilde{b}_0)$ be the length of $\widetilde{\beta}$ with respect to $\widetilde{\alpha}$ such that $\widetilde{F}$ is a positive definite Finsler metric. Let $\Phi(t)$ and ϵ be defined by (9.2.24) and (9.2.30), respectively. Then, for $\widetilde{b} \in [0, \epsilon)$, any complete BH-minimal graph in $(\mathbb{V}^3, \widetilde{F})$ must be a plane.*

Remark. A similar result on the BH-minimal graph in a 3-dimensional special Minkowski-Randers space was given in [136]. For some non-trivial examples of BH-minimal surfaces in $(\mathbb{V}^3, \widetilde{F})$, readers can refer to the excises of this chapter and [40]. References [135] and [41] provided some rotational minimal (hyper-)surfaces in the special Minkowskian (α, β)-space.

9.3 Harmonic maps

9.3.1 A divergence formula

Let (M, F) be an n-dimensional Finsler manifold. Throughout this section, we shall use the following convention of index ranges unless otherwise stated:

$$i, j, k, l, \cdots = 1, \cdots, n; \quad a, b, c, \cdots = 1, \cdots, n-1; \quad A, B, \cdots = 1, \cdots, 2n-1.$$

Let $\{\omega^i\} = \{\omega^a, \, \omega^n = \omega\}$ be an orthonormal coframe field on $\pi^* T^* M$, and the corresponding Chern connection 1-forms be $\{\omega_j^i\}$. Set $\omega^i = v_j^i dx^j$, $\omega^{n+i} = v_j^i \delta y^j$. It can be proved that $\omega^{n+a} = \omega_n^a$ and $\omega^{2n} \neq \omega_n^n = 0$ ([10]). For simplicity, we write $\bar{a} = n + a$. Thus, $\{\omega^A\} = \{\omega^i, \omega^{\bar{a}}\} = \{\omega^i, \omega_n^a\}$ can be viewed as an orthonormal coframe field on the Riemannian manifold $(SM, \widehat{g})$, whose dual orthonormal frame field is $\{e_A\}$. Denote by D the Levi-Civita connection on the Riemannian manifold $(SM, \widehat{g})$ (cf. §4.1.2). The divergence of any 1-form Ψ on $(SM, \widehat{g})$ is given by

$$\text{div}\Psi = \sum_{A=1}^{2n-1} (D_{e_A}\Psi)(e_A).$$

Lemma 9.5. *The divergence of any 1-form* $\Psi = \sum \Psi_A w^A \in \mathcal{C}(T^* SM)$ *is given by*

$$\text{div}_{\widehat{g}}\Psi = \sum_i \Psi_{i|i} - \sum_a \Psi_a \dot{I}_a + \sum_{\bar{a}} \Psi_{\bar{a};\bar{a}}, \tag{9.3.1}$$

where "|" and ";" denote respectively the horizontal and vertical differentials with respect to the Chern connection, and $\dot{I}_a = I_{a|k}\ell^k$.

Proof. For difference, we write $\theta^A = \omega^A$. Let θ_B^A be the Levi-Civita connection forms with respect to $\widehat{g}$. We have

$$d\theta^A = \theta^B \wedge \theta_B^A, \quad \theta_B^A + \theta_A^B = 0.$$

It follows from [79] that

$$\theta_b^a \equiv \omega_b^a \ (\mathrm{mod} \ \theta^{\bar{a}}), \quad \theta_n^a \equiv 0 \ (\mathrm{mod} \ \theta^{\bar{a}}), \quad \theta_{\bar{b}}^{\bar{a}} = \omega_b^a + \sum_c A_{abc}\theta^{\bar{c}},$$

$$\theta_n^{\bar{a}} \equiv 0 \ (\mathrm{mod} \ \theta^a), \quad \theta_b^{\bar{a}} \equiv -\sum_c \left(A_{abc} - \frac{1}{2}R_{abc} \right)\theta^c + \sum_c P_{abc}\theta^{\bar{c}} \ (\mathrm{mod} \ \theta^n),$$

where $R_{abc} = R_{nabc}$, $P_{abc} = P_{nbc}^a$. Further, we can get

$$\mathrm{div}_{\hat{g}}\Psi = \sum_A (D\Psi_A)(e_A)$$

$$= \sum_a (d\Psi_a - \Psi_b\theta_b^a - \Psi_n\theta_a^n - \Psi_{\bar{b}}\theta_{\bar{a}}^{\bar{b}})(e_a) + (d\Psi_n - \Psi_b\theta_n^b - \Psi_{\bar{b}}\theta_n^{\bar{b}})(e_n)$$

$$+ \sum_{\bar{a}} (d\Psi_{\bar{a}} - \Psi_b\theta_{\bar{a}}^b - \Psi_n\theta_{\bar{a}}^n - \Psi_{\bar{b}}\theta_{\bar{a}}^{\bar{b}})(e_{\bar{a}})$$

$$= \sum_a (d\Psi_a - \Psi_b w_a^b)(e_a) + \sum_{a,b} \Psi_b \left(A_{baa} - \frac{1}{2}R_{baa} \right) + d\Psi_n(e_n)$$

$$+ \sum_a \left(d\Psi_{\bar{a}} - \sum_b \Psi_{\bar{b}}w_a^b \right)(e_{\bar{a}}) + \sum_{a,b}\Psi_b P_{bab} - \sum_{a,b}\Psi_b A_{baa}$$

$$= \sum_i \left(d\Psi_i - \sum_j \Psi_j w_i^j \right)(e_i) + \sum_{a,b}\Psi_b P_{aba} + \sum_{a,b}\left(d\Psi_{\bar{a}} - \Psi_{\bar{b}}w_a^b \right)(e_{\bar{a}}).$$

$$(9.3.2)$$

By the definition of the Chern connection, we have

$$\bigtriangledown \Psi_i = d\Psi_i - \Psi_j w_i^j := \Psi_{i|j}w^j + \Psi_{i;\bar{a}}w^{\bar{a}},$$

$$\bigtriangledown \Psi_{\bar{a}} = d\Psi_{\bar{a}} - \Psi_{\bar{b}}w_a^b := \Psi_{\bar{a}|j}w^j + \Psi_{\bar{a};\bar{b}}w^{\bar{b}}.$$

$$(9.3.3)$$

Inserting (9.3.3) into (9.3.2) and noting that $P_{abc} = -\dot{A}_{abc}$, we complete the proof of Lemma 9.5 immediately. □

In the natural coordinate system, let $\Phi = \sum \Phi_i dx^i + \psi_i \delta y^i \in \mathcal{C}(T^*SM)$. Thus, the divergence of Φ can be expressed as

$$\mathrm{div}_{\hat{g}}\Psi = g^{ij}\left(\Psi_{i|j} - \Psi_i \dot{I}_j + F\frac{\partial \Psi_i}{\partial y^j} \right), \quad \Psi_{i|j} = \frac{\delta \Psi_i}{\delta x^j} - \Gamma_{ij}^k \Psi_k. \quad (9.3.4)$$

Lemma 9.6. *Let (M, F) be a compact Finsler manifold without boundary. For any smooth function f on the sphere bundle SM, we have*

$$\int_{SM} (\ell^H f)dV_{SM} = 0, \quad (9.3.5)$$

where $\ell^H = \ell^i \frac{\delta}{\delta x^i}$ is the horizontal component of the dual vector field of the Hilbert form.

Proof. Let ω be the Hilbert form (§2.3.1). By using (9.3.4), a direct computation gives $\mathrm{div}_{\widehat{g}}(f\omega) = \ell^H f$, which together with Stokes' formula completes the proof. □

In each fibre $T_x M \backslash 0$, there is a natural Riemannian metric $g_{ik} dy^i \otimes dy^k$, which induces a Riemannian metric $\widehat{r}_x = F^{-1} F_{y^i y^k} dy^i \otimes dy^k$ on the sphere fibre $S_x M$, where $\{y^i\}$ can be viewed as the homogenous coordinate on $S_x M$. By virtue of a similar computation, we can obtain the following

Lemma 9.7. *Let* $\alpha = \alpha_i dy^i$ $(\alpha_i y^i = 0)$ *be a 1-form on* $(S_x M, \widehat{r}_x)$. *Then its divergence is given by*

$$\mathrm{div}_{\widehat{r}_x} \alpha = F^2 g^{ik} [\alpha_i]_{y^k} - F g^{ik} \alpha_i I_k. \tag{9.3.5'}$$

Further, we have the following

Lemma 9.8 ([32,54]). *Let* (M, F) *be a Finsler manifold,* ψ *and* ϕ *be smooth functions on* SM. *Then we have*

$$\int_{S_x M} \psi g^{ij} [F^2 \phi]_{y^i y^j} \Omega d\eta = \int_{S_x M} \phi g^{ij} [F^2 \psi]_{y^i y^j} \Omega d\eta. \tag{9.3.6}$$

Particularly,

$$\int_{S_x M} g^{ij} [F^2 \phi]_{y^i y^j} \Omega d\eta = 2n \int_{S_x M} \phi \Omega d\eta. \tag{9.3.6'}$$

Proof. Let $\Delta_{\widehat{r}_x}$ be the Laplacian on $(S_x M, \widehat{r}_x)$. Set $\sqrt{g} = \sqrt{\det(g_{ik})}$, $\alpha = \sqrt{g} I_i \frac{dy^i}{F}$. According to the divergence formula, we have

$$\Delta_{\widehat{r}_x}(\sqrt{g}\phi) = g^{ij} [F^2 \phi]_{y^i y^j} \sqrt{g} + \mathrm{div}_{\widehat{r}_x}(\phi \alpha) - 2n\sqrt{g}\phi.$$

Particularly, $\Delta_{\widehat{r}_x}(\sqrt{g}) = \mathrm{div}_{\widehat{r}_x}(\alpha)$. Thus, one can see

$$\psi g^{ij} [F^2 \phi]_{y^i y^j} \sqrt{g} - \phi g^{ij} [F^2 \psi]_{y^i y^j} \sqrt{g}$$
$$= \psi \Delta_{\widehat{r}_x}(\sqrt{g}\phi) - \phi \Delta_{\widehat{r}_x}(\sqrt{g}\psi) - \langle \psi d\phi, \alpha \rangle + \langle \phi d\psi, \alpha \rangle$$
$$= (\psi \sqrt{g}) \Delta_{\widehat{r}_x} \phi - \phi \Delta_{\widehat{r}_x}(\sqrt{g}\psi) + \psi \phi \, \mathrm{div}_{\widehat{r}_x}(\alpha) + \langle d(\psi \phi), \alpha \rangle.$$

Integrating on both sides of the above equality with respect to the volume element $\frac{\sqrt{g}}{F^n} d\eta$ on $S_x M$, we get the required result immediately. □

9.3.2 Harmonic maps

Let $\phi : (M^n, F) \to (\widetilde{M}^m, \widetilde{F})$ be a smooth map between two (real) Finsler manifolds. If the tangent map $\phi_* = d\phi$ is non-degenerate, i.e. $\ker\phi_* = \{0\}$, then ϕ is said to be *non-degenerate*. For convenience, we use the same letters to denote the same quantities of $(\widetilde{M}, \widetilde{F})$ and (M, F), adding "~" for distinction. For example, their local coordinates can be characterized as $\widetilde{x}$ and x respectively. And also, we use different alphabets to represent their index ranges:

$$1 \le \ i, \ j, \cdots \le n, \quad 1 \le \alpha, \beta, \cdots \le m.$$

For a non-degenerate smooth map ϕ, the *energy density* $e(\phi) : SM \to \mathbb{R}$ of ϕ is defined by

$$e(\phi)(x, y) = \frac{1}{2}|d\phi|_F^2 = \frac{1}{2}g^{ij}(x,y)\phi_i^\alpha \phi_j^\beta \widetilde{g}_{\alpha\beta}(\widetilde{x}, \widetilde{y}), \qquad (9.3.7)$$

where $\phi_i^\alpha = \frac{\partial \phi^\alpha}{\partial x^i}$, $\widetilde{x} = \phi(x)$, $\widetilde{y} = d\phi(y) = \{\widetilde{y}^\alpha\} = \{y^j \phi_j^\alpha\}$, and $\widetilde{g}_{\alpha\beta}$ is the fundamental tensor of $(\widetilde{M}, \widetilde{F})$. The *energy* of ϕ (with the compact support in M) is defined by

$$\begin{aligned}
E(\phi) &= \frac{1}{c_{n-1}} \int_{SM} e(\phi)dV_{SM} \\
&= \frac{1}{2c_{n-1}} \int_{SM} \{g^{ij}\widetilde{g}_{\alpha\beta}\phi_i^\alpha \phi_j^\beta\}dV_{SM} \\
&= \frac{1}{4c_{n-1}} \int_{SM} \{g^{ij}(\widetilde{F}^2)_{y^i y^j}\}dV_{SM} \\
&= \frac{n}{2c_{n-1}} \int_{SM} \frac{\widetilde{F}^2}{F^2}dV_{SM},
\end{aligned} \qquad (9.3.8)$$

where dV_{SM} is expressed by (4.1.4), and (9.3.6′) is used in the last equality. The advantage of the last integral consists in the cancellation of the assumption that ϕ is non-degenerate.

Let v be an arbitrary vector field along ϕ. Construct a variation $\phi_t(x) = \exp_{\phi(x)}(tv(x))$, $t \in (-\epsilon, \epsilon)$, which satisfies $\phi_0 = \phi$ and is non-degenerate for $\epsilon > 0$ small enough. The vector field

$$V(x) = \frac{\partial \phi_t}{\partial t}(x)\Big|_{t=0} := V^\alpha(x)\frac{\partial}{\partial \widetilde{x}^\alpha} = \frac{\partial \phi_t^\alpha}{\partial t}\Big|_{t=0} \frac{\partial}{\partial \widetilde{x}^\alpha} \qquad (9.3.9)$$

is called the *variation vector field* of ϕ. By virtue of the property of the exponential map, one can see that $V(x) = v(x)$.

The variation of the energy $E(\phi)$ is given by

$$\frac{d}{dt}E(\phi(t))\Big|_{t=0} = \frac{n}{2c_{n-1}} \int_{SM} \frac{1}{F^2}\left(\frac{\partial}{\partial t}\widetilde{F}^2(\widetilde{x}, \widetilde{y})\right)\Big|_{t=0} dV_{SM}, \qquad (9.3.10)$$

where $\widetilde{x} = \phi_t(x)$, $\widetilde{y} = d\phi_t(y)$.

It is easy to see that

$$\frac{\partial \widetilde{F}^2}{\partial t}\bigg|_{t=0} = \frac{\partial \widetilde{F}^2}{\partial \widetilde{x}^\alpha}V^\alpha + \frac{\partial \widetilde{F}^2}{\partial \widetilde{y}^\alpha}F\ell^H(v^\alpha).$$

By using Lemmas 9.5-9.8 and $\ell^H(F) = 0$, a direct computation can easily give the following theorem. (See [54], [128].)

Theorem 9.9 ([54, 128]). *Let $\phi : (M, F) \to (\widetilde{M}, \widetilde{F})$ be a non-degenerate smooth map, ϕ_t be a variation of $\phi = \phi_0$, whose variation vector field is $V = \frac{\partial \phi_t}{\partial t}|_{t=0}$. Then the first variation of the energy functional is*

$$\begin{aligned}
\frac{d}{dt}E(\phi(t))|_{t=0} &= -\frac{1}{c_{n-1}}\int_{SM}\langle\tau(\phi), V\rangle_{\widetilde{g}}dV_{SM} \\
&= -\frac{n}{c_{n-1}}\int_{SM}\langle\xi(\phi), V\rangle_{\widetilde{g}}dV_{SM} \\
&= -\frac{n}{c_{n-1}}\int_{SM}\widetilde{\mu}(V)dV_{SM} \\
&= -\int_M \mu_\phi(V)dV_F,
\end{aligned} \qquad (9.3.11)$$

where

$$\begin{aligned}
\xi(\phi) &:= (\widetilde{\nabla}_\ell d\phi)(\ell) = \frac{1}{F^2}\xi^\alpha\frac{\partial}{\partial\widetilde{x}^\alpha}, \\
\xi^\alpha &= \phi_{ij}^\alpha y^i y^j - 2\phi_k^\alpha G^k + 2\widetilde{G}^\alpha, \\
\tau(\phi) &= \tau^\alpha\frac{\partial}{\partial\widetilde{\alpha}^\alpha} := \frac{1}{2}\left(\widetilde{g}^{\alpha\beta}[\widetilde{g}_{\beta\gamma}\xi^\gamma]_{y^i y^j}g^{ij}\right)\frac{\partial}{\partial\widetilde{x}^\alpha}, \\
\widetilde{\mu} &= \frac{1}{F^2}\xi_\alpha d\widetilde{x}^\alpha = \frac{1}{F^2}\xi^\beta\widetilde{g}_{\alpha\beta}d\widetilde{x}^\alpha, \\
\mu_\phi(V) &= \frac{n}{c_{n-1}\sigma_F}\int_{S_xM}\widetilde{\mu}(V)(\det(g_{ij}))d\eta.
\end{aligned} \qquad (9.3.12)$$

Here G^k and $\widetilde{G}^\alpha$ are the spray coefficients of (M, F) and $(\widetilde{M}, \widetilde{F})$, respectively.

Definition 9.4. $\tau(\phi)$ and μ_ϕ in (9.3.12) are called the *tension field* and the *tension form*, respectively. ϕ is said to be *harmonic* if $\mu_\phi = 0$. In this case we have

$$\int_{S_xM}\frac{1}{F^2}\widetilde{g}_{\alpha\beta}(\phi_{ij}^\alpha y^i y^j - 2\phi_k^\alpha G^k + 2\widetilde{G}^\alpha)\Omega d\eta = 0 \qquad (9.3.13)$$

for all β. In particular, ϕ is said to be *totally geodesic* if $\xi(\phi) \equiv 0$ in (9.3.12).

The system (9.3.13) is the Euler-Lagrange equation of the energy functional. Comparing the tensor form with the HT-mean curvature (§9.1.2), we can immediately obtain the following

Proposition 9.4. *An isometric immersion is harmonic if and only if it is HT-minimal.*

Definition 9.5. The *first fundamental form* and the *second fundamental from* of a non-degenerate smooth map $\phi : (M^n, F) \to (\widetilde{M}^m, \widetilde{F})$ are defined respectively by

$$I(\phi) := \phi^* \widetilde{g} = \widetilde{g}_{\alpha\beta}(\phi(x), \phi_*(y))\phi_i^\alpha \phi_j^\beta dx^i \otimes dx^j,$$

$$II(\phi) := {}^b\widetilde{\nabla}^{\phi^{-1}} d\phi = \frac{1}{2}\widetilde{g}^{\alpha\beta}[\widetilde{g}_{\beta\gamma}\xi^\gamma]_{y^i y^j} \frac{\partial}{\partial \widetilde{x}^\alpha} \otimes dx^i \otimes dx^j,$$

where ξ^γ is defined by the second equation of (9.3.12) (see Exercise 5, Chapter 9). Clearly, we have $\tau(\phi) = \text{tr}_g II(\phi)$. If $g = I(\phi)$, then ϕ is an isometric immersion.

It should be remarked that the vanishing tension field $\tau(\phi) = 0$ implies the vanishing tension form $\mu_\phi = 0$. However, the inversion of this statement is not true. Hence, we call ϕ to be *strongly harmonic* if $\tau(\phi) = 0$. If the target manifold $(\widetilde{F}, \widetilde{M})$ is Riemannian, then the condition of non-degeneration of ϕ is not necessary. In this case, the system (9.3.13) is equivalent to the following

$$\int_{S_x M} g^{ij} \left(\phi_{ij}^\alpha - B_{ij}^k \phi_k^\alpha + \widetilde{\Gamma}_{\beta\gamma}^\alpha \phi_i^\beta \phi_j^\gamma \right) \Omega d\eta = 0, \qquad (9.3.14)$$

where $B_{jk}^i = \frac{1}{2}[G^i]_{y^j y^k}$ is the Berwald connection coefficients of F (§3.1.2). X. Mo and Y. Yang studied the solvability of (9.3.14) (cf. [84]).

Theorem 9.10 ([84]). *Let (M, F) be a compact Finsler manifold without boundary, (N, h) a compact Riemannian manifold without boundary. If the sectional curvature of N is non-positive, then any continuous map $\phi : (M, F) \to (N, h)$ is homotopic to a harmonic map with minimizing energy.*

Proof. (i) Set

$$\widetilde{\mathfrak{g}}^{ij}(x) := \frac{\int_{S_x M} g^{ij}(x, y)(\det(g_{kl})) d\eta}{\int_{S_x M} (\det(g_{kl})) d\eta}, \quad (\widetilde{\mathfrak{g}}_{ij}) := (\widetilde{\mathfrak{g}}^{ij})^{-1}. \qquad (9.3.15)$$

It is easy to see that $\widetilde{\mathfrak{g}} = \widetilde{\mathfrak{g}}_{ij}(x) dx^i \otimes dx^j$ is a symmetric positively definite covariant tensor field of the second order. Thus, $(M, \widetilde{\mathfrak{g}})$ can be viewed as a

Riemannian manifold. By (9.3.7) and the first equation of (9.3.8), we have

$$E(\phi) = \frac{1}{2} \int_M \widetilde{\mathfrak{g}}^{ij}(x)\phi_i^\alpha \phi_j^\beta h_{\alpha\beta}(\phi(x))dV_F = \int_M \widetilde{e}(\phi)dV_F,$$

$$dV_F = \sigma_H(x)dx,$$

(9.3.16)

where $\sigma_H(x)$ is defined by (4.1.6), $\widetilde{e}(\phi)$ is the energy density of the map $\widehat{\phi} : (M, \widetilde{\mathfrak{g}}) \to (N, h)$ between two Riemannian manifolds.

(ii) Assume that $n \geq 3$. Take a conformal transformation

$$\widehat{g}_{ij}(x) = \rho^2(x)\widetilde{\mathfrak{g}}_{ij}(x), \quad \rho(x) = \left(\frac{\int_{S_x M}(\det(g_{kl}))d\eta}{c_{n-1}\sqrt{\det(\widetilde{\mathfrak{g}}_{ij}(x))}} \right)^{\frac{1}{n-2}}.$$

We have

$$E(\phi) = \frac{1}{2} \int_M \widehat{g}^{ij}(x)\phi_i^\alpha \phi_j^\beta h_{\alpha\beta}(\phi(x))\sqrt{\det(\widehat{g}_{kl}(x))}\, dx = E(\widehat{\phi}),$$

which is exactly the energy of the map $\widehat{\phi} : (M, \widehat{g}) \to (N, h)$ between Riemannian Manifolds $(M, \widehat{g})$ and (N, h). Thus, $E(\phi)$ and $E(\widehat{g})$ have the same critical point. Hence, by means of the well-known Eells-Sampson theorem ([48]), we can finish the proof.

(iii) For $n = 2$, we can discuss (9.3.14) directly by using the heat flow method. According to Nash's embedding theorem, we can assume that $i : (N, h) \hookrightarrow \mathbb{R}^k$ is an isometric embedding to the Euclidean space. Let $\psi = i \circ \phi : M \to \mathbb{R}^K$, whose image lies on N. Denote A_ψ the second fundamental form of $i : (N, h) \hookrightarrow \mathbb{R}^k$. Thus, considering the Euler-Lagrange equation of harmonic map between Riemannian manifolds, we have similarly([102])

$$\Delta_\sigma \psi - \mathrm{tr}_{\widetilde{\mathfrak{g}}} A_\psi(d\psi, d\psi) = 0,$$

(9.3.17)

where

$$\Delta_\sigma := \frac{1}{\sigma_H} \frac{\partial}{\partial x^i} \left(\sigma_H \widetilde{\mathfrak{g}}^{ij} \frac{\partial}{\partial x^j} \right).$$

By the equation (9.3.17), we consider the following heat equation

$$\frac{\partial \psi}{\partial t} = \Delta_\sigma \psi - \mathrm{tr}_{\widetilde{\mathfrak{g}}} A_\psi(d\psi, d\psi).$$

This heat flow method of harmonic maps began with J. Eells-J. H. Sampson's famous work [48]. A complete systematic lecture about it was given in [102]. Hence, for the above heat equation, readers can see [84] for details, and we do not repeat it any more here. $\qquad\square$

Some examples of Finsler harmonic maps are as follows.

Example 9.2. Let $M = \mathbb{R}$ and $(\widetilde{M}, \widetilde{F})$ be an arbitrary Finsler manifold. Noting that $\widetilde{C}_{\alpha\beta\gamma}\widetilde{y}^\gamma = 0$, the vanishing tension field is equivalent to

$$\frac{d^2\phi^\alpha}{dt^2} + \widetilde{\Gamma}^\alpha_{\beta\gamma}\frac{d\phi^\beta}{dt}\frac{d\phi^\gamma}{dt} = 0,$$

which is exactly the geodesic equation in $(\widetilde{M}, \widetilde{F})$.

If (M, F) is an arbitrary Finsler manifold and $\widetilde{M} = \mathbb{R}$, then (9.3.17) becomes

$$\Delta_\sigma\phi = 0.$$

It can be viewed as the equation of the harmonic function ϕ on (M, F).

Example 9.3. Let (M, h) be a flat Riemannian manifold, (M, F) be a Finsler structure on (M, h), where F is a locally Minkowski metric. Consider the identity maps $\mathcal{I} : (M, F) \to (M, h)$ and $\mathcal{I} : (M, h) \to (M, F)$. In the local coordinate system $\{x^i\}$ on M, the identity map $\mathcal{I}$ can be locally expressed as

$$\mathcal{I}^i(x) = x^i, \quad \mathcal{I}^i_j = \delta^i_j, \quad \mathcal{I}^i_{jk} = 0.$$

Since F is locally Minkowski metric, by §3.1, we can see that

$$\gamma^i_{jk} = 0, \quad G^i = \gamma^i_{jk}y^jy^k = 0, \quad N^i_j = \frac{1}{2}[G^i]_{y^j} = 0.$$

$$\Gamma^i_{jk} = 0, \quad \dot{A}_{ijk} = -\frac{1}{4}y_l[G^l]_{y^iy^jy^k} = 0, \quad A_{ijk} = FC_{ijk}.$$

On the other hand, since h is flat Riemannian metric, the above equations hold in (M, h). By (9.3.12), the identity maps $\mathcal{I} : (M, F) \to (M, h)$ and $\mathcal{I} : (M, h) \to (M, F)$ are (strongly) harmonic maps.

Example 9.4. Let $(M, F = \alpha + \beta)$ be a Randers manifold, where β is parallel with respect to the Riemannian metric α. Consider the identity maps $\mathcal{I} : (M, F) \to (M, \alpha)$ and $\mathcal{I} : (M, \alpha) \to (M, F)$. By (9.3.12), a direct computation gives

$$\tau(\mathcal{I})^i = \frac{1}{2}g^{jk}[{}^\alpha G^i - {}^F G^i]_{y^jy^k},$$

where ${}^\alpha G^i$ and ${}^F G^i$ are spray coefficients of α and $F = \alpha + \beta$, respectively. Since β is parallel with respect to α, F is a Berwald metric (cf. §3.1.2). Hence, ${}^F G^i = {}^\alpha G^i$. Then, $\tau(\mathcal{I})^i = 0$. So, the identity maps $\mathcal{I} : (M, F) \to (M, \alpha)$ and $\mathcal{I} : (M, \alpha) \to (M, F)$ are (strongly) harmonic maps.

9.3.3 Composition maps

Let $\phi_1 : (M, F) \to (\overline{M}, \overline{F})$ and $\phi_2 : (\overline{M}, \overline{F}) \to (\widetilde{M}, \widetilde{F})$ be two non-degenerate smooth maps between Finsler manifolds. Denote by $\psi = \phi_2 \circ \phi_1 : (M, F) \to (\widetilde{M}, \widetilde{F})$ the composition map. Here the ranges of various indices are as follows:

$$1 \le i, j, \cdots \le n; \quad 1 \le a, b, \cdots \le l; \quad 1 \le \alpha, \beta, \cdots \le m.$$

By using the chain rule of the differential and noting that $\nabla_{\ell H} \ell = 0$ where ℓ is the corresponding vector field of the Hilbert form (see §2.3.1), we have

$$
\begin{aligned}
{}^b \widetilde{\nabla}^{\psi^{-1}} d(\psi)(\ell, \ell) &= \nabla_{\ell H}[d(\phi_2 \circ \phi_1)\ell] = \nabla_{\ell H}[d\phi_2 \circ d\phi_1 \ell] \\
&= (\nabla_{d\phi_1 \ell} d\phi_2) d\phi_1 \ell + d\phi_2(\nabla_{\ell H} d\phi_1 \ell) \\
&= \frac{\overline{F}^2}{F^2} {}^b \widetilde{\nabla}^{\phi_2^{-1}} d\phi_2(\overline{\ell}, \overline{\ell}) + d\phi_2(\xi(\phi_1)).
\end{aligned}
$$

It follows (cf. (9.3.12)) that

$$\xi(\phi_2 \circ \phi_1) = \frac{\overline{F}^2}{F^2} \xi(\phi_2) + d\phi_2(\xi(\phi_1)). \tag{9.3.18}$$

Integrating the above on $S_x M$ gives that

$$\mu_{\phi_2 \circ \phi_1}(V) = \frac{n}{c_{n-1}\sigma_H} \int_{S_x M} \left\{ \frac{\overline{F}^2}{F^2} \widetilde{\mu}_{\phi_2}(V) + \widetilde{g}(d\phi_2(\xi(\phi_1)), V) \right\} \Omega d\eta, \tag{9.3.19}$$

where $V \in \mathcal{C}((\phi_1 \circ \phi_2)^{-1} T\widetilde{M})$. Thus, we have the following

Proposition 9.5. *Let* $\phi_1 : (M, F) \to (\overline{M}, \overline{F})$ *and* $\phi_2 : (\overline{M}, \overline{F}) \to (\widetilde{M}, \widetilde{F})$ *be two non-degenerate smooth maps. Assume that* ϕ_2 *is totally geodesic and* $d\phi_2 \circ \overline{C} = \widetilde{C} \circ d\phi_2$. *Then,*
(i) If ϕ_1 *is strongly harmonic, then* $\phi_2 \circ \phi_1$ *is also strongly harmonic;*
(ii) If ϕ_1 *is harmonic, then* $\phi_2 \circ \phi_1$ *is also harmonic.*

Proof. Let $\{x^i\}, \{\overline{x}^a\}$ and $\{\widetilde{x}^\alpha\}$ be local coordinate systems of (M, F), $(\overline{M}, \overline{F})$ and $(\widetilde{M}, \widetilde{F})$, respectively. From (9.3.18) we have

$$\xi_\alpha(\phi_2 \circ \phi_1) = \xi_\alpha(\phi_2) + \widetilde{g}_{\alpha\beta}(\phi_2)^\beta_\alpha \overline{g}^{ab} \xi_b(\phi_1).$$

Since ϕ_2 satisfies $d\phi_2 \circ \overline{C} = \widetilde{C} \circ d\phi_2$, i.e., $(\phi_2)^\alpha_a \overline{C}^a_{bc} = \widetilde{C}^\alpha_{\beta\gamma}(\phi_2)^\beta_b(\phi_2)^\gamma_c$, so $\widetilde{g}_{\alpha\beta}(\phi_2)^\beta_a \overline{g}^{ab}$ is independent of $\overline{y}$. Hence we get (see (9.3.12))

$$\tau_\alpha(\phi_2 \circ \phi_1) = \frac{1}{2} g^{ij}[\xi_\alpha(\phi_2 \circ \phi_1)]_{y^i y^j} + \widetilde{g}_{\alpha\beta}(\phi_2)^\beta_a \overline{g}^{ab} \tau_b(\phi_1).$$

Since $\xi(\phi_2) = 0$ (totally geodesic), that $\tau(\phi_1) = 0$ means that $\tau(\phi_2 \circ \phi_1) = 0$. Integrating both sides of the above equation gives that

$$\mu_\alpha(\phi_2 \circ \phi_1) = \widetilde{g}_{\alpha\beta}(\phi_2)_a^\beta \overline{g}^{ab}\mu_b(\phi_1).$$

This completes the proof. $\qquad\qquad\qquad\qquad\qquad\qquad\qquad\qquad\square$

Assume that $f : (M, F) \to (\widetilde{M}, \widetilde{F})$ is an isometric immersion, where $(\pi^*TM)^\perp$ is the orthogonal complement of π^*TM in $\pi^*(f^{-1}T\widetilde{M})$ with respect to $\widetilde{g}$. Set

$$\nu(M) = \{\widetilde{\theta} \in \mathcal{C}(f^{-1}T^*M)|\widetilde{\theta}(df(X)) = 0, \forall X \in \mathcal{C}(TM)\},$$

which is the normal bundle of f ([106]). It is easy to see that $\xi(f)$, $\tau(f) \in \mathcal{C}(\pi^*TM)^\perp$, $\mu(f) \in \nu(M)$.

Proposition 9.6 (55). *Let* $\phi : (M, F) \to (\overline{M}, \overline{F})$ *be a non-degenerate smooth map,* $\psi : (\overline{M}, \overline{F}) \to (\widetilde{M}, \widetilde{F})$ *be an isometric immersion. Then*

(i) ϕ *is harmonic if and only if* $\mu(\phi \circ \psi)$ *lies in the normal bundle* $\nu(\overline{M})$ *of* ψ;

(ii) ϕ *is strongly harmonic if and only if* $\tau(\phi \circ \psi)$ *lies in* $\mathcal{C}(\pi^*T(\overline{M}))^\perp$ *of* ψ.

Proof. By (9.3.19), we have

$$\mu_{\psi \circ \phi}(d\psi(X)) = \frac{1}{c_{n-1}\sigma_H} \int_{S_{(x)}M} \left\{ \frac{\overline{F}^2}{F^2}\widetilde{\mu}_\psi(d\psi X) + \widetilde{g}(d\psi\xi(\phi), d\psi X) \right\} \Omega d\eta$$

$$= \frac{1}{c_{n-1}\sigma_H} \int_{S_x M} \overline{g}(\xi(\phi), X)\Omega d\eta$$

$$= \mu_\phi(X)$$

for any $X \in \mathcal{C}(\phi^*T\overline{M})$. It implies that the condition that $\mu_\phi = 0$ is equivalent to that $\mu_{\psi \circ \phi} \in \nu(\overline{M})$. Thus, (i) is proved. On the other hand, by (9.3.18), we have

$$\widetilde{g}(\xi(\psi \circ \phi), d\psi X) = \widetilde{g}\left(\frac{\overline{F}^2}{F^2}\xi(\psi) + d\psi\xi(\phi), d\psi X\right) = \overline{g}(\xi(\phi), X)$$

for any $X \in \mathcal{C}(\phi^*T\overline{M})$. Thus,

$$\widetilde{g}(\tau(\psi \circ \phi), d\psi X) = \overline{g}(\tau(\phi), X).$$

This is (ii). $\qquad\qquad\qquad\qquad\qquad\qquad\qquad\qquad\qquad\qquad\square$

A direct corollary is the following

Corollary 9.2. *Let* $(\mathbb{V}^{n+1}, \widetilde{F})$ *be a Minkowski space, and* $i : \mathbb{S}^n \to \mathbb{V}^{n+1}$ *be a standard inclusive map of the Euclidean sphere. Then there is an isometric immersion* $i : (\mathbb{S}^n, i^*\widetilde{F}) \to (\mathbb{V}^{n+1}, \widetilde{F})$. *Suppose that* (M, F) *is an arbitrary Finsler manifold. Then the non-degenerate map* $\phi : (M, F) \to (\mathbb{S}^n, i^*\widetilde{F})$ *is harmonic if and only if there exists a function* $\lambda : M \to \mathbb{R}$ *such that*

$$\mu_\Phi = \lambda\phi,$$

where $\Phi = i \circ \phi$.

Remark. Corollary 9.2 can be viewed as a generalization of Takahashi's theorem (cf. [169]) on minimal submanifolds in the Euclidean sphere in the geometry of Riemannian submanifolds.

Let U be an open set in a Finsler manifold (M, F), $f : U \to \mathbb{R}$ a function on U. If $\xi(f) \geq 0$ on SU everywhere, then f is said to be *convex*.

Proposition 9.7 ([55]). *A non-degenerate smooth map* $\phi : (M, F) \to (\widetilde{M}, \widetilde{F})$ *is totally geodesic if and only if it carries germs of convex functions to germs of convex functions.*

Proof. For a function f on an open set $\widetilde{U}$ in $\widetilde{M}$, by (9.3.18), we have

$$\xi(f \circ \phi) = \frac{\widetilde{F}^2}{F^2}\xi(f) + df(\xi(\phi)).$$

If ϕ is totally geodesic, then $\xi(\phi) = 0$. Thus, the condition that $\xi(f) \geq 0$ on $S\widetilde{U}$ is equivalent to that $\xi(f \circ \phi) \geq 0$ on $S\phi^{-1}(\widetilde{U})$.

Conversely, if ϕ carries germs of convex functions to germs of convex functions, then we claim that ϕ is totally geodesic. We use reductio ad absurdum. Suppose that $\xi(\phi)(x_0, y_0) = w \neq 0$ at a point $(x_0, y_0) \in SU \subset SM$. Let $\widetilde{x}_0 = \phi(x_0)$, $\widetilde{y}_0 = d\phi(y_0)$. We can choose a local coordinate system $\{\widetilde{x}^\alpha\}$ near $\widetilde{x}_0$ such that $\widetilde{G}^\alpha(\widetilde{x}_0, [\widetilde{y}_0]) = 0$. Define a function

$$f = b_\alpha \widetilde{x}^\alpha + \frac{1}{2}\sum(\widetilde{x}^\alpha)^2,$$

where $\{b_\alpha\}$ satisfies

$$b_\alpha w^\alpha < -\frac{\widetilde{F}^2}{F^2}|_{(\widetilde{x}_0, \widetilde{y}_0)}\sum(\widetilde{y}_0^\alpha)^2, \quad w^\alpha = d\widetilde{x}^\alpha(w).$$

Then we have

$$\xi(f)|_{(\widetilde{x}_0, [\widetilde{y}_0])} = \sum(\widetilde{y}_0^\alpha)^2,$$

which means that f is a convex function near $\widetilde{x}_0$. However, we also have

$$\xi(f \circ \phi)|_{(\widetilde{x}_0, \widetilde{y}_0)} = \left[\frac{\widetilde{F}^2}{F^2} \xi(f) + df(w) \right]$$

$$= \frac{\widetilde{F}^2}{F^2}|_{(\widetilde{x}_0, \widetilde{y}_0)} \sum (\widetilde{y}_0^\alpha)^2 + b_\alpha w^\alpha < 0.$$

This contradicts to our assumption. ∎

9.4   Second variation of harmonic maps

9.4.1   The second variation

With the same notations as in Theorem 9.8, we let $V_t := \frac{\partial \phi_t}{\partial t}$. Using $\widetilde{G}^\alpha = \widetilde{N}_\sigma^\alpha \widetilde{y}^\sigma$ and $[\widetilde{G}^\alpha]_{\widetilde{y}^\sigma} = 2\widetilde{N}_\sigma^\alpha$, we have

$$\frac{\partial}{\partial t}[\widetilde{\mu}_t(V_t)]_{t=0} = \frac{\partial}{\partial t}\left[\frac{1}{F_t^2} \widetilde{g}_{t\alpha\beta} V_t^\alpha \xi_t^\beta \right]_{t=0}$$

$$= \frac{1}{F^2}\left\{ (\widetilde{g}_{\alpha\lambda}\Gamma_{\beta\gamma}^\lambda V^\gamma + \widetilde{g}_{\beta\lambda}\Gamma_{\alpha\gamma}^\lambda V^\gamma + 2\widetilde{C}_{\alpha\beta\gamma}W^\gamma)V^\alpha \xi^\beta + \widetilde{g}_{\alpha\beta}\xi^\beta \frac{\partial V_t^\alpha}{\partial t}\Big|_{t=0} \right\}$$

$$+ \frac{1}{F^2}\widetilde{g}_{\alpha\beta}V^\alpha \left\{ V_{kj}^\beta y^k y^j - V_k^\beta G^k + V^\sigma[\widetilde{N}_\gamma^\beta]_{\widetilde{x}_\sigma} \widetilde{y}^\gamma + 2F\widetilde{N}_\sigma^\beta W^\sigma - 2\widetilde{N}_\lambda^\beta \widetilde{N}_\sigma^\lambda V^\sigma \right\},$$
$$(9.4.1)$$

where

$$W = \widetilde{\nabla}_\ell V = \left([V^\alpha]_{x^i} \ell^i + \frac{1}{F}V^\sigma \widetilde{N}_\sigma^\alpha \right) \frac{\partial}{\partial \widetilde{x}^\alpha}.$$

On the other hand, by (9.3.12) and $[\widetilde{N}_\beta^\alpha]_{\widetilde{y}^\sigma} = \widetilde{B}_{\beta\sigma}^\alpha$, we have

$$\widetilde{\nabla}_{y^H}\widetilde{\nabla}_y V = \widetilde{\nabla}_{y^H}(FW)$$

$$= \left\{ \frac{\delta}{\delta x^k}[V_j^\beta y^j + V^\sigma \widetilde{N}_\sigma^\beta]y^k + F\widetilde{N}_\sigma^\beta W^\sigma \right\} \frac{\partial}{\partial \widetilde{x}^\beta}$$

$$= \{ V_{kj}^\beta y^k y^j - V_k^\beta G^k + V^\sigma[\widetilde{N}_\sigma^\beta]_{\widetilde{x}^\gamma} \widetilde{y}^\gamma + 2F\widetilde{N}_\sigma^\beta W^\sigma $$
$$(9.4.2)$$
$$- \widetilde{N}_\lambda^\beta \widetilde{N}_\sigma^\lambda V^\sigma + \widetilde{B}_{\alpha\gamma}^\beta V^\alpha(\xi^\gamma - \widetilde{G}^\gamma) \} \frac{\partial}{\partial \widetilde{x}^\beta}.$$

The flag curvature tensor and Landsberg curvature tensor can be expressed as follows

$$\widetilde{F}^2 \widetilde{R}_\beta^\alpha = [\widetilde{N}_\gamma^\alpha]_{\widetilde{x}^\beta} \widetilde{y}^\gamma - [\widetilde{N}_\beta^\alpha]_{\widetilde{x}^\gamma} \widetilde{y}^\gamma - \widetilde{N}_\lambda^\alpha \widetilde{N}_\beta^\lambda + \widetilde{B}_{\beta\gamma}^\alpha \widetilde{G}^\gamma, \quad \widetilde{P}_{\beta\gamma}^\alpha = -\dot{\widetilde{A}}_{\beta\gamma}^\alpha. \quad (9.4.3)$$

Combining (9.4.1)-(9.4.3), we obtain

$$\frac{\partial}{\partial t}\left[\tilde{\mu}_t(V_t)\right]_{t=0} = \tilde{\mu}(U) + \langle \tilde{\nabla}_{\ell^H}\tilde{\nabla}_\ell V, V\rangle$$

$$+ \left\langle \frac{\tilde{F}^2}{F^2}\tilde{\mathfrak{R}}(V) + \tilde{\mathfrak{P}}(V,\xi), V \right\rangle + 2F\tilde{C}(V,\xi,\tilde{\nabla}_\ell V), \tag{9.4.4}$$

where $\tilde{\mathfrak{R}} = \tilde{R}^\alpha_\beta d\tilde{x}^\beta \otimes \frac{\partial}{\partial \tilde{x}^\alpha}$ and $\tilde{\mathfrak{P}} = \tilde{P}^\alpha_{\beta\gamma} d\tilde{x}^\beta \otimes d\tilde{x}^\gamma \otimes \frac{\partial}{\partial \tilde{x}^\alpha}$ are the flag curvature tensor and Landsberg curvature tensor respectively of $(\widetilde{M},\tilde{F})$, $\tilde{C}$ is Cartan tensor, and

$$U := \left(\tilde{\nabla}_{\frac{\partial}{\partial t}}\frac{\partial \phi}{\partial t}\right)\Big|_{t=0}.$$

Using the Hilbert form ω, we construct a 1-form $\theta := \langle V, W\rangle_{\tilde{g}}\omega$. Then

$$\langle \tilde{\nabla}_{\ell^H}\tilde{\nabla}_\ell V, V\rangle_{\tilde{g}} = \operatorname{div}\theta - \|W\|^2 - 2F\tilde{C}(V,W,\xi).$$

In summary, we have proved the following theorem.

Theorem 9.11 ([54]). *Let* $\phi : (M,F) \to (\widetilde{M},\tilde{F})$ *be a non-degenerate smooth map,* ϕ_t *be a variation of* $\phi = \phi_0$. *Let* $V = \frac{\partial\phi_t}{\partial t}\big|_{t=0}$ *and* $U = (\tilde{\nabla}_{\frac{\partial}{\partial t}}\frac{\partial\phi}{\partial t})|_{t=0}$. *Then the second variation of the energy functional for* ϕ *is given by*

$$I_\phi(V,V) = \frac{d^2}{dt^2}E(\phi_t)|_{t=0}$$

$$= \frac{-n}{c_{n-1}}\int_{SM}\left\{\tilde{\mu}(U) - \|\tilde{\nabla}_\ell V\|^2 + \left\langle\frac{\tilde{F}^2}{F^2}\tilde{\mathfrak{R}}(V) + \tilde{\mathfrak{P}}(V,\xi), V\right\rangle\right\}dV_{SM}$$

$$= \frac{-n}{c_{n-1}}\int_{SM}\left\{\tilde{\mu}(U) + \left\langle\tilde{\nabla}_{\ell^H}\tilde{\nabla}_\ell V + \frac{\tilde{F}^2}{F^2}\tilde{\mathfrak{R}}(V)\right.\right.$$

$$\left.\left. + \tilde{\mathfrak{P}}(V,\xi) + 2F\tilde{C}(\xi,\tilde{\nabla}_\ell V), V\right\rangle\right\}dV_{SM}, \tag{9.4.5}$$

where $\tilde{\mathfrak{R}}$, $\tilde{\mathfrak{P}}$ *and* $\tilde{C}$ *are the flag curvature tensor, Landsberg curvature tensor and Cartan tensor of* $(\widetilde{M},\tilde{F})$, *respectively.*

In particular, if the target manifold is Riemannian and ϕ is harmonic, then the equation (9.4.5) is reduced to ([128])

$$I_\phi(V,V) = \frac{1}{c_{n-1}}\int_{SM}\{\|\tilde{\nabla}V\|^2 + \operatorname{tr}\langle\tilde{R}(d\phi,V)d\phi, V\rangle_{\tilde{g}}\}dV_{SM}, \tag{9.4.6}$$

where $\tilde{R}$ is the Riemannian curvature tensor of $(\widetilde{M},\tilde{g})$.

Definition 9.6. If the second variation of a harmonic map $\phi : (M, F) \to (\widetilde{M}, \widetilde{F})$ is non-negative, then the map is called a *stable harmonic map*.

If the target manifold is Riemannian, then the previous computation still holds for a degenerate ϕ. Hence by (9.4.6), we have

Theorem 9.12 ([128]). *Any stable harmonic map from a compact Finsler manifold without boundary to an Euclidean sphere $\mathbb{S}^m$ ($m > 2$) is a constant map.*

Remark. The standard sphere in the above theorem can be replaced by a super-strongly stable manifold ([126]).

For a harmonic map ϕ, if we take $V = d\phi(X)$, $X \in C(TM)$ as the variation vector field, then by (9.3.12), we get ([54])

$$
\begin{aligned}
\int_{SM} \widetilde{\mu}(U)d\mu_{SM} &= \int_{SM} \widetilde{\mu}\left(\widetilde{\nabla}_X(d\phi X)\right) dV_{SM} \\
&= \int_{SM} \left\{ X^H\left[\widetilde{\mu}(d\phi X)\right] - (\widetilde{\nabla}_{X^H}\widetilde{g})(\xi, d\phi X) - \widetilde{g}(\widetilde{\nabla}_{X^H}\xi, d\phi X)\right\} dV_{SM} \\
&= \int_{SM} \left\{ \operatorname{div}\left[\widetilde{\mu}(d\phi X)X\right] - \widetilde{\mu}\left[(\operatorname{div}X)d\phi X\right] \right\} dV_{SM} \\
&\quad - \int_{SM} \left\{ 2F\widetilde{C}(\xi, d\phi X, (\widetilde{\nabla}_\ell d\phi)(X)) + \widetilde{g}(\widetilde{\nabla}_{X^H}\xi, d\phi X)\right\} dV_{SM} \\
&= \int_{SM} \left\{ -2F\widetilde{C}(\xi, d\phi X, \widetilde{\nabla}_\ell(d\phi X)) - \widetilde{g}(\widetilde{\nabla}_{X^H}\xi, d\phi X)\right\} dV_{SM}. \quad (9.4.7)
\end{aligned}
$$

Let M^n be a compact submanifold without boundary in an Euclidean space $\mathbb{R}^{n+p}$, $\{e_i\}$ and $\{e_\alpha\}$ ($\alpha = n+1, \ldots, n+p$) be the local bases of the tangent bundle and the normal bundle, respectively. Let $A_\alpha = A_{e_\alpha}$ be the shape operator, a be a constant vector field in $\mathbb{R}^{n+p}$. Put $a = a^T + a^N$, where $a^T = \langle a, e_i \rangle e_i$, $a^N = \langle a, e_\alpha \rangle e_\alpha$. Then by (9.4.7), the second variation formula (9.4.5) can be reduced to

$$
\begin{aligned}
I_\phi(d\phi X, d\phi X) = \frac{-n}{c_{n-1}} \int_{SM} &\{\widetilde{g}(2(\nabla_\ell d\phi)(A_{a^N}\ell) + d\phi\nabla_{\ell^H}(A_{a^N}\ell) \\
&+ g(A_\alpha\ell, \ell)A_\alpha X - g(A_\alpha\ell, X)A_\alpha\ell, d\phi X)\}dV_{SM}.
\end{aligned} \quad (9.4.8)
$$

According to (9.4.8) and the fact that $\mathbb{S}^n$ is a totally umbilical hypersurface in $\mathbb{R}^{n+1}$, we can get the following

Theorem 9.13 ([54]). *There is no non-degenerate stable harmonic map from a sphere $\mathbb{S}^n$ ($n > 2$) to any Finsler manifold.*

Recall that a non-degenerate map $\phi : (M, F) \to (\widetilde{M}, \widetilde{F})$ is called totally geodesic if ${}^b\widetilde{\nabla}d\phi \equiv 0$, that is, $\xi \equiv 0$. From (9.4.5), we obtain the following

Proposition 9.8. *Any totally geodesic map from a compact Finsler manifold (M, F) to a Finsler manifold with non-positive flag curvature is a stable harmonic map.*

When $(\widetilde{M}, \widetilde{F})$ is a Berwald manifold, $\widetilde{P} = 0$. In this case, (9.4.5) is reduced to

$$\frac{d^2}{dt^2}E(\phi_t)|_{t=0} = \frac{n}{c_{n-1}} \int_{SM} \left(-\widetilde{\mu}(U) + ||\widetilde{\nabla}_l V||^2 - \left\langle \frac{\widetilde{F}^2}{F^2}\widetilde{\mathfrak{R}}(V), V \right\rangle \right) dV_{SM}.$$
(9.4.9)

By (9.4.9), we have

Proposition 9.9. *Any harmonic map from a compact Finsler manifold (M, F) to a Berwald manifold with non-positive flag curvature is stable.*

9.4.2 Stress-energy tensor

Let $\phi : (M, F) \to (\widetilde{M}, \widetilde{F})$ be a non-degenerate smooth map, the *stress-energy tensor S_ϕ* of ϕ is defined by

$$S_\phi := e(\phi)g - \phi^*\widetilde{g},$$
(9.4.10)

where $e(\phi)$ is the energy density, g and $\widetilde{g}$ are the fundamental tensors of F and $\widetilde{F}$, respectively. If $\mathrm{div}S_\phi = 0$ on M, then S_ϕ is said to be *conservative*.

Lemma 9.9. *Let $\phi : (M, F) \to (\widetilde{M}, \widetilde{F})$ be a non-degenerate smooth map. For any $X \in C(\pi^*TM)$, we have*

$$\mathrm{div}S_\phi(X) = -\widetilde{g}(\tau(\phi), d\phi X) - e(\phi)\dot{\eta}(X) + \mathrm{tr}\widetilde{A}(d\phi, d\phi, (\widetilde{\nabla}_{l^H}d\phi)X)$$
$$+ F^2\mathrm{tr}\widetilde{C}(d\phi, d\phi, d\phi X, \widetilde{\tau}) + 2\mathrm{tr}\widetilde{A}(d\phi X, d\phi, (\widetilde{\nabla}_{l^H}d\phi))$$
$$+ \mathrm{tr}\widetilde{L}(d\phi, d\phi, d\phi X),$$
(9.4.11)

where $\widetilde{C} = \widetilde{C}_{\alpha\beta\gamma\sigma}d\widetilde{x}^\alpha \otimes d\widetilde{x}^\beta \otimes d\widetilde{x}^\gamma \otimes d\widetilde{x}^\sigma$, $\widetilde{C}_{\alpha\beta\gamma\sigma} = \frac{\partial^2\widetilde{g}_{\alpha\beta}}{\partial\widetilde{y}^\gamma\partial\widetilde{y}^\sigma}$, $\widetilde{A} = \widetilde{F}\widetilde{C}$.

Proof. By the definition of divergence, we have

$$\mathrm{div}S_\phi(X) = g^{ij}({}^c\nabla_{\delta_i}S_\phi)(\partial_j, X) - S_\phi(\dot{\eta}^*, X)$$
$$= g^{ij}\{\delta_i(e(\phi)g(\partial_j, X) - \widetilde{g}(d\phi\partial_j, d\phi X)) - S_\phi({}^c\nabla_{\delta_i}\partial_j, X)$$
$$- S_\phi(\partial_j, {}^c\nabla_{\delta_i}X)\} - S_\phi(\dot{\eta}^*, X)$$
$$= \mathrm{tr}\widetilde{A}(d\phi, d\phi, (\widetilde{\nabla}_{l^H}d\phi)X) - \widetilde{g}(\mathrm{tr}^c\widetilde{\nabla}d\phi, d\phi X)$$
$$- 2\mathrm{tr}\widetilde{A}(d\phi, d\phi X, \widetilde{\nabla}_{l^H}d\phi) - S_\phi(\dot{\eta}^*, X),$$

where $\delta_i := \frac{\delta}{\delta x^i}$, $\eta := F\mathbf{I}$, η^* is the dual vector field of η.

Let $\widetilde{C}^\alpha_{\beta\gamma\sigma} = \widetilde{g}^{\alpha\lambda}\widetilde{C}_{\lambda\beta\gamma\sigma}$, $\widetilde{C}^\sharp = \widetilde{C}^\alpha_{\beta\gamma\sigma}\frac{\partial}{\partial\widetilde{x}^\alpha}\otimes d\widetilde{x}^\beta\otimes d\widetilde{x}^\gamma\otimes d\widetilde{x}^\sigma$, by (9.3.12), we obtain

$$\tau(\phi) = \mathrm{tr}^b\widetilde{\nabla}d\phi + F^2\mathrm{tr}\widetilde{C}^\sharp(d\phi, d\phi, \xi) + 4\mathrm{tr}\widetilde{A}(d\phi, \widetilde{\nabla}_{\ell^H}d\phi),$$

from which (9.4.11) follows. $\qquad\square$

By (9.4.11), we obtain the following

Theorem 9.14 ([55]). *Let $\phi : (M, F) \to (\widetilde{M}, \widetilde{F})$ be a non-degenerate smooth map. We have*

$$\mathrm{div}S_\phi(\ell) = \widetilde{g}(\tau(\phi), d\phi\ell). \qquad (9.4.12)$$

Therefore, if ϕ is a strong harmonic map, then S_ϕ is conservative.

Lemma 9.10. *Let $\phi : (M, F) \to (\widetilde{M}, \widetilde{F})$ be a non-degenerate smooth map, Ψ be a smooth section with compact support of π^*T^*M. Then we have*

$$\int_{SM}\{\langle\mathrm{div}S_\phi, \Psi\rangle + \langle S_\phi, {}^c\nabla_H\Psi\rangle\}dV_{SM} = 0, \qquad (9.4.13)$$

where ${}^c\nabla_H$ denotes the horizontal covariant differential.

Proof. Let $X \in C(\pi^*TM)$ be the dual vector field of Ψ. By (9.3.1), we get

$$\mathrm{div}(e(\phi)\Psi) = g^{ij}\{\delta_i[e(\phi)]\Psi(\partial_j) + e(\phi)({}^b\nabla_{\delta_i}\Psi)(\partial_j)\}$$
$$= g^{ij}\delta_i[e(\phi)\Psi(\partial_j)] - g^{ij}e(\phi)\Psi({}^b\nabla_{\delta_i}\partial_j),$$
$$\mathrm{div}[g(d\phi X, d\phi\partial_i)dx^i] = g^{ij}\{\delta_i[g(d\phi X, d\phi\partial_j)] + g(d\phi X, d\phi\partial_k)({}^b\nabla_{\delta_i}dx^k)(\partial_j)\}$$
$$= g^{ij}\delta_i[\widetilde{g}(d\phi X, d\phi\partial_j)] - g^{ij}\widetilde{g}(d\phi X, d\phi^b\nabla_{\delta_i}\partial_j).$$

It follows that

$$\mathrm{div}S_\phi(X) = g^{ij}\{\delta_i[e(\phi)g(\partial_j, X) - \widetilde{g}(d\phi\partial_j, d\phi X)] - S_\phi({}^c\nabla_{\delta_i}\partial_j, X)$$
$$- S_\phi(\partial_j, {}^c\nabla_{\delta_i}X)\} - S_\phi(\dot{\eta}^*, X)$$
$$= \mathrm{div}[e(\phi)\Psi] - \mathrm{div}[g(d\phi X, d\phi\partial_i)dx^i] - g^{ij}S_\phi(\partial_j, {}^c\nabla_{\delta_i}X)$$
$$= \mathrm{div}[e(\phi)\Psi] - \mathrm{div}[g(d\phi X, d\phi\partial_i)dx^i] - \langle S_\phi, {}^c\nabla^H\Psi\rangle.$$

Integrating both sides of the above equation, we get (9.4.13). $\qquad\square$

For any $f \in C(SM)$, Put $\Psi = f\omega$ in (9.4.13). By Lemma 9.10 and ${}^c\nabla_H\omega = 0$, we have

Corollary 9.3. *If ϕ is a non-degenerate map from a compact Finsler manifold (M, F) to an arbitrary Finsler manifold $(\widetilde{M}, \widetilde{F})$, then for any $f \in C(SM)$,*

$$\int_{SM} \langle d^H f, S_\phi(\ell) \rangle dV_{SM} = 0, \qquad (9.4.14)$$

where d^H denotes the horizontal differential.

Corollary 9.4. *If ϕ is a non-degenerate map from a compact Finsler manifold (M, F) to an arbitrary Finsler manifold $(\widetilde{M}, \widetilde{F})$, then*

$$\int_{SM} \langle \tau(\phi), d\phi\ell \rangle dV_{SM} = 0.$$

For a non-degenerate map $\phi : (M, F) \to (\widetilde{M}, \widetilde{F})$, if there exists a positive function $\mu > 0$ on SM such that $\phi^* \widetilde{g} = \mu g$, then we call ϕ a *conformal map*. It can proved that $\mu = \mu(x)$ is independent of y ([101] or §11.1 below). By (9.3.7), the energy density of a conformal map is given by

$$e(\phi) = \frac{n}{2}\mu(x) = \frac{n}{2}\frac{\widetilde{F}^2}{F^2}. \qquad (9.4.15)$$

Proposition 9.10 ([55]). *Let $\phi : (M, F) \to (\widetilde{M}, \widetilde{F})$ be a non-degenerate map. Then $S_\phi = 0$ if and only if ϕ is a conformal map and $n = 2$.*

Proof. By (9.4.10), if $S_\phi = 0$, then ϕ is conformal. Then the necessity follows from (9.4.15). Now we show the sufficiency. If $\phi^* \widetilde{g} = \mu g$ and $n = 2$, then $S_\phi = e(\phi)g - \mu g = (\frac{n}{2} - 1)\mu g = 0$. $\square$

Lemma 9.11. *Let $\phi : (M, F) \to (\widetilde{M}, \widetilde{F})$ be a conformal map and $n = \dim M > 2$. Then S_ϕ is conservative if and only if ϕ is homothetic.*

Proof. Since $S_\phi = (\frac{n}{2} - 1)\mu g$, we have

$$\text{div} S_\phi(\ell) = \left(\frac{n}{2} - 1\right) \{\ell^H(\mu) + \mu \text{div} g(\ell)\}$$

$$= \left(\frac{n}{2} - 1\right) \{\ell(\mu) + \mu g^{ij}({}^c \nabla_{\delta_i} g)(\partial_j, \ell) - \mu \dot{\eta}(\ell)\}$$

$$= \left(\frac{n}{2} - 1\right) \ell(\mu).$$

Clearly, when $n = \dim M > 2$, $\text{div} S_\phi(\ell) = 0$ if and only if μ is constant. $\square$

By Theorem 9.13 and Lemma 9.11, we obtain immediately the following

Proposition 9.11 ([55]). *If ϕ is a conformal and strongly harmonic map from an n-dimensional $(n > 2)$ Finsler manifold (M, F) to any Finsler manifold $(\widetilde{M}, \widetilde{F})$, then ϕ is homothetic.*

Remark. These are the extensions of properties on the stress-energy tensor in the Riemannian case ([46]).

9.5 Harmonic maps between complex Finsler manifolds

9.5.1 Complex Finsler manifolds

Let M be an n-dimensional complex manifold, $T'M$ be its holomorphic tangent bundle. Let $z = (z^1, \cdots, z^n)$ is a holomorphic local coordinate system on M. Any vector in $T'M$ can be written as $v = v^i \partial/\partial z^i$. Then $(z, v) = (z^1, \cdots, z^n; v^1, \cdots, v^n)$ is a holomorphic local coordinate system on $T'M$. A complex Finsler metric on a complex manifold M is a continuous function $F \colon T'M \longrightarrow [0, \infty)$ with the following properties ([3]):

    (i) $G := F^2$ is smooth on $\widetilde{M} = T'M \setminus \{0\}$;

    (ii) $F(z, v) \geq 0$, where the inequality holds if and only if $v = 0$;

    (iii) For any $\lambda \in \mathbb{C}$, $F(z, \lambda v) = |\lambda| F(z, v)$.

The pair (M, F) is called a *complex Finsler manifold*.

Example 9.5. Let M be an n-dimensional complex manifold. Define

$$F_K(z, v) = \inf\{|\xi| : \exists \phi \in \text{Hol}(\Delta, M), \phi(0) = z, d\phi_0(\xi) = v\},$$

where Δ is a unit disc on a complex plane, $\text{Hol}(\Delta, M)$ is the set of holomorphic maps from Δ to M. $F_K(z, v)$ is called the *Kobayashi metric* on M. Define

$$F_C(z, v) = \sup\{d\phi_z(v) : \phi \in \text{Hol}(M, \Delta), \phi(z) = 0\}.$$

$F_C(z, v)$ is called the *Carathéodory metric* on M.

In general, the Carathéodory metric and the Kobayashi metric are not smooth, and they are even degenerate at some points. When M is a strongly convex domain, the above Carathéodory metric and Kobayashi metric are smooth on $\widetilde{M} = T'M \setminus \{0\}$ ([67]).

Moreover, if the Levi matric

$$(G_{i\bar{j}}) := (\dot{\partial}_i \dot{\partial}_{\bar{j}} G), \quad \dot{\partial}_i := \frac{\partial}{\partial v^i}$$

is positive definite, then F is said to be *strongly pseudo-convex*. Unless otherwise stated, all complex Finsler metrics discussed in this section are strongly pseudo-convex.

The holomorphic pulled-back bundle $\pi^*T'M$ induced by the natural projection $\pi : \widetilde{M} \to M$ is a Hermite vector bundle with metric $G_{i\bar{j}}dz^i \otimes d\bar{z}^j$. There exists a unique Hermite connection on $\pi^*T'M$. To describe this connection, we take a direct decomposition for $T_{\mathbb{C}}\widetilde{M}$. Let

$$\frac{\delta}{\delta z^i} := \frac{\partial}{\partial z^i} - N_i^j \frac{\delta}{\delta v^j}, \quad \delta v^i := dv^i + N_j^i dz^j, \tag{9.5.1}$$

where $N_j^i := G^{i\bar{k}}G_{\bar{k},j}$, $(G^{i\bar{k}}) = (G_{i\bar{k}})^{-1}$. Here "," denotes the partial derivative with respect to z, for example $G_{i,j} = \frac{\partial^2 G}{\partial v^i \partial z^j}$.

Then, we obtain a decomposition

$$T_{\mathbb{C}}\widetilde{M} = \mathcal{H} \oplus \overline{\mathcal{H}} \oplus \mathcal{V} \oplus \overline{\mathcal{V}},$$

where $\mathcal{H} = \text{span}\{\delta/\delta z^i\}$ is called the *horizontal bundle*, $\mathcal{V} = \text{span}\{\partial/\partial v^i\}$ is called the *vertical bundle*.

Under this decomposition, the Hermite connection on $\pi^*T'M$ can be expressed by

$$\nabla\frac{\partial}{\partial z^j} = \omega_j^i \otimes \frac{\partial}{\partial z^i}, \quad \omega_j^i := G^{i\bar{l}}\partial G_{j\bar{l}} = \Gamma_{j,k}^i dz^k + C_{jk}^i \delta v^k, \tag{9.5.2}$$

where

$$\Gamma_{j,k}^i = G^{i\bar{l}}\delta_k G_{j\bar{l}}, \quad C_{jk}^i = G^{i\bar{l}}G_{j\bar{l}k}. \tag{9.5.3}$$

This connection is called the *Chern-Finsler connection* of F. According to the definition of Hermite connection, the Chern-Finsler connection is a connection of type $(1,0)$ which is compatible with the metric. When F is a Hermite metric, the Chern-Finsler connection is exactly the Hermite connection of F ([3]).

The vertical part of the Chern-Finsler connection $\{C_{jk}^i\}$ forms the component of the *Cartan tensor*. Its trace $C_k dz^k := C_{ik}^i dz^k$ is called the *Cartan form*. Similar to the real case, we have the following Deicke Theorem.

Theorem 9.15 ([34]). *A complex Finsler metric F is a Hermite metric if and only if its Cartan form vanishes.*

Readers can prove the above theorem by a method similar to that for Theorem 2.1 in Chapter 2.

It is easy to see that the pulled-back bundle $\pi^* T'M$ is isomorphic to the horizontal bundle $\mathcal{H}$ and the vertical bundle $\mathcal{V}$, respectively. So,

$$G_{i\bar{j}} dz^i \otimes d\bar{z}^j + G_{i\bar{j}} \delta v^i \otimes \delta \bar{v}^j$$

can be viewed as a Hermite metric on $\mathcal{H} \oplus \mathcal{V}$ $(= T'\widetilde{M})$. The Chern-Finsler connection can also be seen as a connection on $\mathcal{H} \oplus \mathcal{V}$, i.e.

$$\nabla \frac{\delta}{\delta z^j} = \omega^i_j \otimes \frac{\delta}{\delta z^i}, \quad \nabla \frac{\partial}{\partial v^j} = \omega^i_j \otimes \frac{\partial}{\partial v^i}. \tag{9.5.4}$$

Furthermore, we can define $(2,0)$-type *torsion* θ

$$\theta(X,Y) = \nabla_X Y - \nabla_Y X - [X,Y], \quad X,Y \in \mathcal{C}(T'\widetilde{M}). \tag{9.5.5}$$

It is not difficult to verify that in a local coordinate system, the $(2,0)$-type torsion of the Chern-Finsler connection can be expressed as follows ([34])

$$\theta = \Gamma^i_{j,k} dz^k \wedge dz^j \otimes \frac{\delta}{\delta z^i} + C^i_{jk} \delta v^k \wedge dz^j \otimes \frac{\delta}{\delta z^i} = \omega^i_j \wedge dz^j \otimes \frac{\delta}{\delta z^i}.$$

Define a real 2-form on $\widetilde{M}$ by

$$\Phi = \sqrt{-1} G_{i\bar{j}} dz^i \wedge d\bar{z}^j, \tag{9.5.6}$$

which is called the *Kähler form* of F. According to the horizontal and vertical decomposition of $T_{\mathbb{C}}\widetilde{M}$, the exterior derivative can also be decomposed to the horizontal and vertical parts,

$$d = d_{\mathcal{H}} + d_{\mathcal{V}} = \partial_{\mathcal{H}} + \bar{\partial}_{\mathcal{H}} + \partial_{\mathcal{V}} + \bar{\partial}_{\mathcal{V}}. \tag{9.5.7}$$

Then,

$$d_{\mathcal{H}}\Phi = \partial_{\mathcal{H}}\Phi + \bar{\partial}_{\mathcal{H}}\Phi = \sqrt{-1} \frac{\delta G_{i\bar{j}}}{\delta z^k} dz^k \wedge dz^i \wedge d\bar{z}^j + \sqrt{-1} \frac{\delta G_{i\bar{j}}}{\delta \bar{z}^k} d\bar{z}^k \wedge dz^i \wedge d\bar{z}^j.$$

Note that when F is a Hermite metric, $d_{\mathcal{H}}\Phi = d\Phi$.

Definition 9.7. Let F be a complex Finsler metric and Φ be its Kähler form. Set $\chi = v^i \delta/\delta z^i$.
(1) If $d_{\mathcal{H}}\Phi = 0$ then F is called a *strongly Kähler Finsler metric*;
(2) If $d_{\mathcal{H}}\Phi(\chi,\cdot,\cdot) = 0$, then F is called a *Kähler Finsler metric*;
(3) If $d_{\mathcal{H}}\Phi(\chi,\bar{\chi},\cdot) = 0$, then F is called a *weakly Kähler Finsler metric*.

It is easy to verify ([34]) that, in the local coordinate system, the complex Finsler metric F is strongly Kähler (Kähler or weakly Kähler) if and only if $\Gamma^i_{j,k} = \Gamma^i_{k,j}$ $(\Gamma^i_{j,k} v^j = \Gamma^i_{k,j} v^j$ or $G_i \Gamma^i_{j,k} v^j = G_i \Gamma^i_{k,j} v^j)$.

Theorem 9.16 ([33]). *A complex Kähler Finsler metric F must be a strongly Kähler Finsler metric.*

Proof. According to the definition, we have

$$
\begin{aligned}
\Gamma^i_{j,k} &= G^{i\bar{l}}\delta_k G_{j\bar{l}} = G^{i\bar{l}}G_{j\bar{l},k} - G^{i\bar{l}}N^p_k G_{j\bar{l}p} \\
&= (G^{i\bar{l}}G_{\bar{l},k})_{v^j} - (G^{i\bar{l}})_{v^j}G_{\bar{l},k} - G^{i\bar{l}}N^p_k G_{j\bar{l}p} \\
&= (N^i_k)_{v^j} + G^{i\bar{q}}G^{p\bar{l}}G_{p\bar{q}j}G_{\bar{l},k} - G^{i\bar{l}}N^p_k G_{j\bar{l}p}r \\
&= (N^i_k)_{v^j} + G^{i\bar{q}}G_{p\bar{q}j}N^p_k - G^{i\bar{l}}N^p_k G_{j\bar{l}p} = (N^i_k)_{v^j}.
\end{aligned}
$$

So, we can get $\Gamma^i_{j,k}v^j = N^i_k$ by the Euler Theorem. If F is Kähler, i.e. $\Gamma^i_{j,k}v^j = \Gamma^i_{k,j}v^j$, then

$$
(N^i_j v^j)_{v^k} = (N^i_j)_{v^k}v^j + N^i_k = \Gamma^i_{k,j}v^j + N^i_k = \Gamma^i_{j,k}v^j + N^i_k = 2N^i_k.
$$

Then

$$
2\Gamma^i_{j,k} = 2(N^i_k)_{v^j} = (N^i_l v^l)_{v^k v^j} = 2\Gamma^i_{k,j},
$$

i.e. F is strongly Kähler. Obviously, strongly Kähler implies Kähler. $\square$

By the above theorem, (1) and (2) in Definition 9.6 are actually equivalent. So, in complex Finsler geometry, there are only two kinds of Kähler metrics, i.e. Kähler Finsler metrics and weakly Kähler Finsler metrics ([33]).

By a simply calculation, we can know that the curvature form of the Chern-Finsler connection satisfies

$$
\Omega^i_j := d\omega^i_j - \omega^k_j \wedge \omega^i_k = \bar{\partial}\omega^i_j. \tag{9.5.8}
$$

It can be further expressed

$$
\Omega^i_j = R^i_{j,k\bar{l}}dz^k \wedge d\bar{z}^l + S^i_{jk,\bar{l}}\delta v^k \wedge d\bar{z}^l + P^i_{j\bar{l},k}dz^k \wedge \delta\bar{v}^l + Q^i_{jk\bar{l}}\delta v^k \wedge \delta\bar{v}^l, \tag{9.5.8$'$}
$$

where the four parts are called the $h\bar{h}$-*curvature*, $v\bar{h}$-*curvature*, $h\bar{v}$-*curvature* and $v\bar{v}$-*curvature*, respectively. Define

$$
K(z,v) = 2R_{i\bar{j},k\bar{l}}\frac{v^i}{F}\frac{\bar{v}^j}{F}\frac{v^k}{F}\frac{\bar{v}^l}{F}, \quad R_{i\bar{j},k\bar{l}} = R^s_{i,k\bar{l}}G_{s\bar{j}}. \tag{9.5.9}
$$

$K(z,v)$ is called the *holomorphic curvature* of F in the direction v. The Kobayashi metric on strongly convex domain is a weakly Kähler Finsler metric whose holomorphic curvature is -4.

The projective tangent bundle of (M^n, F) is defined as $P\widetilde{M} := \widetilde{M}/\mathbb{C}^*$, whose fiber is exactly the complex projective space $\mathbb{C}P^{n-1}$. On $P\widetilde{M}$ there is a natural Hermite metric

$$
G_{i\bar{j}}dz^i \otimes d\bar{z}^j + (\ln G)_{i\bar{j}}\delta v^i \otimes \delta\bar{v}^j,
$$

the second part corresponds to the Fubini-Study metric on the fiber. It is easy to verify that the invariant volume form of $\widetilde{PM}$ is given by ([163])

$$d\mu_{\widetilde{PM}} = \frac{\omega_{\mathcal{V}}^{n-1}}{(n-1)!} \wedge \frac{\omega_{\mathcal{H}}^{m}}{m!}, \tag{9.5.10}$$

where

$$\omega_{\mathcal{V}} = \sqrt{-1}(\ln G)_{i\bar{j}}\delta v^i \wedge \delta\bar{v}^j, \quad \omega_{\mathcal{H}} = \sqrt{-1}G_{i\bar{j}}dz^i \wedge d\bar{z}^j.$$

Then we have

$$d\mu_{\widetilde{PM}} = \det(G_{i\bar{j}})d\sigma \wedge dz, \tag{9.5.11}$$

where

$$d\sigma = \frac{\omega_{\mathcal{V}}^{n-1}}{(n-1)!}, \quad dz = \left(\sqrt{-1}\sum_{i=1}^{n} dz^i \wedge d\bar{z}^i\right)^n. \tag{9.5.12}$$

Using the volume form on the projective tangent bundle, we can discuss the variation problems of harmonic maps between complex Finsler manifolds.

9.5.2 Harmonic maps between complex Finsler manifolds

Let (M, F) be an n-dimensional complex Finsler manifold, (N, H) be an m-dimensional Hermite manifold and $\phi : M \to N$ be a smooth map. Take a local holomorphic coordinate system $z = (z^1, \cdots, z^n)$ on M and a local holomorphic coordinate system $w = (w^1, \cdots, w^m)$ be N. Then ϕ can be locally expressed by

$$w^\alpha = \phi^\alpha(z^1, \cdots, z^n, \bar{z}^1, \cdots, \bar{z}^n), \quad 1 \le \alpha, \beta, \cdots \le m, \quad 1 \le i, j, \cdots \le n.$$

The tangent map of ϕ, $d\phi : TM \to TN$, can be linearly extended to a map between complexified tangent bundles $T^{\mathbb{C}}M \to T^{\mathbb{C}}N$. According to the decomposition below

$$T^{\mathbb{C}}M = T'M \oplus T''M, \quad T^{\mathbb{C}}N = T'N \oplus T''N,$$

we have

$$d\phi|_{T'M} = \partial\phi + \partial\bar{\phi}, \quad d\phi|_{T''M} = \bar{\partial}\phi + \overline{\partial\bar{\phi}}, \tag{9.5.13}$$

where

$$\partial\phi : T'M \to T'N, \quad \bar{\partial}\phi : T''M \to T'N, \quad \overline{\bar{\partial}\phi} = \bar{\partial}\bar{\phi}, \quad \overline{\partial\phi} = \bar{\partial}\bar{\phi}.$$

In local coordinates, they can be expressed by

$$\partial\phi = \phi_i^\alpha dz^i \otimes \frac{\partial}{\partial w^\alpha}, \quad \bar{\partial}\phi = \phi_{\bar{i}}^\alpha d\bar{z}^i \otimes \frac{\partial}{\partial w^\alpha}, \tag{9.5.14}$$

where

$$\phi_i^\alpha = \frac{\partial \phi^\alpha}{\partial z^i}, \quad \phi_{\bar{i}}^\alpha = \frac{\partial \phi^\alpha}{\partial \bar{z}^i}.$$

It is obvious that ϕ is a holomorphic (resp. anti-holomorphic) map if and only if $\bar{\partial}\phi = 0$ (resp. $\partial\phi = 0$).

Let

$$G(z,v) = G_{i\bar{j}}(z,v)v^i\bar{v}^j, \quad H(w) = H_{\alpha\bar{\beta}(w)w^\alpha\overline{w}^\beta}.$$

Then the $\bar{\partial}$-*energy density* of ϕ is defined as

$$|\bar{\partial}\phi|^2(z,v) = G^{\bar{i}j}(z,v)\phi_{\bar{i}}^\alpha\phi_j^{\bar{\beta}}H_{\alpha\bar{\beta}}(\phi(z)).$$

Using the volume form on the projecting tangent bundle $P\widetilde{M}$, the $\bar{\partial}$-*energy* of ϕ is defined as

$$E_{\bar{\partial}}(\phi) = \frac{1}{c_M}\int_{P\widetilde{M}}|\bar{\partial}\phi|^2 d\mu_{P\widetilde{M}}, \tag{9.5.15}$$

where c_M denotes the standard volume on the complex projecting space $\mathbb{C}P^{n-1}$.

Consider a smooth variation of $\phi = \phi_0$, i.e. a family of smooth maps

$$\phi_t : M \to N, \quad t \in \mathcal{D} = \{z \in \mathbb{C}|\ |z| < \varepsilon\}.$$

The corresponding variation of $\bar{\partial}$-energy is given by

$$\phi_t : M \to N, \quad t \in \mathcal{D} = \{z \in \mathbb{C}|\ |z| < \varepsilon\}.$$

$\{\phi_t\}$ induces a vector field on the pulled-back bundle $\phi_t^{-1}T^{\mathbb{C}}N$,

$$V := d\phi_t\left(\frac{\partial}{\partial t}\right) = \partial\phi_t\left(\frac{\partial}{\partial t}\right) + \bar{\partial}\phi_t\left(\frac{\partial}{\partial t}\right) = V' + V'', \tag{9.5.16}$$

where

$$V' = \frac{\partial\phi_t^\alpha}{\partial t}\frac{\partial}{\partial w^\alpha}, \quad V'' = \frac{\partial\overline{\phi}_t^\alpha}{\partial t}\frac{\partial}{\partial \overline{w}^\alpha}.$$

At $t = 0$, it is a *variation vector field*

$$V_0 := V|_{t=0}.$$

Let

$$U = d\phi_t\left(\frac{\partial}{\partial \bar{t}}\right) = \partial\bar{\phi}_t\left(\frac{\partial}{\partial \bar{t}}\right) + \overline{\partial}\phi_t\left(\frac{\partial}{\partial \bar{t}}\right) := U' + U'';$$

$$T_i = d\phi_t\left(\frac{\partial}{\partial z^i}\right) = \partial\bar{\phi}_t\left(\frac{\partial}{\partial z^i}\right) + \partial\bar{\phi}_t\left(\frac{\partial}{\partial z^i}\right) := T_i' + T_i'';$$

$$S_i = d\phi_t\left(\frac{\partial}{\partial \bar{z}^i}\right) = \bar{\partial}\phi_t\left(\frac{\partial}{\partial \bar{z}^i}\right) + \overline{\partial}\phi_t\left(\frac{\partial}{\partial \bar{z}^i}\right) := S_i' + S_i''.$$

It is obvious that

$$|\overline{\partial}\phi_t|^2 = G^{\overline{i}j}(z,v)\phi_{ti}^{\alpha}\phi_{tj}^{\overline{\beta}}H_{\alpha\overline{\beta}}(\phi(z)) = G^{\overline{i}j}\langle S_i^{\prime\mathcal{H}}, S_j^{\prime\mathcal{H}}\rangle_N,$$

where $\langle\cdot,\cdot\rangle_N$ is the Hermite inner product on the pulled-back bundle $\phi_t^{-1}T'\widetilde{N}$, $X^{\mathcal{H}} = X^{\alpha}\delta/\delta w^{\alpha}$ is the horizontal lift of $X = X^{\alpha}\partial/\partial w^{\alpha}$. Then, we have

$$\frac{\partial}{\partial t}|\overline{\partial}\phi_t|^2 = G^{\overline{i}j}\frac{\partial}{\partial t}\langle S_i^{\prime\mathcal{H}}, S_j^{\prime\mathcal{H}}\rangle_N.$$

By a direct computation, we get ([53])

$$\frac{\partial}{\partial t}E_{\overline{\partial}}(\phi_t) = \frac{1}{c_M}\int_{P\widetilde{M}}G^{\overline{i}j}\Big\{S_i^{\mathcal{H}}\langle V'^{\mathcal{H}}, S_j^{\prime\mathcal{H}}\rangle_N + \overline{S_j^{\mathcal{H}}}\langle S_i^{\prime\mathcal{H}}, \overline{V''^{\mathcal{H}}}\rangle_N$$

$$- \langle V'^{\mathcal{H}}, \nabla_{\overline{S_j^{\mathcal{H}}}}S_j^{\prime\mathcal{H}}\rangle_N - \langle\nabla_{\overline{S_j^{\mathcal{H}}}}S_i^{\prime\mathcal{H}}, \overline{V''^{\mathcal{H}}}\rangle_N \qquad (9.5.16')$$

$$+ \langle\theta(V'^{\mathcal{H}}, S_i^{\prime\mathcal{H}}), S_j^{\prime\mathcal{H}}\rangle_N + \langle S_i^{\prime\mathcal{H}}, \theta(\overline{V''^{\mathcal{H}}}, S_j^{\prime\mathcal{H}})\rangle_N\Big\}d\mu_{P\widetilde{M}}.$$

Define an $(n, n-1)$-form

$$\widetilde{\Psi} = G^{\overline{i}j}\langle V'^{\mathcal{H}}, S_j^{\prime\mathcal{H}}\rangle_N\mathcal{I}_{\delta_{\overline{i}}}(d\mu_{P\widetilde{M}}),$$

where $\mathcal{I}_{\delta_{\overline{i}}}$ denotes the interior differential with respect to $\delta_{\overline{i}}$. Then

$$d\widetilde{\Psi} = G^{\overline{i}j}\{S_i^{\mathcal{H}}\langle V'^{\mathcal{H}}, S_j^{\prime\mathcal{H}}\rangle_N - \langle V'^{\mathcal{H}}, S_j^{\prime\mathcal{H}}\rangle_N({}^M\Gamma_{\overline{i},\overline{k}}^{\overline{k}} - {}^M\Gamma_{\overline{k},\overline{i}}^{\overline{k}})\}d\mu_{P\widetilde{M}},$$

where ${}^M\Gamma_{\overline{i},\overline{j}}^{\overline{k}} = \overline{{}^M\Gamma_{i,j}^{k}}$. According to the Stokes' formula, we have

$$\int_{P\widetilde{M}}G^{\overline{i}j}S_i^{\mathcal{H}}\langle V'^{\mathcal{H}}, S_j^{\prime\mathcal{H}}\rangle_Nd\mu_{P\widetilde{M}} = \int_{P\widetilde{M}}G^{\overline{i}j}\langle V'^{\mathcal{H}}, S_j^{\prime\mathcal{H}}\rangle_N({}^M\Gamma_{\overline{i},\overline{k}}^{\overline{k}} - {}^M\Gamma_{\overline{k},\overline{i}}^{\overline{k}})d\mu_{P\widetilde{M}},$$

i.e.,

$$\int_{P\widetilde{M}}G^{\overline{i}j}S_i^{\mathcal{H}}\langle V'^{\mathcal{H}}, S_j^{\prime\mathcal{H}}\rangle_Nd\mu_{P\widetilde{M}} = \int_{P\widetilde{M}}G^{\overline{i}j}V'^{\alpha}\frac{\partial\overline{\phi_t^{\beta}}}{\partial z^j}({}^M\Gamma_{\overline{i},\overline{k}}^{\overline{k}} - {}^M\Gamma_{\overline{k},\overline{i}}^{\overline{k}})H_{\alpha\overline{\beta}}d\mu_{P\widetilde{M}}.$$

Similarly, we have

$$\int_{P\widetilde{M}}G^{\overline{i}j}\overline{S_j^{\mathcal{H}}}\langle S_i^{\prime\mathcal{H}}, \overline{V''^{\mathcal{H}}}\rangle_Nd\mu_{P\widetilde{M}} = \int_{P\widetilde{M}}G^{\overline{i}j}\frac{\partial\phi_t^{\alpha}}{\partial z^{\overline{i}}}V''^{\beta}({}^M\Gamma_{j,k}^{k} - {}^M\Gamma_{k,j}^{k})H_{\alpha\overline{\beta}}d\mu_{P\widetilde{M}}.$$

Theorem 9.17 ([53]). *Let (M, F) be a closed complex Finsler manifold, (N, H) be an Hermite manifold. If $\phi : M \to N$ is a smooth map, then the first variation of its $\overline{\partial}$-energy is given by*

$$\frac{\partial}{\partial t}E_{\overline{\partial}}(\phi_t)\Big|_{t=0} = -\frac{1}{c_M}\int_{P\widetilde{M}}\overline{V_0^{\beta}}Q^{\alpha}H_{\alpha\overline{\beta}}d\mu_{P\widetilde{M}} - \frac{1}{c_M}\int_{P\widetilde{M}}V_0^{\alpha}\overline{Q^{\beta}}H_{\alpha\overline{\beta}}d\mu_{P\widetilde{M}},$$
$$(9.5.17)$$

where

$$Q^{\alpha} = G^{\overline{i}j}\Big\{({}^M\Gamma_{l,j}^{l} - {}^M\Gamma_{j,l}^{l})\phi_{\overline{i}}^{\alpha} + \phi_{\overline{i}j}^{\alpha} + {}^N\Gamma_{\sigma,\rho}^{\alpha}\phi_{\overline{i}}^{\sigma}\phi_j^{\rho}$$

$$- \frac{1}{2}H^{\overline{\delta}\alpha}H_{\sigma\overline{\gamma}}({}^N\Gamma_{\overline{\rho},\overline{\delta}}^{\overline{\gamma}} - {}^N\Gamma_{\overline{\delta},\overline{\rho}}^{\overline{\gamma}})\phi_{\overline{i}}^{\sigma}\phi_j^{\overline{\rho}}\Big\}.$$
$$(9.5.18)$$

By the above theorem, we immediately obtain the following

Corollary 9.5. *Let (M, F) be a closed Kähler Finsler manifold, (N, H) be an Hermite manifold. If $\phi : M \to N$ is a smooth map, then the first variation of its $\overline{\partial}$-energy is given by*

$$\frac{\partial}{\partial t} E_{\overline{\partial}}(\phi_t)|_{t=0} = -\frac{1}{c_M} \int_{P\widetilde{M}} \overline{V_0^\beta} \Xi^\alpha H_{\alpha\overline{\beta}} d\mu_{P\widetilde{M}} - \frac{1}{c_M} \int_{P\widetilde{M}} V_0^\alpha \overline{\Xi^\beta} H_{\alpha\overline{\beta}} d\mu_{P\widetilde{M}},$$

where

$$\Xi^\alpha = G^{\overline{i}j}\left\{ \phi_{\overline{i}j}^\alpha + {}^N\Gamma_{\sigma,\rho}^\alpha \phi_{\overline{i}}^\sigma \phi_j^\rho - \frac{1}{2} H^{\overline{\delta}\alpha} H_{\sigma\overline{\gamma}}({}^N\Gamma_{\overline{\rho},\overline{\delta}}^{\overline{\gamma}} - {}^N\Gamma_{\overline{\delta},\overline{\rho}}^{\overline{\gamma}}) \phi_{\overline{i}}^\sigma \phi_j^{\overline{\rho}} \right\}. \quad (9.5.19)$$

Definition 9.8. ϕ *is called a* harmonic map *if*

$$\|Q\| := \sup_{V_0 \in \mathcal{C}(\phi^{-1}T^C N)} \left\{ \frac{\left| \int_{P\widetilde{M}} \overline{V_0^\beta} Q^\alpha H_{\alpha\overline{\beta}} dV_{P\widetilde{M}} \right|}{\|V_0\|} \right\} \equiv 0.$$

It follows that a holomorphic map must be harmonic.

Lemma 9.12. *Let F be a complex Finsler metric on M, and*

$$\gamma^{\overline{i}j}(z) := \frac{\int_{P_z\widetilde{M}} G^{\overline{i}j}(z, v) \det(G_{k\overline{l}}(z, v)) d\sigma}{\sigma(z)}, \quad \sigma(z) := \int_{P_z\widetilde{M}} \det(G_{k\overline{l}}(z, v)) d\sigma,$$

where $d\sigma$ is defined by (9.5.12), then $\gamma = \gamma_{i\overline{j}} dz^i \otimes dz^{\overline{j}}$ is a Hermitian metric on M, where $(\gamma_{i\overline{j}}) = (\gamma^{\overline{i}j})^{-1}$.

Proof. It is easy to see that $(\gamma^{\overline{i}j})$ is a positive definite Hermitian matrix. It suffices to show γ is independent of the choice of a particular local coordinate system. Let $(\widetilde{z}^i)$ be another local holomorphic coordinate system. We have that $d\widetilde{z}^j = \frac{\partial \widetilde{z}^j}{\partial z^i} dz^i$ and $\widetilde{G}_{i\overline{j}} = G_{k\overline{l}} \frac{\partial z^k}{\partial \widetilde{z}^i} \frac{\partial z^{\overline{l}}}{\partial \widetilde{z}^{\overline{j}}}$ in the intersection of two local coordinate neighborhoods. Furthermore, $\det(\widetilde{G}_{i\overline{j}}) = \det(G_{k\overline{l}})|\frac{\partial z^l}{\partial \widetilde{z}^j}|^2$. Since $d\sigma$ is an invariant, it follows that $\widetilde{\sigma} = \sigma|\frac{\partial z^l}{\partial \widetilde{z}^j}|^2$, $\gamma^{\overline{i}j} = \widetilde{\gamma}^{\overline{k}l} \frac{\partial \widetilde{z}^i}{\partial z^k} \frac{\partial z^j}{\partial \widetilde{z}^l}$. Hence γ is exactly a tensor, then we obtain a Hermitian metric. $\quad\square$

Let (M, F) be a compact Kähler-Finsler manifold without boundary and (N, H) be a compact Kähler manifold without boundary. By Corollary 9.5, it follows that the smooth map $\phi : M \to N$ is harmonic if and only if

$$\int_{P\widetilde{M}} G^{\overline{i}j}(\phi_{\overline{i}j}^\alpha + {}^N\Gamma_{\sigma,\rho}^\alpha \phi_{\overline{i}}^\sigma \phi_j^\rho) \overline{V_0^\beta} H_{\alpha\overline{\beta}} d\mu_{P\widetilde{M}} = 0 \quad (9.5.20)$$

for any variation vector field V_0. Deducing from (9.5.11), for any function $f : P\widetilde{M} \to \mathbb{R}$, we obtain

$$\int_{P\widetilde{M}} f d\mu_{P\widetilde{M}} = \int_M dz \int_{P_z\widetilde{M}} f \det(G_{i\overline{j}}) d\sigma.$$

Therefore, (9.5.20) can be expressed as

$$\int_M \gamma^{\bar{i}j}(z)(\phi_{i\bar{j}}^{\alpha} + {}^{N}\Gamma_{\sigma,\rho}^{\alpha}\phi_{\bar{i}}^{\sigma}\phi_{j}^{\rho})\overline{V_0^{\beta}}H_{\alpha\bar{\beta}}\sigma(z)dz = 0, \qquad (9.5.21)$$

where $\gamma^{\bar{i}j}$ is the Hermitian metric defined in Lemma 9.12. Since $\sigma(z)dz$ is a volume measure while V_0 is arbitrary, then ϕ is a harmonic map if and only if

$$\gamma^{\bar{i}j}(\phi_{i\bar{j}}^{\alpha} + {}^{N}\Gamma_{\sigma,\rho}^{\alpha}\phi_{\bar{i}}^{\sigma}\phi_{j}^{\rho}) = 0. \qquad (9.5.22)$$

This system of differential equations are exactly the equations ([60]) satisfied by a Hermitian harmonic map from a Hermitian manifold (M, γ) to a Riemannian manifold (N, H). Consequently, according to the results in [60], we have the following

Theorem 9.18 ([53]). *Let (M, F) be a closed compact Kähler-Finsler manifold and (N, H) be a closed compact Kähler manifold with negative sectional curvature. Let $\psi : M \to N$ be a continuous map. Suppose that $\varphi(M)$ is not homotopic to any closed geodesic. Then there exists a harmonic map ϕ which is homotopic to ψ.*

Theorem 9.19 ([53]). *Let (M, F) be a closed compact Kähler-Finsler manifold and (N, H) be a closed compact Kähler manifold with non-positive sectional curvature. Let $\psi : M \to N$ be a continuous map. Suppose that φ induces a non-zero Euler class $e(g^*TN)$. Then there exists a harmonic map ϕ which is homotopic to ψ.*

Let (M, F) be a complex Finsler manifold, (N, H) be a Hermitian manifold and $\phi : M \to N$ be a smooth map. Similar to the $\bar{\partial}$-energy, we can define the ∂-energy of ϕ is given by

$$E_{\partial}(\phi) = \frac{1}{c_M}\int_{P\widetilde{M}}|\partial\phi|^2 d\mu_{P\widetilde{M}}. \qquad (9.5.23)$$

Then the total energy of ϕ is

$$E(\phi) = E_{\partial}(\phi) + E_{\bar{\partial}}(\phi). \qquad (9.5.24)$$

Obviously, ϕ is holomorphic (anti-holomorphic) if and only if $E_{\bar{\partial}} = 0$ ($E_{\partial} = 0$). Let

$$K(\phi) = E_{\partial}(\phi) - E_{\bar{\partial}}(\phi). \qquad (9.5.25)$$

Now, assume that (M, F) is a Kähler-Finsler manifold and (N, H) is a Kähler manifold. By a direct computation ([53]), we obtain that for any smooth variation $\{\phi_t : M \to N\}$ $(0 \leqslant t \leqslant 1)$,

$$
\begin{aligned}
\frac{\partial}{\partial t} E_{\overline{\partial}}(\phi_t) = & -\frac{1}{c_M} \int_{P(\widetilde{M})} G^{\overline{i}j} \langle V'^{\mathcal{H}}, \nabla_{\overline{S_i^{\mathcal{H}}}} S_j'^{\mathcal{H}} \rangle_N \, d\mu_{P\widetilde{M}} \\
& -\frac{1}{c_M} \int_{P(\widetilde{M})} G^{\overline{i}j} \langle \nabla_{\overline{S_j^{\mathcal{H}}}} S_i'^{\mathcal{H}}, U'^{\mathcal{H}} \rangle_N \, d\mu_{P\widetilde{M}}
\end{aligned}
\tag{9.5.26}
$$

and

$$
\begin{aligned}
\frac{\partial}{\partial t} E_{\partial}(\phi_t) = & -\frac{1}{c_M} \int_{P(\widetilde{M})} G^{i\overline{j}} \langle V'^{\mathcal{H}}, \nabla_{\overline{T_i^{\mathcal{H}}}} T_j'^{\mathcal{H}} \rangle_N \, d\mu_{P\widetilde{M}} \\
& -\frac{1}{c_M} \int_{P(\widetilde{M})} G^{i\overline{j}} \langle \nabla_{\overline{T_j^{\mathcal{H}}}} T_i'^{\mathcal{H}}, U'^{\mathcal{H}} \rangle_N \, d\mu_{P\widetilde{M}}.
\end{aligned}
\tag{9.5.26$'$}
$$

In local coordinates, (9.5.25) and (9.5.26) can be expressed as

$$
\begin{aligned}
\frac{\partial}{\partial t} E_{\overline{\partial}}(\phi_t) = & -\frac{1}{c_M} \int_{P(\widetilde{M})} G^{\overline{i}j} \frac{\partial \phi_t^\alpha}{\partial t} \left(\frac{\partial^2 \overline{\phi_t^\beta}}{\partial \overline{z}^i \partial z^j} + \frac{\partial \overline{\phi_t^\gamma}}{\partial \overline{z}^i} \frac{\partial \overline{\phi_t^\sigma}}{\partial z^j} \,^N\Gamma_{\overline{\gamma},\overline{\sigma}}^{\overline{\beta}} \right) H_{\alpha\overline{\beta}} \\
& -\frac{1}{c_M} \int_{P(\widetilde{M})} G^{\overline{i}j} \frac{\partial \overline{\phi_t^\beta}}{\partial t} \left(\frac{\partial^2 \phi_t^\alpha}{\partial \overline{z}^i \partial z^j} + \frac{\partial \phi_t^\gamma}{\partial \overline{z}^i} \frac{\partial \phi_t^\sigma}{\partial z^j} \,^N\Gamma_{\gamma,\sigma}^{\alpha} \right) H_{\alpha\overline{\beta}},
\end{aligned}
$$

$$
\begin{aligned}
\frac{\partial}{\partial t} E_{\partial}(\phi_t) = & -\frac{1}{c_M} \int_{P(\widetilde{M})} G^{i\overline{j}} \frac{\partial \phi_t^\alpha}{\partial t} \left(\frac{\partial^2 \overline{\phi_t^\beta}}{\partial z^i \partial \overline{z}^j} + \frac{\partial \overline{\phi_t^\gamma}}{\partial z^i} \frac{\partial \overline{\phi_t^\sigma}}{\partial \overline{z}^j} \,^N\Gamma_{\overline{\gamma},\overline{\sigma}}^{\overline{\beta}} \right) H_{\alpha\overline{\beta}} \\
& -\frac{1}{c_M} \int_{P(\widetilde{M})} G^{i\overline{j}} \frac{\partial \overline{\phi_t^\beta}}{\partial t} \left(\frac{\partial^2 \phi_t^\alpha}{\partial z^i \partial \overline{z}^j} + \frac{\partial \phi_t^\gamma}{\partial z^i} \frac{\partial \phi_t^\sigma}{\partial \overline{z}^j} \,^N\Gamma_{\gamma,\sigma}^{\alpha} \right) H_{\alpha\overline{\beta}}.
\end{aligned}
$$

Therefore, it can be seen from the expression above that

$$
\frac{d}{dt} K(\phi_t) = \frac{\partial}{\partial t} E_{\partial}(\phi_t) - \frac{\partial}{\partial t} E_{\overline{\partial}}(\phi_t) = 0,
$$

i.e. $K(\phi)$ is constant along any variation. This proves the following

Theorem 9.20 ([53]). *Let (M, F) be a closed compact Kähler-Finsler manifold and (N, H) be a Kähler manifold. For any smooth map $\phi : M \to N$, $K(\phi)$ is a smooth homotopic invariant, i.e. $\mathcal{C}(M, N)$ is constant on each connected component.*

Remark. If (M, F) is a general Kähler manifold, this theorem was shown by A. Lichnerowicz in a different method.

Therefore, under the assumption of this theorem, it follows that

$$
\frac{\partial}{\partial t} E_{\partial}(\phi_t) = \frac{\partial}{\partial t} E_{\overline{\partial}}(\phi_t) = \frac{1}{2} \frac{\partial}{\partial t} E(\phi_t).
$$

Corollary 9.6. *Let (M, F) be a compact Kähler-Finsler manifold without boundary and (N, H) be a Kähler manifold. Then the critical points of E_∂, $E_{\overline{\partial}}$ and E coincide. In each homotopy class, the minimal points of E_∂, $E_{\overline{\partial}}$ and E coincide as well.*

Now, let (M, F) be an n-dimensional complex Finsler manifold, (N, H) be an m-dimensional Hermitian manifold and $\phi : M \to N$ be a harmonic map. We consider the second variation of $\overline{\partial}$-energy functional. Using the similar technique in calculating (9.5.16), after a long computation, we deduce that the second variation of $\overline{\partial}$-energy functional can be expressed as ([172])

$$
\frac{\partial}{\partial \overline{t}} \left[\frac{\partial}{\partial t} |\overline{\partial} \phi_t|^2 \right] \Big|_{t=0}
$$

$$
= \frac{1}{c_M} \int_{P\widetilde{M}} G^{\overline{i}j} [\langle \nabla_{V^{\mathcal{H}}} S_i'^{\mathcal{H}}, \nabla_{V^{\mathcal{H}}} S_j'^{\mathcal{H}} \rangle_N + \langle \nabla_{U^{\mathcal{H}}} S_i'^{\mathcal{H}}, \nabla_{U^{\mathcal{H}}} S_j'^{\mathcal{H}} \rangle_N] dV_{P\widetilde{M}}
$$

$$
- \frac{1}{c_M} \int_{P\widetilde{M}} \frac{1}{2} G^{\overline{i}j} [\langle \Omega(S_i'^{\mathcal{H}}, U''^{\mathcal{H}}) V'^{\mathcal{H}}, S_j'^{\mathcal{H}} \rangle_N + \langle S_i'^{\mathcal{H}}, \Omega(S_j'^{\mathcal{H}}, V''^{\mathcal{H}}) U'^{\mathcal{H}} \rangle_N] dV_{P\widetilde{M}}
$$

$$
- \frac{1}{c_M} \int_{P\widetilde{M}} \frac{1}{2} G^{\overline{i}j} [\langle \Omega(V'^{\mathcal{H}}, U''^{\mathcal{H}}) S_i'^{\mathcal{H}}, S_j'^{\mathcal{H}} \rangle_N + \langle S_i'^{\mathcal{H}}, \Omega(U'^{\mathcal{H}}, V''^{\mathcal{H}}) S_j'^{\mathcal{H}} \rangle_N] dV_{P\widetilde{M}}
$$

$$
+ \frac{1}{c_M} \int_{P\widetilde{M}} G^{\overline{i}j} [\langle \Omega(U'^{\mathcal{H}}, S_i''^{\mathcal{H}}) V'^{\mathcal{H}}, S_j'^{\mathcal{H}} \rangle_N + \langle S_i'^{\mathcal{H}}, \Omega(V'^{\mathcal{H}}, S_j''^{\mathcal{H}}) U'^{\mathcal{H}} \rangle_N] dV_{P\widetilde{M}}
$$

$$
+ \frac{1}{c_M} \int_{P\widetilde{M}} G^{\overline{i}j} [\langle \Lambda(S_i'^{\mathcal{H}}, U'^{\mathcal{H}}) V'^{\mathcal{H}}, S_j'^{\mathcal{H}} \rangle_N + \langle S_i'^{\mathcal{H}}, \Lambda(S_j'^{\mathcal{H}}, V'^{\mathcal{H}}) U'^{\mathcal{H}} \rangle_N] dV_{P\widetilde{M}}
$$

$$
+ \frac{1}{c_M} \int_{P\widetilde{M}} G^{\overline{i}j} [\langle \theta^*(U'^{\mathcal{H}}, S_i'^{\mathcal{H}}), \nabla_{V^{\mathcal{H}}} S_j'^{\mathcal{H}} \rangle_N + \langle \nabla_{U^{\mathcal{H}}} S_i'^{\mathcal{H}}, \theta^*(V'^{\mathcal{H}}, S_j'^{\mathcal{H}}) \rangle_N] dV_{P\widetilde{M}},
$$

where the integrand takes value at $t = 0$. In particular, if N is a Kähler manifold, then the second variation of $\overline{\partial}$-energy functional can be written as

$$
\frac{\partial}{\partial \overline{t}} \left[\frac{\partial}{\partial t} |\overline{\partial} \phi_t|^2 \right] \Big|_{t=0}
$$

$$
= \frac{1}{c_M} \int_{P\widetilde{M}} G^{\overline{i}j} [\langle \nabla_{V^{\mathcal{H}}} S_i'^{\mathcal{H}}, \nabla_{V^{\mathcal{H}}} S_j'^{\mathcal{H}} \rangle_N + \langle \nabla_{U^{\mathcal{H}}} S_i'^{\mathcal{H}}, \nabla_{U^{\mathcal{H}}} S_j'^{\mathcal{H}} \rangle_N] dV_{P\widetilde{M}}
$$

$$
+ \frac{1}{c_M} \int_{P\widetilde{M}} G^{\overline{i}j} [\langle \Omega(U'^{\mathcal{H}}, S_i''^{\mathcal{H}}) V'^{\mathcal{H}}, S_j'^{\mathcal{H}} \rangle_N - \langle \Omega(S_i'^{\mathcal{H}}, U''^{\mathcal{H}}) V'^{\mathcal{H}}, S_j'^{\mathcal{H}} \rangle_N] dV_{P\widetilde{M}}
$$

$$
+ \frac{1}{c_M} \int_{P\widetilde{M}} G^{\overline{i}j} [\langle \overline{S_j''^{\mathcal{H}}}, \Omega(V'^{\mathcal{H}}, \overline{S_i'^{\mathcal{H}}}) U'^{\mathcal{H}} \rangle_N - \langle \overline{S_j''^{\mathcal{H}}}, \Omega(U'^{\mathcal{H}}, V''^{\mathcal{H}}) \overline{S_i''^{\mathcal{H}}} \rangle_N] dV_{P\widetilde{M}}.
$$

If the second variation of energy function is non-negative, then the harmonic map is said to be *stable*. From the expression above, we can easily deduce the following result.

Theorem 9.21 ([172]). *Let (M, F) be a compact complex Finsler manifold and (N, H) be a flat Kähler manifold. Then any harmonic map from (M, F) to (N, H) is stable.*

9.5.3 Holomorphic maps

Holomorphic maps are a kind of special harmonic maps. In Hermitian geometry, we have the Schwarz Lemma on holomorphic maps ([150], [165]). We will extend it to complex Finsler manifolds.

Let (M, F) be complex Finsler manifolds and $v \in \widetilde{M} = T'M \setminus \{0\}$. The holomorphic curvature in (5.5.9), $K_F(v)$, can be expressed as follows ([3],§2.5.2)

$$K_F(v) = K_F(\chi(v)) = \frac{\langle \Omega(\chi, \widetilde{\chi})\chi, \chi \rangle_v}{G(v)^2},$$

where χ means the horizontal lift from $T^{1,0}M$ to $\mathcal{H}TM := \text{span}\{\frac{\delta}{\delta z^i}\}$ and Ω is the curvature form of Chern-Finsler connection.

For any holomorphic map $\varphi : \Delta \to M$ (M is the unit disk on the complex plane) such that $\varphi'(0) \neq 0$, $\mathfrak{h} := \varphi^* G$ is a Hermitian metric in a neighborhood of the origin. It follows that the Gaussian curvature $K_{\mathfrak{h}}(0)$ is meaningful. Consequently, for any point $z \in M$ and direction $v \in \widetilde{M}_z$, the holomorphic curvature $K_F(v)$ in the direction v can also be written as ([3], (2.5.16), p.110)

$$K_F(v) = \sup_\varphi\{K_{\mathfrak{h}}(0)\}, \quad \mathfrak{h} = \varphi^* G, \tag{9.5.27}$$

where sup runs all holomorphic maps $\varphi : \Delta \to M$ such that $\varphi(0) = z$ and $\varphi'(0) = \lambda v$ ($\lambda \in \mathbb{C}^*$).

Set $\Sigma := \varphi(\Delta) \hookrightarrow M$ and consider $(\mathfrak{h}, \Sigma)$ as a piece of an isometrically immersed (2-dimensional real) surface in (M, G), such that $[v] = \lambda v$ is tangent to Σ at point z. Therefore, (9.5.27) can be transformed as

$$K_F(v) = \sup_\sigma\{K_{\mathfrak{h}}([v])\}. \tag{9.5.27'}$$

Obviously, $K_{\mathfrak{h}}([v])$ is the Gaussian curvature of surface Σ at point z.

Theorem 9.22 ([124]). *Let (M_1, F_1) and (M_2, F_2) be two complex Finsler manifolds where (M_1, F_1) is compact. Assume that their holomorphic curvatures satisfy $K_{F_1} \geqslant -B$ and $K_{F_2} \leqslant -A$, where A and B are positive constants. Then for any holomorphic map $f : M_1 \to M_2$, we have*

$$f^* F_2^2 \leq \frac{B}{A} F_1^2. \tag{9.5.28}$$

Proof. For $i = 1, 2$, let $G_i = F_i^2$, $K_{F_i}(v) = \sup_{\Sigma_i} K_{\mathfrak{h}_i}([v])$, $\mathfrak{h}_i = \varphi_i^* G_i$, $\Sigma_i = \varphi(\Delta) \hookrightarrow M_i$, φ_i be a holomorphic map.

The holomorphic map $f : M_1 \to M_2$ induces a holomorphic map from Σ_1 to Σ_2, we still denote it by f. Let $f^* G_2 = \mu(z, v) G_1$, where μ is a positive function depending on z and v. Since $\mathfrak{h}_1$ is a Hermite metric, we can express it as $\mathfrak{h}_1 = \lambda dz d\overline{z}$, where z is the complex coordinate on Σ_1. Then,

$$f^* \mathfrak{h}_2 = \mu \mathfrak{h}_1 = \mu \left(\varphi_1(z), d\varphi_1 \left(\frac{\partial}{\partial z} \right) \right) \lambda dz d\overline{z}.$$

By the formula for the Gaussian curvature, we obtain

$$\sup_{\Sigma_1} K_{f^* \mathfrak{h}_2}([v]) = \sup_{\Sigma_1} \left(- \frac{\Delta_z \log\mu + \Delta_z \log\lambda}{\mu\lambda} \right), \qquad (9.5.29)$$

where Δ_z is the Laplacian related to $f^* \mathfrak{h}_2$.

Since M_1 is compact, then PTM_1 is compact too. Consequently, μ can reach its maximal value on PTM_1. Put

$$\mu_0 := \mu(z_0, v_0) = \max_{PTM_1} \{\mu\} \geq \mu \left(\varphi_1(z), d\varphi_1 \left(\frac{\partial}{\partial z} \right) \right), \quad (z_0, v_0) \in PTM_1.$$

Then for $\varphi_1(0) = z_0$, $d\varphi_1(\frac{\partial}{\partial z}) = v_0$,

$$\Delta_z \log\mu \left(\varphi_1(0), d\varphi_1 \left(\left. \frac{\partial}{\partial z} \right|_0 \right) \right) := \Delta_z \log\mu(0) \leq 0. \qquad (9.5.30)$$

From (9.5.27) we deduce that

$$K_{f^* F_1}(v) = \sup_{\Sigma_1} \{ K_{\mathfrak{h}_1}([v]) \} = \sup_{\varphi_1} \{ K_{\varphi_1^* G_1}(0) \},$$

where the holomorphic map φ_1 satisfies $\varphi_1(0) = z$, $d\varphi_1(\frac{\partial}{\partial z}) = v$.

Similarly, we have

$$K_{f^* F_2}(v) = \sup_{\Sigma_1} \{ K_{f^* \mathfrak{h}_2}([v]) \} = \sup_{\varphi_1} \{ K_{(\varphi_1^* \circ f_* G_2)}(0) \},$$

$$K_{F_2}(f_* v) = \sup_{\Sigma_2} \{ K_{\mathfrak{h}_2}([f_* v]) \} = \sup_{\varphi_2} \{ K_{(\varphi_2^* G_2)}(0) \},$$

where the holomorphic map φ_2 satisfies $\varphi_2(0) = f(z)$, $d\varphi_2(\frac{\partial}{\partial z}) = f_* v$.

It is easy to see that $K_{f^* F_2}(v) \leqslant K_{F_2}(f_* v)$. By using (9.5.29), (9.5.30) and the assumption of the theorem, we have

$$\frac{1}{\mu_0} \sup_{\Sigma_1} \left(- \frac{\Delta_z \log \lambda}{\lambda} \right) \leqslant \sup_{\Sigma_1} K_{f^* \mathfrak{h}_2}([v]) \leqslant -A.$$

Therefore, based on the expression of $K_{F_1}(v)$ and the assumption of the theorem, we deduce from the above expression that

$$f^*G_2 = \mu G_1 \leq \mu_0 G_1$$

$$\leq -\frac{1}{A}\sup_{\Sigma_1}\left(-\frac{\Delta_z \log\lambda}{\lambda}\right)G_1$$

$$= -\frac{1}{A}K_{F_1}(v)G_1 \leq \frac{B}{A}G_1.$$

This proves the theorem. □

Exercises

9.1 Let $f : \mathcal{D} \to (\mathbb{V}^{n+1}, \widetilde{F})$ be a graph defined on a hyperplane $\mathcal{P}$, where $\mathcal{P}$ is perpendicular to $\widetilde{\beta}^\sharp$, f is given by (9.2.13). Let $\Phi(t)$ be defined by (9.2.24). Prove that if there is a $t_0 \in (0, \widetilde{b}^2)$ such that $\Phi(t_0) = 0$, then

$$u(x^1, \cdots, x^n) = \sqrt{\frac{t_0}{\widetilde{b}^2 - t_0}}\sqrt{(x^1)^2 + \cdots + (x^n)^2}$$

is a BH-minimal or HT-minimal graph with a singular point at the origin. ([40])

9.2 Let $(\mathbb{V}^3, \widetilde{F} = \sqrt{\sum_{\alpha=1}^{3}(\widetilde{y}^\alpha)^2} + \widetilde{b}\widetilde{y}^3)$ be a 3-dimensional special Minkowski-Randers space, $f : \mathbb{R}^2 \to (\mathbb{V}^3, \widetilde{F})$ be a graph given by $f(x^1, x^2) = (x^1, x^2, u(x^1, x^2))$ on the $x^1 x^2$-plane. Substituting $\sigma_B(t) = (1 - t^2)^{\frac{3}{2}}$ into (9.2.24), we obtain

$$\Phi(t) = (1 - t)^{\frac{1}{2}}(1 - 3\widetilde{b}^2 + 2t), \quad \Phi'(t) = \frac{3[1 - t + (\widetilde{b}^2 - t)]}{2(1 - t)^{\frac{1}{2}}},$$

$\widetilde{b} \in [0, 1)$. It is easy to see that $\Phi'(t) \geq 0$ for $t \in [0, \widetilde{b}^2]$. Prove that if $\frac{1}{\sqrt{3}} < \widetilde{b} < 1$, then $\Phi(t_0) = 0$ for $t_0 = \frac{3\widetilde{b}^2 - 1}{2}$. So, the cone

$$u(x^1, x^2) = \sqrt{\frac{3\widetilde{b}^2 - 1}{1 - \widetilde{b}^2}}\sqrt{(x^1)^2 + (x^2)^2}$$

is a HT-minimal surface with a singular point at the origin. In particular, the cone $u(x^1, x^2) = \sqrt{(x^1)^2 + (x^2)^2}$ is BH-minimal when $\widetilde{b} = \frac{1}{\sqrt{2}}$. ([135])

9.3 Let $f : \mathbb{R}^2 \supset \mathcal{D} \to (\mathbb{V}^3, \widetilde{F} = \frac{\widetilde{\alpha}^2}{\widetilde{\alpha} - \widetilde{\beta}})$ be a graph defined on $\mathcal{D}$, where $\widetilde{\alpha} = \sqrt{\sum_{\alpha=1}^{3}(\widetilde{y}^\alpha)^2}$ and $\widetilde{\beta} = \widetilde{b}\widetilde{y}^3$. Substituting $\sigma_B(t) = (2 + t^2)^{-1}$ into

(9.2.24) gives

$$\Phi(t) = \frac{2(1 - \widetilde{b}^2) + 3t}{(2 + t)^2}, \quad \Phi'(t) = \frac{2 + \widetilde{b}^2 + 3(\widetilde{b}^2 - t)}{(2 + t)^3}.$$

Prove that $\widetilde{F}$ is positively definite if and only if $\widetilde{b} \in [0, \frac{1}{2})$. So, we have $\frac{\Phi'(t)}{\Phi(t)} > 0$ for $\forall\, t \in [0, \widetilde{b}^2]$. Hence, $f(\mathcal{D})$ is a BH-minimal graph ([40]).

9.4 Let $f : \mathbb{R}^2 \to (\mathbb{V}^3, \widetilde{F}_b = \frac{(\widetilde{\alpha} + \widetilde{\beta})^2}{\widetilde{\alpha}})$, where $\widetilde{\alpha} = \sqrt{\sum_{\alpha=1}^{3}(\widetilde{y}^\alpha)^2}$, $\widetilde{\beta} = \widetilde{b}\widetilde{y}^3$ be a graph defined on the plane $x^1 x^2$. Set $\sigma_B(t) = \frac{2(1-t^2)^{\frac{7}{2}}}{2+3t^2}$. By (9.2.24) we obtain

$$\Phi(t) = \frac{2(1 - t)^{\frac{5}{2}}[2(1 - 10\widetilde{b}^2) + 3t(7 - 5\widetilde{b}^2 + 4t)]}{(2 + 3t)^2},$$

$$\Phi'(t) = \frac{5(1 - t)^{\frac{3}{2}}[(76 + 72t + 27t^2)(\widetilde{b}^2 - t) + (1 - t)(4 + 3t)(2 + 3t)]}{(2 + 3t)^3}.$$

Prove that $\widetilde{F}$ is positively definite if and only if $\widetilde{b} \in [0, 1)$. It follows that $\Phi'(t) \geq 0$ for $t \in [0, \widetilde{b}^2]$. When $\frac{1}{\sqrt{10}} < \widetilde{b} < 1$, one can see that

$$t_0 = \frac{1}{24}\left[15\widetilde{b}^2 - 21 + \sqrt{15(15\widetilde{b}^4 + 22\widetilde{b}^2 + 23)}\right]$$

is a zero point of $\Phi(t)$. Hence, the cone

$$u(x^1, x^2) = \sqrt{\frac{15\widetilde{b}^2 - 21 + \sqrt{15(15\widetilde{b}^4 + 22\widetilde{b}^2 + 23)}}{9\widetilde{b}^2 + 21 - \sqrt{15(15\widetilde{b}^4 + 22\widetilde{b}^2 + 23)}}}\sqrt{(x^1)^2 + (x^2)^2}$$

defined on $\mathcal{D} = \{x^3 = 0\} \setminus \{0\}$ is a BH-minimal surface with a singular point at the origin. In particular, when $\widetilde{b}^2 = \frac{\sqrt{505}-19}{18}$, the cone $u(x^1, x^2) = \sqrt{(x^1)^2 + (x^2)^2}$ is a BH-minimal graph ([40]).

9.5 Prove that the system (9.3.13) is equivalent to that

$$\int_{S_x M} g^{ij}\left(\phi_{ij}^\alpha - B_{ij}^k \phi_k^\alpha + \widetilde{B}_{\beta\gamma}^\alpha \phi_i^\beta \phi_j^\gamma\right)\Omega d\eta = 0,$$

where $B_{jk}^i = \frac{1}{2}[G^i]_{y^j y^k}$ and $\widetilde{B}_{\beta\gamma}^\alpha = \frac{1}{2}[\widetilde{G}^\alpha]_{\widetilde{y}^\beta \widetilde{y}^\gamma}$ are the Berwald connection coefficients of F and $\widetilde{F}$, respectively (§3.1.2). Thus, the tension field can be written as

$$\tau(\phi) = g^{ij}\left(\phi_{ij}^\alpha - B_{ij}^k \phi_k^\alpha + \widetilde{B}_{\beta\gamma}^\alpha \phi_i^\beta \phi_j^\gamma\right)\frac{\partial}{\partial \widetilde{x}^\alpha}.$$

9.6 Let $(M, F = \alpha + \beta)$ be a Randers-Berwald manifold, i.e., β is parallel with respect to the Riemannian metric α. Prove that spray coefficients of α and $F = \alpha + \beta$ are the same.

9.7 Prove Theorem 9.14 by using the similar way in the proof of Theorem 2.1.

9.8 Compute (9.5.25) and (9.5.26) in details.

9.9 Prove Theorem 9.20 in details.

Chapter 10

Einstein Metrics

In this chapter, we will focus on Einstein metrics in Finsler geometry. By Definition 5.4 (§5.4.3), a Finsler metric $F = F(x, y)$ on an n-dimensional manifold M is called an *Einstein metric* if its Ricci curvature satisfies $Ric = (n-1)K(x)F^2$. Moreover, it is said to have *Einstein constant* σ if $K(x) = \sigma = $ constant.

Finsler metrics with isotropic flag curvature are Einstein metrics. However, there are a lot of Einstein metrics without isotropic flag curvatures. As it is well known, Riemannian Einstein metrics with dimension $n \geq 3$ must be of constant Ricci curvature. However, the analogous proposition in the Finsler case is still open. We have already studied Einstein-Randers metrics in Chapter 5 (§5.4.3). In virtue of the navigation construction, Einstein-Randers metrics can be determined completely. Actually, Einstein-Randers metrics with dimension $n \geq 3$ must have constant Ricci curvature. We shall further study other types of Finsler-Einstein metrics in this chapter.

10.1 Projective rigidity and m-th root metrics

10.1.1 Projective rigidity of Einstein metrics

Two Finsler metrics $F(x, y)$ and $\widetilde{F}(x, y)$ on an n-dimensional manifold M are said to be (locally) projectively equivalent (§6.1) if their geodesics coincide as oriented curves in the same orientation. In a local standard coordinate system (x^i, y^i) on TM, $F(x, y)$ and $\widetilde{F}(x, y)$ are projectively equivalent if and only if their geodesic coefficients $G^i = G^i(x, y)$ and $\widetilde{G}^i = \widetilde{G}^i(x, y)$ satisfy (§6.1)

$$\widetilde{G}^i = G^i + Py^i, \tag{10.1.1}$$

where $P = P(x, y)$ is a positive homogeneous function of degree 1 in y. From (6.1.4) and (6.1.5) we see that their Ricci curvatures have the following relationship.

Lemma 10.1. *Let F and $\widetilde{F}$ be two Finsler metrics on an n-dimensional manifold M. If their geodesic coefficients satisfy (10.1.1), then their Ricci curvatures satisfy*

$$\widetilde{Ric} = Ric + (n-1)\{P^2 - P_{|k}y^k\}. \tag{10.1.2}$$

(10.1.2) is equivalent to the following equation

$$\widetilde{\lambda}\widetilde{F}^2 - \lambda F^2 = \Big[\frac{\widetilde{F}_{|k}y^k}{2\widetilde{F}}\Big]^2 - \Big[\frac{\widetilde{F}_{|k}y^k}{2\widetilde{F}}\Big]_{|l}y^l, \tag{10.1.3}$$

where

$$\lambda := \frac{Ric}{(n-1)F^2}, \quad \widetilde{\lambda} := \frac{\widetilde{Ric}}{(n-1)\widetilde{F}^2}.$$

Let $c(t)$ and $\widetilde{c}(\widetilde{t})$ be the geodesics with unit velocity of F and $\widetilde{F}$ respectively, such that $c = \widetilde{c}$ as oriented curves, i.e.,

$$c(t) = \widetilde{c}(\widetilde{t}), \quad \frac{d\widetilde{t}}{dt} > 0.$$

Put

$$f(t) := \frac{1}{\sqrt{\widetilde{F}(c(t), \dot{c}(t))}}, \quad \widetilde{f}(\widetilde{t}) := \frac{1}{\sqrt{F(\widetilde{c}(\widetilde{t}), \dot{\widetilde{c}}(\widetilde{t}))}}.$$

We have

$$f' = -f\frac{\widetilde{F}_{|k}\dot{c}^k}{2\widetilde{F}},$$

$$f'' = -f'\frac{\widetilde{F}_{|k}\dot{c}^k}{2\widetilde{F}} - f\Big(\frac{\widetilde{F}_{|k}\dot{c}^k}{2\widetilde{F}}\Big)_{|k}\dot{c}^k.$$

Restricting (10.1.3) to the lifting of $c(t)$ on TM, one can get

$$f''(t) + \lambda(t)f(t) = \frac{\widetilde{\lambda}(\widetilde{t})}{f^3(t)}. \tag{10.1.4}$$

Similarly,

$$\widetilde{f}''(\widetilde{t}) + \widetilde{\lambda}(\widetilde{t})\widetilde{f}(\widetilde{t}) = \frac{\lambda(t)}{\widetilde{f}^3(\widetilde{t})}. \tag{10.1.5}$$

(10.1.4) and (10.1.5) can be expressed as

$$-\frac{1}{2}\Big(\frac{d\widetilde{t}}{dt}\Big)\frac{d^3\widetilde{t}}{dt^3} + \frac{3}{4}\Big(\frac{d^2\widetilde{t}}{dt^2}\Big)^2 + \lambda(t)\Big(\frac{d\widetilde{t}}{dt}\Big)^2 = \widetilde{\lambda}(\widetilde{t})\Big(\frac{d\widetilde{t}}{dt}\Big)^4. \tag{10.1.6}$$

$$-\frac{1}{2}\left(\frac{dt}{d\widetilde{t}}\right)\frac{d^3t}{d\widetilde{t}^3} + \frac{3}{4}\left(\frac{d^2t}{d\widetilde{t}^2}\right)^2 + \widetilde{\lambda}(\widetilde{t})\left(\frac{dt}{d\widetilde{t}}\right)^2 = \lambda(t)\left(\frac{dt}{d\widetilde{t}}\right)^4. \tag{10.1.7}$$

(10.1.7) is the inverse of (10.1.6), and vice versa.

We suppose that F and $\widetilde{F}$ are all Einstein metrics with Einstein constants, i.e., λ and $\widetilde{\lambda}$ are all constants. Then, (10.1.4) is solvable in this case. The general solution can be represented by some elemental functions. Under the initial data:

$$f(0) = a > 0, \quad f'(0) = b \neq 0,$$

the solution of (10.1.4) is determined by

$$\int_a^{f(t)} \frac{s}{\sqrt{-\lambda s^4 + 2Cs^2 - \widetilde{\lambda}}}\, ds = \pm t, \tag{10.1.8}$$

where $\pm$ in (10.1.8) has the same sign of $f'(0) = b$, and the constant

$$C := \frac{1}{2}\left(\lambda a^2 + \frac{\widetilde{\lambda}}{a^2} + b^2\right). \tag{10.1.9}$$

The solution is given by $b \to 0$ when $b = 0$.

By estimating the integral in (10.1.8), we can prove the following

Theorem 10.1 ([114]). *Let F and $\widetilde{F}$ be two locally projectively equivalent Finsler metrics on an n-dimensional manifold M. If F and $\widetilde{F}$ are geodesically complete Einstein metrics with*

$$Ric = -(n-1)F^2, \quad \widetilde{Ric} = -(n-1)\widetilde{F}^2,$$

then $\widetilde{F} = F$.

Proof. Let $c(t)$ be a geodesic with $c(0) = x$ and $\dot{c}(0) = y$ for any fixed $y \in T_xM$ with $F(x,y) = 1$. When $\lambda = \widetilde{\lambda} = -1$, it follows from (10.1.8) that $f(t) := 1/\sqrt{\widetilde{F}(c(t), \dot{c}(t))}$ should be

$$f(t) = \sqrt{(a^2 + C)\cosh(2t) + ab\sinh(2t) - C}, \tag{10.1.10}$$

where

$$C = \frac{1}{2}\left(-a^2 - \frac{1}{a^2} + b^2\right). \tag{10.1.11}$$

By (10.1.11), the expression (10.1.10) can be rewritten as

$$f(t) = \begin{cases} \sqrt{\sqrt{C^2-1}\,\cosh\left[\cosh^{-1}\left(\frac{a^2+C}{\sqrt{C^2-1}}\right) \pm 2t\right] - C}, & \text{if } C^2 - 1 > 0, \\[2ex] \sqrt{e^{\pm 2t}\left(a^2 + C\right) - C}, & \text{if } C^2 - 1 = 0, \\[2ex] \sqrt{\sqrt{-C^2+1}\,\sinh\left[\sinh^{-1}\left(\frac{a^2+C}{\sqrt{-C^2+1}}\right) \pm 2t\right] - C}, & \text{if } C^2 - 1 < 0. \end{cases} \tag{10.1.12}$$

The sign $\pm$ in (10.1.12) is the same as $f'(0) = b \, (\neq 0)$.

The completeness of F implies that $f(t) > 0$ can be defined on $(-\infty, \infty)$. It follows form the completeness of $\widetilde{F}$ that

$$\int_{-\infty}^{0} \frac{1}{f(t)^2} dt = \infty = \int_{0}^{\infty} \frac{1}{f(t)^2} dt.$$

It is easy to see that $f(t) = 1$. Particularly, $\widetilde{F}(x, y) = 1$ when $t = 0$. Thus,

$$F(x, y) = \widetilde{F}(x, y), \quad \forall \, y \in T_x M. \qquad \square$$

Remark. The geodesic completeness in the theorem is indispensable. In the local case, projectively related Riemann-Einstein metrics may not be rigid, e.g., see [167].

All Finsler metrics considered here are positively definite. If a manifold is closed (compact without boundary), then it must be geodesically complete. Hence, the following corollary is immediate.

Corollary 10.1. *Let F and $\widetilde{F}$ be two Finsler-Einstein metrics on a closed manifold with $Ric = -(n-1)F^2$ and $\widetilde{Ric} = -(n-1)\widetilde{F}^2$. If they are locally projectively equivalent, then $F = \widetilde{F}$.*

The rigidity theorem fails for Finsler metrics with non-negative constant Ricci curvature.

10.1.2 m-th root Einstein metrics

An m-th root Finsler metric on an n-dimensional manifold M is the following form (cf. §2.1.2)

$$F = \left\{ a_{i_1 i_2 \cdots i_m}(x) y^{i_1} y^{i_2} \cdots y^{i_m} \right\}^{\frac{1}{m}},$$

where $a_{i_1 i_2 \cdots i_m}(x)$ are local scalar functions on M, which are symmetric with respect to indices $i_1, i_2, \cdots, i_m$. Because of positive definiteness, m must be even. It is easy to see that

$$F = \{ a_{i_1 j_1}(x) \cdots a_{i_k j_k}(x) y^{i_1} y^{j_1} \cdots y^{i_k} y^{j_k} \}^{\frac{1}{m}}$$

is an m-th root metric for any positive even number $m = 2k$ if $\alpha = \sqrt{a_{ij}(x)y^i y^j}$ is a Riemannian metric. Hence, Riemannian metrics are a special class of m-th ($m = 2$) root metrics.

For an m-th root metric $F = \sqrt[m]{a_{i_1 i_2 \cdots i_m}(x) y^{i_1} y^{i_2} \cdots y^{i_m}}$, let

$$A = a_{i_1 i_2 \cdots i_m}(x) y^{i_1} \cdots y^{i_m} = F^m,$$

$$A_i = a_{i i_2 \cdots i_m}(x) y^{i_2} \cdots y^{i_m} = \frac{1}{m} \frac{\partial A}{\partial y^i},$$

$$A_{ij} = a_{i j i_3 \cdots i_m}(x) y^{i_3} \cdots y^{i_m} = \frac{1}{m(m-1)} \frac{\partial^2 A}{\partial y^i \partial y^j},$$

$$A_{ijk} = a_{i j k i_4 \cdots i_m}(x) y^{i_4} \cdots y^{i_m} = \frac{1}{m(m-1)(m-2)} \frac{\partial^3 A}{\partial y^i \partial y^j \partial y^k}.$$

It follows that

$$F_{y^i} = \frac{A_i}{F^{m-1}}, \quad F_{y^i y^j} = (m-1) \frac{A_{ij}}{F^{m-2}} - (m-1) \frac{A_i A_j}{F^{2m-2}},$$

$$g_{ij} = (m-1) \frac{A_{ij}}{F^{m-2}} - (m-2) \frac{A_i A_j}{F^{2(m-1)}}. \tag{10.1.13}$$

Then

$$A_{ij} = \frac{F^{m-2}}{m-1} g_{ij} + \frac{m-2}{m-1} \frac{A_i A_j}{F^m}.$$

So, (A_{ij}) is positively definite. Let

$$(A^{ij}) = (A_{ij})^{-1},$$

which are rational functions in y, since A_{ij} is a homogeneous polynomial in y with degree $m-2$. We now have the following lemma.

Lemma 10.2. *Spray coefficients of an m-th root metric F are rational functions in y and*

$$G^i = \frac{A^{il}}{2(m-1)} \left\{ \frac{\partial A_l}{\partial x^k} y^k - \frac{1}{m} \frac{\partial A}{\partial x^l} \right\}. \tag{10.1.14}$$

Proof. It follows from (10.1.13) that

$$g^{ij} = \frac{F^{m-2}}{m-1} A^{ij} + \frac{m-2}{m-1} \frac{y^i y^j}{F^2}.$$

Moreover,

$$[F^2]_{x^l} = \frac{2 A_{x^l}}{m F^{m-2}},$$

$$[F^2]_{x^k y^l} y^k = \frac{2 (A_l)_{x^k} y^k}{F^{m-2}} - \frac{2(m-2)}{m} \frac{A_{x^k} y^k}{F^{2(m-1)}} A_l.$$

Thus geodesic coefficients of F are

$$G^i = \frac{1}{4} g^{il} \{ [F^2]_{x^k y^l} y^k - [F^2]_{x^l} \}$$

$$= \Big\{ \frac{F^{m-2}}{4(m-1)} A^{il} + \frac{m-2}{4(m-1)} \frac{y^i y^l}{F^2} \Big\}$$

$$\times \Big\{ \frac{2(A_l)_{x^k} y^k}{F^{m-2}} - \frac{2(m-2)}{m} \frac{A_{x^k} y^k}{F^{2(m-1)}} A_l - \frac{2A_{x^l}}{mF^{m-2}} \Big\}$$

$$= \frac{A^{il}}{2(m-1)} \Big\{ (A_l)_{x^k} y^k - \frac{1}{m} A_{x^l} \Big\}.$$

Hence, G^i are rational functions in y. □

Using the formula (3.3.15) of the Riemann curvature, we can see that $R^i_{\;j}$ are rational functions in y. Especially, the Ricci curvature $Ric = R^k_{\;k}(x, y)$ is a rational function in y. Suppose that F is an Einstein metric, i.e., $Ric = (n-1)\sigma F^2$. $F^2 = \frac{1}{(n-1)\sigma} Ric$ is a rational function in y if $\sigma \neq 0$. On the other hand, $F^2 = A^{2/m}$ is a rational function in y if and only if it is quadratic in y. Thus, we have proved the following theorem.

Theorem 10.2 ([156]). *Any non-Riemannian Einstein m-th root metric is Ricci flat.*

A nature problem is to study geometric the properties of Ricci flat m-th root metrics. We may begin to consider Ricci flat Douglas m-th root metrics.

10.2 The Ricci rigidity and Douglas-Einstein metrics

10.2.1 The Ricci rigidity

From Lemmas 5.3 and 5.4 one can see that a Randers metric $F = \alpha + \beta$ is Einsteinian if and only if there is a constant c such that (5.4.34) and (5.4.38) hold, i.e.,

$$\begin{cases} {}^\alpha Ric = (n-1)\{(K - 3c^2)\alpha^2 + (K + c^2)\beta^2 - s_{0,0} - s_0^2\} + 2t_{00} + \alpha^2 t^m_{\;m}, \\ r_{00} + 2s_0\beta = 2c(\alpha^2 - \beta^2). \end{cases}$$

$$(10.2.1)$$

The navigation representation of the above system is just Theorem 5.12. Let $\{h, W\}$ be the navigation data of an Einstein-Randers metric, i.e., h is a Riemann-Einstein metric, and W is a homothetic field with respect to h (denoted by V in Theorem 5.12).

Lemma 10.3 ([13]). *Let (M,h) be a compact Riemannian manifold without boundary. Any homothetic field W on (M,h) must be a Killing vector field. If h is a Riemann-Einstein metric with Ricci curvature K, then $\{h,W\}$ determines an Einstein-Randers metric with Ricci curvature K.*

Proof. Suppose that $W_{i,j} + W_{j,i} = -ch_{ij}$, where c is a constant and "," denotes the covariant differential with respect to h. Since (M,h) is compact without boundary, it follows from the divergence theorem in Riemann geometry that

$$0 = \int_M W^i_{,i}dV_h = -\frac{1}{2}\int_M nc\,dV_h,$$

where dV_h is the Riemannian volume form with respect to h. Thus, $c = 0$. The lemma follows from Theorem 5.12. $\square$

Now we present the Ricci rigidity theorem on Randers metrics.

Theorem 10.3 ([13]). *Let (M,F) be a compact Einstein-Randers manifold without boundary whose Ricci curvature is $K = \sigma = $ constant. Then*
(1) F is Riemannian if $\sigma < 0$;
(2) F is Berwaldian if $\sigma = 0$.

Proof. Let $\{h,W\}$ be the navigation data of an Einstein-Randers metric, where W is a Killing vector field according to Lemma 10.3. Let

$$w := h_{ij}W^j dx^i = W_i dx^i$$

be the dual 1-form to W. Denote by $\Delta := d\delta + \delta d$ the Laplacian on (M,h). By the Weitzenböck formula ([169], Ch. 3, §4), we have

$$\Delta w = (-W_{i,jk}h^{jk} + {}^h R_{ij}W^j)dx^i,$$

where ${}^h R_{ij}$ is the Ricci tensor related to h. From the condition of the theorem and Lemma 10.3 it follows that

$${}^h R_{ij}W^j = \sigma W_i.$$

Since W is a Killing vector field, then $W^i_{,i} = 0$. The Ricci identity shows that $W^j_{,ji} - W^j_{,ij} = -{}^h R_{ij}W^j$, from which it follows that

$$\Delta w = 2\sigma w.$$

Denote by $(,)$ the global inner product on (M,h) (L^2-inner product). The above formulas give rise to

$$\int_M \{W_{i,j}W^{i,j} + \sigma|w|^2\}dV_h = (\Delta w, w) = 2\sigma\int_M |w|^2 dV_h.$$

Hence,

$$\int_M \{W_{i,j} W^{i,j}\} dV_h = \sigma \int_M |w|^2 dV_h.$$

(1) If $\sigma < 0$, then $w = W = 0$. By using the navigation (5.4.16) of Randers metrics $F = \alpha + \beta$, one can see that $\beta = 0$, i.e., F is Riemannian.

(2) If $\sigma = 0$, then $W_{i,j} = 0$, i.e., W is a parallel vector field. By (5.4.16), β is also parallel with respect to h. Hence, F is Berwaldian. $\square$

Theorem 10.3 can be viewed as a generalization of the Akbar-Zadeh rigidity theorem (Theorem 5.7) within Randers metrics. A nature question is: Does Theorem 10.3 still hold for (α, β)-metrics?

10.2.2 Douglas (α, β)-metrics

Recall that a Finsler metric $F = F(x, y)$ with vanishing Douglas tensor is called a Douglas metric (§6.1.2, (6.1.10)). It is equivalent to that the geodesic coefficients of F are given in the following form

$$G^i = \frac{1}{2} \Gamma^i_{jk}(x) y^j y^k + P(x, y) y^i.$$

If a Douglas metric F is also Einsteinian with $Ric = (n-1)K(x)F^2$, then F is called a Douglas-Einstein metric. There are various Douglas-Einstein metrics in Finsler geometry.

A Randers metric $F = \alpha + \beta$ is of Douglas type if and only if β is closed ([18]). In such a case, we have $s_{ij} = 0$, $t_{ij} = 0$. Thus, the following proposition follows from (10.2.1) directly.

Proposition 10.1 ([13]). *Let $F = \alpha + \beta$ be a Douglas-Randers metric on an n-dimensional $(n \geq 2)$ manifold M. F is an Einstein metric if and only if there is a constant c such that α and β satisfy*

$$\begin{cases} {}^\alpha Ric = (n-1)\{(K - 3c^2)\alpha^2 + (K + c^2)\beta^2\}, \\ r_{00} = 2c(\alpha^2 - \beta^2). \end{cases} \tag{10.2.2}$$

A quadratic (α, β)-metric F is a Finsler metric in the following form

$$F = \frac{(\alpha + \beta)^2}{\alpha},$$

whose spray coefficients are given by (6.2.7). It is easy to prove that $F = (\alpha + \beta)^2/\alpha$ is Douglasian if and only if

$$s^i_{\ 0} = 0, \quad r_{00} = 2\tau\{(1 + 2b^2)\alpha^2 - 3\beta^2\},$$

which is equivalent to

$$b_{i,j} = 2\tau\{(1 + 2b^2)a_{ij} - 3b_ib_j\}, \tag{10.2.3}$$

where $\tau = \tau(x)$ is a scalar function on M. Thus, the spray coefficients of F are

$$G^i = {}^\alpha G^i + 2\tau\alpha^2 b^i + 2\tau(\alpha - 2\beta)y^i. \tag{10.2.4}$$

The Ricci curvature of F is given by

$$\begin{aligned} Ric = {}^\alpha Ric &- 2(n-1)(\tau_0 + 4\tau^2\beta)\alpha + 4(\tau_i + 4\tau^2 b_i)b^i\alpha^2 \\ &+ 4(n-2)(\tau_0 + 4\tau^2\beta)\beta - 24(n-2)\tau^2\beta^2 \\ &+ 4\tau^2\{5(n-1) + 2(2n-5)b^2\}\alpha^2. \end{aligned} \tag{10.2.5}$$

By a direct computation, we have the following

Theorem 10.4 ([37,160,176]). *Let* $F = \frac{(\alpha+\beta)^2}{\alpha}$ *be a quadratic* (α, β)-*metric on an n-dimensional manifold* M. *F is a Douglas-Einstein metric if and only if F is Ricci flat and satisfies*

$$\begin{aligned} {}^\alpha Ric &= 4\tau^2\{-\left[5(n-1) + 2(2n-5)b^2\right]\alpha^2 + 6(n-2)\beta^2\}, \\ b_{i,j} &= 2\tau\{(1 + 2b^2)a_{ij} - 3b_ib_j\}, \\ \tau_i &= -4\tau^2 b_i, \end{aligned} \tag{10.2.6}$$

where $\tau = \tau(x)$ *is a function on* M, $b^2 = \|\beta\|_\alpha^2$ *and* $b_{i,j}$ *denote the covariant derivative of* β *with respect to* α.

Proof. If F is Einsteinian, i.e., $Ric = (n-1)K(x)F^2$, then

$$\alpha^2 Ric = (n-1)K(x)\{\alpha^4 + 6\alpha^2\beta^2 + \beta^4 + 4(\alpha^2 + \beta^2)\beta\alpha\}.$$

From (10.2.5) it follows that

$$-(\tau_0 + 4\tau^2\beta)\alpha^2 = 2K(x)(\alpha^2 + \beta^2)\beta, \tag{10.2.7}$$

which means that the left hand side of (10.2.7) can be divided by β. Thus, $\tau_0 + 4\tau^2\beta$ can be divided by β, i.e.,

$$\tau_0 + 4\tau^2\beta = \delta\beta,$$
$$-\delta\alpha^2 = 2K(x)(\alpha^2 + \beta^2),$$

where $\delta = \delta(x)$ is a function on M. If $K(x) \neq 0$, then

$$\beta^2 = -\Big(\frac{\delta}{2K(x)} + 1\Big)\alpha^2,$$

which is impossible. So $K(x) = 0$, i.e., $Ric = 0$. It follows from (10.2.7) that

$$\tau_0 + 4\tau^2\beta = 0, \qquad (10.2.8)$$

which yields $(10.2.6)_3$. On the other hand, (10.2.5) can be reduced to

$$Ric = {}^\alpha Ric - 24(n-2)\tau^2\beta^2 + 4\tau^2\{5(n-1) + 2(2n-5)b^2\}\alpha^2. \quad (10.2.9)$$

Thus, by $Ric = 0$, we obtain

$$^\alpha Ric = 24(n-2)\tau^2\beta^2 - 4\tau^2\{5(n-1) + 2(2n-5)b^2\}\alpha^2.$$

So, the necessity of the theorem has been proved and the sufficiency is obvious. □

We now can give the structure of Douglas-Einstein quadratic metrics by means of solving equation (10.2.6).

Theorem 10.5. *Let* $F = \frac{(\alpha+\beta)^2}{\alpha}$ *be a non-Berwald quadratic* (α, β)-*metric on* n-*dimensional manifold* M. F *is a Douglas-Einstein metric if and only if it is Ricci flat and* α *is a warped product metric on* $M = R \times \breve{M}$, β *is a 1-form determined by the first factor* R. *Precisely,*

$$\alpha^2 = dt \otimes dt + (\varphi')^2\breve{\alpha}^2,$$
$$\beta = \frac{1}{10}\varphi^{-3/5}\varphi'dt.$$

where $\varphi = \varphi(t)$ *satisfies*

$$\varphi'' = 20\varphi^{1/5} + \frac{2}{5}\varphi^{-1}(\varphi')^2.$$

Moreover, the Riemannian metric $\breve{\alpha}$ *on* $\breve{M}$ *is an Einstein metric*

$$\breve{Ric} = (n-2)\lambda\breve{\alpha}^2,$$

where $\lambda = 400(1 - b^2)\varphi^{2/5}$ *is a constant.*

Proof. By Theorem 10.4, if $\tau = 0$, then β is parallel and α is Ricci flat. In virtue of the de Rham decomposition theorem, α is a direct sum of R and a Ricci flat metric, and β is a parallel covector field on R. Such a metric is Berwaldian.

So, we have $\tau \neq 0$. Without loss of generality, we can suppose that τ is positive, otherwise, we can choose $\widetilde{\beta} = -\beta$ and $\widetilde{\tau} = -\tau$. On putting

$$f = \frac{1}{\tau}, \qquad (10.2.10)$$

we have from $(10.2.5)_2$ and $(10.2.5)_3$ that

$$ff_{ij} + \frac{3}{2}f_if_j = 8(1 + 2b^2)a_{ij}, \tag{10.2.11}$$

where f_{ij} is the Hessian of f with respect to α. Let

$$\varphi = f^{5/2}. \tag{10.2.12}$$

Then (10.2.11) can be rewritten as

$$\varphi_{ij} = 20f^{1/2}(1 + 2b^2)a_{ij}. \tag{10.2.13}$$

Since $b \neq 0$, one can see easily that $d\varphi \neq 0$. We now need the following lemma, of which the proof is easy (as an exercise).

Lemma 10.4 (177). *If there are smooth functions φ and λ on a Riemannian manifold (M, α) such that $\mathrm{Hess}_\alpha \varphi = \lambda\alpha^2$ with $d\varphi \neq 0$, then the Riemannian structure is a warped product. In other words, $M = R \times \check{M}$, φ depends only on the first factor, $\check{M}$ is the level set of φ and $\alpha^2 = dt \otimes dt + (\varphi'(t))^2\check{\alpha}^2$.*

By the above lemma, we see that the Riemannian metric α in the theorem is a local warped product, i.e.,

$$\alpha^2 = dt \otimes dt + (\varphi'(t))^2\check{\alpha}^2, \quad \varphi = \varphi(t). \tag{10.2.14}$$

Moreover we have

$$\beta = d\left(\frac{1}{4\tau}\right) = d\left(\frac{\varphi^{2/5}}{4}\right) = \frac{1}{10}\varphi^{-3/5}\varphi'dt. \tag{10.2.15}$$

The norm of β with respect to α is

$$b^2 = \frac{1}{100}\varphi^{-6/5}(\varphi')^2. \tag{10.2.16}$$

It follows form Lemma 10.4 that

$$\varphi_{ij} = \varphi''a_{ij}. \tag{10.2.17}$$

By (10.2.12), (10.2.13), (10.2.16) and (10.2.17), we see that φ satisfies the following differential equation

$$\varphi'' = 20f^{1/2}(1 + 2b^2) = 20\varphi^{1/5}(1 + 2b^2) = 20\varphi^{1/5} + \frac{2}{5}\varphi^{-1}\varphi'\varphi'. \tag{10.2.18}$$

Since φ satisfies (10.2.18), α and β determined by (10.2.14) and (10.2.15) respectively are the solutions of $(10.2.5)_2$ and $(10.2.5)_3$. Now we verify the Ricci curvature equation $(10.2.5)_1$. Substituting (10.2.14) and (10.2.15) into the Ricci curvature equation yields that

$$^\alpha Ric = 4\tau^2\left\{-\left[5(n-1) + 2(2n-5)b^2\right](\varphi')^2\check{\alpha}^2 + (n-1)(2b^2 - 5)y^1y^1\right\}. \tag{10.2.19}$$

By (10.2.19), one can get the Ricci curvature of the warped product metric (10.2.14)

$$^\alpha Ric = \check{Ric} - \left[\varphi''' \varphi' + (n-2)(\varphi'')^2 \right] \check{\alpha}^2 - (n-1)\frac{\varphi'''}{\varphi'} y^1 y^1. \qquad (10.2.20)$$

Since $\check{\alpha}$ and $\check{Ric}$ are independent of y^1, we have from (10.2.19) and (10.2.20)

$$-\frac{\varphi'''}{\varphi'} = 4\tau^2(2b^2 - 5), \qquad (10.2.21)$$

$$\check{Ric} = \left\{ \varphi''' \varphi' + (n-2)(\varphi'')^2 - 4\tau^2(\varphi')^2 \left[5(n-1) + 2(2n-5)b^2 \right] \right\} \check{\alpha}^2. \qquad (10.2.22)$$

Differentiating (10.2.18) with respect to t yields (10.2.21). Inserting (10.2.16), (10.2.18) and (10.2.21) into (10.2.22), we find surprisingly that

$$\check{Ric} = 400(n-2)(1-b^2)\varphi^{2/5}\check{\alpha}^2,$$

i.e., $\check{\alpha}$ is an $(n-1)$-dimensional Einstein metric.

Finally, we want to show that $(1-b^2)\varphi^{2/5}$ is constant. By a direct computation, we have

$$(b^2)' = \frac{2}{5}\varphi^{-1}\varphi'(1-b^2),$$

which implies that

$$1 - b^2 = c_1 \varphi^{-2/5},$$

where c_1 is a constant. This completes the proof of Theorem 10.5. $\qquad\square$

By the proof of Lemma 4.2 in [159], we can see that if $F = \frac{(\alpha+\beta)^2}{\alpha}$ has constant Ricci curvature, then β must satisfy

$$s^k{}_0 s_{k0} = 0, \quad r_{ij} = \tau\{(1+2b^2)a_{ij} - 3b_i b_j\}, \qquad (10.2.23)$$

where τ is a smooth function on the manifold. The first condition means s_{k0} (as a vector) is zero, so β is closed. Therefore, F is of Douglas type. Namely, the word "Douglas" in Theorems 10.4 and 10.5 above can be removed. This is observed in [117].

Using suitable deformations of α and β, we can express a square metric $F = (\alpha+\beta)^2/\alpha$ using another choice of Riemannian metric $\overline{\alpha}$ and 1-form $\overline{\beta}$ so that the square metric is an Einstein metric if and only if $\overline{\alpha}$ is an Einstein metric and $\overline{\beta}$ is conformal. This is very similar to Randers metrics. Then we can also determine the local structure of Einstein square metrics.

Theorem 10.5* ([117]) *Let $F = \frac{(\alpha+\beta)^2}{\alpha}$ be a Finsler metric on an n-dimensional manifold M. Then the following are equivalent:*

(1) F is an Einstein metric;

(2) The Riemannian metric $\overline{\alpha} := (1-b^2)^{\frac{3}{2}}\sqrt{\alpha^2-\beta^2}$ and the 1-form $\overline{\beta} := (1-b^2)^2\beta$ satisfy

$$\overline{Ric} = 0, \quad \overline{b}_{i|j} = k\overline{a}_{ij}, \tag{10.2.24}$$

where k is a constant number, $\overline{b} = \|\overline{\beta}\|_{\overline{\alpha}}$ and $\overline{b}_{i|}$ is the covariant derivation of $\overline{\beta}$ with respect to $\overline{\alpha}$. In this case, F is given in the following form

$$F = \frac{\left(\sqrt{\left(1-\overline{b}^2\right)\overline{\alpha}^2 + \overline{\beta}^2} + \overline{\beta}\right)^2}{\left(1-\overline{b}^2\right)^2\sqrt{\left(1-\overline{b}^2\right)\overline{\alpha}^2 + \overline{\beta}^2}} \tag{10.2.25}$$

with $\overline{b} = b$.

10.3 Einstein (α, β)-metrics

10.3.1 Polynomial (α, β)-metrics

As in section 2.1.2, an (α, β)-metric is a Finsler metric $F = \alpha\phi(s)$ defined by (2.17), where $\phi(s)$ satisfies conditions in Lemma 2.1. Here α is a Riemannian metric and β is a 1-form, $s = \beta/\alpha$. If $\phi(s)$ is a polynomial in s, i.e.,

$$\phi(s) = \sum_{i=0}^{k} C_k s^k, \quad C_0 := 1, \quad C_k \neq 0,$$

then it is called a *polynomial (α, β)-metric*. Clearly, this is a Randers metric when $k = 1$.

If we denote by G^i and G^i_α geodesic coefficients of F and α respectively, then they are related by (6.2.7) and (6.2.8). Thus, by using (3.3.15), we can directly compute the relation between flag curvature tensors $R^i_{\ j}$ and $^\alpha R^i_{\ j}$. Furthermore, we can get the relation between Ricci curvatures Ric and $^\alpha Ric$. The following lemma was given in [38], whose detailed proof is omitted here.

Lemma 10.5 ([38]). *Let $F = \alpha\phi(s)$, $s = \beta/\alpha$, be a polynomial (α, β)-metric. Then the relation between Ricci curvatures Ric and $^\alpha Ric$ is*

$$Ric = {}^\alpha Ric + RT^m_m,$$

where

$$RT_m^m$$

$$= \frac{r_{00}^2}{\alpha^2}\left[(n-1)c_1 + c_2\right] + \frac{1}{\alpha}\left\{r_{00}s_0\left[(n-1)c_3 + c_4\right] + r_{00}r_0\left[(n-1)c_5 + c_6\right]\right.$$
$$\left. + r_{00;0}\left[(n-1)c_7 + c_8\right]\right\} + \left\{s_0^2\left[(n-1)c_9 + c_{10}\right] + (rr_{00} - r_0^2)c_{11}\right.$$
$$+ r_0 s_0\left[(n-1)c_{12} + c_{13}\right] + (r_{00}r^m{}_m - r_{0m}r^m{}_0 + r_{00;m}b^m - r_{0m;0}b^m)c_{14}$$
$$+ r_{0m}s^m{}_0\left[(n-1)c_{15} + c_{16}\right] + s_{0;0}\left[(n-1)c_{17} + c_{18}\right] + s_{0m}s^m{}_0 c_{19}\right\}$$
$$+ \alpha\left\{rs_0 c_{20} + s_m s^m{}_0\left[(n-1)c_{21} + c_{22}\right] + (3s_m r^m{}_0 - 2s_0 r^m{}_m + 2r_m s^m{}_0\right.$$
$$\left. - 2s_{0;m}b^m + s_{m;0}b^m)c_{23} + s^m{}_{0;m}c_{24}\right\} + \alpha^2\left\{s_m s^m c_{25} + s^i{}_m s^m{}_i c_{26}\right\}.$$

Here we use the notations in (4.3.4), and

$$A_1 := \phi - s\phi', \qquad A_2 = \phi - s\phi' + (b^2 - s^2)\phi'',$$

$$c_1 = \frac{\bar{c}_1}{\phi^2 A_2^3}, \quad c_2 = \frac{\bar{c}_2}{A_2^4}, \quad c_3 = \frac{\bar{c}_3}{\phi^2 A_1 A_2^3}, \quad c_4 = \frac{\bar{c}_4}{A_1 A_2^4}, \quad c_5 = \frac{\bar{c}_5}{\phi A_2^2},$$

$$c_6 = \frac{\bar{c}_6}{A_2^3}, \quad c_7 = \frac{\bar{c}_7}{\phi A_2}, \quad c_8 = \frac{\bar{c}_8}{A_2^2}, \quad c_9 = \frac{\bar{c}_9}{\phi^2 A_1^2 A_2^3}, \quad c_{10} = \frac{\bar{c}_{10}}{A_1^3 A_2^4},$$

$$c_{11} = \frac{\bar{c}_{11}}{A_2^2}, \quad c_{12} = \frac{\bar{c}_{12}}{\phi A_1 A_2^2}, \quad c_{13} = \frac{\bar{c}_{13}}{A_1 A_2^3}, \quad c_{14} = \frac{\bar{c}_{14}}{A_2}, \quad c_{15} = \frac{\bar{c}_{15}}{\phi A_1 A_2},$$

$$c_{16} = \frac{\bar{c}_{16}}{A_1 A_2^2}, \quad c_{17} = \frac{\bar{c}_{17}}{\phi A_1 A_2}, \quad c_{18} = \frac{\bar{c}_{18}}{A_1 A_2^2}, \quad c_{19} = \frac{\bar{c}_{19}}{A_1^3}, \quad c_{20} = \frac{\bar{c}_{20}}{A_1 A_2^2},$$

$$c_{21} = \frac{\bar{c}_{21}}{\phi A_1^2 A_2}, \quad c_{22} = \frac{\bar{c}_{22}}{A_1^2 A_2^2}, \quad c_{23} = \frac{\bar{c}_{23}}{A_1 A_2}, \quad c_{24} = \frac{\bar{c}_{24}}{A_1}, \quad c_{25} = \frac{\bar{c}_{25}}{A_1^2 A_2},$$

and

$$c_{26} = \frac{\bar{c}_{26}}{A_1^2},$$

where $\bar{c}_i$ are all polynomials in s. Every c_i are in the form of

$$c_i = \frac{\bar{c}_i}{\phi^{j_i} A_1^{k_i} A_2^{l_i}}, \quad i = 1, 2, \cdots, 26$$

and

$$j_i \in \{0, 1, 2\}, \quad k_i \in \{0, 1, 2, 3\}, \quad l_i \in \{0, 1, 2, 3, 4\}.$$

Now we establish the following theorem.

Theorem 10.6 ([38]). *Let* $F = \alpha\phi(s)$, $s = \beta/\alpha$, *be a polynomial* (α, β)-*metric with degree* $k \geq 2$. *Then* F *is Einsteinian if and only if* F *is Ricci flat.*

The skeleton of the proof. Since the degree of $\phi(s)$ is $\deg(\phi) = k \geq 2$, and $\deg(A_1) = \deg(A_2) = \deg(\phi)$, then a direct computation shows the degree of each $\bar{c}_i$ satisfies $\deg(\bar{c}_i) < \deg(\phi^{j_i} A_1^{k_i} A_2^{l_i})$.

Now suppose $F = \alpha\phi(s)$ is Einsteinian, i.e., $Ric = (n-1)K(x)F^2$. By Lemma 10.5, a long and cumbersome computation (see [38] for detail) gives rise to
$$E_{11k}s^{11k} + E_{11k-1}s^{11k-1} + E_{11k-2}s^{11k-2} + \cdots + E_{9k+2}s^{9k+2} + \cdots + E_1 s + E_0 = 0.$$
Since s is arbitrary, it shows $E_i \equiv 0$, $i = 0, 1, \cdots, 11k$. On the other hand, a direct computation shows
$$E_{11k} = C_k{}^{11} K(x) b^4 (k+1)^4 (k-1)^7 (n-1).$$
Since $k \geq 2$, $C_k \neq 0$, $b \neq 0$ and $n \geq 2$, then it follows from the above equation that $K = 0$, i.e., F is Ricci flat. $\qquad\square$

10.3.2 Kropina metrics

Kropina metrics are a kind of (α, β)-metrics with $\phi(s) = 1/s$, i.e., $F = \alpha^2/\beta$. It is introduced by the Russian physicist V. K. Kropina ([64]). Although there are singularities ($\beta = 0$), it has important applications in the general dynamic system represented by Lagrangian functions. Recently, there are some new developments in the study of Kropina metrics ([96, 155]).

In this section we focus on Einstein Kropina metrics $F = \alpha^2/\beta$. We always assume that $s = \beta/\alpha > 0$ if unless otherwise stated. Firstly, we discuss the Ricci curvature of Kropina metrics.

By means of (6.2.7), (6.2.8) and (3.3.15), and using notations in (4.3.4), the Ricci curvature of a Kropina metric F is ([158])
$$Ric = {}^{\alpha}Ric + T, \tag{10.3.1}$$
where ${}^{\alpha}Ric$ denotes the Ricci curvature of α, and
$$
\begin{aligned}
T = {}&- \frac{\alpha^2}{b^4\beta} s_0 r - \frac{r}{b^4} r_{00} + \frac{\alpha^2}{b^2\beta} b^k s_{0|k} + \frac{1}{b^2} b^k r_{00|k} + \frac{n-2}{b^2} s_{0|0} \\
&+ \frac{n-1}{b^2\alpha^2} \beta r_{00|0} + \frac{1}{b^2} \left(\frac{\alpha^2}{\beta} s_0 + r_{00} \right) r^k{}_k \\
&- \frac{\alpha^2}{\beta} s^k{}_{0|k} - \frac{1}{b^2} r_{0|0} - \frac{2(2n-3)}{b^4} r_0 s_0 - \frac{n-2}{b^4} s_0^2 \\
&- \frac{4(n-1)}{b^4\alpha^2} \beta r_{00} r_0 + \frac{2(n-1)}{b^4\alpha^2} \beta r_{00} s_0 \\
&+ \frac{3(n-1)}{b^4\alpha^4} \beta^2 r_{00}^2 + \frac{2n}{b^2} s^k{}_0 r_{0k} + \frac{1}{b^4} r_0^2 - \frac{\alpha^2}{b^2\beta} s^k{}_0 r_k \\
&+ \frac{n-1}{b^2\beta} \alpha^2 s^k{}_0 s_k - \frac{\alpha^4}{2b^2\beta^2} s^k s_k - \frac{\alpha^2}{b^2\beta} s^k r_{0k} - \frac{\alpha^4}{4\beta^2} s^j{}_k s^k{}_j.
\end{aligned}
\tag{10.3.2}
$$

From now on, "$|$" and "$.$" denote the horizontal and vertical covariant differentials with respect to the Berwald connection given by G^i_α, respectively.

Lemma 10.6. *Let* $F = \alpha\phi(s)$ *be an* (α, β)-*metric with* $r_{00} = c(x)\alpha^2$. *If* α *is an Einstein metric, i.e.,* $^\alpha Ric = \lambda(x)\alpha^2$, *then the following formulas hold:*

$$\begin{cases} s^i_{\ 0|i} = (n-1)c_0 + \lambda\beta, \\ b^k s^i_{\ k|i} = (n-1)b^k c_k + \lambda b^2, \\ 0 = (n-1)b^k c_k + \lambda b^2 + s^k_{\ |k} + s^k_{\ j} s^j_{\ k}, \end{cases}$$

where $c_k := \partial c/\partial x^k$, $c_0 = c_k y^k$.

Proof. Since β satisfies $r_{00} = c(x)\alpha^2$, a direct computation yields that

$$\begin{cases} b^j s^k_{\ j|i} = (b^j s^k_{\ j})_{|i} - b^j_{\ |i} s^k_{\ j} = -s^k_{\ |i} - (r^j_{\ i} + s^j_{\ i})s^k_{\ j} \\ \qquad = -s^k_{\ |i} - c s^k_{\ i} - s^k_{\ j} s^j_{\ i}, \\ b^j s^k_{\ j|k} = -s^k_{\ |k} - s^k_{\ j} s^j_{\ k}. \end{cases} \qquad (10.3.3)$$

We have the Ricci identity $b_{j|k|l} - b_{j|l|k} = b^s \overline{R}_{jskl}$ for a Riemannian metric $\alpha = \sqrt{a_{ij}y^i y^j}$, where $\overline{R}_{jskl}$ is the Riemannian curvature tensor with respect to α. Contracting it with a^{jl} and noting that α is an Einstein metric, one can get

$$a^{jl}(b_{j|k|l} - b_{j|l|k}) = b^l_{\ |k|l} - b^l_{\ |l|k} = (r^l_{\ k} + s^l_{\ k})_{|l} - (r^l_{\ l} + s^l_{\ l})_{|k}$$
$$= -(n-1)c_k + s^l_{\ k|l} = b^s a^{jl}\overline{R}_{jskl}$$
$$= b^s\ {}^\alpha R_{sk} = \lambda b^s a_{sk} = \lambda b_k,$$

i.e.,

$$s^l_{\ k|l} = (n-1)c_k + \lambda b_k, \quad s^k_{\ 0|k} = (n-1)c_0 + \lambda\beta.$$

Contracting it with b^k yields that $b^k s^l_{\ k|l} = (n-1)b^k c_k + \lambda b^2$. Comparing it with the second equation in (10.3.3), we obtain

$$0 = (n-1)b^k c_k + \lambda b^2 + s^k_{\ |k} + s^k_{\ j} s^j_{\ k}. \qquad \square$$

Theorem 10.7 ([158]). *Let* $F = \frac{\alpha^2}{\beta}$ *be a non-Riemannian Kropina metric on n-dimensional manifold* M.

(1) For $n = 2$, F *is an Einstein metric if and only if there are functions* $c = c(x)$, $\lambda = \lambda(x)$ *such that* α *and* β *satisfy*

$$\begin{cases} r_{00} = c\alpha^2, \\ ^\alpha Ric = \lambda\alpha^2, \\ 0 = \lambda\, b^2\beta - cs_0 + b^k c_k\beta + b^k s_{0|k} - b^2 s^k_{\ 0|k} + s^k_{\ 0} s_k. \end{cases} \qquad (10.3.4)$$

(2) *For* $n \geq 3$, *F is an Einstein metric if and only if there are functions*
$c = c(x)$, $f = f(x)$ *such that* α *and* β *satisfy*

$$
\begin{cases}
r_{00} = c\alpha^2, \\
f\alpha^2 = {}^\alpha Ric\, b^4 + (n-2)\{b^2 s_{0|0} + b^2 c_0 \beta - 2c\beta s_0 \\
\qquad - s_0^2 - c^2 \beta^2\}, \\
0 = \{(n-2)s_k s^k - b^2 s^k{}_{|k} - b^2 s^i{}_j s^j{}_i\}\beta + (n-3)b^2 c s_0 \\
\qquad + b^2 b^k s_{0|k} - b^4 s^k{}_{0|k} + (n-1)b^2 s^k{}_0 s_k,
\end{cases}
\tag{10.3.5}
$$

where

$$
f = -(n-2)b^2 c^2 - b^2 b^k c_k + (n-2)s^k s_k - b^2 s^k{}_{|k} - b^2 s^i{}_j s^j{}_i. \tag{10.3.6}
$$

In each case, for $n \geq 2$, *we have* $\sigma = -\frac{1}{2b^2} s^k s_k - \frac{1}{4} s^i{}_j s^j{}_i$.

Proof. Let $F = \frac{\alpha^2}{\beta}$ be an Einstein metric such that $Ric = (n-1)\sigma(x)F^2$. Inserting it into (10.3.1) and multiplying both sides by $b^4 \alpha^4 \beta^2$, we can obtain that

$$
\begin{aligned}
0 = {}& 3(n-1)\beta^4 r_{00}^2 + (n-1)\{b^2 r_{00|0} - 4r_{00}r_0 + 2r_{00}s_0\}\beta^3 \alpha^2 \\
& + \{{}^\alpha Ric\, b^4 - r_{00}r + b^2 b^k r_{00|k} + (n-2)b^2 s_{0|0} + b^2 r_{00}r^k{}_k \\
& \quad - b^2 r_{0|0} - (4n-6)r_0 s_0 - (n-2)s_0^2 + 2nb^2 r_{0k} s^k{}_0 + r_0^2\}\beta^2 \alpha^4 \\
& + \{-s_0 r + b^2 b^k s_{0|k} + b^2 s_0 r^k{}_k - b^4 s^k{}_{0|k} - b^2 s^k{}_0 r_k \\
& \quad + (n-1)b^2 s^k{}_0 s_k - b^2 r_{0k} s^k\}\beta \alpha^6 \\
& - b^2\{\frac{1}{2}s^k s_k + \frac{b^2}{4}s^i{}_j s^j{}_i + \sigma(x)b^2\}\alpha^8,
\end{aligned}
\tag{10.3.7}
$$

which implies that $3(n-1)\beta^4 r_{00}^2$ can be divided by α^2. Since α^2 is irreducible and β is a linear form, r_{00}^2 must be divided by α^2, i.e., there is a function $c(x)$ such that

$$
r_{00} = c(x)\alpha^2, \tag{10.3.8}
$$

which implies that β is a conformal form with respect to α, i.e., the duality of β is a conformal vector field. It follows obviously from (10.3.8) that

$$
\begin{cases}
r_{00} = c\alpha^2, \quad r_{ij} = ca_{ij}, \quad r_{0i} = cy_i, \quad r_i = cb_i, \quad r = cb^2, \quad r^i{}_j = c\delta^i{}_j, \\
r_{0k}s^k{}_0 = 0, \quad r_{0k}s^k = cs_0, \quad r_0 = c\beta, \quad s^k{}_0 r_k = cs_0, \\
r_{00|k} = c_k \alpha^2, \quad r_{00|0} = c_0 \alpha^2, \quad r^k{}_k = nc, \quad r_{0|0} = c_0\beta + c^2\alpha^2,
\end{cases}
$$

where $y_i := a_{ij}y^j$, $c_k := \partial c/\partial x^k$, $c_0 = c_k y^k$.

Substituting all of the above into (10.3.7) and dividing both sides with α^4, we have

$$
\begin{aligned}
0 = {}^\alpha Ric\, b^4\beta^2 &+ (n-2)\{b^2 s_{0|0} + b^2 c_0\beta - 2c\beta s_0 - s_0^2 - c^2\beta^2\}\beta^2 \\
&+ b^2\{(n-3)cs_0 + (n-2)c^2\beta + b^k c_k\beta + b^k s_{0|k} - b^2 s^k{}_{0|k} \\
&+ (n-1)s^k{}_0 s_k\}\beta\alpha^2 - b^2\left\{\frac{1}{2}s^k s_k + \frac{b^2}{4}s^i{}_j s^j{}_i + \sigma b^2\right\}\alpha^4.
\end{aligned}
\tag{10.3.9}
$$

In the following, we consider two cases separably.

Case I: $n = 2$. Now (10.3.9) becomes

$$
\begin{aligned}
0 = {}^\alpha Ric\, b^2\beta^2 &+ \{-cs_0 + b^k c_k\beta + b^k s_{0|k} - b^2 s^k{}_{0|k} + s^k{}_0 s_k\}\beta\alpha^2 \\
&- \left\{\frac{1}{2}s^k s_k + \frac{b^2}{4}s^i{}_j s^j{}_i + \sigma b^2\right\}\alpha^4,
\end{aligned}
\tag{10.3.10}
$$

which implies that there is $\lambda = \lambda(x)$ such that

$$
{}^\alpha Ric = \lambda\alpha^2,
$$

i.e., α is a Riemann-Einstein metric. Thus, (10.3.10) is equivalent to

$$
\begin{cases}
\eta = \lambda\, b^2\beta - cs_0 + b^k c_k\beta + b^k s_{0|k} - b^2 s^k{}_{0|k} + s^k{}_0 s_k, \\
0 = \beta\eta - \left\{\dfrac{1}{2}s^k s_k + \dfrac{b^2}{4}s^i{}_j s^j{}_i + \sigma b^2\right\}\alpha^2.
\end{cases}
\tag{10.3.11}
$$

The second equation of (10.3.11) means that

$$
\beta\eta = f\alpha^2, \qquad f = \frac{1}{2}s^k s_k + \frac{b^2}{4}s^i{}_j s^j{}_i + \sigma b^2.
$$

There are two cases. (i) If $\eta = t\beta$ where $t = t(x)$ is a function, then $tb_i b_j = fa_{ij}$. Comparing matrices in both sides yields that $t = f = 0$. Hence $\eta = 0$. (ii) If $\eta \neq t\beta$, we can choose a direction y such that $\eta(y) = 0$. Since α is positively definite, $\alpha(y) \neq 0$ and $f = 0$. In either case, we have $f = 0$ and $\eta = 0$.

Now (10.3.11) turns to

$$
\begin{cases}
0 = \lambda b^2\beta - cs_0 + b^k c_k\beta + b^k s_{0|k} - b^2 s^k{}_{0|k} + s^k{}_0 s_k, \\
\sigma = -\dfrac{1}{2b^2}s^k s_k - \dfrac{1}{4}s^i{}_j s^j{}_i.
\end{cases}
\tag{10.3.12}
$$

Conversely, if (10.3.4) holds, we insert it into (10.3.1) and obtain $Ric = \sigma F^2$, where σ is determined by the second equation of (10.3.12). Hence, F is an Einstein metric.

Case II: $n \geq 3$. From (10.3.9) we see that there is a function $f = f(x)$ such that

$$^\alpha Ric\, b^4 + (n-2)\{b^2 s_{0|0} + b^2 c_0 \beta - 2c\beta s_0 - s_0^2 - c^2 \beta^2\} = f\alpha^2.$$

Thus, (10.3.9) becomes

$$0 = \beta\{(n-3)b^2 cs_0 + (n-2)b^2 c^2 \beta + b^2 b^k c_k \beta + b^2 b^k s_{0|k}$$
$$- b^4 s^k{}_{0|k} + (n-1)b^2 s^k{}_0 s_k + f\beta\}$$
$$- b^2 \left\{\frac{1}{2} s^k s_k + \frac{b^2}{4} s^i{}_j s^j{}_i + \sigma(x)b^2\right\}\alpha^2,$$

which is equivalent to

$$\begin{cases} 0 = (n-3)b^2 cs_0 + (n-2)b^2 c^2 \beta + b^2 b^k c_k \beta + b^2 b^k s_{0|k} \\ \quad - b^4 s^k{}_{0|k} + (n-1)b^2 s^k{}_0 s_k + f\beta, \\ 0 = \frac{1}{2} s^k s_k + \frac{b^2}{4} s^i{}_j s^j{}_i + b^2 \sigma, \end{cases} \tag{10.3.13}$$

since α cannot be divided by β. Differentiating the first formula of (10.3.13) by y^i, one can obtain

$$0 = (n-3)b^2 cs_i + (n-2)b^2 c^2 b_i + b^2 b^k c_k b_i + b^2 b^k s_{i|k}$$
$$- b^4 s^k{}_{i|k} + (n-1)b^2 s^k{}_i s_k + fb_i.$$

Contracting it with b^i yields (10.3.6). Substituting it into the first one of (10.3.13) yields

$$0 = \{(n-2)s_k s^k - b^2 s^k{}_{|k} - b^2 s^i{}_j s^j{}_i\}\beta + (n-3)b^2 cs_0$$
$$+ b^2 b^k s_{0|k} - b^4 s^k{}_{0|k} + (n-1)b^2 s^k{}_0 s_k.$$

From the second equation of (10.3.13) it follows that

$$\sigma = -\frac{1}{2b^2} s^k s_k - \frac{1}{4} s^i{}_j s^j{}_i. \tag{10.3.14}$$

Conversely, if (10.3.5) and (10.3.6) hold, inserting them into (10.3.1), one can see that F is an Einstein metric $Ric = (n-1)\sigma F^2$, where σ is given by (10.3.14). The proof of the theorem is completed. $\square$

If an (α, β)-metric F satisfies that $r_{ij} = 0$ and $b = ||\beta||_\alpha = $ constant, then β is called a *constant Killing form* with respect to α. From Theorem 10.7 we obtain the following

Theorem 10.8 ([158]). *Let $F = \frac{\alpha^2}{\beta}$ be a non-Riemannian Kropina metric on n-dimensional manifold M with $n \geq 2$. If β is a constant Killing form with respect to α, then F is an Einstein metric if and only if α is a Riemann-Einstein metric. In this case, $\sigma = \frac{1}{4}\lambda b^2 \geq 0$, where $\lambda = \lambda(x)$ is the Einstein factor of α. When $n \geq 3$, $\sigma = $ constant.*

Proof. Let F be an Einstein metric. Substituting $r_{ij} = 0$ and $s_i = 0$ into (10.3.9) and dividing both sides with b^4, one can obtain

$$0 = {}^\alpha Ric\, \beta^2 - s^k{}_{0|k}\beta\alpha^2 - \left\{\frac{1}{4}s^i{}_j s^j{}_i + \sigma\right\}\alpha^4, \qquad (10.3.15)$$

which implies that ${}^\alpha Ric$ can be divided by α^2, i.e., there is a function $\lambda(x)$ such that

$$ {}^\alpha Ric = \lambda\alpha^2.$$

Thus, α is a Riemann-Einstein metric. Inserting the above into (10.3.15) yields that

$$0 = \{\lambda\beta - s^k{}_{0|k}\}\beta - \left\{\frac{1}{4}s^i{}_j s^j{}_i + \sigma\right\}\alpha^2. \qquad (10.3.16)$$

By Lemma 10.6, we have $s^k{}_{0|k} = \lambda\beta, b^k s^i{}_{k|i} = \lambda b^2 = -s^i{}_j s^j{}_i$. Thus, (10.3.16) is equivalent to

$$\sigma = -\frac{1}{4}s^i{}_j s^j{}_i = \frac{1}{4}\lambda b^2.$$

Since $\lambda b^2 = b^k s^l{}_{k|l} = -s^i{}_j s^j{}_i = \|s_{ij}\|_\alpha^2 \geq 0$, then λ is non-negative. Hence, $\sigma = \frac{1}{4}\lambda b^2 \geq 0$.

Conversely, suppose that $r_{ij} = s_i = 0$ and α is a Riemann-Einstein metric, i.e., ${}^\alpha Ric = \lambda(x)\alpha^2$. By Lemma 10.6, we have $s^k{}_{0|k} = \lambda\beta, b^k s^i{}_{k|i} = \lambda b^2 = -s^i{}_j s^j{}_i$. Substituting those into (10.3.1) and (10.3.2) and noting that $r_{ij} = 0, s_i = 0$, we can obtain that $0 = Ric - \sigma F^2$, where $\sigma = \frac{1}{4}\lambda b^2$. Hence, F is an Einstein metric.

When $n \geq 3$, one can get from Riemannian geometry that $\lambda =$ constant ([169]), so that $\sigma = \frac{1}{4}\lambda b^2 =$ constant. $\qquad\square$

We now introduce the navigation expression for Kropina metrics (§5.4). Let $h = \sqrt{h_{ij}(x)y^i y^j}$ be a Riemannian metric and $W = W^i \frac{\partial}{\partial x^i}$ be a vector field on M. We define a Finsler metric $F = F(x, y)$ by the following equation

$$\left\|\frac{y}{F} - W\right\|_h = \sqrt{h_{ij}(x)\left(\frac{y^i}{F} - W^i\right)\left(\frac{y^j}{F} - W^j\right)} = 1,$$

which is equivalent to

$$\frac{h^2}{F^2} - 2\frac{W_0}{F} + \|W\|_h^2 = 1, \qquad (10.3.17)$$

where $W_i := h_{ij}W^j$, $\|W\|_h^2 = W_i W^i$ and $W_0 := W_i y^i$.

Let $F = \frac{\alpha^2}{\beta}$. We can solve h and W from (10.3.17). Firstly, it follows that

$$0 = h^2\beta^2 - 2W_0\beta\alpha^2 + (||W||_h^2 - 1)\alpha^4, \qquad (10.3.18)$$

which implies $h^2\beta^2$ can be divided by α^2. Thus, there is a function $\rho = \rho(x)$ such that $h^2 = e^{2\rho}\alpha^2$. Inserting it into (10.3.18) we get

$$0 = (e^{2\rho}\beta - 2W_0)\beta + (||W||_h^2 - 1)\alpha^2,$$

which implies

$$\begin{cases} \eta := e^{2\rho}\beta - 2W_0, \\ 0 = \eta\beta + (||W||_h^2 - 1)\alpha^2. \end{cases} \qquad (10.3.19)$$

We now consider (10.3.19) in two cases separably: (i) If $\eta = t\beta \ \forall \ t = t(x)$, then $tb_ib_j = (||W||_h^2 - 1)a_{ij}$. Comparing ranks of matrices on both sides yields that $t = ||W||_h^2 - 1 = 0$, so that $\eta = 0$. (ii) If $\eta \neq t\beta$, we can choose a direction y such that $\eta(y) = 0$. Since α is positively definite, then $||W||_h^2 - 1 = 0$. In either case, $||W||_h - 1 = 0$, so that $\eta = 0$. Thus, we obtain

$$h_{ij} = \frac{4}{b^2}a_{ij}, \quad W_i = \frac{2}{b^2}b_i. \qquad (10.3.20)$$

Conversely, if $||W||_h = \sqrt{h_{ij}(x)W^iW^j} = 1$, then we can solve F from (10.3.17) that $F = \frac{h^2}{2W_0}$, where $W_0 > 0$. Take $\alpha^2 = h^2$ and $\beta = 2W_0 > 0$. Thus, $F = \frac{\alpha^2}{\beta}$ is a Kropina metric. $\{h, W\}$ here is called the navigation data of F. Hence, We have proved the following

Proposition 10.2 ([158]). *A Finsler metric F is of Kropina type if and only if it is solved from the navigation equation (10.3.17) by a Riemannian metric $h = \sqrt{h_{ij}(x)y^iy^j}$ and a unit vector field $= W^i\frac{\partial}{\partial x^i}$ with $||W||_h = 1$.*

Remark. Recall that Randers metrics determined by the navigation data h and W (§5.4, Example 5.6). It is required that $||W||_h < 1$. Now we require $||W||_h = 1$ for Kropina metrics. Hence, a Kropina metric can be viewed as the limit of Randers metrics ($||W||_h \to 1$) in the navigation sense.

Let $\{h, W\}$ be the navigation data of a Kropina metric $F = \frac{\alpha^2}{\beta}$. Write

$$\begin{aligned} \mathcal{R}_{ij} &:= \frac{1}{2}(W_{i;j} + W_{j;i}), \quad \mathcal{S}_{ij} := \frac{1}{2}(W_{i;j} - W_{j;i}), \quad \rho := \ln\frac{2}{b}, \\ \mathcal{S}^i{}_j &:= h^{ik}\mathcal{S}_{kj}, \quad \mathcal{S}_j := W^i\mathcal{S}_{ij}, \quad \mathcal{R}_j := W^i\mathcal{R}_{ij}, \quad \mathcal{R} := \mathcal{R}_jW^j, \end{aligned} \qquad (10.3.21)$$

where ";" is the covariant differential with respect to h. It follows easily from (10.3.20) and (10.3.21) that

$$r_{ij} = 2e^{-2\rho}(\mathcal{R}_{ij} - W^k\rho_k h_{ij}),$$
$$s_{ij} = 2e^{-2\rho}(\mathcal{S}_{ij} + \rho_i W_j - \rho_j W_i), \tag{10.3.22}$$

where $\rho_i = \frac{\partial\rho}{\partial x^i}$.

Lemma 10.7. $r_{00} = c(x)\alpha^2$ is equivalent to $\mathcal{R}_{ij} = 0$. In this case, $W^k\rho_k = -\frac{1}{2}c$.

Proof. Let $r_{00} = c(x)\alpha^2$, i.e., $r_{ij} = ca_{ij}$. Contracting it with $b^i b^j$ yields that $r := r_{ij}b^i b^j = cb^2$.

Differentiating the third equation of (10.3.21), one can get

$$0 = b^2\rho_k + r_k + s_k,$$

where $r_k = b^j r_{jk}$, $s_k = b^j s_{jk}$. Contracting it with b^k yields that

$$0 = b^2\rho_k b^k + r = 2b^2\rho_k W^k + cb^2.$$

Thus, $W^k\rho_k = -\frac{1}{2}c$.

Substituting the first equation of (10.3.22) into $r_{ij} = ca_{ij}$, we have

$$ce^{-2\rho}h_{ij} = 2e^{-2\rho}(\mathcal{R}_{ij} - W^k\rho_k h_{ij})$$
$$= 2e^{-2\rho}(\mathcal{R}_{ij} + \frac{1}{2}ch_{ij}).$$

It follows that $\mathcal{R}_{ij} = 0$.

Conversely, from $\mathcal{R}_{ij} = 0$ and the first equation of (10.3.22) we have

$$r_{ij} = -2e^{-2\rho}W^k\rho_k h_{ij},$$

i.e., $r_{ij} = ca_{ij}$, where $c = c(x) = -2W^k\rho_k$. □

Theorem 10.9 ([158]). *Let $F = \frac{\alpha^2}{\beta}$ be a non-Riemannian Kropina metric on an n-dimensional ($n \geq 2$) manifold M, and $\{h, W\}$ be its navigation data. Then F is an Einstein metric if and only if h is a Riemann-Einstein metric and W is a unit Killing vector field with respect to h. In this case F and h have the same non-negative Einstein factors. Clearly, when $n \geq 3$, the Einstein metric F has constant Ricci curvature.*

Proof. Let $F = \frac{\alpha^2}{\beta} = \frac{h^2}{2W_0}$ be an Einstein Kropina metric. We have $r_{00} = c(x)\alpha^2$ by Theorem 10.7. It follows that $\mathcal{R}_{ij} = 0$ from Lemma 10.7. Thus, W_0 is a unit Killing form with respect to h. Since $F = \frac{\alpha^2}{\beta} = \frac{h^2}{2W_0}$ is Einsteinian, then h is a Riemann-Einstein metric by means of Theorem 10.8.

Conversely, let h be a Riemann-Einstein metric and W be a unit Killing vector field with respect to h. Then W_0 is a unit Killing form with respect to h. It follows from Theorem 10.8 that $\frac{h^2}{W_0}$ is an Einstein metric. Thus, $F = \frac{\alpha^2}{\beta} = \frac{h^2}{2W_0}$ is an Einstein metric.

By Theorem 10.8, the Einstein factor of $\frac{h^2}{W_0}$ is

$$\frac{1}{4}\lambda\|W\|_h^2 = \frac{1}{4}\lambda = -\frac{1}{4}\mathcal{S}^i{}_j\mathcal{S}^j{}_i = \frac{1}{4}\|\mathcal{S}_{ij}\|_h^2 \geq 0,$$

where λ is the Einstein factor of h. Hence, the Einstein factor of $F = \frac{h^2}{2W_0}$ is $\sigma \geq 0$. $\qquad\square$

Example 10.1. By Theorem 10.9, a Riemann-Einstein metric h and a unit Killing vector field W with respect to h can be used to construct an Einstein Kropina metric. Particularly, Riemannian metrics with constant sectional curvature can be used. Let h be an n-dimensional $(n \geq 2)$ Riemannian metric with constant sectional curvature μ. In the standard local coordinate system, we can write $h^2 = \|dx\|^2/H^2$, where $H := 1 + \frac{\mu}{4}\|x\|^2$, $\|\cdot\|^2$ is the standard Euclidean inner product. By [166], the general solution of the Killing vector field W is

$$W_i(x) = \frac{1}{H^2}\left\{\sum_j Q_{ij}x^j + c_i - \frac{1}{4}\mu\|x\|^2 c_i + \frac{1}{2}\left[\sum_k \mu c_k x^k\right]x^i\right\},$$
$$(10.3.23)$$

where $Q_{ij} = -Q_{ji}$ and c_i are $\frac{1}{2}n(n+1)$ arbitrary constants. We can choose the constant Killing vector field.

Let (M, h) be a 3-dimensional Riemannian manifold with constant sectional curvature $\mu = 1$, where $h = \sqrt{\|dx\|^2/H^2}$ is the standard metric. Define a matrix by

$$Q = \begin{pmatrix} 0 & a & b \\ -a & 0 & c \\ -b & -c & 0 \end{pmatrix}, \quad (c_1, c_2, c_3) = \pm(c, -b, a),$$

where $a^2 + b^2 + c^2 = 1$ and a, b, c are non-vanishing constants. Thus, the unit Killing vector field W_i with respect to h can be expressed by (10.3.23). Therefore, $F = \frac{h^2}{2W_0}$ is a 3-dimensional Einstein Kropina metric.

Corollary 10.2 ([158]). *Let $F = \frac{\alpha^2}{\beta}$ be a non-Riemannian Kropina metric on $n(\geq 2)$-dimensional manifold M. If F is Ricci flat, then F is a Berwald metric.*

Proof. Let F be Ricci flat. It follows from Theorem 10.9 that

$$0 = \sigma = \lambda = \|\mathcal{S}_{ij}\|_h^2,$$

which implies W_0 is closed. Hence W_0 is parallel with respect to h. Thus, $G^i = {}^\alpha G^i$, where ${}^\alpha G^i$ are geodesic coefficients of h. Hence, F is a Berwald metric. $\qquad\qquad\square$

Finsler metrics with constant flag curvature are, of course, Einstein metrics with constant Einstein factor. By the same method as in Theorems 10.8 and 10.9, the following corollary is obvious.

Corollary 10.3 ([158], [155]). *Let $F = \frac{\alpha^2}{\beta}$ be a non-Riemannian Kropina metric on n-dimensional $(n \geq 2)$ manifold M with the navigation data $\{h, W\}$. F has constant flag curvature if and only if h is a Riemannian metric with constant sectional curvature and W is a unit Killing vector field with respect to h. Moreover, F and h have the same non-negative constant curvature.*

Remark. By the further discussion, we can easily show: (1) the **S**-curvature of an Einstein Kropina metric with respect to the Busemann-Hausdorff volume form vanishes identically; (2) Any conformal transformation between Einstein Kropina metrics must be homothetic. See [158] for details.

We cite S. T. Yau's problem ([152], 275-319, Problem 1) to end this chapter. It illustrates the importance of studying Finsler-Einstein metrics.

S. T. Yau's problem. Find a general method to construct canonical metrics on compact Riemannian manifold. All the known canonical metrics are obtained by variational principle. In the past, geometers studied the critical points of the functionals defined by the total scalar curvature, the L^2-norm of the Riemannian curvature or those functionals coupled with the Yang-Mills fields. If there is a compact group acting on the manifold, one can reduce the variational problem to a lower dimensional problem which may be easier to be solved. The last approach was used by relativists in looking for exact solutions for the Einstein equation. A possible fruitful approach to find canonical metrics is to use singular perturbation method. For example, if two compact manifolds admit Einstein metric with scalar curvature of the same sign, can we connect these two manifolds along certain submanifold so that the sum of the manifold admits an approximate Einstein metric which we can perturb to form an Einstein manifold. Donaldson and Friedman has demonstrated this for self-dual metrics where they take connected sum. Recently, Taubes (refer to *J. Diff. Geom.*, 36(1992), 163-253.) has proved a general existence theorem for self-dual metrics. Since the connected sum of four dimensional torus does not admit Einstein metric, the problem for Einstein metric is more complicated. Perhaps one has to select the submanifold suitably before we do the perturbation. Would this procedure be much easier for dimension greater than five because there is no known obstruction for these dimensions?

We can generalize this problem to some class of metrics which are more general than Riemannian metrics. For example, we can look for Finsler metrics or Riemannian metrics whose connection may not be Riemannian but satisfies other conditions related to the Lagrangian.

Exercises

10.1 Verify the formula in the proof of Theorem 10.3:

$$\int_M \{W_{i,j}W^{i,j} + \sigma|w|^2\}dV_h = (\Delta w, w) = 2\sigma \int_M |w|^2 dV_h.$$

10.2 Prove Lemma 10.4. (Hints: Choose a coordinate change such that level surfaces $\varphi = $ constant are a family of coordinate hypersurfaces.)

10.3 Give a proof of the sufficiency of Theorem 10.4.

10.4 Verify (10.3.2) in detail.

10.5 By conformal transformations of h and α in (10.3.20), prove (10.3.22).

10.6 Prove that the **S**-curvature of Einstein Kropina metrics vanishes identically with respect to the Busemann-Hausdorff volume form ([158]).

10.7 Prove that any conformal transformation between Einstein Kropina metrics must be homothetic ([158]).

10.8 Prove Corollary 10.3 completely.

10.9 Consider a 5-dimensional Riemannian metric α in the local coordinate system $(x^1, x^2, x^3, x^4, x^5)$ on M^5:

$$\alpha^2 = a_{ij}dx^i dx^j$$
$$:= x^1(dx^1)^2 + \frac{1}{x^1}(dx^2)^2 \qquad (1)$$
$$+ (x^1)^2\{(dx^3)^2 + (dx^4)^2\} + (dx^5)^2, \quad \forall x^1 > 0.$$

Prove it is a non-Euclidean Ricci flat Einstein metric.

10.10   Under the condition of Exercise 10.9, consider the 1-form

$$\beta = cdx^5, \quad c \neq 0, \tag{2}$$

where c is a non-zero constant. Prove the Matsumoto metric $F = \alpha^2/(\alpha - \beta)$ is Ricci flat, where α and β are given by (1) and (2), respectively.

Chapter 11

Miscellaneous Topics

11.1 Conformal changes

11.1.1 Conformal changes

Let $F(x,y)$ and $\widetilde{F}(x,y)$ be two Finsler metrics on an n-dimensional manifold M. Then $F(x,y)$ and $\widetilde{F}(x,y)$ are said to be *(locally) conformally equivalent*, or $\widetilde{F}(x,y)$ is *(locally) conformal to* $F(x,y)$ if there is a smooth positive function $\varphi(x,y)$ such that

$$\widetilde{F}(x,y) = \varphi(x,y)F(x,y). \tag{11.1.1}$$

From now on we shall omit the "locally" since there is no global discussion here.

By squaring on both sides of (11.1.1) and differentiating three times with respect to y, we have

$$\widetilde{C}_{ijk} = \varphi^2 C_{ijk} + \frac{1}{2}[\varphi^2]_{y^k} g_{ij} + \frac{F}{2}[\varphi^2]_{y^j y^k}[F]_{y^i},$$

where C_{ijk} (resp. $\widetilde{C}_{ijk}$) are coefficients of the Cartan tensor (§2.2.1). Exchanging indices j and k, one can get from the symmetry that

$$[\varphi^2]_{y^k} g_{ij} = [\varphi^2]_{y^j} g_{ik}.$$

Thus,

$$[\varphi]_{y^k} = 0.$$

It shows that φ is independent of y and the function of point x only ([63]). We use the notation $\varphi(x) = e^{\rho(x)}$, where $\rho(x)$ is a smooth function on M. Then (11.1.1) can be rewritten as

$$\widetilde{F}(x,y) = e^{\rho(x)}F(x,y), \quad \widetilde{g}_{ij}(x,y) = e^{2\rho(x)}g_{ij}(x,y). \tag{11.1.2}$$

A change of Finsler metrics satisfying (11.1.2) is said to be *conformal*, and the function $\rho(x)$ is called a *conformal factor*. Thus, a non-Riemannian Finsler metric cannot be conformal to a Riemannian metric.

Formula (11.1.2) gives that

$$\widetilde{g}^{ij} = e^{-2\rho}g^{ij}, \quad \widetilde{\gamma}^i_{jk} = \gamma^i_{jk} + \rho_j\delta^i_k + \rho_k\delta^i_j - g^{il}\rho_l g_{jk}, \tag{11.1.3}$$

where γ^i_{jk} are defined by (2.3.4), $\rho_j = \partial\rho/\partial x^j$. By (3.1.15) and (11.1.3), one can see that their spray coefficients satisfy

$$\widetilde{G}^i = G^i + \rho_k y^k y^i - \frac{1}{2}F^2\rho^i, \quad \rho^i := g^{ik}\rho_k. \tag{11.1.4}$$

A direct corollary of these equations is the following

Proposition 11.1. *The conformal change (11.1.2) leaves geodesic invariant if and only if the conformal factor ρ is a constant.*

Proof. By (11.1.4) and (6.1.1), the conformal change (11.1.2) leaves geodesic invariant if and only if there is a scalar function $Q(x,y)$ which is homogeneous of degree one in y such that

$$F^2 g^{ik}\rho_k = Q(x,y)y^i, \quad Q(x,\lambda y) = \lambda Q(x,y).$$

It is equivalent to

$$F^2\rho_k = Q(x,y)y^i g_{ik}.$$

Contracting it with y^k yields that

$$\rho_k y^k = Q(x,y).$$

Since $Q(x,y)$ is homogeneous of degree one in y, then for any positive number λ, we have

$$\lambda^n \rho_k y^k = \rho_k(\lambda y^k) = Q(x,\lambda y) = \lambda Q(x,y) = \lambda\rho_k y^k.$$

When dimension $M = n > 1$, the above implies that $\rho_k = 0$, i.e., $\rho =$ constant. $\square$

From Proposition 11.1 we see that a Finsler metric is uniquely determined by its projective and conformal characteristics up to a constant. A conformal change is said to be *homothetic* if ρ is constant, and to be *isometric* if $\rho = 0$.

It follows from (11.1.2) that

$$\widetilde{h}_{ij} = e^{2\rho}h_{ij}, \quad \widetilde{C}_{ijk} = e^{2\rho}C_{ijk}, \tag{11.1.5}$$

where h_{ij} is an angle metric tensor (§4.3).

By $N^i_j = \partial G^i/\partial y^j$ (See (3.1.17)), we get from (11.1.4) that

$$\widetilde{N}^i_j = N^i_j + \rho_j y^i + \rho_k y^k \delta^i_j - FF_{y^j}\rho^i + F^2 \rho^k C^i_{kj}, \quad C^i_{jk} = g^{il}C_{ljk}. \quad (11.1.6)$$

From (2.2.2), (11.1.3) and (11.1.6) we obtain that

$$\widetilde{C}^i_{jk} = C^i_{jk}, \quad \widetilde{\mathbf{I}}_i = \mathbf{I}_i, \quad \widetilde{F}^2||\widetilde{\mathbf{I}}||^2 = F^2||\mathbf{I}||^2, \quad (11.1.7)$$

where $||\mathbf{I}||^2 := g^{ij}\mathbf{I}_i\mathbf{I}_j$. We immediately get the following ([77])

Proposition 11.2. *The Cartan form* $\mathbf{I}$ *and* $F^2||\mathbf{I}||^2$ *are conformal invariants.*

Define

$$\theta := \rho_k y^k, \quad ||d\rho||^2_F := g^{ij}\rho_i\rho_j, \quad Q^i := \frac{1}{2}F^2\rho^i, \quad Q^i_j := [Q^i]_{y^j}, \quad Q^i_{jk} := [Q^i_j]_{y^k}. \quad (11.1.8)$$

Recall that G^i and Q^i are homogeneous of degree two. By means of the expression (3.3.15) of the flag curvature $R^i{}_j$, (11.1.4) and (11.1.8), a direct calculation gives ([16])

$$\widetilde{R}^i{}_j = R^i{}_j + \Xi\delta^i_j + P_j y^i - 2Q^i_{;j} + Q^i_{j;k}y^k \qquad (11.1.9)$$
$$+ 2Q^k Q^i_{kj} - Q^i_k Q^k_j - F^2||d\rho||^2_F \delta^i_j,$$

where the semicolon ";" denotes the covariant differentiation with respect to the Berwald connection (§3.1.2),

$$\Xi := \theta^2 - [\theta]_{;k}y^k, \quad P_j := 3([\theta]_{;j} - \theta\rho_j) + [\Xi]_{y^j} + \rho_k Q^k_j. \quad (11.1.10)$$

Contracting on both sides of (11.1.9) yields the formula of Ricci curvatures in a conformal change

$$\overline{Ric}(y) = Ric(y) + (n-1)(\Xi - F^2||d\rho(y)||^2_F) \qquad (11.1.11)$$
$$- 2Q^k_{;k} + y^j Q^k_{k;j} + 2Q^j Q^k_{jk} - Q^k_j Q^j_k.$$

According to the definition of Q^i and $\rho^i_{;j} = 2\rho^k L^i_{kj} + g^{ik}\rho_{k;j}$ where L^i_{jk} is defined by (3.1.18), we can expand the last four items of (11.1.11) and obtain ([16])

$$\overline{Ric}(y) = Ric(y) + (n-2)(\Xi - F^2||d\rho(y)||^2_F) \qquad (11.1.12)$$
$$- F^2\{2\rho_k J^k + \widetilde{\Delta}\rho + [\rho^j I_j]_{;k}y^k + 2\theta\rho^j I_j\}$$
$$+ F^4\rho^j\rho^k\{2I_s C^s_{jk} - [I_j]_{y^k} - C^s_{ji}C^i_{ks}\},$$

where J^k are defined by (3.1.19), I_i are coefficients of Cartan form, and $\widetilde{\Delta}\rho = g^{ij}\rho_{i;j}$. When ρ is constant, i.e., the change is homothetic, the Ricci curvature is invariant.

We now turn to the **S**-curvature with respect to the Busemann-Hausdorff volume measure (§4.1). By (4.1.1), we firstly consider the change of the measure function σ_B. Define

$$B_x^n := \{(y^i) \in \mathbb{R}^n | F(y) < 1\},$$

$$\widetilde{B}_x^n := \{(y^i) \in \mathbb{R}^n | \widetilde{F}(y) < 1\} = \{(y^i) \in \mathbb{R}^n | F(e^{\rho(x)}y) < 1\},$$

and set $z^i = e^\rho y^i$. Denoting by Vol the Euclidean volume, we have

$$\mathrm{Vol}(\widetilde{B}_x^n) = \int_{\widetilde{B}_x^n} dy^1 \wedge \cdots \wedge dy^n = e^{-n\rho(x)} \int_{B_x^n} dz^1 \wedge \cdots \wedge dz^n = e^{-n\rho(x)} \mathrm{Vol}(B_x^n).$$

Thus, from (4.1.1) it follows that

$$\widetilde{\sigma}_{\widetilde{F}} = e^{n\rho(x)} \sigma_F.$$

By using (4.2.5) and (11.1.4) we obtain

$$\widetilde{\mathbf{S}}(y) = \frac{\partial \widetilde{G}^k}{\partial y^k} - \frac{y^k}{\widetilde{\sigma}_{\widetilde{F}}} \frac{\partial \widetilde{\sigma}_{\widetilde{F}}}{\partial x^k} = \mathbf{S}(y) + F^2 \rho^k I_k. \qquad (11.1.13)$$

From the above formulas we see that if the conformal factor ρ is not constant, then it is difficult to find other geometric conformal invariants except the Cartan form $\mathbf{I}$ and $F^2\|\mathbf{I}\|^2$. This fact is different from one in Riemannian geometry, where there is a famous Weyl conformal curvature tensor which is a conformal invariant (see [169]). But in Finsler geometry, there is no such a conformal invariant.

11.1.2   Conformally flat metrics

A Finsler metric $\widetilde{F}$ is said to be (locally) *conformally flat* if $\widetilde{F}$ is conformal to a locally Minkowskian metric ([58]), i.e., in a local coordinate system $\widetilde{F}(x,y) = e^{\rho(x)}F(y)$, where $F(y)$ is a locally Minkowskian metric (see Definition 5.3).

In Riemann geometry, a Riemannian metric of constant curvature is not only conformally flat, but also projectively flat ([169]). In fact, when the dimension $n \geq 3$, the Beltrami theorem (Theorem 6.3) shows that a Riemannian metric is projectively flat if and only if it is of constant curvature, so that it is also conformally flat. But in Finsler geometry, such analogous theorem does not hold. Thus, we consider naturally the following question: Describe all of Finsler metrics which are both conformally and projectively flat. This question is still open for general Finsler metrics. In this section we will describe all of (α, β)-metrics which are both conformally and projectively flat. Particularly, we consider Randers metrics.

Lemma 11.1. *Any conformal change leaves the type of (α, β)-metrics invariant. In particular, the type of Randers metrics is invariant. Thus, a conformally flat Randers metric F can be expressed in a local coordinate system as*

$$F(x,y) = e^{\rho(x)}[\sqrt{\Sigma_i(y^i)^2} + b_iy^i], \quad b_i = \text{const.} \tag{11.1.14}$$

Proof. Let $F = \alpha\phi(s), s = \frac{\beta}{\alpha}$. Under the conformal transformation (11.1.2), we put $\widetilde{\alpha} = e^\rho\alpha$, $\widetilde{\beta} = e^\rho\beta$. Then $\widetilde{F} = \widetilde{\alpha}\phi(s)$, where $s = \frac{\widetilde{\beta}}{\widetilde{\alpha}} = \frac{\beta}{\alpha}$. Thus, $\widetilde{F} = e^\rho F$ is also the same type of (α, β)-metrics.

Now let $\widetilde{F}(x,y)$ be conformally flat Randers metric, i.e., there is a conformal factor $\rho(x)$, such that $\widetilde{F} = e^\rho F$, where the Randers metric $F = \alpha + \beta$ is locally Minkowskian. Thus, $\alpha = \sqrt{a_{ij}y^iy^j}$ and $\beta = b_iy^i$ should be independent of the point x. Hence, a_{ij} and b_i should be constants, which implies that $\alpha = \sqrt{a_{ij}y^iy^j}$ is a Euclidean metric. So, we see that there is a local coordinate system such that $\alpha = \sqrt{\Sigma(y^i)^2}$. $\square$

Theorem 11.1 ([173])**.** *Let (M, F) be an n-dimensional $(n \geq 3)$ Randers manifold. F is both conformally and projectively flat if and only if one of the following cases holds:*

(i) F is a Riemannian metric of constant curvature;

(ii) There is a local coordinate system (x^i, y^i) such that F can be expressed as

$$F = \frac{1}{|A + Bb_kx^k|}\left(\sqrt{\Sigma_i(y^i)^2} + b_iy^i\right), \tag{11.1.15}$$

where b_i, A and B are constants with $A + Bb_kx^k \neq 0$.

Proof. If F is a conformally flat Randers metric, by Lemma 11.1, F can be expressed as (11.1.14). Now if F is also projectively flat, by Theorem 6.4 (§6.2), the Riemannian metric $\alpha = e^\rho\sqrt{\Sigma_i(y^i)^2}$ has constant sectional curvature. Moreover, $\beta = e^\rho b_iy^i$ is a closed 1-form. It follows that $d(e^\rho b_i dx^i) = e^\rho(\rho_i b_j dx^i \wedge dx^j) = 0$. Thus,

$$b_i\rho_j - b_j\rho_i = 0,$$

which implies that there a scalar function $c(x)$ such that

$$\rho_i = c(x)b_i. \tag{11.1.16}$$

Differentiating on both sides of (11.1.16) in x^j yields that

$$c_ib_j = \rho_{ij} := \frac{\partial^2\rho}{\partial x^i\partial x^j} = c_jb_i.$$

Thus, we can put $c_j = d(x)b_j$, where $d(x)$ is a scalar function. Thus

$$\rho_{ij} = d(x)b_i b_j. \qquad (11.1.17)$$

On the other hand, a conformally flat Riemannian metric $\alpha = e^\rho \sqrt{\Sigma_i(y^i)^2}$ has constant sectional curvature if and only if

$$\rho_{ij} - \rho_i \rho_j = K(x)\delta_{ij},$$

where $K(x)$ is a scalar function ([169], Chapter 3, §3.3). Substituting (11.1.16) and (11.1.17) into the above yields that

$$b_i b_j (d - c^2) = K(x)\delta_{ij}.$$

Since dimension $n \geq 3$, then $d - c^2 = 0$, i.e.,

$$\rho_{ij} - \rho_i \rho_j = 0.$$

On putting $\varphi = e^{-\rho}$, one can get from the above $\frac{\partial^2 \varphi}{\partial x^i \partial x^j} = 0$. Noting (11.1.16), we have

$$e^\rho = \varphi^{-1} = \frac{1}{|A + Bb_k x^k|},$$

where A and B are arbitrary constants such that $A + Bb_k x^k \neq 0$.

Conversely, if F can be expressed as (11.1.15), then it is conformally flat. Let $\alpha = \frac{B}{|A+b_k x^k|}\sqrt{\Sigma_i(y^i)^2}$, $\beta = \frac{B}{|A+b_k x^k|}b_i y^i$. A direct calculation shows that α has constant sectional curvature and the 1-form β is closed. According to Theorem 6.4, $F = \alpha + \beta$ is projectively flat. The theorem is proved completely. $\qquad\square$

As it is well known, a projectively flat Finsler metric must have scalar flag curvature (Proposition 6.4, §6.2). So, it is natural to ask whether or not the projectively flat condition in Theorem 11.1 can be replaced by the scalar flag curvature. The following theorem give a positive answer.

Theorem 11.2 ([173]). *If F is a conformally flat Randers metric with scalar flag curvature on n-dimensional ($n \geq 3$) manifold M, then F is projectively flat.*

To prove the theorem we need the following two lemmas, whose proofs are omitted here.

Lemma 11.2 ([18]). *A Randers metric $F = \alpha + \beta$ is Douglasian if and only if β is a closed 1-form.*

Lemma 11.3 ([120]). *A Randers metric $F = \alpha + \beta$ of scalar flag curvature if and only if*

$$^\alpha R^i{}_j = \kappa(\alpha^2 \delta^i_j - y_j y^i) + \alpha^2 t^i{}_j + t_{00}\delta^i_j - t_{j0}y^i - t^i{}_0 y_j - 3s^i{}_0 s_{j0}, \quad (11.1.18)$$

$$s_{ij,k} = \frac{1}{n-1}(a_{ik}s^m{}_{j,m} - a_{jk}s^m{}_{i,m}), \quad (11.1.19)$$

where $^\alpha R^i{}_k$ is the flag curvature tensor of the Riemannian metric α, the comma "," denotes the covariant differentiation with respect to α, $\kappa = \kappa(x)$ is a scalar function and

$$t^i{}_j = a^{ik}t_{kj}, \quad t_{ij} = s_{ik}s^k{}_j, \quad s_{ij} = \frac{1}{2}(b_{i,j} - b_{j,i}), \quad s^i{}_j = a^{ik}s_{kj}.$$

The proof of Theorem 11.2. If F is a Riemannian metric with scalar flag curvature, then it has constant sectional curvature for $n \geq 3$. A Riemannian metric of constant curvature is projectively flat naturally. So, we suppose that F is non-Riemannian in the following.

According to Lemma 11.1, a conformally flat Randers metric F can be expressed as (11.1.14) in a local coordinate system, i.e.,

$$F = \alpha + \beta = e^\rho(\widetilde{\alpha} + \widetilde{\beta}), \quad \widetilde{\alpha} := \Sigma_i(y^i)^2, \quad \widetilde{\beta} := \widetilde{b}_i y^i, \quad \widetilde{b}_i = \text{const}.$$

Thus,

$$\alpha := \sqrt{a_{ij}y^i y^j}, \quad a_{ij} = e^{2\rho}\delta_{ij}, \quad \beta := b_i y^i, \quad b_i = e^\rho \widetilde{b}_i.$$

If the Randers metric F of scalar flag curvature, then equations (11.1.18) and (11.1.19) hold by Lemma 11.3. Contracting i with j on both sides of (11.1.18) and differentiating it twice in y^i and y^j, we have

$$^\alpha R_{ij} = ((n-1)\kappa + t^m{}_m)a_{ij} + (n+1)t_{ij}, \quad (11.1.20)$$

where $^\alpha R_{ij}$ is the Ricci tensor of α. Contracting (11.1.20) with $a^{ij} = e^{-2\rho}\delta_{ij}$ yields that

$$^\alpha R = n(n-1)\kappa + (2n+1)t^m{}_m, \quad (11.1.21)$$

where $^\alpha R$ is the scalar curvature of α.

Introduce the following notations

$$f(x) := \delta^{ij}\widetilde{b}_i \rho_j = \widetilde{b}^j \rho_j = \widetilde{b}^j \frac{\partial \rho}{\partial x^j}, \quad f_i := \frac{\partial f}{\partial x^i},$$

$$\rho^i := \delta^{ij}\rho_j, \quad \rho_{ij} := \frac{\partial \rho_i}{\partial x^j}, \quad \widetilde{b}^2 := \delta^{ij}\widetilde{b}_i \widetilde{b}_j.$$

Noting that α is a conformal Euclidean metric, a direct calculation gives that

$$r_{ij} = \frac{1}{2}(b_{i,j} + b_{j,i}) = \frac{e^\rho}{2}(2f\delta_{ij} - \widetilde{b}_i\rho_j - \widetilde{b}_j\rho_i),$$

$$s_{ij} = \frac{1}{2}(b_{i,j} - b_{j,i}) = \frac{e^\rho}{2}(\widetilde{b}_i\rho_j - \widetilde{b}_j\rho_i),$$

$$t_{ij} = a^{pq}s_{ip}s_{qj} = \frac{1}{4}(f\widetilde{b}_i\rho_j + f\widetilde{b}_j\rho_i - \widetilde{b}_i\widetilde{b}_j\rho^k\rho_k - \rho_i\rho_j\widetilde{b}^2), \qquad (11.1.22)$$

$$s_{ij,k} = \frac{1}{2}e^\rho\{-2(\widetilde{b}_i\rho_j - \widetilde{b}_j\rho_i)\rho_k + \widetilde{b}_i\rho_{jk} - \widetilde{b}_j\rho_{ik}$$
$$+ f(\delta_{ik}\rho_j - \delta_{jk}\rho_i) + \rho^m\rho_m(\widetilde{b}_i\delta_{jk} - \widetilde{b}_j\delta_{ik})\}.$$

Since α is a conformal Euclidean metric with the conformal factor ρ, then the Ricci tensor and the scalar curvature of α can be expressed respectively as

$$^\alpha R_{ij} = -(n-2)(\rho_{ij} - \rho_i\rho_j) - \{\triangle\rho + (n-2)\rho^k\rho_k\}\delta_{ij},$$
$$e^{2\rho}(^\alpha R) = -2(n-1)\triangle\rho - (n-1)(n-2)\rho^k\rho_k, \qquad (11.1.23)$$

where $\triangle\rho := \delta^{ij}\rho_{ij}$. Substituting $(11.1.23)_2$ into $(11.1.21)$, and using $(11.1.22)_3$, we can obtain

$$\kappa = \frac{e^{-2\rho}}{n(n-1)}\left\{-2(n-1)\left(\triangle\rho + \frac{n-2}{2}\rho^k\rho_k\right) - \frac{2n+1}{2}(f^2 - \rho^m\rho_m\widetilde{b}^2)\right\}.$$

Substituting the above formula into $(11.1.20)$, comparing it with $(11.1.23)_1$ and using $(11.1.22)_3$ give that

$$\left\{\frac{n-2}{n}(\triangle\rho - \rho^k\rho_k) + \frac{n+1}{2n}(f^2 - \widetilde{b}^2\rho^k\rho_k)\right\}\delta_{ij}$$
$$= \frac{n+1}{4}(f\widetilde{b}_i\rho_j + f\widetilde{b}_j\rho_i - \widetilde{b}_i\widetilde{b}_j\rho^k\rho_k - \rho_i\rho_j\widetilde{b}^2) \qquad (11.1.24)$$
$$+ (n-2)(\rho_{ij} - \rho_i\rho_j).$$

Contracting the above with $\widetilde{b}^j$ yields that

$$f_i - f\rho_i = \left\{\frac{1}{n}(\triangle\rho - \rho^k\rho_k) - \frac{n+1}{4n}(f^2 - \widetilde{b}^2\rho^k\rho_k)\right\}\widetilde{b}_i. \qquad (11.1.25)$$

Inserting $(11.1.19)$ into $(11.1.22)_4$ and using $(11.1.22)_2$, one can get

$$\delta_{ik}f_j - \delta_{jk}f_i - (\triangle\rho - 2\rho^m\rho_m)(\delta_{ik}\widetilde{b}_j - \delta_{jk}\widetilde{b}_i)$$
$$= 2f(\delta_{ik}\rho_j - \delta_{jk}\rho_i) - 2(n-1)(\widetilde{b}_i\rho_j - \widetilde{b}_j\rho_i)\rho_k \qquad (11.1.26)$$
$$+ (n-1)(\widetilde{b}_i\rho_{jk} - \widetilde{b}_j\rho_{ik}).$$

Contracting the above with $\tilde{b}^k$ and noting that $n \geq 3$, we have
$$2f(\tilde{b}_i \rho_j - \tilde{b}_j \rho_i) = (\tilde{b}_i f_j - \tilde{b}_j f_i),$$
which implies that there is a scalar function $p = p(x)$ such that
$$2f\rho_j - f_j = p(x)\tilde{b}_j. \tag{11.1.27}$$
Comparing (11.1.27) with (11.1.25) yields that there is a scalar function $q = q(x)$ such that
$$f\rho_j = q(x)\tilde{b}_j. \tag{11.1.28}$$

If $f \neq 0$, then (11.1.28) and (11.1.22)$_2$ give rise to $s_{ij} = 0$, i.e., β is closed. Thus, by Lemma 11.2, the Douglas tensor of F vanishes identically. Since F of scalar flag curvature, then by Lemma 6.1, the Weyl projective curvature tensor of F also vanishes identically. From Theorem 6.2 it follows that F is projectively flat.

Now consider the case when $f = 0$. Contracting (11.1.26) with $\tilde{b}^i$ and using (11.1.27), we have
$$\tilde{b}^2 \{\triangle \rho + p(x) - 2\rho^m \rho_m\}\delta_{jk} = -2(n-1)\tilde{b}^2 \rho_j \rho_k$$
$$+ (n-1)\tilde{b}^2 \rho_{jk} + \{\triangle \rho + np(x) - 2\rho^m \rho_m\}\tilde{b}_j \tilde{b}_k.$$

Substituting the above into (11.1.24) and eliminating the factor $(\rho_{jk} - \rho_j \rho_k)$, we obtain
$$\begin{aligned}&\left\{\frac{(n-1)(n-2)}{n}(\triangle \rho - \rho^m \rho_m) - (n-2)(\triangle \rho + p(x) - 2\rho^m \rho_m)\right.\\ &\left. - \frac{n^2-1}{2n}\tilde{b}^2 \rho^m \rho_m \right\}\tilde{b}^2 \delta_{jk}\\ &= (n-1)\left(n-2-\frac{n+1}{4}\tilde{b}^2\right)\tilde{b}^2 \rho_j \rho_k\\ &\quad - \left\{\frac{n^2-1}{4}\tilde{b}^2 \rho^m \rho_m + (n-2)(\triangle \rho + np(x) - 2\rho^m \rho_m)\right\}\tilde{b}_j \tilde{b}_k. \end{aligned} \tag{11.1.29}$$

Consider the $n \times n$ matrices on both sides of (11.1.29). If it is non-zero, then the rank of the matrix on the left hand side is $n \geq 3$, while the rank of the matrix $(\tilde{b}_j \tilde{b}_k)$ as well as $(\rho_j \rho_k)$ on the right hand side is 1. This is a contradiction. So, if F is non-Riemannian metric, i.e., $\tilde{b}^2 \neq 0$, then (11.1.29) gives
$$\begin{aligned}0 &= (n-1)\left(n-2-\frac{n+1}{4}\tilde{b}^2\right)\tilde{b}^2 \rho_j \rho_k\\ &\quad - \left\{\frac{n^2-1}{4}\tilde{b}^2 \rho^m \rho_m + (n-2)(\triangle \rho + np(x) - 2\rho^m \rho_m)\right\}\tilde{b}_j \tilde{b}_k. \end{aligned} \tag{11.1.30}$$

Contracting (11.1.30) with $\rho^j \rho^k$ and noting that $f = \widetilde{b}_i \rho^i = 0$, we can get

$$0 = (n-1)\left(n - 2 - \frac{n+1}{4}\widetilde{b}^2\right)\widetilde{b}^2(\rho_j \rho^j)^2.$$

Since $||\widetilde{\beta}||_{\widetilde{\alpha}}^2 = \widetilde{b}^2 < 1$ for the Randers metric $\widetilde{\alpha} + \widetilde{\beta}$, we have $\rho_j = 0$, i.e., ρ is a constant. Hence, the Randers metric $F = e^\rho(\widetilde{\alpha} + \widetilde{\beta})$ is flat. $\qquad\square$

Theorem 11.2 implies that Theorem 11.1 is true under the same hypothesis as in Theorem 11.2. This gives a complete classification of n-dimensional ($n \geq 3$) conformally flat Randers metrics with scalar flag curvature.

11.1.3 Conformally flat (α, β)-metrics

As it is well known, an (α, β)-metric F is a Berwald metric if and only if β is parallel with respect to α ([17]).

Proposition 11.3. *An (α, β)-metric F is locally Minkowskian if and only if α is flat and β is parallel with respect to α.*

Proof. Geodesic coefficients of an (α, β)-metric $F = \alpha\phi(\frac{\beta}{\alpha})$ can be expressed as (6.2.7) and (6.2.8).

If F is locally Minkowskian, then it is a flat Berwald metric naturally. Thus, β is parallel with respect to α. So, $r_{ij} = s_{ij} = 0$, which implies that $G^i = G^i_\alpha$ by means of (6.2.7). Thus F is affinely equivalent to α. Since F is flat, then α is flat.

Conversely, if α is flat and β is parallel with respect to α, then there is a local coordinate system such that α and β can be expressed respectively as $\alpha = \sqrt{\Sigma_i (y^i)^2}$ and $\beta = b_i y^i$, where b_i are constants. Hence, in the coordinate system F is independent of x, i.e., F is locally Minkowskian. $\qquad\square$

Theorem 11.3. *Let $\widetilde{F} = \widetilde{\alpha}\phi(\frac{\widetilde{\beta}}{\widetilde{\alpha}})$ be a non-Riemannian n-dimensional ($n \geq 3$) conformally flat (α, β)-metric. If $\widetilde{F}$ is projectively flat, then it is either a locally Minkowskian metric or a Randers metric.*

Proof. If $\widetilde{F}$ is a conformally flat (α, β)-metric, then there is a local coordinate system such that

$$\widetilde{F} = \widetilde{\alpha}\phi(s), \quad s = \frac{\widetilde{\beta}}{\widetilde{\alpha}}, \quad \alpha := \sqrt{\widetilde{a}_{ij}y^i y^j}, \quad \beta := \widetilde{b}_i y^i,$$
$$\widetilde{\alpha} = e^\rho \alpha = e^\rho \sqrt{\Sigma_i (y^i)^2}, \quad \widetilde{\beta} = e^\rho \beta = e^\rho b_i y^i, \quad b_i = \text{const.}, \tag{11.1.31}$$

according to Lemma 11.1 and Proposition 11.3. Obviously, $\|\widetilde{\beta}\|_{\widetilde{\alpha}} = \|\beta\|_\alpha = \sqrt{\Sigma_i(b_i)^2} := b$ is a positive constant.

We now employ Theorem 6.6 in §6.2.2, where the condition (c) has been satisfied. We will show that if $\widetilde{F}$ is projectively flat, then conditions (a) and (b) in Theorem 6.6 are not satisfied simultaneously.

We use reductio ad absurdum. Suppose that conditions (a) and (b) in Theorem 6.6 hold simultaneously. Then there is a function $\phi(s)$ such that (6.2.9) and (6.2.10) hold, i.e.,

$$\widetilde{b}_{i\|j} = 2\tau\{(1 + k_1b^2)\widetilde{a}_{ij} + (k_2b^2 + k_3)\widetilde{b}_i\widetilde{b}_j\}, \qquad (11.1.32)$$

where "$\|$" represents the covariant differentiation with respect to $\widetilde{\alpha}$. The right hand side of (11.1.32) is symmetric with respect to indices i and j, so that $\widetilde{b}_{i\|j} = \widetilde{b}_{j\|i}$, i.e., $\widetilde{\beta}$ is closed. Thus, (11.1.16) and (11.1.17) hold. Expanding the left hand side of (11.1.32) and noting that $\widetilde{\alpha}$ is conformally flat, we have

$$[b^2c(x) - 2\tau e^\rho(1 + k_1b^2)]\delta_{ij} = [2e^\rho\tau(k_2b^2 + k_3) + c(x)]b_ib_j.$$

Since dimension $n \geq 3$, we obtain

$$b^2c(x) - 2\tau e^\rho(1 + k_1b^2) = 0,$$
$$2e^\rho\tau(k_2b^2 + k_3) + c(x) = 0,$$

from which it follows that

$$(1 + k_1b^2) + b^2(k_2b^2 + k_3) = 0. \qquad (11.1.33)$$

Substituting (11.1.33) into (6.2.9) and putting $s = b$, one can see that

$$(k_1 + k_2b^2)(\phi(b) - s\phi'(b)) = 0.$$

Since $\phi(b) - b\phi'(b) > 0$ ([17]), we have

$$k_1 + k_2b^2 = 0, \quad 1 + k_3b^2 = 0.$$

Moreover, (6.2.9) can be expressed as

$$(1 + k_1s^2)\phi''(s) = \phi(s) - \phi'(s).$$

The solution of this equation is $\phi = c_1s + c_2\sqrt{1 + k_1s^2}$, i.e., $\widetilde{F}$ is of Randers type. This is a contradiction to the condition (b) of Theorem 6.6. Therefore, our claim is proved.

Conditions (a) and (b) do not hold simultaneously. If the condition (a) is not satisfied, i.e., $\widetilde{\beta}$ is parallel with respect to $\widetilde{\alpha}$, then $\widetilde{F}$ is a Berwald metric ([17]). Thus, the flat metric $F = \alpha\phi(\beta/\alpha)$ is a Berwald metric naturally. Since $\widetilde{F} = e^\rho F$, we have

$$\widetilde{b}_{i||j} = e^\rho(b_{i,j} - \rho_i b_j + \delta_{ij} b^s \rho_s),$$

where "," represents the covariant differentiation with respect to α. Since they are Berwaldian, i.e., $\widetilde{b}_{i||j} = b_{i,j} = 0$, we have

$$\rho_i b_j = \delta_{ij} b^s \rho_s, \quad \rho_s b_s = 0.$$

Hence $\rho_i b_j = 0$. Since $b \neq 0$, we obtain $\rho_i = 0$, i.e., ρ is constant. Hence, $\widetilde{F}$ is locally Minkowskian.

If condition (b) is not satisfied, then $\widetilde{F}$ is of Randers type. $\qquad\square$

Remark. By [72], in Theorem 11.3 the condition that $\widetilde{F}$ is projectively flat can be replaced by that $\widetilde{F}$ is Douglasian. Moreover, we can get the following corollary from the last part of the proof.

Corollary 11.1. *Any conformal change between Berwald (α, β)-metrics must be homothetic.*

Combining Theorem 11.1 with Theorem 11.3 yields the following

Theorem 11.4 ([174]). *Let (M, F) be an n-dimensional $(n \geq 3)$ (α, β)-manifold. Then F is both conformally and projectively flat if and only if one of the following holds:*

(i) F is a Riemannian metric of constant curvature;

(ii) There is a local coordinate system (x^i, y^i) such that F can be expressed as

$$F = \frac{1}{|A + Bb_k x^k|}\left(\sqrt{\Sigma_i (y^i)^2} + b_i y^i\right),$$

where b_i, A and B are constants satisfying $A + Bb_k x^k \neq 0$.

Remark. Please refer to [83] for the conformally flat compact Finsler manifolds.

11.2 Conformal vector fields

11.2.1 Conformal vector fields

Let (M, F) be an n-dimensional Finsler manifold, $\varphi : M \to M$ be a diffeomorphism. φ is called a *conformal transformation* if there is a smooth projective function $\rho = \rho(x)$ such that $F(\varphi(x), d\varphi(y)) = e^{\rho(x)}F(x, y)$. A vector field v on M is call a *conformal vector field* on M ([74]) if the one parameter transformation group $\{\varphi_t\}$ generated by v is a conformal transformation group, i.e.,

$$\varphi_t^* F(x,y) = F(\varphi_t(x), d(\varphi_t)(y)) = e^{\rho(x)t} F(x,y), \qquad (11.2.1)$$

Let Φ_t be the lifting of φ_t onto the tangent bundle TM, i.e., $\Phi_t(x,y) := (\varphi_t(x), (d\varphi_t)(y))$. Then $\{\Phi_t\}$ is a one parameter transformation group on TM, i.e.,

$$\Phi_t^* F = e^{\rho t} F.$$

In particular, v is called a *homothetic vector field* on M if ρ is constant, and a *Killing vector field* on M if $\rho = 0$. A conformal vector field v is said to be *essential* if v is not a Killing vector field.

Proposition 11.4 ([118]). *Let v be a vector field on an n-dimensional Finsler manifold (M, F). In a standard local coordinate system (x^i, y^i), the following conditions are equivalent:*

(1) $v = v^i(x)\frac{\partial}{\partial x^i}$ *is a conformal vector field on* (M, F);

(2) $\frac{\partial g_{ij}}{\partial x^p} v^p + g_{pj}\frac{\partial v^p}{\partial x^i} + g_{ip}\frac{\partial v^p}{\partial x^j} + 2C_{ijp}\frac{\partial v^p}{\partial x^q} y^q = 2\rho g_{ij}$;

(3) $v_{i|j} + v_{j|i} + 2C_{ij}^p v_{p|q} y^q = 2\rho g_{ij}$;

(4) $\frac{\partial F}{\partial x^i} v^i + \frac{\partial F}{\partial y^i}\frac{\partial v^i}{\partial x^j} y^j = \rho F$,

where g_{ij} and C_{ijp} are components of the fundamental tensor and the Cartan tensor, $C_{ij}^p = g^{pq}C_{ijq}$, $v_i = g_{ij}v^j$, and "$|$" denotes the horizontal covariant differentiation with respect to the Chern connection.

Proof. $(1) \Leftrightarrow (2)$. Suppose that v is a conformal vector field on M and φ_t is a one parameter group generated by v such that $\varphi_0(x) = x$. By $(11.2.1)$ we have

$$g_{ij}(\varphi_t(x), (d\varphi_t)(y))\frac{\partial \varphi_t^i}{\partial x^k} y^k \frac{\partial \varphi_t^j}{\partial x^l} y^l = e^{2\rho(x)t} g_{ij}(x,y) y^i y^j. \qquad (11.2.2)$$

Note that $v(x) = \frac{d\varphi(x,t)}{dt}\big|_{t=0}$ and φ_0 is an identity. Differentiating with respect to t on both sides of $(11.2.2)$ and taking value at $t = 0$, we obtain

$$\frac{\partial g_{ij}}{\partial x^k} v^k y^i y^j + g_{ij}\frac{\partial v^i}{\partial x^k} y^k y^j + g_{ij}\frac{\partial v^j}{\partial x^k} y^k y^i = 2\rho g_{ij} y^i y^j, \qquad (11.2.3)$$

where we have used $(2.2.3)$. Differentiating $(11.2.3)$ with respect to y^i and y^j respectively yields (2).

Conversely, contracting (2) with y^i and y^j gives $(11.2.3)$, which implies

$$\frac{d(\Phi_t^* F)}{dt}\big|_{t=0} = \rho F, \quad \text{equivalently}, \quad \frac{d}{dt}(\Phi_t^* F - e^{\rho t} F)\big|_{t=0} = 0. \qquad (11.2.4)$$

Obviously,

$$
\begin{aligned}
\frac{d}{dt}(\Phi_t^* F)|_{t=s} &= \lim_{t \to 0} \frac{\Phi_{t+s}^* F - \Phi_s^* F}{t} \\
&= \lim_{t \to 0} \frac{\Phi_t^* \cdot \Phi_s^* F - \Phi_s^* F}{t} \\
&= \Phi_s^* \left(\frac{d}{dt} \Phi_t^* F|_{t=0} \right) = \rho \Phi_s^* F.
\end{aligned}
\tag{11.2.5}
$$

Thus, we obtain

$$
\frac{d}{dt}(\Phi_t^* F - e^{\rho t} F)|_{t=s} = \rho(\Phi_s^* F - e^{\rho s} F).
\tag{11.2.6}
$$

If $\rho = 0$, then $\frac{d}{dt}(\Phi_t^* F - F)|_{t=s} = 0$, which implies that $\Phi_t^* F - F$ is independent of t. From (11.2.4) we have $\Phi_t^* F = F$, i.e., Φ_t is an infinitesimal isometry. Hence, (1) holds.

If $\rho \neq 0$ and $\Phi_t^* F - e^{\rho t} F \neq 0$, then (11.2.6) gives that

$$
\Phi_t^* F - e^{\rho t} F = e^{\rho_1} e^{\rho t},
$$

where ρ_1 is a constant. Substituting the above into (11.2.4) yields that $e^{\rho_1} = 0$, which is impossible. Thus, either $\rho = 0$ or $\Phi_t^* F - e^{\rho t} F = 0$. Hence, (1) always holds in any case.

(2) $\Leftrightarrow$ (3). From the definition of the Chern connection (§3.1.1) we can show this directly.

(2) $\Leftrightarrow$ (4). Contracting (2) with y^i and y^j gives (11.2.3). Noting that $F^2(y) = g_{ij}(y)y^i y^j$, we have

$$
\frac{\partial F^2}{\partial x^k} v^k + \frac{\partial F^2}{\partial y^k} \frac{\partial v^k}{\partial x^l} y^l = 2\rho F^2,
$$

which is equivalent to (4). Conversely, if (4) holds, i.e., the above equation holds, then one can get (2) by differentiating with respect to y^i and y^j. $\quad \square$

Remark. Let $X_v = v^i \frac{\partial}{\partial x^i} + y^j \frac{\partial v^i}{\partial x^j} \frac{\partial}{\partial y^i}$ be a vector field induced by Φ on TM. The condition (4) in Theorem 11.4 is equivalent to $X_v F = \rho F$.

Proposition 11.5 ([174]). *Let $F = \alpha \phi(\beta/\alpha)$ be an (α, β)-metric on an n-dimensional manifold M. A vector field v on M is conformal if and only if*

$$
\begin{cases}
v_{i,j} + v_{j,i} = 2\rho a_{ij}, \\
v^j b_{i,j} + b^j v_{j,i} = \rho b_i,
\end{cases}
\tag{11.2.7}
$$

where $\alpha^2 = a_{ij}y^i y^j$, $v_i = a_{ij}v^j$, $b^i = a^{ij}b_j$, the comma "," denotes the covariant differentiation with respect to the Riemannian metric α. (11.2.7) can be expressed equivalently as

$$\begin{cases} \mathcal{L}_V \alpha^2 = 2\rho\alpha^2, \\ \mathcal{L}_V \beta = \rho\beta, \end{cases} \tag{11.2.7'}$$

where $\mathcal{L}_V$ denotes the Lie derivative with respect to v.

Proof. Clearly, we need only to prove the necessity. Suppose that $v = v^i \frac{\partial}{\partial x^i}$ is a conformal vector field on M. By means of the condition (4) in Proposition 11.4, v satisfies

$$v_{i,j}y^i y^j + \alpha Q(s)(v^i b_{j,i} + b^i v_{i,j})y^j = \frac{2\rho\alpha F}{\phi - s\phi'}, \tag{11.2.8}$$

where $Q(s) := \frac{\phi'}{\phi - s\phi'}$. Here the condition $(2.1.5')$ for (α, β)-metrics implies $\phi - s\phi' > 0$.

Fix a point $x \in M$. There is a local coordinate system at the point x such that $\alpha = \sqrt{\delta_{ij}y^i y^j}$ and $\beta = by^1$. Write $\tilde{\alpha} = \sqrt{\sum_{a=2}^n (y^a)^2}$. Thus,

$$y^1 = \frac{s}{\sqrt{b^2 - s^2}}\tilde{\alpha}, \quad y^a = y^a \quad (2 \le a \le n) \tag{11.2.9}$$

define a local coordinate change $\psi : (s, y^a) \to (y^1, y^a)$. In the new coordinate system we have

$$\alpha = \frac{b}{\sqrt{b^2 - s^2}}\tilde{\alpha}, \quad \beta = \frac{bs}{\sqrt{b^2 - s^2}}\tilde{\alpha}. \tag{11.2.10}$$

Substituting (11.2.9) and (11.2.10) into (11.2.8) and using the irrationality of α, we can get

$$\begin{cases} s\tilde{\alpha}^2 \left(sv_{1,1} + bQb_{1,j}v^j + b^2 Qv_{1,1} \right) + (b^2 - s^2)v_{a,c}y^a y^c = \frac{2\rho b^2 \phi}{\phi - s\phi'}\tilde{\alpha}^2, \\ \left(sv_{1,a} + sv_{a,1} + b^2 Qv_{1,a} + Qbb_{a,j}v^j \right) y^a = 0, \end{cases}$$

where $1 \le j \le n$ and $2 \le a, c \le n$. Putting $s = 0$ in the above and using them, we obtain

$$v_{i,j} + v_{j,i} = 2\rho\delta_{ij}, \quad b_{j,i}v^i + bv_{1,j} = \rho b\delta_{1j}.$$

These hold in the new coordinate system (s, y^a). By coming back to the original coordinate system (y^1, y^a), we have (11.2.7).

Setting $\alpha^2 = a_{ij}dx^i \otimes dx^j$ and $\beta = b_i dx^i$. By the definition of the Lie derivative (refer to [74]), one can get $(11.2.7')$. □

Remark. For a vector field X_v on TM, a direct calculation shows that (11.2.7) is equivalent to

$$\begin{cases} X_v(\alpha^2) = 2\rho\alpha^2, \\ X_v(\beta) = \rho\beta. \end{cases} \tag{11.2.7''}$$

If $\rho = 0$, i.e., v is a Killing vector field, then (11.2.7') was given in [71]. If F is a Riemannian metric ($\beta = 0$), then those are just the equations of conformal vector fields and Killing vector fields in Riemannian geometry.

Taking the covariant differentiation with respect to the Riemannian metric α on both sides of $(11.2.7)_1$ and using the Ricci identity and the Bianchi identity in Riemannian geometry, we can obtain

$$v_{i,jk} = \rho_j a_{ik} + \rho_k a_{ij} - \rho_i a_{jk} + v_s {}^\alpha R_k{}^s{}_{ji}, \tag{11.2.11}$$

where $\rho_i = \partial\rho/\partial x^i$, ${}^\alpha R_k{}^s{}_{ji}$ denote the components of the Riemannian curvature tensor of α. Differentiating (11.2.11) yields that

$$v_{i,jkl} = \rho_{k,l} a_{ij} + \rho_{j,l} a_{ik} - \rho_{i,l} a_{jk} + (v_s {}^\alpha R_k{}^s{}_{ji})_{,l}.$$

Skew-symmetrizing with respect to indices k and l in the above and using the Ricci identity, we get

$$\rho_{j,l} a_{ik} - \rho_{i,l} a_{jk} - \rho_{j,k} a_{il} + \rho_{i,k} a_{jl} = T_{ijkl}, \tag{11.2.12}$$

where

$$T_{ijkl} := -(v_s {}^\alpha R_k{}^s{}_{ji})_{,l} + (v_s {}^\alpha R_l{}^s{}_{ji})_{,k} + v_{s,j} {}^\alpha R_i{}^s{}_{kl} + v_{i,s} {}^\alpha R_j{}^s{}_{kl}.$$

Contracting (11.2.12) with a^{jl} yields that

$$\rho^l{}_{,l} a_{ik} + (n-2)\rho_{i,k} = a^{jl} T_{ijkl}. \tag{11.2.13}$$

Contracting (11.2.13) with a^{ik} gives

$$2(n-1)\rho^l{}_{,l} = a^{jl} a^{ik} T_{ijkl}.$$

Substituting this into (11.2.13), we have for $n \geq 3$

$$(n-2)\rho_{i,k} = a^{jl}\left(T_{ijkl} - \frac{1}{2(n-1)} a^{pq} T_{pjql} a_{ik}\right). \tag{11.2.14}$$

It follows from (11.2.11), (11.2.12) and (11.2.14) that the covariant derivatives of arbitrary order for v^i are completely determined by v^i, $v_{i,j}$, ρ_i and ρ. So, the solution of $(11.2.7)_1$ admits at most $\frac{1}{2}(n+1)(n+2)$ independent parameters.

Taking covariant differentiation on (11.2.7) with respect to the Riemannian metric α and using (11.2.11), we can get

$$\rho_i b_k + \rho b_{i,k} - f a_{ik} = U_{ik}, \qquad (11.2.15)$$

where

$$f := b^s \rho_s, \quad U_{ik} := v_s b^j R_k{}^s{}_{ji} - v^j{}_{,k} b_{i,j} - v^j b_{i,j,k} + b^j{}_{,k} v_{i,j}.$$

Contracting (11.2.15) with a^{ik} yields that

$$\rho b^i{}_{,i} - (n-1)f = U^i{}_i.$$

Contracting (11.2.15) with b^k and using the above, we get

$$b^2 \rho_i = \rho \left(\frac{1}{n-1} b^k{}_{,k} b_i - b_{i,k} b^k \right) + U_{ik} b^k - \frac{1}{n-1} U^k{}_k b_i. \qquad (11.2.16)$$

All those are tensor equations, so that they are independent of the choice of the coordinate system. We now choose a special coordinate system such that $\beta = by^1$. Then $(11.2.7)_2$ can be expressed as

$$v_{i,1} = \frac{1}{b} v^j b_{i,j}.$$

Thus, in this local coordinate system, derivatives of arbitrary order for v^i can be completely determined by $\frac{1}{2} n(n-1) + 2$ parameters ρ, v^i, $v_{a,b}$ ($2 \le a \le b \le n$). However, the number of parameters is independent of the choice of coordinate systems. Hence, we have the following

Proposition 11.6 ([174]). *Let M be an n-dimensional ($n \ge 2$) differentiable manifold and $F = \alpha \phi(\frac{\beta}{\alpha})$ be a non-Riemannian (α, β)-metric. Then the maximum rank of the group of essentially conformal transformations on (M, F) is $\frac{1}{2} n(n-1) + 2$.*

The following theorem shows there exist non-Riemannian (α, β)-metrics such that the rank of the group of essential conformal transformations reaches the maximum.

Theorem 11.5 (174). *Let M be an n-dimensional ($n \ge 3$) compact differential manifold without boundary, and $\widetilde{F} = \widetilde{\alpha} \phi(\frac{\widetilde{\beta}}{\widetilde{\alpha}})$ be a non-Riemannian (α, β)-metric on M, where $\widetilde{\alpha}$ is a conformally flat Riemannian metric. If the rank of the group of essentially conformal transformations on $(M, \widetilde{F})$ is $\frac{1}{2} n(n-1) + 2$, then $\widetilde{F}$ is conformally flat.*

Proof. Since $\widetilde{\alpha}$ is conformally flat, there is a function $\rho(x)$ on M such that $\alpha := e^\rho \widetilde{\alpha}$ is a flat metric. Let

$$\beta := e^\rho \widetilde{\beta}, \quad F := e^\rho \widetilde{F} = \alpha \phi(\beta/\alpha).$$

Then an essential conformal field on $(M, \widetilde{F})$ is also an essential conformal field on (M, F), and vice versa. Thus, the maximum rank of the group of essential conformal transformations on (M, F) is also $\frac{1}{2}n(n-1) + 2$. By Proposition 11.3, we need only to prove β is parallel with respect to α, so that F is a locally Minkowskian (α, β)-metric, which implies that $\widetilde{F}$ is conformally flat.

In the following, we will prove that β is parallel with respect to α. The proof is divided into three steps.

Step one. $b^2 = ||\beta||^2_\alpha$ is constant.

Suppose that b^2 is not constant. $(11.2.7)_1$ implies $v_{i,j}v^i v^j = \rho b^2$. Contracting $(11.2.7)_2$ with b^i yields that $v^j b_{i,j} b^i = 0$. Since F is non-Riemannian, i.e., $b^2 \neq 0$, then there is a k such that $b_{i,k}b^i \neq 0$. Thus, we can see from the above that v^k can be determined by other $n-1$ v^j. In other word, the maximum rank of the group of essentially conformal transformations is $\frac{1}{2}n(n-1) + 1$. It contradicts to the assumption in the theorem. Hence, $b_{i,j}b^i = 0$, i.e., b^2 is constant.

Step two. All essentially conformal vector fields are homothetic vector fields, i.e., $\rho_i = 0$.

Since α is flat, $(11.2.14)$ implies that $\rho_{i,j} = 0$. Note that $b^2 =$const., and the curvature tensor and its derivatives for α vanish identically. Differentiating on both sides of $(11.2.16)$ yields that

$$
\begin{aligned}
0 = {} & \rho_j \left(\frac{1}{n-1} b^k{}_{,k} b_i - b_{i,k} b^k \right) + \rho \left(\frac{1}{n-1} b^k{}_{,k} b_i - b_{i,k} b^k \right)_{,j} \\
& + \left(-v^s{}_{,k} b^k b_{i,s} - v^s b_{i,sk} b^k + b^s{}_{,k} v_{i,s} b^k \right)_{,j} \\
& + \frac{1}{n-1} \left(v^s b^k{}_{,sk} b_i \right)_{,j}.
\end{aligned}
\tag{11.2.17}
$$

Contracting $(11.2.17)$ with $b^i b^j$ and using $(11.2.7)_2$, $(11.2.11)$ and $(11.2.16)$, we have

$$\rho A + v^i D_i = 0, \tag{11.2.18}$$

where

$$A := \frac{b^2}{(n-1)^2}(b^k{}_{,k})^2 + \frac{2b^2}{n-1} b^k{}_{,ki} b^i - 2b_{i,kj} b^i b^j b^k - b^i{}_{,s} b^s b_{i,k} b^k,$$

$$D_i := \frac{b^2}{(n-1)^2} b^K{}_{,k} b^j{}_{,ji} - b_{s,jki} b^s b^j b^k - b_{s,ik} b^s b^k{}_{,j} b^j + \frac{b^2}{n-1} b^k{}_{,kij} b^j$$

$$- b_{s,j} b^j{}_{,i} b^s{}_{,k} b^k - b_{s,ik} b^s{}_{,j} b^k b^j - b_i{}^j b_{s,jk} b^s b^k - b_{s,i} b^s{}_{,k} b^k{}_{,j} b^j$$

$$- b^k{}_{,i} b_{s,kj} b^s b^j - b_{s,i} b^s{}_{,kj} b^k b^j + \frac{b^2}{n-1} b^j{}_{,i} b^k{}_{,kj}.$$

Similarly, contracting (11.2.17) with a^{ij} and using (11.2.7)$_2$, (11.2.11) and (11.2.16), one can get

$$\rho B + v^i E_i = 0, \tag{11.2.19}$$

where

$$B := \frac{1}{(n-1)^2} (b^k{}_{,k})^2 - \frac{2(n-2)}{n-1} b^k{}_{,kj} b^j - \frac{n-2}{b^2} b^j{}_{,s} b^s{}_{,jk} b^k - b^j{}_{,k} b^k{}_{,j},$$

$$E_i := - b^j{}_{,jki} b^k - b^j{}_{,ik} b^k{}_{,j} + \frac{1}{n-1} (b^k{}_{,ki} b^j){}_{,j} - \frac{n-2}{(n-1)^2} b^k{}_{,k} b^j{}_{,ji}$$

$$- \frac{n-2}{n-1} b^j{}_{,i} b^k{}_{,kj} - \frac{n-2}{b^2} b_{k,j} b^j{}_{,i} b^k{}_{,s} b^s - \frac{n-2}{b^2} b_{j,ik} b^k b^j{}_{,s} b^s.$$

We can see from (11.2.18) and (11.2.19) that if one of A, B, D_i, E_i is non-zero, then the $(n+1)$ quantities $\{\rho, v^i\}$ are not independent, which contradicts to the assumption in the theorem. Hence, all of A, B, D_i, E_i vanish identically.

$A = 0$ and $B = 0$ imply respectively that

$$\frac{b^2(2n-3)}{(n-1)^2} (b^k{}_{,k})^2 - b^i{}_{,j} b^j b_{i,k} b^k = \frac{b^2}{n-1} (b^k{}_{,k} b^i){}_{,i},$$

$$\frac{(n-2)^2}{(n-1)^2} (b^k{}_{,k})^2 - \frac{n-2}{b^2} b^i{}_{,j} b^j b_{i,k} b^k = \frac{n-3}{n-1} (b^k{}_{,k} b^i){}_{,i} + (b^i{}_{,k} b^k){}_{,i}.$$

Denote by $dx := \sqrt{\det(a_{ij})} dx^1 \wedge \cdots \wedge dx^n$ the volume form of the flat Riemannian metric α. Integrating both sides of the above two formulas on M respectively, we obtain from the divergence theorem that

$$\frac{b^2(2n-3)}{(n-1)^2} \int_M (b^k{}_{,k})^2 dx - \int_M b^i{}_{,j} b^j b_{i,k} b^k dx = 0,$$

$$\frac{(n-2)^2}{(n-1)^2} \int_M (b^k{}_{,k})^2 dx - \frac{n-2}{b^2} \int_M b^i{}_{,j} b^j b_{i,k} b^k dx = 0.$$

From these we can get for $n \geq 3$ that

$$\int_M (b^k{}_{,k})^2 dx = \int_M b^i{}_{,j} b^j b_{i,k} b^k dx = 0.$$

Obviously, the integrand functions are non-negative. Hence, we obtain

$$b^k_{,k} = b^i_{,k} b^k = 0. \tag{11.2.20}$$

Substituting (11.2.20) into (11.2.16) yields that

$$b^2 \rho_i = -v^k (b_{i,j} b^j)_{,k} = 0.$$

Since F is non-Riemannian , $b^2 \neq 0$. Thus, $\rho_i = 0$ and ρ is a constant.

Step three. From the above we see that (11.2.15) can be expressed as

$$\rho b_{i,k} = -v^j_{,k} b_{i,j} - v^j b_{i,jk} + b^j_{,k} v_{i,j}.$$

Choose a special local coordinate system such that $b^i = b\delta^i_1$. Then $b_{i,j} b^j = 0$ implies that $b_{i,1} = 0$. In such a case, (11.2.20) implies that $b_{1,i} = 0$. Thus, the above equation can be rewritten as

$$\rho b_{a,b} = -\sum_{c \neq b} v^c_{,b} b_{a,c} - v^j b_{i,jk} + \sum_{c \neq b} b^c_{,b} v_{a,c}, \quad (2 \leq a, b \leq n).$$

It follows that for essentially conformal vector fields, if there are indices a, b such that $b_{a,b} \neq 0$, then ρ can be determined by $v_{a,b}$ $(a \neq b)$ and v^i. It contradicts to the assumption in the theorem. Hence, we have $b_{i,j} = 0$. This property is independent of the choice of local coordinate systems. Therefore, β is parallel with respect to α. $\square$

Please see [82] and [83] for further results on conformal vector fields.

11.2.2   Conformal vector fields on a Randers manifold

In this section we will use the navigation method (§5.4) to study conformal vector fields on a Randers manifold. Given a Riemannian metric $h(x,y) = \sqrt{h_{ij}(x)y^i y^j}$ and a vector field $W = W^i(x)\frac{\partial}{\partial x^i}$ on M such that $h(x, -W_x) < 1$, we can obtain a Finsler metric $F(x,y)$ by the following formula:

$$h\left(x, \frac{y}{F(x,y)} - W\right) = 1, \quad \forall x \in M, \quad y \in T_x M. \tag{11.2.21}$$

Let

$$W_i = h_{ij} W^j, \quad W_0 = W_i y^i = \langle W, y \rangle_h, \quad \lambda = 1 - |W|^2_h > 0.$$

By solving the equation (11.2.21) for F (see (5.4.12)), we may get a Randers metric $F = \alpha + \beta$, where $\alpha = \sqrt{a_{ij} y^i y^j}$, $\beta = b_i(x) y^i$,

$$a_{ij} = \frac{h_{ij}}{\lambda} + \frac{W_i W_j}{\lambda^2}, \quad b_i = -\frac{W_i}{\lambda}. \tag{11.2.22}$$

Proposition 11.7 ([118]). *Let $F = \alpha + \beta$ be a Randers metric on an n-dimensional manifold M, $\{h, W\}$ be the navigation data given by (11.2.21). Then a vector field V on M is conformal if and only if V satisfies*

$$V_{i;j} + V_{j;i} = 2\rho h_{ij},$$
$$V^i W_{j;i} + W^i V_{i;j} = \rho W_j,$$

(11.2.23)

where we drop down superscripts of V and W by h_{ij}, the semicolon ";" denotes the covariant differentiation with respect to h.

Proof. According to Proposition 11.5 and (11.2.7″), a vector field V is conformal if and only if

$$X_V(\alpha^2) = 2\rho\alpha^2,$$
$$X_V(\beta) = \rho\beta,$$

where $\rho = \rho(x)$ is a smooth function on M. By using (11.2.22), it is equivalent to

$$\lambda[X_V(h^2) - 2\rho h^2] = h^2 X_V(\lambda),$$
$$\lambda[X_V(W_0) - \rho W_0] = W_0 X_V(\lambda).$$

(11.2.24)

We consider two different cases separately.

Case I: $X_V(h^2) - 2\rho h^2 = 0$, which implies that $X_V(\lambda) = 0$. Since $\lambda > 0$, then (11.2.24) is equivalent to $X_V(h^2) - 2\rho h^2 = 0$ and $X_V(W_0) - \rho W_0 = 0$.

Noticing

$$X_V(h^2) = 2V_{i;j}y^i y^j,$$
$$X_V(W_0) = X_V(h_{ij}W^i y^j) = V^i W_{j;i}y^j + W^i V_{i;j}y^j,$$

(11.2.25)

we have $V_{i;j}y^i y^j = 2\rho h_{ij}y^i y^j$ and $V^i W_{j;i}y^j + W^i V_{i;j}y^j = \rho W_i y^i$. This is just (11.2.23).

Case II: $X_V(h^2) - 4\rho h^2 \neq 0$, which implies that $X_V(\lambda) \neq 0$. Thus, (11.2.24) is equivalent to

$$\lambda[X_V(h^2) - 2\rho h^2] = h^2 X_V(\lambda),$$
$$h^2[X_V(W_0) - \rho W_0] = W_0[X_V(h^2) - 2\rho h^2].$$

(11.2.26)

From (11.2.25) and (11.2.26)$_2$ it follows that

$$h^2(V^i W_{j;i}y^j + W^i V_{i;j}y^j - \rho h_{ij}W^i y^j) = 2W_0(V_{i;j}y^i y^j - \rho h_{ij}y^i y^j).$$

Differentiating on both sides with respect to y yields that

$$h_{kl}(V^i W_{j;i} + W^i V_{i;j} - \rho W_j) + h_{jl}(V^i W_{k;i} + W^i V_{i;k} - \rho W_k)$$
$$+ h_{jk}(V^i W_{l;i} + W^i V_{i;l} - \rho W_l) = W_l(V_{k;j} + V_{j;k} - 2\rho h_{jk})$$

(11.2.27)

$$+ W_k(V_{j;l} + V_{l;j} - 2\rho h_{jl}) + W_j(V_{k;l} + V_{l;k} - 2\rho h_{kl}).$$

At any point $x \in M$, we choose a local coordinate system such that

$$h_{ij} = \delta_{ij}, \quad W^i = W^1 \delta_{1i}, \quad W_i = W_1 \delta_{1i}.$$

Putting $k = l \neq j$ and $k = j = l$ respectively in (11.2.27), we obtain

$$V^i W_{j;i} + W^i V_{i;j} - \rho W_j = 2W_l(V_{l;j} + V_{j;l}) + 2W_j(V_{l;l} - \rho), \quad l \neq j \quad (11.2.28)$$

and

$$V^i W_{j;i} + W^i V_{i;j} - \rho W_j = 2W_j(V_{j;j} - \rho), \quad \text{for any } j, \ 1 \le j \le n. \quad (11.2.29)$$

We consider two subcases separately in the following.

Case II.1: $\dim M = n \le 2$. We firstly consider the case when $n = 2$. Putting $j = 1, l = 2$ in (11.2.28) and $j = 1$ in (11.2.29), one can get

$$V^i W_{1;i} + W^i V_{i;1} - \rho W_1 = 2W_1(V_{2;2} - \rho) = 2W_1(V_{1;1} - \rho),$$

which implies that $V_{1;1} = V_{2;2}$. Set $\tau(x) = \frac{1}{2}(V_{1;1} - \rho)$. The above equality becomes that

$$V^i W_{1;i} + W^i V_{i;1} - \rho W_1 = 2\tau W_1.$$

Similarly, by putting $j = 2$ and $l = 1$ in (11.2.28) and $j = 2$ in (11.2.29), we obtain

$$V^i W_{2;i} + W^i V_{i;2} = V_{1;2} + V_{2;1} = 0.$$

From those equalities it follows that

$$V_{i;j} + V_{j;i} = 2(\rho + \tau)h_{ij}, \quad V^k W_{j;k} + W^k V_{k;j} = (\rho + 2\tau)W_j. \quad (11.2.30)$$

In the case when $n = 1$, (11.2.27) implies (11.2.30) directly.

Case II.2: $\dim M = n \ge 3$. Since the left hand side of (11.2.28) is independent of l, we have for every j

$$W_l(V_{l;j} + V_{j;l}) + W_j(V_{l;l} - \rho) = W_k(V_{k;j} + V_{j;k}) + W_j(V_{k;k} - \rho), \quad k \neq j, l \neq j.$$

Setting $j \neq 1, k \neq 1$ and $l = 1$ in the above, one get

$$V_{1;j} + V_{j;1} = 0, \quad j \neq 1.$$

Combining it with (11.2.28) yields that

$$V^i W_{j;i} + W^i V_{i;j} - \rho W_j = 0, \quad j \neq 1. \quad (11.2.31)$$

Taking $j = 1$ in (11.2.29), we get

$$V^i W_{1;i} + W^i V_{i;1} - \rho W_1 = 2(V_{1;1} - \rho)W_1.$$

Set $\tau(x) = \frac{1}{2}(V_{1;1} - \rho)$. Then the above equality can be rewritten as

$$V^i W_{1;i} + W^i V_{i;1} - \rho W_1 = 4\tau W_1,$$

from which and (11.2.31) it follows that

$$V^i W_{j;i} + W^i V_{i;j} = (\rho + 2\tau)W_j, \quad 1 \le j \le n. \tag{11.2.32}$$

Substituting (11.2.32) into (11.2.27) and putting $l = 1, j \ne 1, k \ne 1$, we obtain

$$V_{k;j} + V_{j;k} = 2(\rho + \tau)\delta_{jk}, \quad j \ne 1, k \ne 1. \tag{11.2.33}$$

By virtue of that $V_{1;1} - \rho = 2\tau$, from (11.2.31)-(11.2.33) we see that (11.2.30) holds in any local coordinate system.

So far we have proved that $(11.2.24)_2$ implies (11.2.30) for any n.

We now show that $\tau(x) = 0$. Since $X_V(\lambda) = -2W_{i;k}W^i V^k$, then $(11.2.24)_1$ can be rewritten as

$$\lambda(V_{i;j} y^i y^j - \rho h^2) + h^2 W_{i;k} W^i V^k = 0,$$

which is equivalent to that

$$W_{i;k} W^i V^k + \lambda\tau = 0$$

by means of (11.2.30). Combining it with $(11.2.30)_2$ yields that

$$V_{i;j} W^i W^j = (\rho + 2\tau) - (\rho + \tau)\lambda. \tag{11.2.34}$$

On the other hand, it follows from $(11.2.30)_1$ that

$$V_{i;j} W^i W^j = (\rho + \tau)(1 - \lambda).$$

Combining the above with (11.2.34) yields that $\tau = 0$. Thus, (11.2.23) holds.

Conversely, it is easy to verify that (11.2.23) implies that V is a conformal vector field. $\qquad\square$

We now have the following

Theorem 11.6 (118). *Let $F = \alpha + \beta$ be a Randers metric on an n-dimensional $(n \ge 3)$ manifold M, and V be a conformal vector field on (M, F) with the conformal factor $\rho(x)$. Let $\widetilde{F} = \widetilde{F}(x, y)$ be a Randers metric obtained from $\{F, V\}$ by the navigation construction, i.e.,*

$$F\left(x, \frac{y}{\widetilde{F}(x, y)} - V_x\right) = 1, \quad y \in T_x M. \tag{11.2.35}$$

Then

(1) If F has isotropic $\mathbf{S}$-curvature $S(x, y) = (n + 1)\sigma F(x, y)$, then $\widetilde{F}$ has isotropic $\mathbf{S}$-curvature $\widetilde{S}(x, u) = (n + 1)(\sigma - \rho)\widetilde{F}(x, u)$;

(2) If F has weakly isotropic flag curvature $K(x,y) = \frac{3\theta}{F}(x,y) + \zeta$, then $\widetilde{F}$ has weakly isotropic flag curvature $\widetilde{K}(x,u) = \frac{3\widetilde{\theta}}{\widetilde{F}}(x,u) + \widetilde{\zeta}$;

(3) If F is a weak Einstein metric, i.e.,

$$Ric(x,y) = (n-1)\left(\frac{3\theta}{F(x,y)} + \zeta\right)F(x,y)^2,$$

then $\widetilde{F}$ is also a weak Einstein metric with

$$\widetilde{Ric}(x,u) = (n-1)\left(\frac{3\widetilde{\theta}}{\widetilde{F}(x,u)} + \widetilde{\zeta}\right)\widetilde{F}(x,u)^2,$$

where

$$\begin{cases} u := y + F(x,y)V = y + \widetilde{F}(x,u)V, \\ \widetilde{\theta} := (\theta_m - \rho_{x^m})u^m, \\ \widetilde{\zeta} := \zeta - \rho^2 + 2\rho_{x^m}V^m, \end{cases} \qquad (11.2.36)$$

$\theta := \theta_m y^m$ and $\widetilde{\theta}$ are 1-forms on M, ζ and $\widetilde{\zeta}$ are scalar functions on M.

To prove the theorem, first we need the following

Lemma 11.4 ([118]). *Let (M,F) be a Finsler manifold, W be a vector field on M such that $F(x,-W) < 1$. Suppose that $\widetilde{F}(x,y)$ is a Finsler metric obtained from $\{F,W\}$ by the navigation construction (11.2.35) and V is a vector field on M satisfying $\widetilde{F}(x,-W) < 1$. Then the Finsler metric $\widetilde{\widetilde{F}}(x,y)$ obtained from $\{\widetilde{F},V\}$ by the navigation (11.2.35) satisfies the following equality*

$$\widetilde{\widetilde{F}}(x,u) = F\left(x,u - \widetilde{\widetilde{F}}(x,u)(V+W)\right),$$

where $u = y + \widetilde{F}(x,y)V$.

Proof. By the assumption and (11.2.35), we have

$$\widetilde{F}(x,y) = F\left(x,y - \widetilde{F}(x,y)W\right), \quad \widetilde{\widetilde{F}}(x,y) = \widetilde{F}\left(x,y - \widetilde{\widetilde{F}}(x,y)V\right). \tag{11.2.37}$$

Let $y = u - \widetilde{\widetilde{F}}(x,u)V$. From (11.2.37) it follows that

$$\begin{aligned} \widetilde{\widetilde{F}}(x,u) &= \widetilde{F}\left(x,u - \widetilde{\widetilde{F}}(x,u)V\right) \\ &= F\left(x,u - \widetilde{\widetilde{F}}(x,u)V - \widetilde{F}\left(x,u - \widetilde{\widetilde{F}}(x,u)V\right)W\right) \\ &= F\left(x,u - \widetilde{\widetilde{F}}(x,u)(V+W)\right). \end{aligned}$$

By means of $(11.2.37)_2$ we get

$$\widetilde{F}(x,u) = \widetilde{F}\left(x, u - \widetilde{F}(x,u)V\right) = \widetilde{F}(x,y).$$

Thus, $u = y + \widetilde{F}(x,y)V$. The lemma is proved. □

Proof of Theorem 11.6. By the assumption, V is a conformal vector field on (M,F) with conformal factor $\rho(x)$. According to Proposition 11.7, V is a conformal vector field on (M,h) with conformal factor $\rho(x)$.

(1) Since F has isotropic **S**-curvature $S(x,y) = (n+1)\sigma F(x,y)$, by the main theorem of literature [146], $-W$ is a conformal vector field with respect to h satisfying $-W_{i;j} - W_{j;i} = 2\sigma h_{ij}$. Thus, $V + W$ is also a conformal vector field on (M,h) with the conformal factor $\rho - \sigma$, i.e., $(V_{i;j} + W_{i;j}) + (V_{j;i} + W_{j;i}) = 2(\rho - \sigma)h_{ij} = -2(\sigma - \rho)h_{ij}$.

On the other hand, by means of Lemma 11.4, $\widetilde{F}$ constructed from $\{F,V\}$ by the navigation (11.2.35) satisfies

$$\widetilde{F}(x,u) = h\left(x, u - \widetilde{F}(x,u)(V+W)\right).$$

Thus, $\widetilde{F}$ may be viewed as a Finsler metric determined from $\{h, V + W\}$ by (11.2.35). By using again the main theorem of [146], $\widetilde{F}(u)$ has isotropic **S**-curvature $(\sigma - \rho)$, i.e., $\widetilde{S}(x,u) = (n+1)(\sigma - \rho)\widetilde{F}(x,u)$, where $u = y + F(x,y)V = y + \widetilde{F}(x,u)V$. Since the **S**-curvature of F is isotropic along any direction y, the **S**-curvature of $\widetilde{F}$ is isotropic along any direction. If y is replaced by $y - F(x,y)V$, then (1) is proved.

(2) Since F has weakly isotropic flag curvature $K_F = \frac{3\theta}{F} + \zeta$, by Theorem 1.2 of [120], the metric F has isotropic **S**-curvature $\sigma(x)$, where $\theta = \sigma_{x^m}y^m$. Theorem 5.1 of [30] implies that the sectional curvature of h is $K_h = \mu$ ($\mu =$ constant for $\dim M \geq 3$) and $\zeta = \mu - \sigma^2 - 2\sigma_{x^m}W^m$. On the other hand, $\widetilde{F}$ can be viewed as a Finsler matric determined from $\{h, V + W\}$ by (11.2.35). Hence, from (1) and Theorem 5.1 of [30] it follows that $\widetilde{F}(x,u)$ of scalar flag curvature $\widetilde{K}_{\widetilde{F}}(x,u)$:

$$\widetilde{K}_{\widetilde{F}}(x,u) = \frac{3(\sigma_{x^m} - \rho_{x^m})u^m}{\widetilde{F}(x,u)} + \mu - (\sigma - \rho)^2 - 2(\sigma_{x^m} - \rho_{x^m})(V^m + W^m),$$

where $u = y + F(x,y)V = y + \widetilde{F}(x,u)V$. The above formula can be rewritten as

$$\widetilde{K}_{\widetilde{F}}(x,u) = \frac{3\widetilde{\theta}}{\widetilde{F}(x,u)} + \widetilde{\zeta},$$

where $\widetilde{\theta} := (\sigma_{x^m} - \rho_{x^m})u^m = (\theta_{y^m} - \rho_{x^m})u^m$ and

$$\widetilde{\zeta} := \zeta - \rho(\rho - 2\sigma) + 2(\rho_{x^m} - \sigma_{x^m})V^m + 2\rho_{x^m}W^m. \qquad (11.2.38)$$

Since $n \geq 3$, from (11.2.38) we see that $\widetilde{\zeta} = \zeta - \rho^2 + 2\rho_{x^m}V^m$. Similar to the case (1), the flag curvature of $\widetilde{F}$ is weakly isotropic along any direction. Now (2) is proved.

(3) Since F is a weak Einstein metric with Ricci curvature $Ric_F = (n-1)\left(\frac{3\theta}{F} + \zeta\right)F^2$, by Proposition 5.1 of [120], we see that F has isotropic S-curvature $\sigma(x)$. Thus, by Theorem 4.2 of [30], h is an Einstein metric with Ricci curvature $^hRicci = (n-1)\mu h^2$, where $\mu = \zeta + \sigma^2 + 2\sigma_{x^m}W^m$. In this case $\theta = \sigma_{x^m}y^m$. The remainder of the proof is similar to (2) and will be omitted here. This proves Theorem 11.6 completely. $\qquad \square$

11.3   A class of critical Finsler metrics

11.3.1   The Einstein-Hilbert functional

In Riemannian geometry, Einstein metric is the critical point of the following Einstein-Hilbert functional (totally scalar curvature functional) ([20]):

$$\frac{1}{\mathrm{Vol}^{1-2/n}(M)} \int_M R \, dV_M,$$

where R is the scalar curvature of Riemannian metric, dV_M is the Riemannian volume element. In Finsler geometry, we introduce the generalized Einstein-Hilbert functional ([6, 32]) by

$$\mathcal{E}(F) = \frac{1}{\mathrm{Vol}^{1-2/n}(SM)} \int_{SM} Ric \, dV_{SM}. \qquad (11.3.1)$$

We can easily prove the above two functionals are consistent in Riemannian case by (9.3.6) of Lemma 9.7.

Definition 11.1. A Finsler metric is called an $\mathcal{E}$-*critical metric*, if it is a critical point of a functional $\mathcal{E}$.

Remark. In [6] it is claimed that the critical point of functional $\mathcal{E}$ is a Finsler-Einstein metric (§5.4.3). Unfortunately there is an error in the computation and the critical metric is not necessarily a Finsler-Einstein metric ([32]).

Now we will find equations to characterize the $\mathcal{E}$-critical metric. Suppose that $F(t)$ is a variation of F, such that $F(0) = F$, $F(t)|_{\partial(SM)} = F(0)|_{\partial(SM)}$. Denote the variation function V as

$$V = \left.\frac{\partial}{\partial t}\right|_{t=0} \ln F^2.$$

V can be an arbitrary function on SM. In fact, for an arbitrary $V(x, y)$, we can construct variation $F(t) := F(0)e^{tV/2}$. For simplicity, all the derivations about t will be evaluated at $t = 0$ in the following, more remarks will be given.

The variation of fundamental tensor can be expressed as

$$\frac{\partial}{\partial t}g_{ik} = v_{ik}, \quad v_{ik} = \frac{1}{2}[F^2 V]_{y^i y^k}, \quad v_{k0} = \frac{1}{2F}[F^2 V]_{y^k}, \quad v_{00} = V. \quad (11.3.2)$$

Where "0" represents contraction with vector ℓ, such as $v_{0k} = v_{ik}\ell^i$, $v_{00} = v_{0k}\ell^k$.

Hence, the variation of volume element is

$$\frac{\partial}{\partial t}dV_{SM} = \frac{1}{2}\left(g^{ik}[F^2 V]_{y^i y^k} - nV\right)dV_{SM}, \quad (11.3.3)$$

$$\frac{\partial}{\partial t}g^{il} = -g^{ip}v_{pq}g^{ql} := -v^{il}. \quad (11.3.4)$$

The variation of Cartan tensor is given by

$$\frac{\partial}{\partial t}C_{ijk} = \frac{1}{2F}v_{ij;k}, \quad v_{0j;k} = v_{i0;k} = v_{ij;0} = 0. \quad (11.3.5)$$

Let

$$H^i_{kj} := \frac{1}{2}g^{il}\left(v_{lj|k} + v_{lk|j} - v_{jk|l}\right), \quad (11.3.6)$$

then

$$2H^i_{kj} = -v^{il}\left(\frac{\delta g_{lj}}{\delta x^k} + \frac{\delta g_{lk}}{\delta x^j} - \frac{\delta g_{jk}}{\delta x^l}\right) + g^{il}\left(\frac{\delta v_{lj}}{\delta x^k} + \frac{\delta v_{lk}}{\delta x^j} - \frac{\delta v_{jk}}{\delta x^l}\right). \quad (11.3.7)$$

Therefore the variation of Christoffel symbols satisfies

$$2\frac{\partial}{\partial t}\gamma^p_{kq} = -v^{pl}\left(\frac{\partial g_{lq}}{\partial x^k} + \frac{\partial g_{lk}}{\partial x^q} - \frac{\partial g_{kq}}{\partial x^l}\right) + g^{pl}\left(\frac{\partial v_{lq}}{\partial x^k} + \frac{\partial v_{lk}}{\partial x^q} - \frac{\partial v_{kq}}{\partial x^l}\right)$$

$$= 2H^p_{kq} - 2v^{pl}(N^i_k C_{lqi} + N^i_q C_{lki} - N^i_l C_{kqi})$$

$$+ \frac{1}{F}g^{pl}(N^i_k v_{lq;i} + N^i_q v_{lk;i} - N^i_l v_{kq;i}). \quad (11.3.8)$$

Contracting above formula with y, the variation of Geodesic coefficients is

$$\frac{\partial}{\partial t}G^p = \frac{\partial}{\partial t}\gamma^p_{kq}y^k y^q = \frac{1}{2}g^{pl}(v_{lk|q} + v_{lq|k} - v_{kq|l})y^q y^k = F^2 H^p_{00}. \quad (11.3.9)$$

Denote $T_k^p := \frac{1}{F}\frac{\partial}{\partial t}N_k^p$, formulas (3.1.15), (3.1.17) and (11.3.9) show that

$$T_k^p = \frac{1}{F}\frac{\partial}{\partial t}N_k^p = H_{k0}^p - A_{kq}^p H_{00}^q. \tag{11.3.10}$$

Noticing

$$\left[\frac{\partial}{\partial t}, \frac{\delta}{\delta x^i}\right] = -T_i^k F\frac{\partial}{\partial y^k}, \tag{11.3.11}$$

and according to (3.1.15), (3.1.17) and (3.1.18), formulas (11.3.10) and (11.3.11) imply

$$\frac{y^j}{F^2}\frac{\partial}{\partial t}\left(\frac{\delta N_j^i}{\delta x^i}\right) = \frac{y^j}{F^2}\frac{\delta}{\delta x^i}\left(\frac{\partial N_j^i}{\partial t}\right) - \frac{y^j}{F}T_i^k\frac{\partial N_j^i}{\partial y^k} = \frac{\delta H_{00}^i}{\delta x^i}, \tag{11.3.12}$$

$$\frac{y^j}{F^2}\frac{\partial}{\partial t}\left(\frac{\delta N_i^i}{\delta x^j}\right) = \ell^H(T_i^i) - H_{00}^k(\Gamma_{ik}^i + \dot{I}_k). \tag{11.3.13}$$

Put

$$\theta := g_{ik}H_{00}^i dx^k - T_k^k\omega.$$

By (11.3.12), (11.3.13), Lemma 9.4 and

$$Ric(x, y) = \frac{y^j}{F^2}\left[\frac{\delta N_j^i}{\delta x^i} - \frac{\delta N_i^i}{\delta x^j}\right],$$

we obtain

$$\frac{\partial}{\partial t}Ric = -V\,Ric + \text{div}_{\widehat{g}}\theta + 2H_{00}^i J_i, \tag{11.3.14}$$

where $J = J_i dx^i$ is the dual form of the mean Landsberg curvature (§3.1, (3.1.19)).

Now we calculate the third item on the right hand side of (11.3.14)

$$2H_{00}^i J_i = 2v_{k0|0}J_i g^{ki} - V_{|k}J_i g^{ki}.$$

Using the divergence formula again, we can get

$$\begin{aligned}
2v_{k0|0}J_i g^{ki} &= 2[v_{k0}J_i g^{ki}]_{|0} - 2v_{k0}\dot{J}_i g^{ki}\\
&= 2[v_{k0}J_i g^{ki}]_{|0} - V_{;k}\dot{J}_i g^{ki}\\
&= \text{div}_{\widehat{g}}(2[v_{k0}J_i g^{ki}]\omega - V\dot{J}_i\delta y^i) + V\text{div}_{\widehat{g}}(\dot{J}_i\delta y^i).
\end{aligned} \tag{11.3.15}$$

Since $\dot{J}_i\ell^i = 0$, the above 1-form of divergence indeed is defined on the projective sphere bundle. Moreover it is easy to see that

$$-V_{|k}J_i g^{ki} = -\text{div}_{\widehat{g}}(VJ) + V\text{div}_{\widehat{g}}(J). \tag{11.3.16}$$

Defining two 1-forms as follows

$$\xi := g_{ik}H_{00}^i dx^k + [2v_{k0}J_i g^{ki} - T_i^i]\omega - V\dot{J}_i\delta y^i - VJ,$$
$$\kappa := J_i dx^i + \dot{J}_i \delta y^i. \tag{11.3.17}$$

Combining (11.3.14), (11.3.15) and (11.3.16), one can get

$$\frac{\partial}{\partial t}Ric = \mathrm{div}_{\hat{g}}\xi - VRic + V\mathrm{div}_{\hat{g}}\kappa. \tag{11.3.18}$$

Integrating both sides of the above formula, we get

$$\begin{aligned}
&\frac{d}{dt}\int_{SM} Ric\, dV_{SM}\\
&= \int_{SM}\left(\frac{\partial Ric}{\partial t}\right)dV_{SM} + \int_{SM} Ric\left(\frac{\partial}{\partial t}dV_{SM}\right)\\
&= \int_{SM} V\left(-Ric + \mathrm{div}_{\hat{g}}\kappa\right) + \frac{1}{2}\int_{SM} Ric\left(g^{ik}[F^2V]_{y^iy^k} - nV\right)\\
&= \frac{1}{2}\int_{SM} V\left(g^{ik}[F^2 Ric]_{y^iy^k} - (n+2)Ric + 2\mathrm{div}_{\hat{g}}\kappa\right).
\end{aligned} \tag{11.3.19}$$

Here we have used Lemma 9.8 and $\xi|_{\partial(SM)} = 0$.

Similarly, using Lemma 9.8, we can show the volume variation

$$\frac{d}{dt}\mathrm{Vol}(SM) = \int_{SM}\frac{1}{2}\left(g^{ik}[F^2V]_{y^iy^k} - nV\right) = \frac{n}{2}\int_{SM} V. \tag{11.3.20}$$

Then

$$\begin{aligned}
&\frac{d}{dt}\mathcal{E}(F)\\
&= \frac{1}{2\mathrm{Vol}^{1-2/n}(SM)}\int_{SM} V\left(F^2 g^{ik}[Ric]_{y^iy^k} + (n-2)(Ric - r) + 2\mathrm{div}_{\hat{g}}\kappa\right),
\end{aligned}$$

where

$$r = \frac{1}{\mathrm{Vol}(SM)}\int_{SM} Ric\, dV_{SM}. \tag{11.3.21}$$

Since V is arbitrary, we arrive at the following theorem.

Theorem 11.7 ([32]). *The Euler-Lagrange equation of the functional (11.3.1) $\mathcal{E}(F)$ is*

$$F^2 g^{ik}[Ric]_{y^iy^k} + (n-2)(Ric - r) + 2\mathrm{div}_{\hat{g}}\kappa = 0, \tag{11.3.22}$$

where $\kappa = J_i dx^i + \dot{J}_i\delta y^i$ and r is defined by (11.3.21).

Using the divergence theorem and expanding $\text{div}_{\widehat{g}}\kappa$, one can show that (11.3.22) is equivalent to

$$Ric(x, y) = \frac{2}{n+2}\left(\text{trace}_g\widetilde{\mathcal{R}}c + \text{trace}_g\mathcal{J} - \frac{n-2}{2}r\right), \qquad (11.3.23)$$

where

$$\widetilde{\mathcal{R}}c := \frac{1}{2}[F^2 Ric]_{y^i y^k}dx^i \otimes dx^k, \quad \mathcal{J} := (J_{i|k} + \dot{J}_{i;k} - J_i J_k)dx^i \otimes dx^k. \quad (11.3.24)$$

Besides, using the Riemannian metric $\widehat{r}_x$ which is on projective fiber $S_x M$, (11.3.23) can be rewritten as

$$\Delta_{\widehat{r}_x}Ric + \langle\nabla_{\widehat{r}_x}Ric, \nabla_{\widehat{r}_x}\tau\rangle_{\widehat{r}_x} + (n-2)(Ric - r) + 2\text{div}_{\widehat{g}}\kappa = 0, \quad (11.3.25)$$

where τ is the distortion with respect to the Holmes-Thompson volume element, $\Delta_{\widehat{r}_x}$ represents the Laplacian of the Riemannian metric $\widehat{r}_x$.

Theorem 11.8 ([32]). *A Riemannian metric F is the $\mathcal{E}$-critical metric if and only if F is a Riemannian-Einstein metric.*

Proof. Since F is a Riemannian metric, $\tau = 1$, $I = 0$ and $\kappa = 0$. Substituting into (11.3.25) gives

$$\Delta_{\widehat{r}_x}(Ric - r) = -(n-2)(Ric - r). \qquad (11.3.26)$$

When $n = 2$, $Ric - r$ is independent of y. Noticing that in Riemannian geometry $(S_x M, \widehat{r}_x)$ is a standard sphere whose first eigenvalue is $n - 1$. Thus, when $n \geq 3$, equation (11.3.26) means $Ric - r = 0$. $\qquad \square$

The above theorem indicates that Riemannian-Einstein metrics also preserve the critical proposition even in Finsler setting, i.e., any normal Riemannian-Einstein metric is an $\mathcal{E}$-critical metric. On the other hand, there are non-Riemannian $\mathcal{E}$-critical metrics ([32]).

Remark. As shown in Chapter 10, Einstein metrics in Finsler geometry are important and interesting. Although every Riemannian-Einstein metric is the $\mathcal{E}$-critical metric, a general Finsler Einstein metric is not necessary an $\mathcal{E}$-critical metric. The deceased geometry grandmaster S. S. Chern has proposed the following question

Chern's question ([13]). Whether there is a Finsler-Einstein metric on each smooth manifold?

This question has not been resolved. In [13] the authors propose the following Finsler Ricci flow

$$\frac{\partial}{\partial t}\ln F = -Ric$$

to discuss this question, but it has no conclusion. The proof of Theorem 11.7 might provide a way for the local calculation of the Finsler Ricci flow.

11.3.2 Some special $\mathcal{E}$-critical metrics

Suppose M is an n-dim compact closed manifold, F is a Finsler metric with constant flag curvature K on M. Since the homogeneous property of F in equation (11.3.22), we may suppose $K = 1, 0, -1$. According to Akbar-Zadeh's rigidity theorem of closed manifolds, we only need to consider the case when $K = 1$. It gives

$$\dot{J} = -KI = -I \quad \text{and} \quad \kappa = J_i dx^i - I_i \frac{\delta y^i}{F}. \tag{11.3.27}$$

Equation (11.3.22) can be rewritten as

$$\text{div}_{\widehat{g}}\kappa = 0. \tag{11.3.28}$$

By the definitions of distortion and **S**-curvature in §4.2, we have ([112])

$$d\tau = \tau_{|i}dx^i + I_i\frac{\delta y^i}{F},$$

$$S_{y^i} = \tau_{|i} + \tau_{|k;i}\ell^k = \tau_{|i} + \tau_{;i|k}\ell^k + \tau_{;j}L^j{}_{ki}\ell^k = \tau_{|i} + J_i.$$

The above formulas and (11.3.27) imply

$$\kappa + d\tau = (J_i + \tau_{|i})dx^i = S_{y^i}dx^i,$$

by which and (11.3.28), we can see that F is an $\mathcal{E}$-critical metric if and only if

$$\Delta_{\widehat{g}}\tau = \text{div}_{\widehat{g}}(S_{y^i}dx^i).$$

Recall Definition 4.4 in §4.3 that F having almost isotropic **S** curvature, if $S = \lambda F + df(y)$, where λ and f are scalar functions on M and F having *almost constant* **S** *curvature*, if λ is constant. Thus, if F with constant flag curvature $K = 1$ and almost constant **S** curvature, then Lemma 9.5 gives

$$\Delta_{\widehat{g}}\tau = \text{div}_{\widehat{g}}(\lambda\omega + df) = \Delta_{\widehat{g}}f. \tag{11.3.29}$$

According to the Hopf maximum principle, if M is a compact closed manifold, then $\tau(x, y) - f(x)$ is a constant. Thus τ is independent of y and F is a Riemannian metric. On the other hand, Theorem 1.1 in [26] tells us that if F has constant flag curvature and almost isotropic **S** curvature, then F must admit almost constant **S** curvature. Thus we get the following proposition from (11.3.29).

Proposition 11.8. *Suppose that M is a compact closed manifold, F is a Finsler metric with constant flag curvature and almost isotropic $\mathbf{S}$ curvature on a closed manifold M. Then F is an $\mathcal{E}$-critical metric if and only if F is a Riemannian metric.*

Since Randers metric with constant flag curvature must has almost constant $\mathbf{S}$ curvature (refer to [112], §11). So Proposition 11.8 gives the following

Corollary 11.2. *On a compact closed manifold, any $\mathcal{E}$-critical Randers metric with constant flag curvature must be a Riemannian metric.*

Example 11.1 (Berwald-Randers metrics)**.** Suppose that $F = \alpha + \beta$ is a Randers metric, we call F a Berwald-Randers metric if β is parallel about α. Obviously, the norm $b := \|\beta\|_\alpha$ of β about α is constant. For any Berwald metric, we have $\kappa = 0$ for the quantity κ in (11.3.17). Thus, (11.3.22) can be rewritten as
$$(n-2)r = g^{ik}[F^2 Ric]_{y^i y^k} - (n+2)Ric.$$
Let $^\alpha Rc = R_{ik}dx^i \otimes dx^k$ be the Ricci tensor of Riemannian metric α, according to §2.1.3 of [13], since β is parallel with respect to α,
$$^\alpha Rc(b, y) = 0, \quad Ric(x, y) = R_{ik}y^i y^k/F^2.$$
All of the above formulas show
$$(n-2)rF^3 = 2\alpha F^2\, {}^\alpha R + (2\alpha\|b\|^2 - (n+2)\alpha - n\beta)R_{ik}y^i y^k,$$
where $^\alpha R$ is the scalar curvature of α. Since α is even homogeneous in y, β is odd homogeneous in y, so the above equation is equivalent to
$$\begin{cases} (n-2)r(\alpha^2 + 3\beta^2) = 2(\alpha^2 + \beta^2)\, {}^\alpha R + (2\|b\|^2 - n - 2)R_{ik}y^i y^k, \\ (n-2)r(3\alpha^2\beta + \beta^3) = 4\alpha^2\beta\, {}^\alpha R - n\beta R_{ik}y^i y^k. \end{cases}$$
$$(11.3.30)$$
Letting $y = b$ in (11.3.30) and noticing $0 < \|b\| < 1$, we have $r = {}^\alpha R = 0$. Applying (11.3.30) again gives $Ric(x, y) = R_{ik}y^i y^k/F^2 = 0$. Conversely, if α is Ricci flat, then (11.3.30) holds naturally. So we have the following

Proposition 11.9. *Let $F = \alpha + \beta$ be a non-Riemannian Berwald-Randers metric. Then, F is an $\mathcal{E}$-critical metric if and only if α is Ricci flat.*

Example 11.2 (Product metrics)**.** Suppose that (M, g) and (N, h) are two Riemannian metrics, their local expressions are
$$g = g_{i_1 j_1}y^{i_1}y^{j_1}, \quad h = h_{i_2 j_2}y^{i_2}y^{j_2}.$$
Considering product manifold $L = M \times N$. Suppose $\phi : [0, \infty) \times [0, \infty) \to [0, \infty)$ is a smooth function satisfying

(a) $\phi(\lambda s, \lambda t) = \lambda\phi(s,t), (\lambda > 0)$ and $\phi(s,t) = 0 \Leftrightarrow (s,t) = 0$;

(b) $\phi_s > 0, \phi_t > 0, \phi_s + 2s\phi_{ss} > 0, \phi_t + 2t\phi_{tt} > 0$;

(c) $\phi_s\phi_t - 2\phi\phi_{st} + 4st[\phi_{ss}\phi_{tt} - \phi_{st}\phi_{st}] > 0.$

An example of such function is $\phi_{\epsilon,k} = s + t + \epsilon\sqrt[k]{s^k + t^k}$, where ϵ is an non-negative real number, k is a positive integer.

Now let

$$F(x,y) := \sqrt{\phi(g(x_1,y_1), h(x_2,y_2))},$$

where $x = (x_1, x_2) \in L$ and $y = y_1 \oplus y_2 \in T_xL$. F is a Berwald metric on L ([112], §5, §14), its Ricci curvature is

$$Ric(F) = \frac{g}{F^2}Ric(g) + \frac{h}{F^2}Ric(h).$$

It is easy to verify that the above product Finsler metric $F(x,y)$ is an $\mathcal{E}$-critical metric if (M,g) and (N,h) are two Riemannian metrics which are Ricci flat. As known, every Calabi-Yau manifold is a Ricci flat Riemannian manifold. Thus we can construct many non-Riemannian $\mathcal{E}$-critical metrics.

11.4 The first eigenvalue of Finsler Laplacian and the generalized maximal principle

11.4.1 Finsler Laplacian and weighted Ricci curvature

Let $(M, F, d\mu)$ be an n-dimensional $(n \geq 2)$ Finsler manifold with volume measure $d\mu$, $u : M \to \mathbb{R}$ be a C^∞ function on M. Put

$$M_u := \{x \in M | du(x) \neq 0\}.$$

According to the last paragraph of §5.1.2, we define

$$\nabla u(x) := \begin{cases} g^{ij}(x, \nabla u)\dfrac{\partial u}{\partial x^j}\dfrac{\partial}{\partial x^i}, & x \in M_u, \\ 0, & x \in M \setminus M_u, \end{cases} \tag{11.4.1}$$

which is a smooth vector field on open set M_u and continuous on $M \setminus M_u$. We write

$$\ell_u := \nabla u = u^i\frac{\partial}{\partial x^i}, \quad u^i(x) := \begin{cases} g^{ij}(x, \ell_u)\dfrac{\partial u}{\partial x^j}\dfrac{\partial}{\partial x^i}, & x \in M_u, \\ 0, & x \in M \setminus M_u. \end{cases} \tag{11.4.2}$$

For a smooth vector field V on M and $x \in M_V := \{x \in M | V(x) \neq 0\}$, we define $\nabla V(x) \in T_x^*M \otimes T_xM$ by

$$\nabla V(X) := D_X^V V(x) \in T_xM, \quad X \in T_xM, \tag{11.4.3}$$

where D^V is the restriction of the Chern connection on V. In local coordinate system, it is given by

$$D^V_X V(x) := X^j \left\{ \frac{\partial V^i}{\partial x^j}(x) + \Gamma^i_{jk}(x, V) V^k(x) \right\} \frac{\partial}{\partial x^i},$$

where $\Gamma^i_{jk}(x, V)$ are the coefficients Γ^i_{jk} of the Chern connection evaluated at (x, V).

For any C^∞ function $u : M \to \mathbb{R}$ and any point $x \in M_u$, let

$$\nabla^2 u(x) := \nabla(\nabla u)(x) = \nabla(\ell_u)(x).$$

Let $\{e_a\}^n_{a=1}$ be a local g_{ℓ_u} orthogonal basis on M_u (in order to discriminate local orthogonal basis about g_{ℓ_u}, we use index $1 \leq a, b, \cdots \leq n$) and $\{\omega^a\}^n_{a=1}$ be the dual basis. Noting that $C_{\ell_u}(\ell_u, e_a, e_b) = 0$, (11.4.3) yields

$$\begin{aligned}
\nabla^2 u &= \sum \left(\nabla^2 u(e_b) \right) \omega^b = \sum \left(D^{\ell_u}_{e_b}(\ell_u) \right) \omega^b \\
&= \sum g_{\ell_u} \left(D^{\ell_u}_{e_b}(\ell_u), e_a \right) e_a \omega^b \\
&= \sum \{ e_b \left(g_{\ell_u}(\ell_u, e_a) \right) - g_{\ell_u}(\ell_u, D^{\ell_u}_{e_b} e_a) \} e_a \omega^b \\
&= \sum \{ e_b(e_a(u)) - \left(D^{\ell_u}_{e_b} e_a \right)(u) \} e_a \omega^b \\
&= \sum u_{a|b} e_a \omega^b,
\end{aligned}$$

where "$|$" is the horizontal derivative with respect to the Chern connection (the restriction on ℓ_u). It is easy to verify

$$u_{a|b} = u_{b|a}.$$

Now let

$$d\mu = \sigma(x) dx^1 \wedge \cdots \wedge dx^n,$$

where $\sigma(x)$ is a positive function on M. By (5.1.9), the divergence of a vector field $V = V^i \frac{\partial}{\partial x^i}$ with respect to $d\mu$ is given by

$$\operatorname{div}_\mu V = \nabla^V_i V^i - \mathbf{S}_\mu(V) = \sum_i \left(\frac{\partial V^i}{\partial x^i} + V^i \frac{\partial \ln \sigma}{\partial x^i} \right), \tag{11.4.4}$$

where $\mathbf{S}_\mu$ is the $\mathbf{S}$-curvature with respect to $d\mu$. So the Laplacian of u on M is given by

$$\Delta u := \operatorname{div}_\mu \ell_u = \sum_i \left(\frac{\partial u^i}{\partial x^i} + u^i \frac{\partial \ln \sigma}{\partial x^i} \right), \tag{11.4.5}$$

where u^i is defined in (11.4.2).

According to [91] and [144], for a vector field V on M with no zero point, we can define the *weighted gradient field* and the *weighted Laplacian* on Riemannian manifold (M, g_V) as

$$\nabla^V u := \begin{cases} g^{ij}(V)\dfrac{\partial u}{\partial x^j}\dfrac{\partial}{\partial x^i}, & \text{on } M_u, \\ 0, & \text{on } M \backslash M_u, \end{cases} \qquad \Delta^V u := \mathrm{div}(\nabla^V u).$$

Obviously, formulas (11.4.1) and (11.4.5) give

$$\nabla^{\ell_u} u = \nabla u = \ell_u, \quad \Delta^{\ell_u} u = \Delta u.$$

So we call Δu is the *Finsler Laplacian* of function u on (M, F).

For any function $f \in C^2(M)$, if there is a constant λ satisfying

$$\Delta f = -\lambda f,$$

then λ is called the *eigenvalue* of Δ, and the function f is called an *eigenfunction* corresponding to λ. The minimum non-zero positive eigenvalue λ_1 of Δ on $(M, F, d\mu)$ is called the *first eigenvalue*.

Suppose that $\Omega \subset M$ is a domain with compact closure and non-empty boundary $\partial\Omega$. The first eigenvalue $\lambda_1(\Omega)$ of Ω is defined as ([103])

$$\lambda_1(\Omega) = \inf_{u \in L_0^{1,2}(\Omega)} \frac{\int_\Omega (F^*(du))^2 d\mu}{\int_\Omega u^2 d\mu},$$

where $L_0^{1,2}(\Omega)$ is the C_0^∞ completion with respect to the following norm

$$\|\varphi\|_\Omega^2 = \int_\Omega \varphi^2 d\mu + \int_\Omega (F^*(d\varphi))^2 d\mu.$$

If $\Omega_1 \subset \Omega_2$ are bounded domains, then $\lambda_1(\Omega_1) \geq \lambda_1(\Omega_2) \geq 0$. If $\Omega_1 \subset \Omega_2 \subset \cdots \subset M$ is a sequence of bounded domains satisfying $\bigcup \Omega_i = M$, then the following limit exists

$$\lambda_1(M) = \lim_{i \to \infty} \lambda_1(\Omega_i) \geq 0.$$

Moreover, it is independent of the choice of $\{\Omega_i\}$. ([103])

In order to estimate the first eigenvalue and according to [88, 91], we introduce the definition of weighted Ricci curvature which is inspired by Lott-Villani and Sturm's work on measurable metric spaces.

Definition 11.2. Given a vector $V \in T_x M$ on $(M, F, d\mu)$, let $\gamma : (-\varepsilon, \varepsilon) \to M$ be a geodesic satisfying $\gamma(0) = x$ and $\gamma'(0) = V$. Define

$$\dot{\mathbf{S}}(V) := F^{-2}(V)\frac{\partial}{\partial t}[\mathbf{S}(\gamma(t), \dot{\gamma}(t)]_{t=0}, \qquad (11.4.6)$$

where $\mathbf{S}(V)$ is the $\mathbf{S}$ curvature of (x, V). So

$$\dot{\mathbf{S}}(x, y) = \frac{1}{F^2}\mathbf{S}_{|i}y^i = \frac{1}{F^2}\{\mathbf{S}_{x^i}y^i - 2\mathbf{S}_{y^i}G^i\}.$$

The definition of *weighted Ricci curvature* is given by

$$\begin{cases} Ric_n(V) := \begin{cases} Ric(V) + \dot{\mathbf{S}}(V), & \text{when } \mathbf{S}(V) = 0, \\ -\infty, & \text{when } \mathbf{S}(V) \neq 0, \end{cases} \\ Ric_N(V) := Ric(V) + \dot{\mathbf{S}}(V) - \dfrac{\mathbf{S}(V)^2}{(N-n)F(V)^2}, \quad \forall\, N \in (n, \infty), \\ Ric_\infty(V) := Ric(V) + \dot{\mathbf{S}}(V), \end{cases}$$

$$(11.4.7)$$

where $n = \dim M$ and $Ric(V)$ is the Ricci curvature with respect to $F(x, V)$.

Remark. The above definition is a little different from the definition in [88], where the weighted Ricci curvature is homogeneous of degree two in literature. Obviously, the weighted Ricci curvature reduces to the Ricci curvature when F is a Riemannian metric.

11.4.2 Lichnerowicz-Obata estimates

In this section we will establish the following Lichnerowicz-Obata theorems for Finsler manifolds.

Theorem 11.9 ([153]). *Let $(M, F, d\mu)$ be an n-dimensional forward complete connected Finsler manifold. If there is a positive constant $k > 0$ and $N \in (n, \infty)$, such that the weighted Ricci curvature and $\mathbf{S}$-curvature of $(M, F, d\mu)$ satisfy*

$$Ric_N \geq (n-1)k \quad and \quad \dot{\mathbf{S}} \leq \frac{(N-n)(n-1)}{N-1}k,$$

then

$$\lambda_1 \geq \frac{n-1}{N-1}Nk.$$

Moreover, $\mathrm{diam}(M) = \sqrt{\frac{N-1}{n-1}}\frac{\pi}{\sqrt{k}}$ *if* $Ric_N = (n-1)k$.

In order to prove the theorem, we first enumerate the following lemmas, whose detailed proofs can be founded in related literatures.

Lemma 11.5 ([91]). *Let (M, F) be an n-dimensional Finsler manifold. Given a function $u \in C^\infty(M)$, the following formulas hold at every point of M_u for $N \in [n, \infty]$*

$$\Delta^{\ell_u}\left(\frac{F(\ell_u)^2}{2}\right) - D(\Delta u)(\ell_u) = \|\nabla u\|^2 Ric_\infty(\ell_u) + \|\nabla^2 u\|^2_{HS(\ell_u)} \quad (11.4.8)$$

and

$$\Delta^{\ell_u}\left(\frac{F(\ell_u)^2}{2}\right) - D(\Delta u)(\ell_u) \geq \|\nabla u\|^2 Ric_N(\ell_u) + \frac{(\Delta u)^2}{N}, \qquad (11.4.9)$$

where $\ell_u = \nabla u$ and $\|\nabla^2 u\|^2_{HS(\ell_u)}$ is the Hilbert-Schmidt norm with respect to g_{ℓ_u}.

According to Lemma 3.3 of [143], Lemma 3.2 of [91] and the paragraph of $\nabla^2 u$ in §11.4.1, we can rewrite the above lemma as

Lemma 11.6. *Let $(M, F, d\mu)$ be an n-dimensional Finsler manifold and $u : M \to \mathbb{R}$ be a smooth function. Then the following equality holds*

$$\Delta u = \text{tr}(\nabla^2 u) - \mathbf{S}(\ell_u) = \sum_a u_{a|a} - \mathbf{S}(\ell_u), \qquad (11.4.10)$$

where $u_{a|a} = g_{\ell_u}\left(\nabla^2 u(e_a), e_a\right)$, $\mathbf{S}$ is the $\mathbf{S}$-curvature with respect to $d\mu$ and $\{e_a\}_{a=1}^n$ is a local g_{ℓ_u} orthogonal basis on M_u.

Proof of Theorem 11.9. Firstly, in the assumption of Theorem 11.9, (11.4.7) gives

$$Ric = Ric_N - \dot{\mathbf{S}} + \frac{\mathbf{S}^2}{(N-n)F^2} \geq \frac{(n-1)^2}{N-1}k. \qquad (11.4.11)$$

According to Bonnet-Myers theorem 5.3, M is compact.

Suppose that $u : M \to \mathbb{R}$ is an eigenfunction corresponding to the first eigenvalue λ_1 of the Finsler Laplacian on $(M, F, d\mu)$, i.e.

$$\Delta u = -\lambda_1 u.$$

From the formula

$$\Delta^{\ell_u}(u^2) = \text{div}(\nabla^{\ell_u}(u^2)) = \text{div}(2u\nabla u) = 2u\Delta u + 2\|\nabla u\|^2,$$

we obtain

$$(\Delta u)^2 = -\lambda_1 u \Delta u = \lambda_1\left(\|\nabla u\|^2 - \frac{1}{2}\Delta^{\ell_u}(u^2)\right). \qquad (11.4.12)$$

On the other hand, taking the integral of both sides of (11.4.9) on M and using the divergence theorem, we get

$$\int_M \lambda_1 \|\nabla u\|^2 d\mu \geq \int_M \left(\|\nabla u\|^2 Ric_N(\ell_u) + \frac{(\Delta u)^2}{N}\right) d\mu.$$

By the assumption of Theorem 11.9 and (11.4.12) we get

$$\int_M \left(\frac{N-1}{N}\lambda_1 - (n-1)k\right)\|\nabla u\|^2 d\mu \geq 0,$$

i.e.

$$\lambda_1 \geq \frac{n-1}{N-1} Nk.$$

If $\lambda_1 = \frac{n-1}{N-1} Nk$, all inequalities become equality. Recall (11.4.9) which originates from formula (11.4.8) and the following inequality

$$\|\nabla^2 u\|_{HS(\ell_u)}^2 = \text{tr}(B(0)^2) = \frac{(\text{tr}B(0))^2}{n} + \left\| B(0) - \frac{\text{tr}(B(0))}{n} I_n \right\|_{HS(\ell_u)}^2$$

$$\geq \frac{(\text{tr}B(0))^2}{n} = \frac{(\Delta u + \mathbf{S}(\ell_u))^2}{n}$$

$$= \frac{(\Delta u)^2}{N} - \frac{(\mathbf{S}(\ell_u))^2}{N-n} + \frac{N(N-n)}{n} \left(\frac{\Delta u}{N} + \frac{\mathbf{S}(\ell_u)}{N-n} \right)^2$$

$$\geq \frac{(\Delta u)^2}{N} - \frac{(\mathbf{S}(\ell_u))^2}{N-n},$$

$$(11.4.13)$$

where the matrix $B(0) = (u_{a|b})$ (cf. [91], pp.11-12). When $\lambda_1 = \frac{n-1}{N-1} Nk$, we have

$$B(0) = \frac{\text{tr}(B(0))}{n} I_n, \qquad (11.4.14)$$

$$\frac{\Delta u}{N} = -\frac{\mathbf{S}(\ell_u)}{N-n}. \qquad (11.4.15)$$

(11.4.14) gives

$$u_{a|a} = u_{b|b}, \quad \forall\, a, b,$$
$$u_{a|b} = 0, \quad \text{when } a \neq b. \qquad (11.4.16)$$

Substituting (11.4.15) into (11.4.13) yields

$$\|\nabla^2 u\|_{HS(\ell_u)}^2 = \frac{(\Delta u + \mathbf{S}(\ell_u))^2}{n} = \frac{n}{N^2} (\Delta u)^2 = \frac{n\lambda_1^2}{N^2} u^2.$$

Combining (11.4.16) with the formula gives

$$u_{a|a}^2 = \frac{\lambda_1^2 u^2}{N^2}, \quad \forall a. \qquad (11.4.17)$$

From Lemma 11.6 and (11.4.16), we have

$$-\lambda_1 u = \Delta u = n u_{a|a} - \mathbf{S}(\ell_u), \quad \forall a,$$

which combining with (11.4.15) and (11.4.17) yields

$$u_{a|a} = -\frac{\lambda_1 u}{N}, \quad \forall a.$$

Let $f(x) := \|\nabla u\|^2 + \frac{\lambda_1}{N} u^2$. f is smooth on the open set $M_u = \{x \in M | dx \neq 0\}$ and continuous on $M \backslash M_u$. The derivative of f along $e_c \, (\forall c)$ on M_u is

$$df(e_c) = dg_{\nabla u}(\ell_u, \ell_u)(e_c) + \frac{2\lambda_1}{N} u u_c$$

$$= 2g_{\ell_u}(\nabla^2 u, \ell_u)(e_c) + \frac{2\lambda_1}{N} u u_c$$

$$= 2g_{\ell_u}\left(\sum u_{a|b} e_a \omega^b, \sum u_d e_d\right)(e_c) + \frac{2\lambda_1}{N} u u_c$$

$$= 2u_c u_{c|c} + \frac{2\lambda_1}{N} u u_c = 0,$$

which shows that f is a constant on M_u. On the other hand, f is a constant on $M \backslash M_u$. In fact, if $x \in M \backslash M_u$ is an inner point, then $f = \frac{\lambda_1}{N} u^2$ holds in a neighbourhood U containing x. Then $df = 0$ holds, or f is a constant on U. If $x \in M \backslash M_u$ is a boundary point, we can choose a sequence of $\{x_k\} \subset M_u$ such that $x_k \to x \, (k \to \infty)$. The continuity of f gives $f(x) = f|_{M_u}$. By the continuity of f and the connectivity of M again, we get $f(x)$ is a constant on M.

Suppose u reaches the maximum $u_{\max}$ and minimum $u_{\min}$ respectively at points $p \in M$ and $q \in M$. Since $\|\nabla u\|^2 = 0$ at points p and q, $f(p) = \frac{\lambda_1}{N}(u_{\max})^2 = f(q) = \frac{\lambda_1}{N}(u_{\min})^2$, i.e. $|u_{\max}| = |u_{\min}|$. Without loss of generality, we can assume that $u_{\max} = 1$ and $u_{\min} = -1$. Suppose $\gamma(s)$ is a minimum regular geodesic from p to q on (M, F) with tangent vector $\dot{\gamma}(s)$. It can be assumed that there is no other extremum point along $\gamma(s)$. Otherwise, since the continuity of u, p is not the focal point of minimum extremum point of u. Thus we can assume that $q' \in \gamma(s)$ is the first minimum extremum point of u from p. By the same method, we get maximum extremum point $p' \in \gamma(s)$ from q' to p along $\overleftarrow{\gamma}(s)$. So $\gamma(s)|_{\widehat{p'q'}}$ is a minimum regular geodesic without any other extremum point of u. It can be assumed that $\gamma(s)$ has such property. This shows $\|\nabla u\|(x) > 0, \forall x \in \gamma(s) \backslash \{p, q\}$. Hence, $\gamma(s) \backslash \{p, q\} \subset M_u$. Since $\lambda_1 = \frac{n-1}{N-1} Nk$, we have $\frac{\|\nabla u\|}{\sqrt{1-u^2}} = \sqrt{\frac{n-1}{N-1} k}$ along $\gamma(s)$.

Let d_M be the diameter of (M, F),

$$\sqrt{\frac{n-1}{N-1}} k d_M \geq \sqrt{\frac{n-1}{N-1}} k \int_\gamma F(\dot{\gamma}) ds = \int_\gamma F(\dot{\gamma}) \frac{\|\nabla u\|}{\sqrt{1-u^2}} ds. \quad (11.4.18)$$

$|\frac{du}{ds}| = |g_{\nabla u}(\nabla u, \dot{\gamma})| \leq F(\dot{\gamma})\|\nabla u\|$ implies

$$\int_\gamma F(\dot{\gamma}) \frac{\|\nabla u\|}{\sqrt{1-u^2}} ds \geq \int_{-1}^{1} \frac{du}{\sqrt{1-u^2}} = \pi. \quad (11.4.19)$$

(11.4.18) and (11.4.19) give $d_M \geq \sqrt{\frac{N-1}{n-1}} \frac{\pi}{\sqrt{k}}$.

On the other hand, (11.4.11) and the Bonnet-Myers theorem give

$$d_M \leq \sqrt{\frac{N-1}{n-1}} \frac{\pi}{\sqrt{k}}.$$

Hence, $d_M = \sqrt{\frac{N-1}{n-1}} \frac{\pi}{\sqrt{k}}$. The proof of Theorem 11.9 is completed. $\square$

Theorem 11.10 ([153, 180]). *Let $(M, F, d\mu)$ be an n-dimensional forward complete connected Finsler manifold. If $\mathbf{S} \equiv 0$ and there is a positive constant $k > 0$ such that the Ricci curvature of F satisfies $Ric \geq (n-1)k$, then*

$$\lambda_1 \geq nk.$$

If the equality holds, then the diameter of M is $\frac{\pi}{\sqrt{k}}$, F is an Einstein metric and M is homeomorphic to $\mathbb{S}^n$.

Proof. If $\mathbf{S} \equiv 0$, then $Ric_N = Ric$ by Definition 11.2. We can easily get the first part of Theorem 11.10 by Theorem 11.9. Now we prove that M is homeomorphic to $\mathbb{S}^n$ if $\lambda_1 = nk$.

By the condition of Theorem 11.10, $f(x) = \|\nabla u\|^2 + \frac{\lambda_1}{n} u^2 =$ constant. Let

$$M^+ = \{x \in M | u(x) > 0\},$$
$$M^0 = \{x \in M | u(x) = 0\},$$
$$M^- = \{x \in M | u(x) < 0\},$$

where M^+, M^- is an open set on M and M^0 is a closed set with zero measure. Suppose that p and q are maximum and minimum point of u respectively, and $u(p) = 1$, $u(q) = -1$. $\frac{\|\nabla u\|}{\sqrt{1-u^2}} = \sqrt{k}$ when $\lambda_1 = nk$. Let $\gamma(s) \subset (M, F)$ be a minimizing geodesic from p to q with tangent vector $\dot{\gamma}(s)$. Denote by $L(\gamma)$ the lengthen of γ.

$$\sqrt{k}L(\gamma) = \int_\gamma F(\dot{\gamma}) \frac{\|\nabla u\|}{\sqrt{1-u^2}} ds \geq \int_{-1}^{1} \frac{du}{\sqrt{1-u^2}} = \pi, \qquad (11.4.20)$$

which implies $L(\gamma) = d(p, q) = \text{diam}(M)$. Similarly, we can get $d(q, p) = \text{diam}(M)$. In addition, we claim $B(p, \frac{d}{2}) \subset M^+$. In fact, if there is a point $x_0 \in M^- \cup M^0$ such that $x_0 \in B(p, \frac{d}{2})$, then

$$\sqrt{k}L(\eta) = \int_\eta F(\dot{\eta}) \frac{\|\nabla u\|}{\sqrt{1-u^2}} ds \geq \int_0^1 \frac{du}{\sqrt{1-u^2}} = \frac{\pi}{2}, \qquad (11.4.21)$$

by letting η be a minimizing geodesic from p to x_0 on (M, F) with tangent vector $\dot\eta(s)$. This shows $L(\eta) = d(p, x_0) \geq \frac{d_M}{2}$, which is a contradiction to the hypothesis. In the same way, $B(q, \frac{d_M}{2}) \subset M^-$.

$$B\left(p, \frac{d_M}{2}\right) \cap B\left(q, \frac{d_M}{2}\right) = \emptyset. \tag{11.4.22}$$

Note that $V_{k,0,n}(r) = \mathrm{Vol}(\mathbb{S}^n(k; r))$ when $S = 0$ and $k > 0$, where $V_{k,0,n}(r) = V_{p,k,0,n}(r)$ is defined by (7.1.8) (for $h = 0$). The volume comparison theorem 7.2 gives

$$\frac{\mathrm{Vol}_F^{d\mu}(B(p, \frac{\pi}{2\sqrt{k}}))}{\mathrm{Vol}(\mathbb{S}^n(k; \frac{\pi}{2\sqrt{k}}))} \geq \frac{\mathrm{Vol}_F^{d\mu}(B(p, \frac{\pi}{\sqrt{k}}))}{\mathrm{Vol}(\mathbb{S}^n(k; \frac{\pi}{\sqrt{k}}))} = \frac{\mathrm{Vol}_F^{d\mu} M}{\mathrm{Vol}\mathbb{S}^n(\frac{1}{\sqrt{k}})},$$

which implies

$$\mathrm{Vol}_F^{d\mu}\left(B\left(p, \frac{d_M}{2}\right)\right) \geq \frac{1}{2}\mathrm{Vol}_F^{d\mu} M. \tag{11.4.23}$$

Replacing p by q, one can also get

$$\mathrm{Vol}_F^{d\mu}\left(B\left(q, \frac{d_M}{2}\right)\right) \geq \frac{1}{2}\mathrm{Vol}_F^{d\mu} M. \tag{11.4.24}$$

From (11.4.22), (11.4.23) and (11.4.24), we see

$$B\left(p, \frac{d_M}{2}\right) = M^+, \quad B\left(q, \frac{d_M}{2}\right) = M^-, \tag{11.4.25}$$

M^0 is the boundary of $B(p, \frac{d_M}{2})$ and $B(q, \frac{d_M}{2})$. We can prove that $d(p, x) = \frac{d_M}{2}$, for any point $x \in M^0$. In fact, $d(p, x) \geq \frac{d_M}{2}$ by (11.4.21). On the other hand, if $d(p, x) > \frac{d_M}{2}$, there is a neighbourhood U of x such that for any $\bar{x} \in U$, we have $d(p, \bar{x}) > \frac{d_M}{2}$, which is contradict with (11.4.25). Similarly, $d(q, x) = \frac{d_M}{2}$ for any point $x \in M^0$.

By using reductio ad absurdum we now prove that u only has one maximum point on M. If not, suppose p_1, p_2 are two different maximum points of u and σ_1 is a minimizing regular geodesic from p_1 to q. Then $L(\sigma_1) = d(p_1, q) = d$ and

$$d(p_1, x_1) = L(\sigma_1|_{\widehat{p_1 x_1}}) = d(x_1, q) = L(\sigma_1|_{\widehat{x_1 q}}) = \frac{d_M}{2}$$

by letting $x_1 = \sigma_1 \cap M^0$. Let η be a minimizing regular geodesic from p_2 to x_1. So $d(p_2, x_1) = L(\eta) = \frac{d_M}{2}$. (11.4.20) gives

$$d(p_2, x_1) + d(x_1, q) = d(p_1, q).$$

Suppose that $\sigma_2 := \eta \cup \sigma_1|_{\widehat{x_1 q}}$. Thus σ_2 is a minimizing regular geodesic with $L(\sigma_2) = d_M$ from p_2 to q. Note that the equality holds in (11.4.20) if and only if $\dot{\gamma}$ is parallel to ∇u and u is monotone decreasing along γ. Hence, $\dot{\sigma}_1(x_1) = \dot{\sigma}_2(x_1) = -\frac{\nabla u}{\|\nabla u\|}(x_1)$ in x_1. The uniqueness of geodesic gives $\sigma_1 = \sigma_2$. Therefore $p_1 = p_2$.

In the same way, u only has a one minimum extremum point q on M.

By the proof of Theorem 11.9 and the fact that u is non-degenerate at p, we have

$$u_{a|a} = -ku, \quad \forall a; \quad u_{a|b} = 0, \quad \forall a \neq b; \quad \nabla u = 0.$$

Similarly, q is also a non-degenerate critical point of u. Thus u exactly has two non-degenerate critical points, which means that M is homeomorphic to $\mathbb{S}^n$ according to the analogous Reeb theorem ([169], Theorem 5.4.2). $\qquad\square$

11.4.3 Li-Yau-Zhong-Yang type estimates

Theorem 11.11 ([154]). *Let $(M, F, d\mu)$ be an n-dimensional compact Finsler manifold, whose weighted Ricci curvature is non-negative, i.e., $Ric_\infty \geq 0$. Then*

$$\lambda_1 \geq \frac{\pi^2}{d^2},$$

where d denotes the diameter of $(M, F, d\mu)$.

Proof. Suppose that $u : M \to \mathbb{R}$ is an eigenfunction corresponding to the first eigenvalue λ_1 of the Finsler Laplacian on $(M, F, d\mu)$. Since $\int_M u\, d\mu = -\frac{1}{\lambda_1} \int_M \Delta u\, d\mu = 0$, it can be assumed that

$$1 = \sup u > \inf u = -k \geq -1, \quad 0 < k \leq 1.$$

For $\varepsilon > 0$ small enough, we construct a function

$$v = \frac{u - \frac{1}{2}(1 - k)}{\frac{1}{2}(1 + k)(1 + \varepsilon)}.$$

Obviously, $dv = \frac{2}{(1+k)(1+\varepsilon)} du$ which satisfies

$$\begin{cases} \Delta v = -\lambda_1(v + a_\varepsilon), \quad a_\varepsilon = \dfrac{1 - k}{(1 + k)(1 + \varepsilon)}, \\[2mm] \sup v = \dfrac{1}{1 + \varepsilon}, \qquad \inf v = -\dfrac{1}{1 + \varepsilon}. \end{cases}$$

Since the Legendre transformation $\mathcal{L}^* : T^*M \to TM$ is a bijection satisfying $\mathcal{L}^*(a\zeta) = a\mathcal{L}^*(\zeta)$, $a \in \mathbb{R}^+$, $\zeta \in T^*M$, so

$$\nabla v = \nabla^{\nabla u} v = \frac{2}{(1 + k)(1 + \varepsilon)} \nabla u.$$

Let $v = \sin\theta$. We get

$$-\frac{1}{1+\varepsilon} \leq \sin\theta \leq \frac{1}{1+\varepsilon}, \quad \frac{\|\nabla v\|^2}{1-v^2} = \|\nabla^{\nabla u}\theta\|^2.$$

Now we consider the following function

$$f(x) = \frac{\|\nabla v\|^2}{1-v^2}.$$

We can use Maximum Principle for f on the Riemannian manifold $(M, g_{\nabla u})$ since M is compact. Suppose that $f(x)$ attains its maximum at $x_0 \in M$. Then

$$\nabla^{\nabla u} f(x_0) = 0, \quad \Delta^{\nabla u} f(x_0) \leq 0, \quad x_0 \in M_u.$$

Let $\{e_a\}_{a=1}^n$ be a local $g_{\nabla u}$ orthogonal basis on M_u and $\nabla v = \sum_a v_a e_a$.

Calculating $\nabla^{\nabla u} f(x_0) = 0$ directly gives

$$\sum_b v_b v_{b|a} = \frac{\|\nabla v\|^2(-v)v_a}{1-v^2}, \quad \forall a. \tag{11.4.26}$$

We can get by direct computation that

$$\Delta^{\nabla u} F(x_0) = \Delta^{\nabla u}\left(\frac{\|\nabla v\|^2}{1-v^2}\right) := A + B + C, \tag{11.4.27}$$

where

$$A = \frac{\Delta^{\nabla u}\left(\|\nabla v\|^2\right)}{1-v^2},$$

$$B = \|\nabla v\|^2 \Delta^{\nabla u}\left(\frac{1}{1-v^2}\right) = \|\nabla v\|^2 \mathrm{div}\left(\nabla^{\nabla u}\left(\frac{1}{1-v^2}\right)\right)$$

$$= \|\nabla v\|^2\left\{\frac{2v}{(1-v^2)^2}\mathrm{div}\left(\nabla^{\nabla u}v\right) + 2g_{\nabla u}\left(\nabla^{\nabla u}v, \nabla^{\nabla u}\left(\frac{v}{(1-v^2)^2}\right)\right)\right\}$$

$$= \|\nabla v\|^2\left\{\frac{2v}{(1-v^2)^2}\Delta v + \frac{2\|\nabla v\|^2}{(1-v^2)^2} + \frac{8v^2\|\nabla v\|^2}{(1-v^2)^3}\right\},$$

$$C = 2g_{\nabla u}\left(\nabla^{\nabla u}\left(\|\nabla v\|^2\right), \nabla^{\nabla u}\left(\frac{1}{1-v^2}\right)\right) = \frac{8v v_a v_b v_{a|b}}{(1-v^2)^2}.$$

Therefore, we have

$$0 \geq \Delta^{\nabla u} F(x_0) = \frac{\Delta^{\nabla u}(\|\nabla v\|^2)}{1-v^2} + \frac{8v \sum v_a v_b v_{a|b}}{(1-v^2)^2}$$

$$- \frac{2\|\nabla v\|^4 + 2v\|\nabla v\|^2\Delta v}{(1-v^2)^2} + \frac{8v^2\|\nabla v\|^4}{(1-v^2)^3}.$$

Substituting (11.4.26) into the above formula gives

$$0 \geq \Delta^{\nabla u}(\|\nabla v\|^2) + \frac{2\|\nabla v\|^4 + 2v\|\nabla v\|^2 \Delta v}{1 - v^2}. \tag{11.4.28}$$

(11.4.8) and the conditions of the theorem imply

$$\Delta^{\nabla u}(\|\nabla v\|^2) = 2\|\nabla v\|^2 Ric_\infty(\nabla v)$$
$$+ 2D(\Delta v)(\nabla v) + 2\|\nabla^2 v\|^2_{HS(\nabla v)}$$
$$\geq 2D(-\lambda_1(v + a_\varepsilon))(\nabla v) + 2\sum_{ab} v^2_{a|b} \tag{11.4.29}$$
$$= -2\lambda_1\|\nabla v\|^2 + 2\sum_{ab} v^2_{a|b}.$$

By Schwarz inequality and (11.4.26), we get

$$\sum_{ab} v^2_{a|b} \sum_b v^2_b \geq \sum_a \left(\sum_b v_b v_{b|a}\right)^2 = \sum_a \frac{\|\nabla v\|^4 v^2 v^2_a}{(1-v^2)^2}.$$

This shows

$$\sum_{ab} v^2_{a|b} \geq \frac{\|\nabla v\|^4 v^2}{(1-v^2)^2}. \tag{11.4.30}$$

It follows from (11.4.28)-(11.2.30) that at the point x_0

$$f(x_0) = \frac{\|\nabla v\|^2}{1-v^2}(x_0) \leq \lambda_1(1 + a_\varepsilon).$$

So, at any $x \in M$ we have

$$\sqrt{f(x)} = \|\nabla^{\nabla u}\theta\| \leq \sqrt{\lambda_1(1 + a_\varepsilon)}. \tag{11.4.31}$$

Suppose that

$$G(\theta) = \max_{\substack{x \in M \\ \theta(x)=\theta}} \|\nabla^{\nabla u}\theta\|^2 = \max_{\substack{x \in M \\ \theta(x)=\theta}} \frac{\|\nabla v\|^2}{1-v^2}.$$

Obviously, $G(\theta) \in C^0\left([-\frac{\pi}{2} + \delta, \frac{\pi}{2} - \delta]\right)$, where δ is determined by the following formula

$$\sin\left(\frac{\pi}{2} - \delta\right) = \frac{1}{1+\varepsilon}, \quad G\left(-\frac{\pi}{2} + \delta\right) = G\left(\frac{\pi}{2} - \delta\right) = 0.$$

(11.4.31) gives

$$G(\theta) \leq \lambda_1(1 + a_\varepsilon).$$

By the above formula, we may assume that

$$G(\theta) = \lambda_1(1 + a_\varepsilon \varphi(\theta)), \quad \varphi(\theta) \in C^0\left([-\frac{\pi}{2} + \delta, \frac{\pi}{2} - \delta]\right).$$

Note that $G(\theta)$ vanishes at the endpoints of the interval $[-\frac{\pi}{2} + \delta, \frac{\pi}{2} - \delta]$. It is easy to see

$$\varphi\left(\frac{\pi}{2} - \delta\right) = \varphi\left(-\frac{\pi}{2} + \delta\right) < -1.$$

The formula (11.4.31) gives $\varphi(\theta) \le 1$.

We use the same method as in [161] (cf. [164]) and get

$$\varphi(\theta) \le \psi(\theta), \tag{11.4.32}$$

where $\psi(\theta)$ is defined as follows

$$\psi(\theta) = \begin{cases} \dfrac{\frac{4}{\pi}(\theta + \cos\theta\sin\theta) - 2\sin\theta}{\cos^2\theta}, & \theta \in \left(-\dfrac{\pi}{2}, \dfrac{\pi}{2}\right), \\ \psi\left(\dfrac{\pi}{2}\right) = 1, & \psi\left(-\dfrac{\pi}{2}\right) = -1. \end{cases} \tag{11.4.33}$$

(11.4.32) implies

$$\|\nabla^{\nabla u}\theta\| \le \sqrt{\lambda_1}\sqrt{1 + a_\varepsilon\psi(\theta)}. \tag{11.4.34}$$

Suppose that $p, q \in M$ satisfy $\theta(p) = -\frac{\pi}{2} + \delta$, $\theta(q) = \frac{\pi}{2} - \delta$. Let γ be the shortest geodesic connecting p and q whose tangent vector is T. Then

$$\|\nabla^{\nabla u}\theta\| = \frac{\|\nabla v\|}{\cos\theta} = \frac{F(\nabla v)}{\cos\theta} \ge \frac{\left|g_{\nabla u}\left(\nabla v, \frac{T}{F(T)}\right)\right|}{\cos\theta}$$

$$= \frac{|Tv|}{F(T)\cos\theta} = \frac{\left|\frac{dv}{ds}\right|}{F(T)\cos\theta} = \frac{\frac{d\theta}{ds}}{F(T)}.$$

Thus (11.4.34) implies

$$\sqrt{\lambda_1}d \ge \int_\gamma \sqrt{\lambda_1}F(T)ds \ge \int_{-\frac{\pi}{2}+\delta}^{\frac{\pi}{2}-\delta} \frac{d\theta}{\sqrt{1 + a_\varepsilon\psi(\theta)}}.$$

By (11.4.33), $\psi(0) = 0, \psi(-\theta) = -\psi(\theta), |a_\varepsilon\psi(\theta)| < 1$. Now we have

$$\int_{-\frac{\pi}{2}+\delta}^{\frac{\pi}{2}-\delta} \frac{d\theta}{\sqrt{1 + a_\varepsilon\psi(\theta)}} = \int_0^{\frac{\pi}{2}-\delta} \left(\frac{1}{\sqrt{1 + a_\varepsilon\psi(\theta)}} + \frac{1}{\sqrt{1 - a_\varepsilon\psi(\theta)}}\right) d\theta$$

$$= 2\int_0^{\frac{\pi}{2}-\delta} \left(1 + \sum_1^\infty \frac{1 \cdot 3 \cdots (4k-1)}{2 \cdot 4 \cdots 4k} a_\varepsilon^{2k}\psi^{2k}\right) d\theta$$

$$\ge 2(\frac{\pi}{2} - \delta) = \pi - 2\delta.$$

Therefore

$$\sqrt{\lambda_1}d \ge \pi - 2\delta.$$

Let $\varepsilon \to 0$, hence $\delta \to 0$. So it holds that

$$\lambda_1 \ge \frac{\pi^2}{d^2}. \qquad \square$$

If $\mathbf{S} = (n+1)cF$ for some constant c, then $\dot{\mathbf{S}} = 0$ which implies $Ric_\infty = Ric$. We obtain the following corollary.

Corollary 11.3. *Let (M, F) be an n-dimensional compact Finsler manifold. If M has constant $\mathbf{S}$-curvature and $Ric \geq 0$, then*

$$\lambda_1 \geq \frac{\pi^2}{d^2},$$

where d is the diameter of (M, F).

Remark. (1) The estimates in Theorems 11.9 and 11.11 have been mentioned in [144], where the authors also gave the best estimation of lower bound of first eigenvalue for Neumann condition. When $n \geq 2$, the estimate of Theorem 11.11 is not the best.

(2) Very recently, Q. L. Xia ([147]) obtained a sharp estimate of λ_1 for the case that the weighted Ricci curvature satisfies $Ric_N \geq k$. It is stated as follows.

Let $(M, F, d\mu)$ be an n-dimensional compact Finsler manifold without boundary or with a convex boundary. Suppose that $Ric_N \geq k$ for $N \in [n, \infty]$ and $k \in \mathbb{R}$. Then

$$\lambda_1 \geq \sup_{s \in (0,1)} \left\{ \frac{1}{4} s(1-s) \frac{\pi^2}{d^2} + sk \right\}.$$

11.4.4 Mckean type estimates

All of the above estimates on the first eigenvalue are for Finsler manifolds with non-negative Ricci curvature. For Finsler metric with strict negative curvature, we have the following Mckean type estimates. The detailed proofs are given in [171], we omit them here. The reader who is interested in it can refer to [171] or [143].

Theorem 11.12 ([143]). *Let $(M, F, d\mu)$ be an n-dimensional complete noncompact simply connected Finsler manifold with finite reversibility λ. If the flag curvature K_F and $\mathbf{S}$-curvature of $(M, F, d\mu)$ satisfy that*

$$K_F \leq -a^2 (a > 0), \quad \sup_M ||\mathbf{S}|| = b < (n-1)a,$$

where a, b are constants, then

$$\lambda_1 \geq \frac{((n-1)a - b)^2}{4\lambda^2}.$$

Theorem 11.13 ([143]). *Let $(M, F, d\mu)$ be an n-dimensional complete non-compact simply connection Finsler manifold with finite reversibility λ and non-positive flag curvature. If*

$$Ric_F \leq -a^2 (a > 0), \quad \sup_M ||\mathbf{S}|| = b < a,$$

where a, b are constants, then

$$\lambda_1 \geq \frac{(a-b)^2}{4\lambda^2}.$$

Remark. By using the weighted Ricci curvature in a Finsler manifold $(M, F, d\mu)$, we can give the generalized maximal principle for C^2 functions on $(M, F, d\mu)$.

It is well-known that Hopf's maximum principle is a powerful tool in global differential geometry. H. Omori and S. T. Yau extended it to complete non-compact Riemannian manifolds ([92, 151]). Their generalized maximal principle says that if M is a complete Riemannian manifold with Ricci curvature bounded from below and u is C^2 function bounded from above, then there exists a sequence of points $\{x_k\}$ on M such that

$$\lim_{k\to\infty} u(x_k) = \sup_M u, \quad \lim_{k\to\infty} |\nabla u|(x_k) = 0, \quad \limsup_{k\to\infty} \Delta u(x_k) \leq 0.$$

Recently, F. Zhang ([178]) extended Yau's result to Finsler manifolds as follows.

Theorem 11.14 ([178]). *Let $(M, F, d\mu)$ be a forward complete Finsler manifold with a volume form $d\mu$. Let u be a non-constant C^2-function bounded from above on M. If the weighted Ricci curvature Ric_N is bounded from below, then there exists a sequence of points $\{x_k\} \subset M$ such that*

$$\lim_{k\to\infty} u(x_k) = \sup_M u, \quad \lim_{k\to\infty} F(\nabla u)(x_k) = 0, \quad \limsup_{k\to\infty} \Delta u(x_k) \leq 0,$$

where Δ is the Finsler Laplacian.

Exercises

11.1 Verify formula (11.1.9) in detail.

11.2 Reduce the transformation formula of **S**-curvature which is similar to (11.1.13) by using the volume measure (4.1.6) induced on the projective sphere bundle.

11.3 Prove Corollary 11.1 in detail.

11.4 Prove that a Finsler metric F is of scalar flag curvature if and only if its projective curvature tensor $\mathbf{W}$ of F vanishes (refer to [138]).

11.5 Let $g_{ij}(x, y)$ be the fundamental tensor of Finsler metric $F(x, y)$. One can define a Riemannian metric by Holmes-Thompson volume element (4.1.6)

$$\widehat{g} := \widehat{g}_{ij}(x)dx^i \otimes dx^j, \quad \widehat{g}_{ij}(x) := \frac{\int_{S_x M} g_{ij}(x, y)(\det(g_{kl}))d\eta}{\int_{S_x M} (\det(g_{kl}))d\eta}.$$

Prove that any conformal vector field (resp. homothetic vector field, or Killing vector field) of $F(x, y)$ is also a conformal vector field (resp. homothetic vector field, or Killing vector field) of the Riemannian metric $\widehat{g}$, and vice versa.

11.6 Verify formula (11.2.7″).

11.7 Let $g = ||dx||^2/H^2$, $H := 1 + \frac{\mu}{4}||x||^2$ be the standard Riemannian metric of constant curvature μ with $x = (x^1, \cdots, x^n)$ being local coordinates, and $|| \cdot ||^2$ denoting the Euclidean inner product. Prove that the general solution (complementary solution) of conformal vector field equation $(11.2.7)_1$ with respect to g is given by

$$v_i(x) = \frac{1}{H^2} \left\{ \sum_j c_{ij} x^j + b_i - \frac{1}{4}(\mu b_i + d_i)||x||^2 \right.$$
$$\left. + \frac{1}{2} \left[\sum_k (\mu b_k + d_k)x^k + a \right] x^i \right\},$$
$$\rho(x) = \frac{1}{2H} \left\{ \sum_j d_j x^j + a - \frac{a\mu}{4}||x||^2 \right\},$$

where $c_{ij} = -c_{ji}$, b_i, d_i and a are $(n+1)(n+2)/2$ arbitrary constants. Particularly, $a = d_i = 0$ when $\rho = 0$. Therefore the general solution (complementary solution) of the Killing vector field equation with respect to g is

$$v_i(x) = \frac{1}{H^2} \left\{ \sum_j c_{ij} x^j + b_i - \frac{1}{4}\mu b_i ||x||^2 + \frac{1}{2} \left[\sum_k \mu b_k x^k \right] x^i \right\},$$

which contains $n(n+1)/2$ arbitrary constants $c_{ij} = -c_{ji}$ and b_i (cf. [166]).

11.8 Prove that a Finsler metric F with constant flag curvature and almost isotropic $\mathbf{S}$-curvature must has almost constant $\mathbf{S}$-curvature (cf. [26]).

11.9 Verify that the product Finsler metric in Example 11.2 is an non-Riemannian $\mathcal{E}$-critical point.

Appendix A

Maple Program

In Finsler geometry, the computations of geometric quantities are usually very complicated. However, using a Maple program, we can quickly check whether or not an expression is correct even though we can derive it manually; we can simplify the expressions in the computation without making mistakes.

A.1 Spray coefficients of two-dimensional Finsler metrics

In this section, we shall compute the spray coefficients for two-dimensional Finsler metrics. For simplicity, we denote a point (x^1, x^2) in R^2 by (x, y) and a tangent vector $y^1 \frac{\partial}{\partial x^1} + y^1 \frac{\partial}{\partial x^2}$ at (x^1, x^2) by $(x, y; u, v)$. Let $F = F(x, y, u, v)$ be a Finsler metric on an open subset $\mathcal{U} \subset \mathbb{R}^2$. Let

$$L(x, y; u, v) := \frac{1}{2} F^2(x, y, u, v).$$

The spray coefficients, $G := G^1(x, y; u, v)$ and $H := G^2(x, y; u, v)$, are given by

$$G := \frac{(L_x L_{vv} - L_y L_{uv}) - (L_{xv} - L_{yu})L_v}{2\left(L_{uu} L_{vv} - (L_{uv})^2\right)}, \tag{A.1}$$

$$H := \frac{(-L_x L_{uv} + L_y L_{uu}) + (L_{xv} - L_{yu})L_u}{2\left(L_{uu} L_{vv} - (L_{uv})^2\right)}. \tag{A.2}$$

Below is a Maple program for computing G and H. Our testing example is the Klein metric on the unit disk in $\mathbb{R}^2$. It is defined by

$$F = \frac{\sqrt{(u^2 + v^2) - ((x^2 + y^2)(u^2 + v^2) - (xu + yv)^2)}}{1 - (x^2 + y^2)}.$$

It takes a while if one computes the spray coefficients G^i by hands. Now we can use a Maple program to find its spray coefficients within a couple of seconds once the metric function is entered.

```
>   restart;
>   GH:=proc(F)
>   local L,Lx,Ly,Lu,Lv,Lxv,Lyu,Luu,Luv,Lvv,Num1,Num2,
>   Den,G,H;
>   L:=F^2/2;
>   Lx:=diff(L,x);
>   Ly:=diff(L,y);
>   Lu:=diff(L,u);
>   Lv:=diff(L,v);
>   Lxv:=diff(L,x,v);
>   Lyu:=diff(L,y,u);
>   Luu:=diff(L,u,u);
>   Luv:=diff(L,u,v);
>   Lvv:=diff(L,v,v);
>   Den:=2*(Luu*Lvv-Luv*Luv);
>   Num1:=(Lx*Lvv-Ly*Luv)-(Lxv-Lyu)*Lv;
>   Num2:=(-Lx*Luv+Ly*Luu)+(Lxv-Lyu)*Lu;
>   G:=Num1/Den;
>   H:=Num2/Den;
>   RETURN([G,H]);
>   end:
>   F:=sqrt(yy-(xx*yy-xy^2))/(1-xx);
```

$$F := \frac{\sqrt{yy - xx\,yy + xy^2}}{1 - xx}$$

```
>   xx:=x^2+y^2:
>   yy:=u^2+v^2:
>   xy:=x*u+y*v:
>   M:=GH(F):
>   G:=M[1]:
>   H:=M[2]:
>   G:=simplify(G);
```

$$G := -\frac{u\,(x\,u + y\,v)}{-1 + x^2 + y^2}$$

```
> H:=simplify(H);
```

$$H := -\frac{v\,(x\,u + y\,v)}{-1 + x^2 + y^2}$$

In the above program, we define a function `GH(F)`. The input is a Finsler metric F and the output is the matrix $[G, H]$ formed by the spray coefficients. For the Klein metric, one gets G and H which can be expressed in the form $G = Pu$ and $H = Pv$. Thus the Klein metric is projectively flat on the unit disk.

The above Maple program can be used to compute the spray coefficients for general two-dimensional Finsler metrics.

The Bryant metrics on the upper (or lower) hemisphere can be pulled to projective metrics defined on $\mathbb{R}^2$ using the same standard map $\psi_{\pm}$ in Example 1.2.4 of [36]. Thus they can be expressed as metrics on $\mathbb{R}^2$

$$F := \sqrt{\frac{\sqrt{A} + B}{2E} + \left(\frac{U}{E}\right)^2} + \frac{U}{E},$$

where

$$A := B^2 + (1 - e^2)\,(u^2 + v^2)^2,$$
$$B := e\,(u^2 + v^2) + [(x^2 + y^2)(u^2 + v^2) - (xu + yv)^2],$$
$$U := \sqrt{1 - e^2}\,(xu + yv),$$
$$V := [e + (x^2 + y^2)]\,(xu + yv),$$
$$E := 1 + 2e\,(x^2 + y^2) + (x^2 + y^2)^2.$$

Below is a portion of a Maple program for computing G and H of a family of Bryant metrics on S^2. We omit the head part of the above Maple program defining `GH(F)`.

```
> F:=sqrt((sqrt(A)+B)/(2*E)+(U/E)^2)+U/E;
```

$$F := \frac{1}{2}\sqrt{2\,\frac{\sqrt{A} + B}{E} + \frac{4\,U^2}{E^2}} + \frac{U}{E}$$

```
> P:=sqrt((sqrt(A)-B)/(2*E)-(U/E)^2)-V/E;
```

$$P := \frac{1}{2}\sqrt{2\,\frac{\sqrt{A} - B}{E} - \frac{4\,U^2}{E^2}} - \frac{V}{E}$$

```
>  A:=(e*yy+(xx*yy-xy^2))^2+(1-e^2)*yy^2:
>  B:=e*yy+(xx*yy-xy^2):
>  U:=sqrt(1-e^2)*xy:
>  V:=(e+xx)*xy:
>  E:=1+2*e*xx+xx^2:
>  xx:=x^2+y^2:
>  yy:=u^2+v^2:
>  xy:=x*u+y*v:
>  M:=GH(F):
>  G:=M[1]:
>  H:=M[2]:
>  x:=-1/2;y:=-3/5;u:=-1;v:=4/5;e:=1/4;
```

$$x := \frac{-1}{2}$$

$$y := \frac{-3}{5}$$

$$u := -1$$

$$v := \frac{4}{5}$$

$$e := \frac{1}{4}$$

```
>  simplify(G/u-H/v);
```
$$0$$

```
>  simplify(G/u-P);
```
$$0$$

```
>  simplify(H/v-P);
```
$$0$$

In the above Maple program, we verified two facts: 1) F is projectively flat, and 2) $G = Pu$ and $H = Pv$ where P is given by

$$P = \sqrt{\frac{\sqrt{A} - B}{2E} - \left(\frac{U}{E}\right)^2} + \frac{V}{E}.$$

One can also use equation $(6.2.1)_3$ to check whether a Finsler metric is projectively flat. Equation $(6.2.1)_3$ in dimension two is given as follows,

$$F_{xu}u + F_{yu}v = F_x, \qquad F_{xv}u + F_{yv}v = F_y. \tag{A.3}$$

If a Finsler metric $F = F(x, y; u, v)$ satisfies (A.3), then by Theorem 6.1, it is projectively flat. In this case, the spray coefficients are in the form $G = Pu$ and $H = Pv$, where

$$P = \frac{F_x u + F_y v}{2F}. \tag{A.4}$$

Below is a Maple program by which we verify that a Bryant metric F in (8.47) of [36] satisfies (A.3), hence it is projectively flat. We also compare the function P in (8.48) of [36] with the function P in (A.4) using fractional numbers. They are always sufficiently close. Thus we conclude that they are equal to each other. A tip is to select small values for the variables, otherwise the computation will go beyond the capacity of Maple.

```
> restart;
> F:=sqrt((sqrt(A)+B)/(2*E)+(U/E)^2)+U/E;
```

$$F := \frac{1}{2}\sqrt{2\,\frac{\sqrt{A}+B}{E} + \frac{4\,U^2}{E^2}} + \frac{U}{E}$$

```
> P:=sqrt((sqrt(A)-B)/(2*E)-(U/E)^2)-V/E;
```

$$P := \frac{1}{2}\sqrt{2\,\frac{\sqrt{A}-B}{E} - \frac{4\,U^2}{E^2}} - \frac{V}{E}$$

```
> A:=(e*yy+(xx*yy-xy^2))^2+(1-e^2)*yy^2:
> B:=e*yy+(xx*yy-xy^2):
> U:=sqrt(1-e^2)*xy:
> V:=(e+xx)*xy:
> E:=1+2*e*xx+xx^2:
> xx:=x^2+y^2:
> yy:=u^2+v^2:
> xy:=x*u+y*v:
> simplify(diff(F,x,u)*u+diff(F,y,u)*v-diff(F,x));
                              0

> simplify(diff(F,x,v)*u+diff(F,y,v)*v-diff(F,y));
                              0

> PP:=(diff(F,x)*u+diff(F,y)*v)/(2*F):
> e:=1/4;x:=1;y:=-1/2;u:=1/3;v:=1/5;
```

$$e := \frac{1}{4}$$

$$x := 1$$

$$y := \frac{-1}{2}$$

$$u := \frac{1}{3}$$

$$v := \frac{1}{5}$$

```
>  simplify(PP-P);
```

$$0$$

A.2   Gauss curvature

The flag curvature in dimension two is called the Gauss curvature. For a Finsler metric $F = F(x, y; u, v)$, the Gauss curvature $\mathbf{K} = \mathbf{K}(x, y; u, v)$ is given by

$$\mathbf{K} := \frac{1}{F^2}\Big\{ 2G_x + 2H_y - G_u^2 - H_v^2 - 2H_u G_v$$

$$- Q_x u - Q_y v + 2GQ_u + 2HQ_v \Big\}, \tag{A.5}$$

where $G = G(x, y; u, v)$ and $H = H(x, y; u, v)$ denote its spray coefficients and $Q = G_u + H_v$. The formula (A.5) is in fact a formula for the Ricci scalar *Ric* divided by F^2. In dimension two, the quotient Ric/F^2 is the Gauss curvature.

Below is a Maple program for the Gauss curvature, by which we compute the Gauss curvature of the Funk metric on the unit disk. As we know, the Gauss curvature of the Funk metric is equal to -0.25. However, our PC does not run fast enough to complete the symbolic computation. Thus we randomly select some point (x, y) in the unit disk and a direction (u, v). If we always obtain a value sufficiently close to -0.25, then we can conclude that the Gauss curvature is equal to -0.25 and look for a rigorous proof.

```
>  restart;
>  GC:=proc(F)
>  local L,Lx,Ly,Lu,Lv,Lxv,Lyu,Luu,Luv,Lvv,Num1,Num2,
>  Den,G,H,Gx,Hy,Gu,Gv,Hu,Hv,Q,Qx,Qy,Qu,Qv,M,N,K;
>  L:=F^2/2;
```

```
>   Lx:=diff(L,x);
>   Ly:=diff(L,y);
>   Lu:=diff(L,u);
>   Lv:=diff(L,v);
>   Lxv:=diff(L,x,v);
>   Lyu:=diff(L,y,u);
>   Luu:=diff(L,u,u);
>   Luv:=diff(L,u,v);
>   Lvv:=diff(L,v,v);
>   Den:=2*(Luu*Lvv-Luv*Luv);
>   Num1:=(Lx*Lvv-Ly*Luv)-(Lxv-Lyu)*Lv;
>   Num2:=(-Lx*Luv+Ly*Luu)+(Lxv-Lyu)*Lu;
>   G:=Num1/Den;
>   H:=Num2/Den;
>   Gx:=diff(G,x);
>   Hy:=diff(H,y);
>   Gu:=diff(G,u):
>   Gv:=diff(G,v):
>   Hu:=diff(H,u):
>   Hv:=diff(H,v):
>   Q:=Gu+Hv:
>   Qx:=diff(Q,x):
>   Qy:=diff(Q,y):
>   Qu:=diff(Q,u):
>   Qv:=diff(Q,v):
>   M:=Qx*u+Qy*v:
>   N:=G*Qu+H*Qv:
>   K:=(2*Gx+2*Hy-Gu^2-Hv^2-2*Hu*Gv-M+2*N)/F^2:
>   RETURN(K);
>   end:
>   F:=sqrt(Y-(X*Y-Z^2))/(1-X)+Z/(1-X);
```

$$F := \frac{\sqrt{Y - X Y + Z^2}}{1 - X} + \frac{Z}{1 - X}$$

```
>   X:=x^2+y^2:Y:=u^2+v^2:Z:=x*u+y*v:
>   K:=GC(F):
>   x:=0.3:y:=-0.6:u:=2.1:v:=0.5:
>   K:=simplify(K);
```

$$K := -.2499999933$$

In the above program, we define a function K:=GC(F). The input is a Finsler metric F and the output is the Gauss curvature **K**. Note that the first half of the program is for computing the spray coefficients G and H.

For a projective flat metric $F = F(x, y; u, v)$, one can first find the projective factor using (A.4), then use the projective factor to compute the flag curvature by the formula in (6.2.2), i.e.,

$$\mathbf{K} = \frac{P^2 - P_x u - P_y v}{F^2}.$$

A.3   Spray coefficients of (α, β)-metrics

In this section, we shall find a formula for the spray coefficients G^i of an (α, β)-metric in *any* dimension. This formula is given in (6.2.7) without detailed computation. We shall start with computing g_{ij}, then find a formula for g^{ij}, by which we derive a formula for G^i. In each step, we introduce some new variables which are expressed in terms of previous variables. We leave them without simplification until we obtain a formula for G^i. Then we simplify all the coefficients involved in the formula of G^i using Maple.

Let

$$F = \alpha\phi(s), \quad s = \frac{\beta}{\alpha}.$$

We have

$$g_{ij} = \rho a_{ij} + \rho_0 b_i b_j + \rho_1 (b_i \alpha_j + b_j \alpha_i) + \rho_2 \alpha_i \alpha_j, \tag{A.6}$$

where $\alpha_i := a_{ij} y^j / \alpha$ and

$$\rho := \phi\{\phi - s\phi'\},$$
$$\rho_0 := \phi\phi'' + \phi'\phi',$$
$$\rho_1 := -\{s(\phi\phi'' + \phi'\phi') - \phi\phi'\},$$
$$\rho_2 := s\{s(\phi\phi'' + \phi'\phi') - \phi\phi'\}.$$

Rewrite g_{ij} as follows:

$$g_{ij} = \rho\{A_{ij} + \mu\, Y_i Y_j\} \tag{A.7}$$

where

$$Y_i := \alpha_i + \varepsilon b_i,$$
$$A_{ij} := a_{ij} + \delta\, b_i b_j,$$
$$\varepsilon := \frac{\rho_1}{\rho_2},$$
$$\delta := \frac{\rho_0 - \epsilon^2 \rho_2}{\rho},$$
$$\mu := \frac{\rho_2}{\rho}.$$

The inverse $(A^{ij}) := (A_{ij})^{-1}$ is given by

$$A^{ij} = a^{ij} - \tau \, b^i b^j,$$

where

$$\tau = \frac{\delta}{1 + \delta b^2}.$$

Using the formula for A^{ij}, we can find a formula for the inverse $(g^{ij}) := (g_{ij})^{-1}$.

$$g^{ij} = \rho^{-1}\{A^{ij} - \eta Y^i Y^j\} = \rho^{-1}\{a^{ij} - \tau \, b^i b^j - \eta \, Y^i Y^j\},$$

where

$$Y^i := A^{ij} Y_j = \frac{y^i}{\alpha} + \lambda \, b^i,$$

$$\lambda := -\tau s + \varepsilon - \varepsilon \tau b^2 = \frac{\varepsilon - \delta s}{1 + \delta b^2},$$

$$\eta := \frac{\mu}{1 + Y^2 \mu},$$

$$Y := \sqrt{Y^i A_{ij} Y^j} = \sqrt{1 + (\lambda + \epsilon)s + \lambda \epsilon b^2}.$$

The geodesic coefficients G^i are given by

$$G^i = G_\alpha^i + \frac{F_{;k} y^k}{2F} y^i + \frac{F}{2} g^{il} \{F_{;k \cdot l} y^k - F_{;l}\},$$

where $F_{;i}$ denote the covariant derivatives of F with respect to α and $F_{;i \cdot j} = [F_{;i}]_{y^j}$. We use the above identity to find a formula for G^i.

Observe that

$$F_{;k} = \phi' b_{i;k} y^i,$$

$$F_{;k \cdot l} y^k = (b_l - s\alpha_l)\phi'' \frac{r_{00}}{\alpha} + \phi' b_{l;k} y^k.$$

Thus

$$F_{;k} y^k = \phi' b_{i;k} y^i y^k = \phi' r_{00},$$

$$F_{;k \cdot l} y^k - F_{;l} = (b_l - s\alpha_l)\phi'' \frac{r_{00}}{\alpha} + 2\phi' s_{l0}.$$

Then we obtain the following formula for G^i

$$G^i = G_\alpha^i + P y^i + Q^i,$$

where

$$P = \Xi s_0 + \alpha^{-1} \Theta r_{00},$$

$$Q^i = Q \alpha s^i{}_0 + \left(\Phi \alpha s_0 + \Psi r_{00}\right) b^i,$$

here

$$Q = \frac{\phi\phi'}{\rho},$$

$$\Xi = -\frac{\eta\lambda}{\rho}\phi\phi',$$

$$\Theta = \frac{\phi'}{2\phi} - \frac{s\phi\phi''}{2\rho} - \frac{(b^2 - s^2)\eta\lambda\phi\phi''}{2\rho},$$

$$\Phi = -\frac{\phi\phi'}{\rho}(\tau + \eta\lambda^2),$$

$$\Psi = \frac{\phi\phi''}{2\rho}\{1 - (b^2 - s^2)(\tau + \eta\lambda^2)\}.$$

We use Maple to simplify Q and Θ as follows,

$$Q = \frac{\phi'}{\phi - s\phi'},$$

$$\Theta = \frac{\phi\phi' - s(\phi\phi'' + \phi'\phi')}{2\phi((\phi - s\phi') + (b^2 - s^2)\phi'')}.$$

We also use Maple to find the following identity,

$$\frac{\Xi}{\Theta} = \frac{\Phi}{\Psi} = -2Q.$$

Let

$$\chi := \frac{\Psi}{\Theta}.$$

χ is given by

$$\chi = \frac{\phi\phi''}{\phi\phi' - s(\phi\phi'' + \phi'\phi')}.$$

Finally, we obtain the following formula for G^i.

$$G^i = G^i_\alpha + Qs^i_{\ 0} + \Theta\{-2Qs_0 + r_{00}\}\left\{\frac{y^i}{\alpha} + \chi b^i\right\}.$$

Below is a Maple program for the above computation.

```
>  restart;
>  f:=phi(s):
>  fs:=diff(f,s):
>  fss:=diff(f,s,s):

>  rho:=f*(f-s*fs):
>  rho0:=f*fss+fs^2:
```

```
>   rho1:=-(s*(f*fss+fs^2)-f*fs):
>   rho2:=s*(s*(f*fss+fs^2)-f*fs):

>   epsilon:=rho1/rho2:
>   delta:=(rho0-epsilon^2*rho2)/rho:
>   mu:=rho2/rho:
>   tau:=delta/(1+delta*b2):
>   lambda:=-tau*s+epsilon-epsilon*tau*b2:
>   Y2:=1+(lambda+epsilon)*s+lambda*epsilon*b2:
>   eta:=mu/(1+Y2*mu):

>   Xi:=-(eta*lambda/rho)*f*fs:
>   Theta1:=fs/(2*f)-s*f*fss/(2*rho):
>   Theta2:=-(b2-s^2)*eta*lambda*f*fss/(2*rho):
>   Theta:=Theta1+Theta2:
>   Q:=f*fs/rho:
>   Phi:=-(f/rho)*(tau+eta*lambda^2)*fs:
>   Psi1:=(f/(2*rho))*(1-(b2-s^2)*(tau+eta*lambda^2))*fss:

>   Q:=simplify(Q);
```

$$Q := -\frac{\frac{\partial}{\partial s}\,\phi(s)}{-\phi(s) + s\left(\frac{\partial}{\partial s}\,\phi(s)\right)}$$

```
>   Theta:=simplify(Theta);
```

$$\Theta := \frac{1}{2}\,\frac{-s\,\phi(s)\left(\frac{\partial^2}{\partial s^2}\,\phi(s)\right) - s\left(\frac{\partial}{\partial s}\,\phi(s)\right)^2 + \phi(s)\left(\frac{\partial}{\partial s}\,\phi(s)\right)}{\phi(s)\left(\phi(s) - s\left(\frac{\partial}{\partial s}\,\phi(s)\right) + \left(\frac{\partial^2}{\partial s^2}\,\phi(s)\right)b2 - s^2\left(\frac{\partial^2}{\partial s^2}\,\phi(s)\right)\right)}$$

```
>   simplify(Xi/Theta-Phi/Psi1);
```
$$0$$

```
>   simplify(Xi/Theta+2*Q);
```
$$0$$

```
>   chi:=simplify(Psi1/Theta);
```

$$\chi := -\frac{\left(\frac{\partial^2}{\partial s^2}\,\phi(s)\right)\phi(s)}{s\,\phi(s)\left(\frac{\partial^2}{\partial s^2}\,\phi(s)\right) + s\left(\frac{\partial}{\partial s}\,\phi(s)\right)^2 - \phi(s)\left(\frac{\partial}{\partial s}\,\phi(s)\right)}$$

Bibliography

[1] J. C. Álvarez-Paiva and G. Berck, *What is wrong with the Hausdorff measure in Finsler spaces*, Adv. in Math., **204**(2)(2006), 647-663.

[2] M. T. Anderson, *Short geodesics and gravitational instantons*, J. Diff. Geom., **31**(1990), 265-275.

[3] M. Abate and G. Patrizio, *Finsler Metrics – A Global Approach*, LNM **1591**, Springer-Verlag, 1994.

[4] G. S. Asanov, *Finsleroid-Finsler spaces of positive-definite and relativistic types*, Reports on Math. Phys., **55**(2006), 275-300.

[5] H. Akbar-Zadeh, *Sur les espaces de Finsler á courbres sectionnelles constants*, Bull. Acad. Roy. Bel. Cl, Sci, 5e Série - Tome LXXXIV (1988), 281-322.

[6] ———, *Generalized Einstein manifolds*, J. Geom. and Phys., **17**(1995), 342-380.

[7] D. Burago, Y. Burago and S. Ivanov, *A course in metric geometry*, Amer. Math. Soc., 2001.

[8] D. Bao and S. S. Chern, *On a notable connection in Finsler geometry*, Houston J. Math., **19**(1)(1993), 135-180.

[9] ———, *A note on the Gauss-Bonnet theorem for Finsler spaces*, Ann. Math., **143**(1996), 1-20.

[10] D. Bao, S. S. Chern and Z. Shen, *An Introduction to Riemann-Finsler Geometry*, GTM **200**, Springer-Verlag, 2000.

[11] ———, *Finsler Geometry* (Joint Summer Research conference on Finsler Geometry in July 16-20, 1995), Contem. Math. **196**, AMS, 1996.

[12] N. Berline, E. Getzler and M. Vergne, *Heat Kernels and Direct Operators*, Grundlehren Text Editions, Springer-Verlag, 2004.

[13] D. Bao and C. Robles, *On Ricci curvature and flag curvature in Finsler geometry*, in *"A Sampler of Finsler Geometry"*, MSRI series **50**, Camb. Univ. Press, 2004, 197-259.

[14] D. Bao, C. Robles and Z. Shen, *Zermelo navigation on Riemannian manifolds*, J. Diff. Geom., **66**(2004), 391-449.

[15] D. Bao and Z. Shen, *Finsler metrics of constant cuevature on the Lie group S^3*, J. London Math. Soc., **66**(2002), 453-467.

[16] S. Bácsó and X. Cheng, *Finsler conformal transformalations and the curvature invariances*, Publ. Math. Debrecen, **70/1-2**(2007), 221-231.

[17] S. Bácsó, X. Cheng and Z. Shen, *Curvature properties of* (α, β)-*metrics*
(Survey article), in "Finsler Geometry", Sapporo 2005 – In Memory of M.
Matsumoto, ed. S. Sabau and H. Shimada, Adv. Studies in Pure Math.
48, Math. Soc. Japan, 2007, 73-110.

[18] S. Bácsó and M. Matsumoto, *On Finsler spaces of Douglas type: A generalization of the notion of Berwald space*, Publ. Math. Debrecen, **51**(1997),
385-406.

[19] A. L. Besse, *Manifolds all of whose geodesics are closed*, Ergebnisse der
Math. **93**, Springer-Verlag, 1978.

[20] ———, *Einstein manifolds*, Ergebnisse der Math. (**3**)10, Springer-Verlag,
1987.

[21] R. L. Bishop and R. Crittenden, *Geometry of Manifolds*, New York, Aca-
demic Press, 1964.

[22] G. E. Bredon, *Topology and Geometry*, GTM**139**, Springer-Verlag, 1993.

[23] R. Bryant, *Projectively flat Finsler 2-spheres of constant curvature*, Selecta
Math., New Ser., **3**(1997), 161-204.

[24] S. S. Chern, *A simple intrinsic proof of the Gauss-Bonnet formula for
closed Riemannian manifolds*, Ann. Math., **45**(1944), 747-752.

[25] I. Chavel, *Riemannian Geometry: A Modern Introduction*, CTM **108**,
New York, Camb. Univ. Press, 1993.

[26] X. Cheng, X. Mo and Z. Shen, *On the flag curvature of Finsler metrics of
scalar curvature*, J. London Math. Soc., **68**(2)(2003), 762-780.

[27] X. Cheng and Z. Shen, *Randers metrics with special curvature properties*,
Osaka J. Math., **40**(2003), 87-101.

[28] ———, *Projectively flat Finsler metrics with almost isotropic S-curvature*,
Acta Mathematica Scientia, Ser. B Engl. Ed., **26**(2006), no. 2, 307-313.

[29] ———, *A class of Finsler metrics with isotropic S-curvature*, Israel J.
Math., **169**(2009), 317-340.

[30] ———, *Randers metrics of scalar flag curvature*, J. Aust. Math.,
87(2009), 359-370.

[31] ———, *Finsler Geometry – An Approach via Randers Spaces*, Science
Press, Beijing, 2012.

[32] B. Chen and Y. B. Shen, *On a class of critical Finsler metrics*, Publ.
Math. Debrecen, **72**(2008), 451-468.

[33] ———, *Kähler Finsler metrics are actually strongly Kähler*, Chin. Ann.
of Math., Ser. B, **30B**(2009), 173-178.

[34] ———, *On complex Randers metrics*, Intern. J. Math., **21**(2010), No.8.,
971-986.

[35] B. Chen, Z. Shen and L. Zhao, *On a class of Ricci-flat metrics in Finsler
geometry*, Journal of Geometry and Physics, **70**(2013), 30-38.

[36] S. S. Chern and Z. Shen, *Riemann-Finsler Geometry*, Nankai Tracts in
Math., Vol. **6**, World Scientific, 2005, Singapore.

[37] X. Cheng and Y. Tian, *Ricci-flat Douglas* (α, β)-*metrics*, Differential Geometry and its Applications, **30**(1)(2012): 20-32.

[38] X. Cheng, Z. Shen and Y. Tian, *A class of Einstein* (α, β)-*metrics*, Israel J. Math., **192**(2012), 221-249.

[39] X. Cheng, H. Wang and M. Wang, (α, β)-*metrics with relatively isotropic mean Landsberg curvature*, Publ. Math. Debrecen, **72**(2008), 475-485.

[40] N. W. Cui and Y. B. Shen, *Bernstein type theorems for minimal surfaces in* (α, β)-*spaces*, Publ. Math. Debrecen, **74/3-4**(2009), 383-400.

[41] ———, *Minimal rotational hypersurfaces in Minkowski-*(α, β)-*space*, Geom. Dedicatae, **151**(2011), 27-39.

[42] ———, *Projective change between two classes of* (α, β)-*metrics*, Diff. Geom. and its Appl., **27**(2009), 566-573.

[43] P. Dazord, *Variétés finslériennes en forme des sphéres*, C. R. Acad. Sc. Paris, **267**(1968), 353-355.

[44] C. E. Duran, *A volume comparison theorem for Finsler manifolds*, Proc. AMS, **126**(1998), 3079-3082.

[45] O. C. Durumeric, *Growth of fundamental groups and isoembolic volume and diameter*, Proc. AMS, **130**(2001), 585-590.

[46] J. Eells and L. Lemaire, *Selected Topics in Harmonic Maps*, CBMS Regional Conf., S. N. **50**, 1983.

[47] ———, *Another report on harmonic maps*, Bull. London Math. Soc., **20**(1988), 385-524.

[48] J. Eells and J. H. Sampson, *Harmonic mappings of Riemannian manifolds*, Amer. J. Math., **86**(1964), 109-160.

[49] L. P. Eisenhart, *Riemannian geometry*, Princeton Univ. Press, 1926, Second printing 1949.

[50] ———, *Non-Riemannian geometry*, Amer. Math. Soc., Collo. Publ., New York, 1927.

[51] M. Gromov, *Metric Structures for Riemannian and Non-Riemannian Spaces*, Based on Structures Métriques des Variété Riemanniennes Edited by J. LaFontaine and P. Pansu, English translation by Sean Michael Bates, PM **152**, Birkhäuser Boston, 1999.

[52] P. Günther, *Einige Sätze über das Volumenelement eines Riemannschen Raumes*, Publ. Math. Deberecen, **7**(1960), 78-93.

[53] J. W. Han and Y. B. Shen, *Harmonic maps from complex Finsler manifolds*, Pacific J. Math., **236**(2008), 341-356.

[54] Q. He and Y. B. Shen, *Some results on harmonic maps for Finsler manifolds*, Internat. J. Math. **16**(2005), no. 9, 1017-1031.

[55] ———, *Some properties of harmonic maps for Finsler manifolds*, Houston J. Math., **33**(2007), 683-699.

[56] ———, *On the mean curvature of Finsler submanifolds*, Chin. J. Contem. Math., **27**(2006), 431-442.

[57] ———, *On Bernstein type theorems in Finsler spaces with the volume form induced from the projective sphere bundle*, Proc. AMS, **134**(2006), 871-880.

[58] Y. Ichijyo and M. Hashiguchi, *On the condition that a Randers space be conformally flat*, Rep. Fac. Sci. Kagoshima Univ., 1989.

[59] M. Ji and Z. Shen, *On strongly convex graphs in Minkowski geometry*,

Can. Math. Bull., **45**(2002), 232-246.

[60] J. Jost and S. T. Yau, *A nonlinear elliptic system for maps from Hermitian to Riemannian manifolds and rigidity theorems in Hermitian geometry*, Acta Math., **170**(1993), 221-254.

[61] C. W. Kim and J. W. Yim, *Finsler manifolds with positive constant flag curvature*, Geom. Dedicata, **98**(2003), 47-56.

[62] W. Klingenberg, *Riemannian Geometry*, de Gruyter Studies Math. **1**, Berlin, New York, 1995.

[63] M. S. Knebelman, *Conformal geometry of generalized metric spaces*, Proc. Nat. Acad. Sci. USA, **15**(1929), 376-379.

[64] V. K. Kropina, *On projective two-dimensional Finsler spaces with a special metric*, Trudy Sem. Vektor. Tenzor. Anal., **11**(1961), 277-292. (in Russian)

[65] P. F. Leung, *On the stability of harmonic maps*, Lecture Notes in Math., **949**, Springer-Verlag (1982), 122-129.

[66] B. Lackey, *On the Gauss-Bonnet formula in Riemannian-Finsler geometry*, Bull. London Math. Soc., **34**(2002), 329-340.

[67] L. Lempert, *La métrique de Kobayashi et la représentation des domaines sur la boule*, Bull. Soc. Math. France, **109**(1981), 427-474.

[68] B. L. Li, *On the classification of projectively flat Finsler metrics with constant flag curvature*, Advances in Math., **257**(2014), 266-284.

[69] A. Lichnerowicz, *Applications harmoniques et varietes Kähleriennes*, Symp. Math. III (Bologna 1970), 341-402.

[70] ———, *Quelques théorémes de géométrie différentielle globale*, Comm. Math. Helv. **22**(1949), 271-301.

[71] X. Li, Z. Chang and X. Mo, *Isometric group of (α, β)-type Finsler space and the symmetry of very special relativity*, arXiv:1001.2667v2, [phisics.gr-qc], 7 Apr. 2010.

[72] B. Li, Y. B. Shen and Z. Shen, *On a class of Douglas metrics*, Studia Scie. Math. Hungarica, **46**(2009), 355-365.

[73] B. Li and Z. Shen, *On a class of projectively flat Finsler metrics with constant flag curvature*, Intern. J. Math., **18**(2007), No.7., 749-760.

[74] M. Matsumoto, *Foundations of Finsler Geometry and Special Finsler Spaces*, Kaiseisha Press, Japan, 1986.

[75] ———, *On C-reducible Finsler spaces*, Tensor N.S., **24**(1972), 29-37.

[76] ———, *Finsler spaces with (α, β)-metric of Douglas type*, Tensor N.S., **60**(1998), 123-134.

[77] ———, *Conformally closed Finsler spaces*, Balkan J. Geom. Appl., **4**(1999), 117-128.

[78] J. Milnor, *A note on curvature and fundamental group*, J. Diff. Geom., **2**(1968), 1-7.

[79] X. H. Mo, *Characterzation and structure of Finsler spaces with constant flag curvature*, Science in China, Ser. A, **41**(1998), 900-917.

[80] ———, *Harmonic maps from Finsler manifolds*, Illinois J. Math. **45**(2001), 1331-1345.

[81] V. Mathai and D. Quillen, *Superconnections, Thom classes and equivariant differential forms*, Topology, **25**(1986), 85-110.

[82] V. S. Matveev, H.-B. Rademacher, M. Troyanov and A. Zeghib, *Finsler conformal Lichnerowicz-Obata conjecture*, Anna. de l'inst. Fourier, **59**(2009), 937-949.

[83] V. S. Matveev and M. Troyanov, *The Binet-Legendre ellipsoid in Finsler geometry*, 2011, preprint.

[84] X. H. Mo and Y. Yang, *The Existence of Harmonic maps from Finsler manifolds*, Science in China, Ser. A, **48**(2005), 115-130.

[85] X. H. Mo, Z. Shen and C. Yang, *Some constructions of projectively flat Finsler metrics*, Science in China, Ser. A, **49**(2006), 703-714.

[86] S. Nishikawa, *Harmonic maps in complex Finsler geometry*, Progress in Nonlinear Diff. Equat. and its Appl., **59**(2004), 113-132.

[87] S. Numata, *On Landsberg spaces of scalar curvature*, J. Korea Math. Phys., **12**(1975), 97-100.

[88] S. Ohta, *Finsler interpolation inequalities*, Calc. Var. PDE, **36**(2009), 211-249.

[89] ———, *Vanishing S-curvature of Randers spaces*, Diff. Geom. and its Appl., **29**(2011), 174-178.

[90] T. Okada, *On models of projectively flat Finsler spaces of constant negative curvature*, Tensor N.S., **40**(1983), 117-123.

[91] S. Ohta and K.-T. Sturm, *Bochner-Weitzenböck formula and Li-Yau estimates on Finsler manifolds*, arXiv: 1105.0983.

[92] H. Omori, *Isometric immersions of Riemannian manifolds*, J. Math. Soc. Japan, **19**(1967), 205-214.

[93] J. C. A. Paiva, *The symplectic geometry of spaces of geodesics*, PhD thesis, Rutgers University, 1995.

[94] P. Petersen, *Riemannian Geometry*, GTM **171**, Springer-Verlag, 1998.

[95] H. B. Rademacher, *Non-reversible Finsler metrics of positive flag curvature*, in "A Sampler of Finsler Geometry", MSRI series **50**, Cambridge Univ. Press, 2004, 261-302.

[96] M. Rafie-Rad, *Time-optimal solutions of parallel navigation and Finsler geodesics,* Nonlinear Anal, RWA, **11**(2010), 3809-3814.

[97] A. Rapcsák, *Über die bahntreuen Abbildungen metrisher Räume*, Publ. Math. Debrecen, **8**(1961), 285-290.

[98] C. Robles, *Einstein metrics of Randers type*, Ph.D. Thesis, University of British Columbia, Canada, 2003.

[99] N. S. Romanvoskii, *Free subgroups of finitely presented groups*, Algebra i Logika, **16**(1977), 88-97.

[100] S. Rosenberg and D. Yang, *Bounds on the fundamental group of a manifold with almost nonnegative Ricci curvature*, J. Math. Soc. Japan, **46**(1994), No.2.

[101] H. Rund, *Differential Geometry of Finsler Spaces*, GMW 101, Springer-Verlag, 1959.

[102] R. Schoen, *Analytic aspects of the harmonic map problem*, Math. Sci. Res. Inst. Publ., **2** (Springer-Verlag, Berlin, 1984), 321-358.

[103] Z. Shen, *Lectures on Finsler Geometry*, World Scientific, 2001, Singapore.

[104] ———, *Finsler spaces of constant positive curvature*, (Joint Summer Re-

search conference on Finsler Geometry in July 16-20, 1995), Contem. Math. **196**, AMS, 1996, 83-92.

[105] ——, *Volume comparison and its applications in Riemann-Finsler geometry*, Adv. Math., **128**(1997), 306-328.

[106] ——, *On Finsler geometry of submanifolds*, Math. Ann., **311**(1998), 549-576.

[107] ——, *Differential Geometry of Spray and Finsler Spaces*, Kluwer Acad. Publ., 2001.

[108] ——, *Projectively flat Randers metrics of constant flag curvature*, Math. Ann., **325**(2003), 19-30.

[109] ——, *Projectively flat Finsler metrics of constant flag curvature*, Trans. AMS, **355**(4)(2003), 1713-1728.

[110] ——, *Finsler metrics with $K = 0$ and $S = 0$*, Cana. J. Math., **55**(2003), 112-132.

[111] ——, *Nonpositively curved Finsler manifolds with constant S-curvature*, Math. Z., **249**(2005), 625-639.

[112] ——, *Landsberg curvature, S-curvature and Riemann curvature*, in "*A Sampler of Finsler Geometry*" MSRI Ser., Cambridge Univ. Press, 2004, 303-355.

[113] ——, *On projectively flat (α, β)-metrics*, Canadian Math. Bull., **52**(1)(2009), 132-144.

[114] ——, *On projectively related Einstein metrics in Riemann-Finsler geometry*, Math. Ann., **320**(2001), 625-647.

[115] ——, *Some formulas of Gauss-Bonnet-Chern type in Riemannian-Finsler geometry*, J. reine. angew. Math. **475**(1996), 149-165.

[116] ——, *A Gauss-Bonnet-Chern formula for Finsler manifolds*, preprint 1996.

[117] Z. Shen and C. Yu, *On Einstein square metrics*, Publ. Math Debrecen, (2014),

[118] Z. Shen and Q. L. Xia, *On conformal vector fields on Randers manifolds*, preprint.

[119] Z. Shen and G. C. Yildirim, *On a class of projectively flat metrics with constant flag curvature*, Canad. J. Math., **60**(2008), 443-456.

[120] ——, *A characterization of Randers metrics of scalar flag curvature*, Survey in Geometric Analysis and Relativity, ALM 23 (2012), 330-343.

[121] E. Spanier, *Algebraic Topology*, McGraw-Hill, 1966.

[122] E. Sevim, Z. Shen and L. Zhao, *On a class of Ricci-flat Douglas metrics*, International Journal of Mathematics, **23**(2012), doi:10.1142/S0129167X12500462.

[123] R. Schoen and K. Uhlenbeck, *Regularity of minimizing harmonic maps into the sphere*, Invent. Math., 78(1)(1984), 89-100.

[124] Y. B. Shen and B. Shen, *Schwarz lemma and Hartogs phenomenon in Complex Finsler manifolds*, Chin. Ann. of Math., Ser. B, **34**(2013), 455-460.

[125] Y. B. Shen and H. Tian, *Measurable (α, β)-spaces with vanishing S-curvature*, Diff. Geom. and Its Appl., **30**(2012), 549-561.

[126] Y. B. Shen and S. W. Wei, *The stability of harmonic maps on Finsler manifolds*, Houston J. Math., **35**(2009).

[127] Y. B. Shen and Y. Y. Yu, *On projectively related Randers metrics*, Intern. J. Math., **19**(2008), 503-520.

[128] Y. B. Shen and Y. Zhang, *Second variation of harmonic maps between Finsler manifolds*, Science in China, Ser. A, **47**(2004), 39-51.

[129] Y. B. Shen and W. Zhao, *Gromov pre-compactness theorems for nonreversible Finsler manifolds*, Diff. Geom. and its Appl., **28**(2010), 565-581.

[130] ——, *On fundamental groups of Finsler manifolds*, Science in China Ser. A, **54**(2011), 1951-1964.

[131] ——, *Some results on fundamental groups and Betti numbers of Finsler manifolds*, Intern. J. Math., **23**(2012).

[132] ——, *A universal volume comparison theorem for Finsler manifolds and related results*, Canad. J. Math., **65**(2013), 1401-1435.

[133] Y. B. Shen and L. Zhao, *Some projectively flat (α, β)-metrics*, Science in China, Ser. A, **49**(2006), 838-851.

[134] L. Simon, *Equations of mean curvature type in 2 independent variables*, Pac. J. Math., **69**(1977), 245-268.

[135] M. Souza and K. Tenenblat, *Minimal surfaces of rotation in a Finsler space with a Randers metric*, Math. Ann., **325**(2003), 625-642.

[136] M. Souza, J. Spruck and K. Tenenblat, *A Bernstein type theorem on a Randers space*, Math. Ann., **329**(2004), 291-305.

[137] Z. Szabó, *Positive definite Berwald spaces (structure theorems on Berwald spaces)*, Tensor, N. S. **35**(1981), 25-39.

[138] ——, *Eine Charakterisierung der Finslerschen Räume von Konstanter Krümmung*, Acta Math. Hungarica, **42**(1983), 233-236.

[139] H. C. Wang, *On Finsler space with completely integrable equations of Killing*, J. London Math. Soc., **22**(1947), 5-9.

[140] A. Weinstein, *On the volume of manifolds all of whose geodesics are closed*, J. Diff. Geom., **9**(1974), 513-517.

[141] G. Wei, *On the fundamental groups of manifolds with almost-nonnegative Ricci curvature*, Proc. AMS, **110**(1990), 197-199.

[142] B. Wu, *A local rigidity theorem for minimal surfaces in Minkowski 3-space of Randers type*, Ann. Glob. Anal. Geom., **31**(2007), 375-384.

[143] B. Wu and Y. L. Xin, *Comparison theorems in Finsler geometry and their application*, Math. Ann., **337**(2007), 177-196.

[144] G. Wang and C. Xia, *A sharp lower bound for the first eigenvalue on Finsler manifolds*, Ann. Inst. H. Poincaré Anal. Non Linéaire, **30**(2013), no.6, 983996.

[145] Y. L. Xin, *Some results on stable harmonic maps*, Duke Math. J., **47**(1980), 643-648.

[146] H. Xing, *Geometric meaning of Randers metrics with isotropic S-curvature*, Chin. Adv. in Math., **34**(2005), 717-730.

[147] Q. L. Xia, *A sharp lower bound for the first eigenvalue on Finsler manifolds*, Preprint.

[148] C. T. Yang, *Odd-dimensional Wiedersehens manifolds are shpere*, J. Diff.

Geom., **15**(1980), 91-96.

[149] H. Yasuda and H. Shimada, *On Randers spaces of scalar curvature*, Rep. Math. Phys., **11**(1977), 347-360.

[150] S. T. Yau, *A General Schwarz Lemma for Kahler Manifolds* , Amer. J. Math, **100**(1978), 197-203.

[151] S. T. Yau, *Harmonic functions on complete Riemannian manifolds*, Comm. Pure and Appl. Math., **28**(1975), 210-228.

[152] S. T. Yau etc., *Chern – A Great Geometer of the Twentieth Century*, edited by S. T. Yau, International Press Co. Ltd. Hong Kong, 1992.

[153] S. T. Yin, Q. He and Y. B. Shen, *On lower bounds of the first eigenvalue of Finsler-Laplacian* , Publ. Math. Debrecen, **83**(2013), 385-405.

[154] S. T. Yin, Q. He and Y. B. Shen, *On the first eigenvalue of Finsler-Laplacian in a Finsler manifold with nonnegative weighted Ricci curvature*, Science in China Math., **56**(2013).

[155] R. Yoshikawa and K. Okubo, *Kropina spaces of constant curvature; II*, Tensor, N. S., **68**(2007), 190-203; arXiv:math/1110.5128v1 [math.DG] 24 Oct. 2011.

[156] Y. Yu and Y. You, *On Einstein m-th root metrics*, Diff. Geom. and its Appl., **28**(2010), 290-294.

[157] S. Zhu, *The comparison geometry of Ricci curvature*, in Comparison Geometry, eds. Grove and Petersen, MSRI Publ. **30**(1997), 221-262.

[158] X. L. Zhang and Y. B. Shen, *On Einstein Kropina metrics*, Diff. Geom. Appl., **31**(2013), 80-92.

[159] L. Zhou, *A local classfication of a class of* (α, β)*-metrics with constant flag curvature*, Diff. Geom. Appl. **28**(2010), 170-193.

[160] M. Zohrehvand, M. Rafie-Rad and M. Rezaii, *On the projectively equivalent Finsler metrics with common anisotropy direction*, preprint.

[161] J. Zhong and H. Yang, *On the estimates of the first eigenvalue of a compact Riemannian manifold*, Science in China, Ser. **A27**(1984), 1265-1273.

[162] W. Zhao and L. Yuan, *A simple proof of the Gauss-Bonnet-Chern formula for Finsler manifolds*, arXiv preprint arXiv:1303.1918 (2013).

[163] C. Zhong and T. Zhong, *Mean-value Laplacian for* (p, q)*-forms on strongly Kähler-Finsler manifolds*, Chin. Adv. in Math., 33(2004), 152-164.

[164] S. T. Yau and R. Schoen, *Lectures on Differential Geometry* (Chinese), Higher Education Press, Beijing, 2004.

[165] Z. Z. Chen and H. C. Yang, *Schearz lemma on complete manifolds with Ricci curvature bounded from below* (Chinese), Acta Math. Sinica, **24**(1981), 945-952.

[166] Y. B. Shen, *General solutions of some differential equations in Riemannian manifolds* (Chinese), J. Math. Research and Exposition, **2**(1982), No.2, 55-60.

[167] ———, *On Einstein spaces with corresponding geodesics and Riemannian spaces* $V(K)$ (Chinese), Acta Math. Sinica, **24**(1981), 217-228.

[168] ———, *Introduction to Global Differential Geometry* (Chinese), Higher Education Press, Beijing, 2009.

[169] Z. G. Bai, Y. B. Shen etc., *Introduction to Riemannian Geometry* (Chi-

nese), Higher Education Press, Beijing, 2004.

[170] X. H. Mo, *Foundations of Riemann-Finsler Geometry* (Chinese), Peking Education Press, Beijing, 2007.

[171] B. Y. Wu, *Global Finsler Geometry* (Chinese), Tongji University Press, Shanghai, 2008.

[172] J. W. Han, *On harmonic maps for Finsler manifolds and projectively flat Asanov metrics* (Chinese), Zhejiang University Ph.D. Thesis, 2008.

[173] L. Kan, *Conformally flat Randers metrics* (Chinese), Science in China: Math., **41**(2011), 439-446.

[174] ———, *Some problems on conformal changes in Finsler geometry* (Chinese), Zhejiang University Ph.D. Thesis, 2011.

[175] L. Kan and B. Shen, *Killing vector fields in (α, β)-spaces* (Chinese), Science in China: Math., **41**(2011), 689-699.

[176] E. S. Sevim, Z. Shen and L. Zhao, *On a class of Ricci-flat Douglas metrics*, International Journal of Mathematics, **23**(2012), doi:10.1142/S0129167X12500462.

[177] P. Petersen, *Warped Product*, (http://www.math.ucla.edu/~petersen/warpedproducts.pdf)

[178] F. Zhang, *On the maximum principle on complete Finsler manifolds*, Diff. Geom. Appl., **31**(2013), 707-717.

[179] M. Y. Zhang, *Mean curvature of a subspace in a Finsler space*, Ann. Mat. Pura Appl., **31**(1950), 297-302.

[180] S. T. Yin, *Some nonlinear problems in global Finsler geometry* (Chinese), Tongji University Ph.D. Thesis, Shanghai, 2014.

Index